SPECTROSCOPY

VOLUME TWO

SPECTROSCOPY

BY

S. WALKER
M.A., B.Sc., D.Phil., F.R.I.C.
Reader in the Department of Chemistry
College of Advanced Technology, Birmingham
(formerly senior lecturer in physical
chemistry, Leicester College of Technology)

AND

H. STRAW, B.Sc.
Lecturer in physical chemistry
College of Technology, Leicester

Volume Two

Ultra-violet, Visible, Infra-red and Raman Spectroscopy

LONDON: CHAPMAN & HALL: 1962

First published 1962

CHAPMAN & HALL LTD
37 ESSEX STREET
LONDON WC2

Catalogue No. 659/4

PRINTED IN GREAT BRITAIN AT
THE UNIVERSITY PRESS
ABERDEEN

To K and M

Preface

THE advanced side of most of the branches of spectroscopy is well treated in such works as those by Gaydon, Herzberg and Ingram, and by the Reviews. However, no full account from one source exists as an introduction to these works or for gaining a view of spectroscopy as a whole. The aim of this two-volume work is to endeavour to fill these gaps and also give a reasonably up to date account. It covers more than the normal requirements for a chemistry degree course. It may also be useful to a first-year research student in one of the main branches of spectroscopy and to research workers who have specialised in one branch but wish to have a more detailed view of the whole.

Volume One deals with four branches of spectroscopy. Three of these—microwave, electron spin resonance and nuclear magnetic resonance—have all evolved since about 1945 and have led to almost a new insight into many of the problems in chemistry and physics. The fourth topic is atomic spectroscopy, and one of the major aims in its treatment is to provide sufficient theoretical background for a reasonably full appreciation of the other three topics. For example, particular emphasis is placed on the *g*-factors as these are so deeply involved in electron spin resonance and nuclear magnetic resonance work.

The title of Volume Two is *Ultra-violet, Visible, Infra-red, and Raman Spectroscopy*. Other topics which are considered in the second volume are instrumentation, molecular quantum numbers, flames, fluorescence, and phosphorescence, dissociation energies, force constants, evaluation of thermodynamic functions from spectroscopic data, and the application of spectroscopy to astrophysics.

The two volumes have been designed to be reasonably independent of each other, although to some extent one enhances the value of the other. In particular, the spectrographs involved in optical spectroscopy are dealt with in Volume Two and have been somewhat neglected in the chapter on atomic spectroscopy in Volume One. Both volumes contain a chapter on the 'Introduction to Molecular Spectra' in which a few of the basic ideas are considered. To a large extent overlap of material between the two volumes was unavoidable in this particular chapter.

To someone approaching spectroscopy for the first time one of the sources of confusion must be in the duplication of symbols and of the use by different authors of the same symbol for different factors. We have tried to minimise this difficulty by giving a symbol index, and our choice of symbols has to a large degree been governed by the extent of its use. As a general rule, though, in the reading of books and papers on spectroscopy the context should be examined in order to identify the symbol.

In many ways this work owes a great deal to other people. We wish to acknowledge the help of the writers of review articles, authors of previous textbooks, and numerous writers and publishers who have permitted us to reproduce their diagrams and spectrograms.

We are indebted to Dr. C. W. N. Cumper for reading a preliminary version of the manuscript. To Mr. N. H. Roche we are particularly grateful for reading part of the manuscript and for many helpful discussions on topics where physics overshadowed physical chemistry. We should like to thank Dr. B. Pagel and Dr. B. Stevens for reading the manuscript and proofs of the chapters on Applications of Spectroscopy to Astrophysics and Phosphorescence and Fluorescence respectively and for several helpful suggestions and material. We are grateful to Dr. R. L. Williams and Dr. A. D. Caunt for reading the manuscript of Chapters 4 and 5 respectively. Our thanks are due to the Instrument Manufacturers, Grubb Parsons, Hilger and Watts, and Unicam Instruments Ltd. for their help and kind cooperation, and in particular to Dr. A. E. Martin for reading the page proofs of the material relating to instrumentation. We are also grateful to Dr. B. Cannon for reading the Appendix. In addition, we should like to mention Mr. L. P. Priestley, the Head of our Department, who has been most sympathetic to this work. In conclusion, we wish to thank the publishers—in particular Mr. G. Parr and Mr. E. W. Hamilton—who have shown much patience and understanding. Finally, we are indebted to Mrs. K. Walker who has done so much at each of the various stages between the written word and the resulting book.

S. W.

H. S.

Note—The spectra on the jacket are (i) ultra-violet: the benzyl radical in absorption. Porter and Strachan, Spectrochim. *Acta* **12** (1958), 299 (ii) visible: the benzyl radical in emission. Bindley and Walker, *Trans. Faraday Soc.* **58** (1962), 217 (iii) Infra-red: the $2\gamma_3$ band of methyl fluoride, Pickworth and Thompson, *Proc. Roy. Soc. Lond.* 222A (1954), 443 (iv) Rotational Raman: fluorine gas, Andrychuk, *Canad. J. Phys.* **29** (1951), 151.

Contents

PLATES

(*All figures are in the text except the following which are inserted as plates*)

List of Symbols

a Class of rotational level of homonuclear molecules, such as $^{35}Cl^{35}Cl$, where on exchange of the positions of the nuclei the total eigenfunction changes sign. Such a rotational level is termed antisymmetric (*a*).

A Helmholtz free energy.

A Integrated intensity of absorption.

A Spectroscopic constant ($\boldsymbol{h}/8\pi^2 cI_A$) for the rotation of a rigid symmetric-top molecule about the *A* axis, where for tetrahedral and pyramidal types of molecule I_A is the moment of inertia about the main axis of symmetry.

A_j Vibrational amplitude for the particle j executing simple harmonic motion.

A_{nm} Einstein probability coefficient of spontaneous emission which indicates the probability of a spontaneous transition in 1 sec from the upper state n to the lower state m.

B Apparent integrated absorption intensity.

B Spectroscopic constant ($\boldsymbol{h}/8\pi^2 cI_B$) of a linear molecule whose moment of inertia is I_B.

B Spectroscopic constant ($\boldsymbol{h}/8\pi^2 cI_B$) of a prolate symmetric-top molecule, where the moment of inertia I_B is greater than I_A, and $I_B = I_C \neq I_A$.

B_e Spectroscopic constant ($\boldsymbol{h}/8\pi^2 cI_e$) for the molecule with the atoms regarded as being in the hypothetical vibrationless condition, i.e. $v = -\frac{1}{2}$.

B_v Spectroscopic constant for the vth vibrational level.

B Slit width.

c Concentration of solute (g moles/l.).

c Velocity of light *in vacuo*.

C_p Molar heat capacity at constant pressure.

c and d A classification employed to characterise the rotational level components resulting from Λ-type doubling in electronic states with $\Lambda > 0$. This classification applies to cases in or between Hund's cases (*a*) and (*b*).

d	Differentiation symbol.
d_{ij}	A constant in Badger's equation.
$d\mathscr{T}$	Infinitesimal element of volume.
D	Diameter of camera lens in a spectroscope.
D	Diameter of collimator lens in a spectroscope.
D	Optical density and equals $\log_{10}\frac{I_0}{I}$.
D	Thermochemical dissociation energy of a diatomic molecule and is $hc\{G(v_{max})-G(0)\}$.
D	Atomic state symbol when the resultant orbital angular momentum quantum number, L, is 2.
D	Centrifugal distortion constant for the rotation of a linear molecule.
D_e	Spectroscopic dissociation energy of a diatomic molecule. D_e = thermal dissociation energy+zero point energy = $hcG(v_{max})$.
D_J, D_K, D_{JK}	Centrifugal distortion constants for the rotation of a symmetric-top molecule.
D_{vJ}, D_{vK}, D_{vJK}	Centrifugal distortion constant for the rotation of a symmetric-top molecule in the vth vibrational level.
$D_{1\lambda_1}$	Optical density of the component 1 at the wavelength λ_1.
e	Charge on the electron in electrostatic units.
E, E_T, E_e, E_v and E_r	Total energy, transitional energy, electronic energy, vibrational energy, and rotational energy of a molecule, respectively.
E	Electron affinity.
E_{vr}	Rotation-vibration energy of a molecule.
E'	Total energy of a molecule or atom in the upper state.
E''	Total energy of a molecule or atom in the lower state.
E_{JK}	Rotational energy of a symmetric-top molecule and equals E_r.
f	Focal length.
f	Shorthand symbol for $f(x)$, a power series in x.
f	Partition function.
f_e, f_T, f_v, f_r, $f_{N.S.}$	Electronic, translational, vibrational, rotational, and nuclear spin partition functions, respectively.
F	Force.
F	Atomic state symbol when the resultant orbital angular momentum quantum number is 3.
F	The F number, the ratio of the focal length of the camera lens to its diameter.
F	The electric field strength in volts per cm (V/cm).
$F(J)$	Rotational energy term (E_r/hc).
$F(J, K)$	Rotational energy term for a symmetric-top molecule (E_{JK}/hc).
F^0	Equilibrium value of the electric field strength.
F_x, F_y, F_z	Components of the electric field strength along the x, y, and z axes, respectively.

g	Degeneracy.
g	Suffix to a molecular state of molecules such as $^{35}Cl—^{35}Cl$ and $^{35}Cl—^{37}Cl$ which indicates that the wave-function is unaltered on reflection of the electron co-ordinates at a centre of symmetry. The concept applies to molecules whose electric field is symmetrical about a centre of symmetry.
G	Gibbs's free energy.
$G(v)$	Vibrational energy term ($E_v/\boldsymbol{h}c$).
$\boldsymbol{h}$	Planck's constant.
H	Shorthand symbol for $H(s)$, a power series in s.
$\mathbf{H}$	Magnetic field strength.
$H_v(s)$	The vth Hermite polynomial.
ΔH	Change in heat content at constant pressure.
i	Angle of incidence.
i	Subscript to all symbols concerning the rarer of two isotopes, for example $\nu - {}_i\nu =$ isotopic displacement.
	$\sqrt{-1}$.
I	Ionisation potential.
I	Intensity of emergent beam.
I	Moment of inertia of a molecule.
I	Nuclear spin quantum number of an atom in a molecule.
I_B	Moment of inertia of a linear molecule about an axis perpendicular to the internuclear axis.
I_A, I_B and I_C	Moments of inertia of a polyatomic molecule about the A, B, and C axes, respectively.
I_c	Central intensity of first diffraction maximum.
I_e	The value of the moment of inertia of a molecule when the nuclei are in their equilibrium positions, i.e. for the hypothetical case of $v = -\frac{1}{2}$.
I_0	Intensity of incident beam.
j	Total angular momentum quantum number for an electron in an atom for Russell–Saunders coupling of the orbital angular momentum ($l^\star \boldsymbol{h}/2\pi$) and the electron spin angular momentum ($s^\star \boldsymbol{h}/2\pi$).
$j^\star$	$\sqrt{j(j+1)}$ where j is defined above.
J	Total angular momentum quantum number of an atom for the Russell–Saunders coupling of the resultant orbital angular momentum ($L^\star \boldsymbol{h}/2\pi$) and the resultant electron spin angular momentum ($S^\star \boldsymbol{h}/2\pi$).
$J^\star$	$\sqrt{J(J+1)}$ where J is defined above.
J	Rotational quantum number of a molecule for the total angular momentum $\sqrt{J(J+1)}\boldsymbol{h}/2\pi$. This includes the nuclear, electronic orbital and electron spin momenta. $\sqrt{J(J+1)}\boldsymbol{h}/2\pi$ is the

resultant of $\Omega \boldsymbol{h}/2\pi$ and $N\boldsymbol{h}/2\pi$ in Hund's cases (*a*) and (*c*), and the resultant of $\sqrt{K(K+1)}\boldsymbol{h}/2\pi$ and $\sqrt{S(S+1)}\boldsymbol{h}/2\pi$ in Hund's cases (*b*) and (*d*). In singlet states $S = 0$ and $J = K$.

J_a — $J_a^\star \boldsymbol{h}/2\pi$ is resultant of $L^\star \boldsymbol{h}/2\pi$ and $S^\star \boldsymbol{h}/2\pi$ for a diatomic molecule when Hund's case (*c*) is applicable, $J_a^\star = \sqrt{J_a(J_a+1)}$.

$\boldsymbol{k}$ — Boltzmann's constant.

k — Force constant.

k_θ — Force constant for a bending vibration.

k_{11} — Force constant of the atom 1 relating to the displacement q_1.

k_{12}, k_{23} — Interaction constants employed in force constant studies.

K — A second rotational quantum number for a symmetric-top molecule which governs the component of the total angular momentum directed along the principal symmetry axis.

K_ν — Absorption coefficient at the wave-number ν.

K_ν^a — Apparent absorption coefficient at the wave-number ν.

K — Rotational quantum number for the resultant angular momentum ($\sqrt{K(K+1)}\boldsymbol{h}/2\pi$) of a diatomic molecule. This includes the contributions from the nuclear and electron angular momenta, but not that for the electron spin momentum. K is non-existent for Hund's cases (*a*) and (*c*).

l — Thickness of an absorbing layer.

L — Resultant orbital angular momentum quantum number for an atom.

$L^\star$ — $\sqrt{L(L+1)}$ where L is defined above.

${}^{2S+1}L_J$ — The notation for atomic sub-states, superscript = multiplicity = $2S+1$, subscript = value of J, while main symbol indicates the value of L. For example, when $L = 0$, 1, 2 and 3, the main symbol would be S, P, D, and F, respectively.

m — $= 1, 2, 3, \ldots$ or $-1, -2, -3, \ldots$ and is the empirical numbering sometimes employed for the lines of a branch of a band instead of the J'' numbering. The positive values of m correspond to the *R*-branch, and the negative values, the *P*-branch. The value $m = 0$ corresponds with the null line or band origin.

m_1 — Mass of the atom 1 in a molecule.

M — Variable electric dipole moment of a molecule, the value of which is dependent on the value of the internuclear distance.

M — Molecular weight.

M — Magnetic quantum number.

M_e — Electron component of the variable electric dipole moment, M.

M_L — The quantum number governing the component of the resultant orbital angular momentum of an atom along the axis of an applied field.

M_n — Nuclear component of the variable electric dipole moment, M.

M_0	Value of the electric dipole moment at the equilibrium internuclear distance.
M_s	The quantum number governing the component of the resultant electron spin orbital angular momentum of an atom projected along the axis of an applied field.
M_x, M_y, M_z	Components of the variable electric dipole moment along the x, y and z axes, respectively.
n	Order of a grating spectrum, and takes the values ± 1, ± 2, ± 3 . . . in equation (2.25).
n	Refractive index.
n_0	Constant in the Hartmann dispersion formula.
N	Avogadro's number.
N	Number of lines on a diffraction grating.
N	Angular momentum (in $\boldsymbol{h}/2\pi$ units) of the pair of nuclei in a diatomic molecule. N is not a quantum number.
O	Branch of Raman bands consisting of lines with $J'-J'' = -2$.
O	Origin of co-ordinates.
P	Pressure of a gas.
P	Atomic state symbol when the resultant angular orbital momentum quantum number, L, is 1.
P	The electric moment induced in a molecule by an electric field.
P	Total angular momentum of a rigid rotor.
P	Branch of a band consisting of lines with $J'-J'' = -1$.
$P(J)$	Wave-number of a line in the P-branch of a band where J is the value of the rotational quantum number in the lower state.
$\bar{q}$	Displacement of the centre of gravity of a system of particles.
q_0	Amplitude of vibration of a harmonic oscillator.
q_v	Vibrational co-ordinate of a harmonic oscillator.
Q	Branch of a band with lines consisting of $J'-J'' = 0$.
Q	A normal co-ordinate.
$Q(J)$	Wave-number of a line in the Q-branch where J is the value of the rotational quantum number.
r	Angle of refraction.
r	Distance between nuclei in a molecule.
r_e	Value of r when the nuclei are in their equilibrium positions.
$\dot{r}$	dr/dt where t is time.
$\ddot{r}$	d^2r/dt^2 where t is time.
$\boldsymbol{R}$	Rydberg's constant.
R	Gas constant.
R	Resolving power.
R	Matrix element.
R	Branch of a band consisting of lines with $J'-J'' = +1$.
$R(J)$	Wave-number of a line in the R-branch of a band, where J is the rotational quantum number in the lower state.

R_x, R_y, R_z Matrix element components along the x, y and z axes, respectively.

R_x^{nm}, R_y^{nm}, R_z^{nm} Matrix elements of the components of the variable electric dipole moment along the axes x, y and z, respectively for a transition between the states n and m.

s Class of rotational levels of homonuclear molecules, as for example, $^{35}Cl^{35}Cl$, where on exchange of the positions of the nuclei the sign of the total eigenfunction remains unaltered. Such a rotational level is termed symmetric (s).

s Spin quantum number of a single valence electron. $s^{\star} = \sqrt{s(s+1)}$.

S Entropy.

S Atomic state symbol when the resultant angular orbital momentum quantum number, L, is 0.

S Total electron spin quantum number for the atom. $S^{\star} = \sqrt{S(S+1)}$.

S Branch of band in a Raman spectrum consisting of lines with $J'-J'' = +2$.

t Time.

T Absolute temperature.

T Kinetic energy.

T Term value symbol (E/hc).

T Intensity of the emergent radiation when not truly monochromatic.

T Total nuclear spin quantum number.

T_e Electronic term value symbol (E_e/hc).

T_0 Intensity of the incident radiation when not truly monochromatic.

$T_{\parallel}$ Kinetic energy of a parallel vibration.

u Suffix to a molecular state which indicates that the wavefunction changes sign on reflection of the electron co-ordinates at a centre of symmetry. The concept applies to molecules such as $^{35}Cl—^{35}Cl$ and $^{35}Cl—^{37}Cl$ whose electric field is symmetrical about a centre of symmetry.

v Vibrational quantum number which may take the values 0, 1, 2, 3, . . . v_{max}. v_{max} is the value of v at which the molecule dissociates.

V Volume.

V Potential energy.

$V_{\parallel}$ Potential energy of parallel vibrations.

$V_{\perp}$ Potential energy of perpendicular vibrations.

x, y and z Cartesian co-ordinates.

$x_0\omega_0$ Defined by equation (5.15).

x_e Anharmonicity constant in the vibrational energy equation.

x_A Electronegativity of the atom A.

y_e	Anharmonicity constant in the vibrational energy equation.
α	Absorption coefficient.
α_e	A constant which takes into account the interaction between the rotational and vibrational energies (see equation (5.72)).
α	A constant in the Morse equation.
α	Polarisability.
α	Phase constant.
α	Angle of incidence of light on to a diffraction grating.
α	Symbol employed in quantum mechanics and defined by equation (A.5).
α_ν	Absorption coefficient at the wave-number ν.
β_e	A constant which takes into account the interaction between the rotational and vibrational energies (see equation (5.73)).
β	Angle of emergence of light from a diffraction grating.
β	Representing I_B/I_A-1.
$\delta\lambda$	Width of a spectral line (in Å) at half its maximum intensity.
θ	Angle.
ΔE	Change in energy $(E'-E'')$.
$\Delta G(v)$	$= G(v+\frac{1}{2})-G(v-\frac{1}{2})$ which equals approximately $\frac{1}{2}[G(v+1)-G(v-1)]$.
$\Delta G(v+\frac{1}{2})$	Interval between two consecutive vibrational levels, i.e. $G(v+1)-G(v)$, and is known as the *first difference*.
$\Delta^2 G(v+1)$	The *second difference* between two consecutive vibrational levels and is $\Delta G(v+\frac{3}{2})-\Delta G(v+\frac{1}{2})$.
$\Delta_1 F'(J)$	$= F_{v'}(J+1)-F_{v'}(J)$.
$\Delta_1 F''(J)$	$= F_{v''}(J+1)-F_{v''}(J)$.
$\Delta_2 F'(J)$	$= F_{v'}(J+1)-F_{v'}(J-1)$.
$\Delta_2 F''(J)$	$= F_{v''}(J+1)-F_{v''}(J-1)$.
Δr	Internuclear distance change.
$\Delta\theta$	Change in an angle between two chemical bonds as a result of a bending vibration.
Δv	Difference in value between the vibrational quantum numbers in their upper and lower states, i.e. $v'-v''$.
ΔJ	Difference in value between the rotational quantum numbers in their upper and lower states, i.e. $J'-J''$.
$\Delta\nu_{1/2}$	Half band width (in cm^{-1}).
$\Delta\nu^a_{1/2}$	Apparent half band width (in cm^{-1}).
$\Delta_i\nu$	$= \nu - {}_i\nu =$ isotopic displacement where ${}_i\nu$ is the wave-number of the molecule containing the rarer of the two isotopes.
$\Delta\nu$	Raman wave-number displacement, and is equal to either the wave-number of the observed line minus that of the exciting line or vice versa.
ε	Dielectric constant.

Symbol	Definition
ε	Molecular extinction coefficient, and is defined by equation (5.82).
ε	Total energy of a molecule.
ε_ν	Molecular extinction coefficient at the wave-number ν.
ε_{max}	Molecular extinction coefficient at the wavelength where the absorption is a maximum.
$\varepsilon_{1_{\lambda_1}}$	Molecular extinction coefficient of the component 1 at the wavelength λ_1.
ζ	Coriolis coupling constant.
λ	Symbol employed in force constant studies and defined by equation (10.28).
λ	Symbol employed in quantum mechanics and defined by equation (A.4).
λ	Wavelength (in Å).
λ_0	Constant in the Hartmann dispersion formula.
λ_0	Wavelength of light from source.
λ_{max}	Wavelength at which the absorption is a maximum.
Λ	Quantum number for a linear molecule governing the component of the resultant orbital angular momentum $\sqrt{L(L+1)}\boldsymbol{h}/2\pi$ about the internuclear axis.
${}^{2S+1}\Lambda_{\Lambda+\Sigma}$	Notation for molecular electronic states and sub-states, where the superscript equals multiplicity $= 2S+1$, and the subscript is the value of $\Lambda+\Sigma$, while the main symbol indicates the value of Λ. For example, when $\Lambda = 0$, 1 and 2, the main symbols would be Σ, Π, and Δ, respectively.
μ	Electric dipole moment as determined experimentally.
μ	Reduced mass, and for the diatomic molecule A—B is $m_A m_B/(m_A+m_B)$ where m_A and m_B are the masses of the atoms A and B, respectively.
ν	Wave-number (in cm^{-1}), and is the reciprocal of the wave-length *in vacuo*.
ν	If ν is the wave number for a particular transition of the molecule containing the main isotope, then ${}_i\nu$ is that for the corresponding transition for the molecule containing the rarer of the two isotopes.
ν_c	Lowest observed wave-number which corresponds with the commencement of a continuum, and molecular dissociation.
ν_0	Wave-number corresponding to the $v'-v''$ transition where $J' = J'' = 0$ and is known as the origin of the band. The transition may be between either vibrational levels in the same or in different electronic states.
ν_{00}	Wave-number of the origin of the (0,0) band.
ν_R, ν_Q, ν_P	Wave-numbers of the lines in the P, Q, and R-branches, respectively, for rotation-vibration transitions.
$\bar{\nu}$	Frequency (in c/sec).

ν_r, ν_v, ν_e Wave-numbers corresponding, respectively, to rotational, vibrational and electronic energy changes.

Π Symbol employed to characterise the electronic state of a linear molecule when the quantum number Λ equals 1.

ρ Square root of the ratio of the reduced mass of a molecule formed from the main isotope to that of the reduced mass of a molecule containing the rarer of the two isotopes.

ρ Depolarisation ratio (see p. 158).

$\mathit{\Sigma}$ (Sloping symbol.) Quantum number governing the component of the resultant electron spin angular momentum of a linear molecule along the internuclear axis. $\mathit{\Sigma}$ does not exist in Hund's cases (*b*) and (*d*).

Σ (Upright symbol.) Symbol employed to characterise the electronic state of a linear molecule when the quantum number Λ equals 0.

Σ^+ A Σ-state where the sign of the wave-function is unchanged by reflection of the electron co-ordinates in any plane through the nuclei of the linear molecule.

Σ^- A Σ-state where the sign of the wave-function changes on reflection of the electron co-ordinates in any plane through the nuclei of the linear molecule.

Σ Summation symbol.

ψ Molecular orbital wave-function.

$\psi^\star$ Complex conjugate of ψ.

ψ_v Eigenfunction for the vth vibrational level.

ψ_e, ψ_v, ψ_r Electron, vibrational, and rotational eigenfunction, respectively.

ω Angular frequency ($2\pi\bar{\nu}$).

ω Wave-number for the vibration of the nuclei in a diatomic molecule based on the assumption that the motion is simple harmonic.

ω_e Wave-number (cm^{-1}) of vibration of the nuclei with infinitesimal amplitude about their equilibrium positions.

${}_i\omega$ Wave-number corresponding to ω for the vibration of the molecule containing the rarer of the two isotopes.

ω_0 Defined by equation (5.14).

Ω Quantum number governing the component of the whole of the electronic angular momentum along the internuclear axis; $\Omega = |\Lambda + \mathit{\Sigma}|$ in Hund's case (*a*); $\Omega \boldsymbol{h}/2\pi$ = component of $\sqrt{J_a(J+{}_a1)}\boldsymbol{h}/2\pi$ in Hund's case (*c*); Ω does not exist in Hund's cases (*b*) and (*d*).

∂ Partial differentiation symbol.

$\int$ Integration symbol.

$'$ and $''$ Right-hand superscripts allotted to any symbol to indicate the upper and lower energy states, respectively, in relation to a transition involving the absorption or emission of energy.

$\rightarrow, \leftarrow, \rightleftarrows$	Indicates emission, absorption, and both emission and absorption of energy, respectively. In molecular spectra, in contrast to atomic spectra, when the transition is represented in terms of the energy state symbols, the symbol for the upper energy state (e.g. $^1\Pi$) is written on the left and that for the lower energy state (e.g. $^1\Sigma^+$) on the right. Thus, a transition between these energy levels which could be observed in both emission and absorption would be represented as $^1\Pi\rightleftarrows{}^1\Sigma^+$.
+ and −	Classification of rotational levels according as to whether the sign of the total eigenfunction remains unchanged (termed +) or changes sign (termed −) on reflection at the origin of co-ordinates.

1

Introductory

Absorption and emission of electromagnetic radiation

MOLECULAR spectroscopy is concerned with the change in internal energy when a molecule absorbs or emits electromagnetic radiation. This energy is divided amongst several different motions within the molecule, and its gain or loss is variously distributed according to the mode of interaction with the radiation and the size of the quantum involved. A *quantum of energy* (ΔE) is related to the *wavelength* (λ) by the equation:

$$\Delta E = \frac{hc}{\lambda} \tag{1.1}$$

where h is Planck's constant and c is the velocity of the electromagnetic radiation in the same medium as the wavelength is measured. In addition, c and λ are related to the frequency ($\bar{\nu}$) of the electromagnetic radiation by the formula:

$$\lambda \times \bar{\nu} = c \tag{1.2}$$

The values of λ and c are slightly dependent on whether the measurements are made in vacuum or air. The corresponding frequency, however, is in each case given by the same type of ratio which is:

$$\frac{c_{\mathrm{air}}}{\lambda_{\mathrm{air}}} = \frac{c_{\mathrm{vac}}}{\lambda_{\mathrm{vac}}} = \bar{\nu} \tag{1.3}$$

If the wavelength measurement is made in air (λ_{air}), it may be corrected to λ_{vac} by the addition to it of $(n-1)\lambda_{\mathrm{air}}$ where n is the refractive index of air at that particular wavelength. With a view to the subsequent analysis it is generally more desirable to employ frequency rather than wavelength. Often it is more convenient to use the reciprocal of the value of the wavelength *in vacuo* to measure frequency; this is known as the wave-number, is given the symbol ν and is in cm^{-1} units.

The units employed for recording wavelength are microns (μ) where $1\mu = 10^{-4}$ cm; one millimicron $= 1\ m\mu = 10^{-7}$ cm; and Ångström units (Å) where $1\mu = 10\,000$ Å $= 1000\ m\mu$. The choice of units is influenced by the region of the spectrum being studied. For example, in the infra-red region microns are used to record wavelengths in order to express them in simple numbers between about 1 to 1000 μ.

For reasons related both to these internal energy differences and to the different experimental techniques required, it is convenient to divide the electromagnetic spectrum into the regions shown in Fig. 1.1.

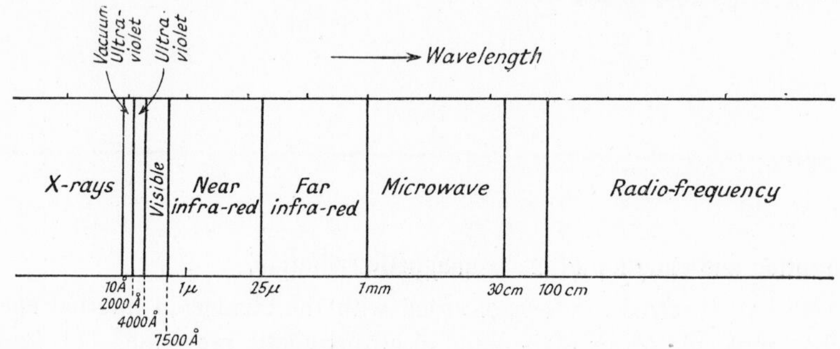

FIG. 1.1 Spectroscopic regions

The instruments employed in spectroscopic studies in the range 10 to 10 000 Å have many features in common. They are all concerned with the dispersion and focusing of electromagnetic radiation where the dispersing unit is either a prism or a grating which separates the radiation into its component frequencies to give what is known as the spectrum of the substance. If, however, it is impossible to resolve the frequencies—and this applies over a fairly wide frequency region—the spectrum is described as being continuous. In the ultra-violet and visible regions one type of instrument which may be employed to separate the light emitted by a molecule into its different frequencies, or to detect its absorption from continuous radiation, is that of the type given in Fig. 1.2. This instrument consists of a slit, a collimating lens, B, a prism, and a focusing lens C. If a set of frequencies $\bar{\nu}_1, \bar{\nu}_2, \bar{\nu}_3$ . . . are directed on to the slit as in Fig. 1.2, this then permits a narrow beam of light to enter the spectroscope;† the lens B collimates the light on to the prism while the latter disperses the light into its respective frequencies. The lens C then focuses these separated frequencies which are monochromatic images of the slit on to a photographic plate. When the photographic plate is developed, and providing the dispersion is sufficient, black 'lines' (really bands, see p. 9) are observed at various positions on the photographic plate corresponding to each of the emitted frequencies $\bar{\nu}_1$, $\bar{\nu}_2$, $\bar{\nu}_3$ . . . . This photographic-plate record of the spectrum is termed a *spectrogram*. In

† A *spectroscope* may be defined as an instrument which splits the light up into a spectrum.

addition, when the spectroscope gives a photographic record it is called a *spectrograph*, the former term sometimes being reserved for instruments where the spectrum is viewed with the eye.

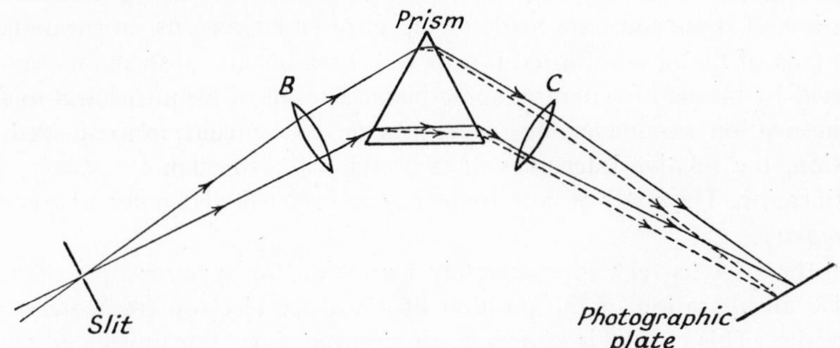

FIG. 1.2 Optical arrangements of one type of spectrograph employed in the visible and ultra-violet regions

A most important feature of a spectrograph is its ability to separate wavelengths of almost the same value, and this is measured by what is known as the resolving power which is defined as $\lambda/d\lambda$ where

$$d\lambda = \lambda_1 - \lambda_2 \tag{1.4}$$

and is the wavelength separation between the two closest lines λ_1 and λ_2 of similar intensity which can just be resolved with the spectrograph at the average wavelength (λ), where

$$\lambda = \frac{\lambda_1 + \lambda_2}{2}$$

The resolving power may vary considerably, depending on the type of spectrograph employed. In addition, for spectrographs employing prisms, the resolution varies considerably according to the wavelength region being considered. For example, the type of spectrograph given in Fig. 1.2 could have moderate resolving power in the ultra-violet region but only poor resolving power in the 5000 to 7500 Å part of the visible region. Much fundamental information has been obtained from spectral studies where a high resolving power has been employed.

Two of the experimental techniques available for the study of the emission spectrum of a molecule are the use of discharges and flames. In both cases the molecules are excited either by collision with electrons, atoms, ions, or other molecules, and then the molecule may either lose this energy by further collision or may emit some form of spectrum. If the spectrum is not completely continuous, then the radiation emitted should be characteristic of the molecule concerned. This type of process has been studied from the vacuum ultra-violet to the infra-red region. It is also possible to examine the absorption of energy by molecules, and this is done by directing energy from a filament lamp (e.g. to study from 3000 to 10 000 Å a tungsten lamp could be employed; it provides a continuous range of wavelengths in this region) through a cell containing the molecules whose absorption spectrum is required. The frequencies which are required to accomplish the particular energy changes are selected by the molecules from the continuous source of radiation. If the studies are made in the ultra-violet regions, in the visible, or in part of the near infra-red (up to 1.3 μ) region, the absorption may be detected by means of a photographic plate. The set of frequencies at which the absorption occurs enables the molecule to be characterised, and in addition, the relative intensities of these 'bands' also helps to achieve this identification. The study of both frequency and intensity is known as *spectrophotometry*.

In the 10 Å to very approximately 1 μ region the spectroscopic changes involve an alteration of the position of a valence electron from one orbit to another. This change is known as an *electronic* one. For molecules which undergo electromagnetic changes in the 1 μ to 100 μ range, the effect is usually to alter simultaneously a vibrational frequency of some or all of the nuclei, together with an alteration in the rotational energy of the molecule. This is known as a *rotation-vibration* change. For wavelengths greater than about 100 μ (to even beyond 30 cm) changes in the rotational energy—known as *pure rotational* energy changes—usually result. However, there is nothing rigid about the types of changes which may occur in these ranges. The quoted figures are quite arbitrary. For example, hydrogen chloride undergoes a pure rotational energy change in the 40 μ region and BeO an electronic transition at about 1.8 μ. In fact, the wavelength at which a particular electronic, rotation-vibration, or a pure rotational energy change occurs is determined in the simplest case of gaseous molecules at low pressures by such factors as the relative size of the atoms, the electron distribution within the chemical bonds, and the geometry of the molecule.

As yet the bulk of the infra-red work has been concerned with the absorption of electromagnetic radiation. It is only in the last few years that infra-red emission spectra have begun to be studied in detail. For electronic spectra, however, both absorption and emission spectra have been studied for a considerable number of years.

For the absorption and emission processes in a molecule involving electronic, rotation-vibration and pure rotational changes it is very rare for only one frequency to be observed. Usually, an appreciable number is involved.

Vibrational and rotational energy

In general, for molecular spectra the number of electronic states between which transitions take place is considerably smaller than those of atomic spectra. However, on the other hand, for electronic and rotation-vibration changes in molecules the spectra becomes more complex in that simultaneous changes in the rotational and vibrational energy occur. The frequencies of these spectral changes may be analysed in terms of changes in the quantum numbers which are allotted to characterise the molecules in their different energy states. The vibrational quantum number v which characterises the vibrational energy will now be considered.

The atoms within a molecule are never stationary, not even in the region of the absolute zero temperature. In the case of a diatomic molecule the nuclei vibrate along the line of the nuclei. The motion may be represented as in Fig. 1.3 where (*a*) indicates the inward motion of the nuclei and (*b*) the

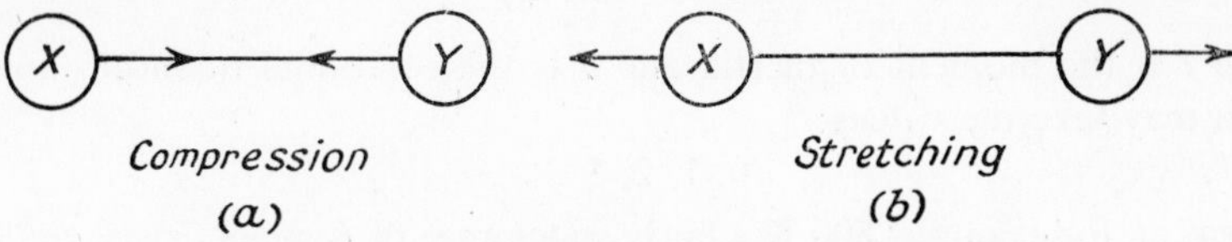

FIG. 1.3 Vibrational mode of a diatomic molecule

outward. Both these movements are characterised by one frequency, ω, where ω is expressed in wave-numbers. In this vibrational motion only a minute displacement of the nuclei takes place and is something of the order of 10^{-10} cm. If the vibrational motion were a simple harmonic one, then the vibrational energy E_v would be given by†:

$$E_v = (v+\tfrac{1}{2})hc\omega \tag{1.5}$$

where v is the vibrational quantum number and may take the values:

$$0, 1, 2, 3 \ldots$$

Thus, the feasible vibrational energy states are:

$$\tfrac{1}{2}hc\omega,\ \tfrac{3}{2}hc\omega,\ \tfrac{5}{2}hc\omega,\ \tfrac{7}{2}hc\omega \ \ldots$$

The number of vibrational levels which a molecule may have is fairly limited.

Although the vibrational motion is sometimes treated as though it were a simple harmonic one, in practice this is never so. In fact, the vibrational energy equation for a diatomic molecule has to be modified to:

$$E_v = (v+\tfrac{1}{2})hc\omega_e-(v+\tfrac{1}{2})^2hcx_e\omega_e+(v+\tfrac{1}{2})^3hcy_e\omega_e+ \ \ldots \tag{1.6}$$

where x_e and y_e are constants termed *anharmonicity constants*, inserted to make the equation fit the experimental data. ω_e is known as the wave-number of mechanical oscillation for small amplitudes; it is constant for a given electronic state and is really the wave-number associated with a hypothetical vibration of infinitesimal amplitude. The terms, $-(v+\tfrac{1}{2})^2hcx_e\omega_e$ and $(v+\tfrac{1}{2})^3hcy_e\omega_e$, thus, allow for the fact that the oscillations of the molecules are not simple harmonic ones. The lowest vibrational energy which a molecule may have is obtained by substituting $v = 0$ into this equation. The corresponding vibrational energy $E_{v=0}$ is given by:

$$E_{v=0} = \tfrac{1}{2}hc\omega_e-\tfrac{1}{4}hcx_e\omega_e+\tfrac{1}{8}hcy_e\omega_e+ \ \ldots \tag{1.7}$$

$E_{v=0}$ is known as the *zero point energy*. Even at room temperature by far the greater proportion of molecules of a given gas, liquid or solid is in the $v = 0$ vibrational state.

† The derivation of this equation is outlined in the Appendix.

When a solid is near the absolute zero temperature, although the molecules vibrate with their zero point energy, they do not rotate. As the temperature is raised rotation of the molecules eventually begins to take place. If the diatomic molecule is regarded as a rigid rotator (one where the internuclear distance does not alter during rotation), then the feasible rotational energy levels of the molecule are given by the equation:

$$E_r = J(J+1)\frac{h^2}{8\pi^2 I} \tag{1.8}$$

where I is the moment of inertia and J is the rotational quantum number which may take the values:

$$0, 1, 2, 3 \ldots$$

In a gas at, for example, 500°K a fairly wide range of J-values exists, e.g. from 0 to 100. The quantum number J defines the total angular momentum, P, of the molecule exclusive of nuclear spin. From quantum mechanics:

$$P = \sqrt{J(J+1)}\frac{h}{2\pi} \tag{1.9}$$

while from classical mechanics:

$$E_r = \frac{1}{2}\frac{P^2}{I} \tag{1.10}$$

Thus, if the value of P is substituted from equation (1.9) into (1.10), then equation (1.8) results.

The moment of inertia (I) depends upon the relative positions of the nuclei in the particular molecule. Every non-linear molecule may rotate about an infinite number of axes. However, from a mathematical point of view its motion can be described in terms of three orthogonal axes intersecting at the centre of mass about which the molecule can rotate, and it is by reference to these axes that the moment of inertia is calculated. Its value referred to one of three axes is determined by multiplying the mass of each atom by the square of its perpendicular distance from the axis and summing these products for all the atoms in the molecule. For example, the moment of inertia of an atom i about a particular axis is given by $I = m_i r_i^2$, where r_i is the distance of atom i from the axis and m_i its mass. The sum of the $m_i r_i^2$ terms for each atom gives the total moment of inertia I of the molecule about the particular axis.

The rotation of the linear molecule may be analysed in terms of rotation about the axes as in Fig. 1.4. The first axis of a linear molecule is chosen as the internuclear axis. The second axis is placed through the centre of mass perpendicular to the first axis, while the third is also placed through the centre of mass at right angles to the other two. The rotation takes place about the centre of mass of the molecule. The moment of inertia of the diatomic molecule may be readily shown to be:

$$I = \frac{m_A m_B}{m_A + m_B} r^2 \tag{1.11}$$

where m_A and m_B are the masses of the two atoms, and r is their internuclear distance. For a diatomic molecule and linear molecules in general the moment of inertia about the internuclear axis is zero since r is zero. Moreover, from symmetry considerations the moment of inertia about the other two axes must be equal.

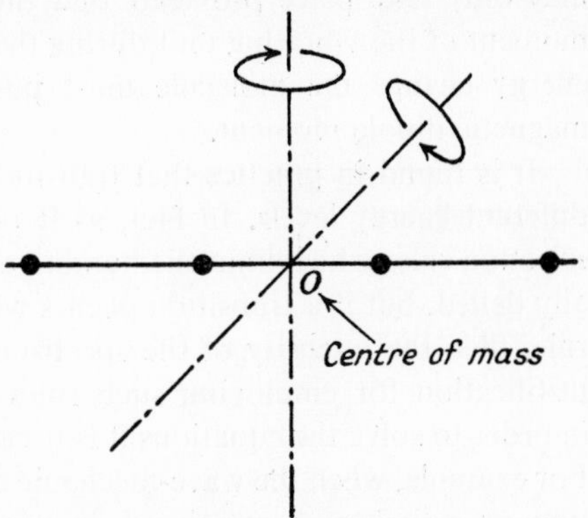

FIG. 1.4 Rotation of a linear molecule about two perpendicular axes

In practice equation (1.8), although a very good approximation, does not exactly fit the experimental data; this is especially true for higher values of J. The reason is that during the rotation of the molecule stretching of the bond occurs, and then the molecule may no longer be regarded as a rigid rotator. This centrifugal distortion in the molecule is taken into account by the addition of the small term:

$$-hcDJ^2(J+1)^2$$

Thus, the revised rotational energy equation† is:

$$E_r = \frac{h^2}{8\pi^2 I}J(J+1) - hcDJ^2(J+1)^2 \tag{1.12}$$

D is known as the centrifugal stretching constant and for a diatomic molecule may be related to the moment of inertia and the vibrational frequency by the equations:

$$D = \frac{4B^3}{\omega^2}\ \ddagger \tag{1.13}$$

where

$$B = \frac{h}{8\pi^2 cI} \tag{1.14}$$

Equations (1.1), (1.6), and (1.12) and the quantum numbers which we have considered may be used to analyse the total changes in energy which occur when the electron in a diatomic molecule changes its orbit. Instead of repeating the full equations for the rotational and vibrational energies, when E_r is mentioned, equation (1.12) will be implied unless indicated otherwise, while E_v will imply equation (1.6).

Energy changes within the molecule

Whether an energy change can occur at all depends on the molecule's ability to interact with the electromagnetic radiation. In each type of change

† Equation (1.12) applies not only to diatomic molecules but to linear polyatomic molecules as well.

‡ This equation would be exact only if the vibration were a harmonic one.

a certain criterion must be satisfied. For example, if the absorption of electromagnetic radiation is to produce a change in vibrational energy, interaction may only take place provided that there is a change in the electric dipole moment of the vibrating unit during the vibration while for a pure rotational energy change the molecule must possess either a permanent electric or magnetic dipole moment.

It is found in practice that transitions do not take place between all the different energy levels. In fact, as is observed for atomic spectra there are selection rules which limit the number of transitions. Such rules are occasionally defied, but if a transition occurs which is not permitted by the selection rule, then the intensity of the spectrum is usually very low. The theoretical justification for employing such rules is given by wave mechanics, where in order to solve the equations it is necessary to introduce certain limitations. For example, when the wave-mechanic equation is formulated for the absorption or emission of rotational energy of a diatomic molecule, between a higher rotational energy state characterised by the rotational quantum number J' and a lower one characterised by J'' it is found necessary, in order to obtain an acceptable solution for the equation, that:

$$J'-J'' = \pm 1 \tag{1.15}$$

where $J'-J''$ is represented by ΔJ. Thus, permissible pure rotational energy changes are limited by this selection rule to transitions between adjacent levels. This selection rule is considered in the Appendix of Volume 1. Transitions such as $\Delta J = \pm 2, \pm 3, \ldots$ are not observed in the pure rotational spectrum of a diatomic molecule in either the infra-red or microwave regions and are termed *forbidden transitions.*

If the eigenfunctions are known for the two energy states between which transitions are being considered, then it is in theory possible to determine the selection rules, that is to decide which transitions are permissible. It should be noted that even if a transition is theoretically permissible, it does not follow that it will necessarily be experimentally detected.

In the analysis of all types of spectra, electronic, rotation-vibration, and pure rotational energy changes, selection rules are found to be necessary. Examples will be found in the chapters on electronic, infra-red, and Raman spectra. For linear molecules the selection rules are fairly simple. However, as the symmetry of the molecule decreases the selection rules become more complex, and the analysis of the spectrum much more involved. In general, a complete analysis of a spectrum is feasible only for small molecules possessing a certain degree of symmetry.

To a first approximation the total energy of a molecule exclusive of any translational energy may be written as the sum of the rotational (E_r), vibrational (E_v), and electronic energies (E_e), that is:

$$E = E_e + E_v + E_r \tag{1.16}$$

The main processes are as follows:

(i) Changes in rotational energy of the molecule. If E_r' and E_r'' are the rotational energies of the molecule in the upper and lower states, respectively, then the change in rotational energy (ΔE_r) is:

$$\Delta E_r = E'_r - E''_r \dagger \tag{1.17}$$

These changes are studied mainly in the microwave region and occasionally in the higher wavelength region of the infra-red.

(ii) Changes in vibrational energy, $\Delta E_v = E_{v'} - E_{v''}$ where $E_{v'}$ and $E_{v''}$ are the vibrational energies in the upper and lower energy states, respectively. These changes are normally observed in the infra-red region requiring more energy than rotational changes. When these changes of vibrational energy occur, they are usually accompanied by simultaneous changes in rotational energy as well. If ΔE_{vr} is the total rotation-vibration energy change, then:

$$\Delta E_{vr} = (E_{v'} - E_{v''}) + (E'_r - E''_r) \tag{1.18}$$

and the electronic energy remains unaltered. Such a spectrum is usually studied by supplying a continuous source of radiation within the 2.5 to 25 μ range, and the changes in the rotation-vibration energy are followed by observing which frequencies are absorbed. For a particular vibrational energy change only one absorption line would be observed; however, if rotational energy changes simultaneously accompany the vibrational energy change, then a number of closely-spaced lines would lie near this line and give what is termed a *band*.‡ Even for a diatomic molecule several bands may, in general, be observed.

(iii) Changes in electronic energy. These occur mainly in the visible and ultra-violet regions, usually requiring more energy than those in the previous classes and, in general:

$$\Delta E_e > \Delta E_v > \Delta E_r$$

Electronic spectra are the most complex forms of spectra considered in this volume, since, in general, for this type all three kinds of energy changes simultaneously occur, that is:

$$\Delta E = (E'_e - E''_e) + (E_{v'} - E_{v''}) + (E'_r - E''_r) = h\bar{\nu} \tag{1.19}$$

For an electron passing from a higher energy orbit to a lower energy one, since electromagnetic radiation is given out, the process is known as one of *emission*. When electromagnetic radiation is taken up and an electron passes from a lower energy state to a higher one, the process is termed *absorption*. In the case of atoms for the transition between two electronic states a single line is observed; however, for the electronic spectrum of a molecule each change between two vibrational energy levels in the different electronic states produces a band, since the transitions simultaneously take place

† In molecular spectra in contrast to atomic spectra it is usual to write the higher energy state first. Thus, an emission transition would be written $E' \rightarrow E''$ while an absorption one would be written $E' \leftarrow E''$.

‡ It should be noted that pure rotational and also rotation-vibration changes in the lowest electronic state of the molecule may also be studied by means of the Raman technique. The mechanism by which the Raman change is accomplished, however, is completely different from the infra-red.

amongst the large number of rotational levels in these two different vibrational states. The observed spectral lines in an electronic change may be analysed in terms of vibrational and rotational quantum numbers of the upper and lower electronic states which are termed, respectively, v' and J' and v'' and J''. Since there is usually a number of $v'-v''$ transitions between these two electronic states, then the corresponding number of bands is observed. The total number of bands resulting from transitions between two electronic states is termed a *band system*. In Fig. 1.5 the band system of CN is given and the bands are identified in the figure in terms of their vibrational quantum number values in the upper and lower electronic states, that is v' and v'' values where the band is termed the (v', v'') band. With a spectrograph of sufficient resolving power each one of these bands may be shown

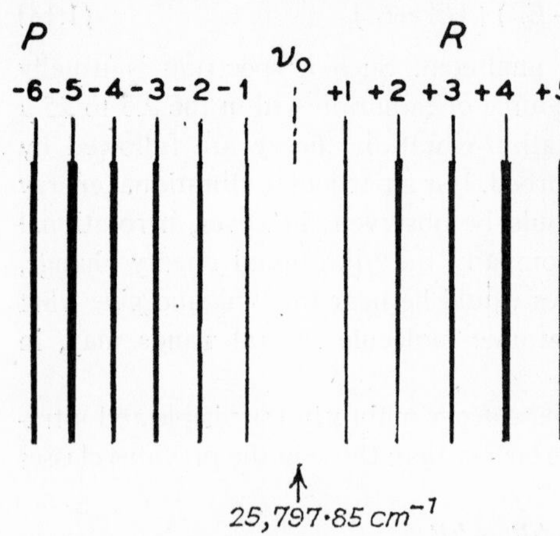

FIG. 1.6 Part of the (0, 0) band of the violet band system of CN, the lines on the higher and lower frequency sides are known as the R and P branches, respectively, and are characterised by their m values (see. p. 209) which equal $J''+1$ and $-J''$ respectively. (*From G. Herzberg*,[2] 'Spectra of Diatomic Molecules', Vol. 1, 2*nd ed.* 1950, *D. Van Nostrand Co., Princeton, N.J.*)

to consist of a number of closely-spaced lines. Each of these lines could be related to particular values of J' and J''. This is illustrated in Fig. 1.6 for part of the (0, 0) band of the violet band system of CN at a low temperature.

Term differences

It is a general principle in spectra that the wave-number of a spectral line is given by the difference of two terms. A term may be defined as the energy value divided by $\boldsymbol{hc}$. For example, a rotational term would be $E_r/\boldsymbol{hc}$, and this is represented by the symbol $F(J)$, that is:

$$\frac{E_r}{\boldsymbol{hc}} = F(J) \tag{1.20}$$

where $F(J)$ is in cm^{-1} units, and it follows from equations (1.20) and (1.12) that:

$$F(J) = J(J+1)\frac{\boldsymbol{h}}{8\pi^2 cI} - DJ^2(J+1)^2 \tag{1.21}$$

where $\boldsymbol{h}/8\pi^2 cI$ is known as the *rotational constant* and is given the symbol B. If E_r' is the rotational energy in an upper rotational state, and E_r'' that in a lower state, then if a transition takes place between them, it follows that the

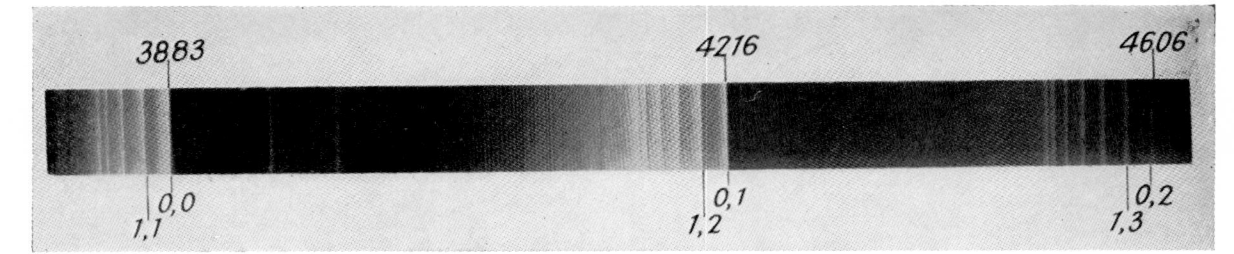

Fig. 1.5 Violet band system of CN at moderate dispersion. (The marked scale is in Ångström units.)
(*After Pearse and Gaydon*[1])

[*To face page* 10

wave-number of the spectral line for this transition would be given by the difference of the two terms E_r'/hc and E_r''/hc, that is:

$$\nu = F(J') - F(J'') \qquad (1.22)\dagger$$

The term value for the vibrational energy is represented by $G(v)$, that is:

$$\frac{E_v}{hc} = G(v) \qquad (1.23)$$

It then follows from equations (1.23) and (1.6) that:

$$G(v) = (v+\tfrac{1}{2})\omega_e - (v+\tfrac{1}{2})^2 x_e\omega_e + (v+\tfrac{1}{2})^3 y_e\omega_e + \ldots \qquad (1.24)$$

On dividing equation (1.16) throughout by hc we obtain:

$$E/hc = E_e/hc + E_v/hc + E_r/hc \qquad (1.25)$$

where E_e/hc is called the *electronic term value* (T_e) and E/hc is the *term value* (T) for the given electronic state. Thus, the term value equation is:

$$T = T_e + G(v) + F(J) \qquad (1.26)$$

In an electronic transition the wave-number of a spectral line is then given by the difference of the term value (T') in the upper electronic state and T'', the term value in the lower electronic state, that is:

$$\nu = T' - T'' = (T_e' - T_e'') + \{G'(v') - G''(v'')\} + \{F_{v'}(J') - F_{v''}(J'')\} \qquad (1.27)$$

In this equation $(T_e' - T_e'')$ is a constant term while $\{G'(v') - G''(v'')\}$ and $\{F_{v'}(J') - F_{v''}(J'')\}$ are the variable terms where the suffix on the F term indicates the vibrational level involved. By inserting the v', v'' and J', J'' values from equations (1.6) and (1.12) the wave-numbers of the spectral lines may be expressed in terms of the vibrational and rotational quantum numbers. For the lines in a particular band the $\{G'(v') - G''(v'')\}$ term is constant, and the wave-numbers of the different lines in the band may then be related to the variable term $\{F_{v'}(J') - F_{v''}(J'')\}$. This term is governed by the selection rule for J which for a diatomic molecule is either $J' - J'' = \pm 1$ or $0, \pm 1$. For another band in the same band system the v', v'' values differ, and $\{G'(v') - G''(v'')\}$ has a different value, and again $\{F_{v'}(J') - F_{v''}(J'')\}$ is the variable part which accounts for the rotational structure of the band. When all the observed v', v'' transitions are taken into account between the two electronic states, then the corresponding set of bands gives the band system.

For a rotation-vibration change in the same electronic state $T_e' = T_e''$ and the wave-numbers of the spectral lines would be given by:

$$\nu = \{G(v') - G(v'')\} + \{F_{v'}(J') - F_{v''}(J'')\} \qquad (1.28)$$

In this case $\{G(v') - G(v'')\}$ has a constant value,‡ and the wave-numbers of the lines in a given band are limited by the selection rule $\Delta J = \pm 1$ or $\Delta J = 0, \pm 1$.

† In general, throughout this volume the single dash $'$ will be employed to signify the higher energy state and the double dash $''$ the lower.

‡ However, when *overtones* (see p. 95) or other $v' - v''$ transitions are taken into account a few values of $\{G(v') - G(v'')\}$ may result, and consequently the corresponding number of bands will be observed.

Thus, for both an electronic and a rotation-vibration change the wave-numbers of the lines in a band are given by a formula of the type:

$$\nu = \nu_0 + F_{v'}(J') - F_{v''}(J'') \tag{1.29}$$

where ν_0 is a constant but differs, of course, in value for an electronic change compared with a rotation-vibration one. When $J'-J'' = +1$ the wave-numbers of the corresponding lines are members of what is known as the R-branch of the band and are given by the formula:

$$\nu = \nu_0 + F_{v'}(J') - F_{v''}(J'') \tag{1.30}$$

and on substitution for J':

$$\nu = \nu_0 + F_{v'}(J''+1) - F_{v''}(J'') = R(J'') \tag{1.31}$$

It is customary to employ $R(J'')$ to represent the wave-number of the R-branch line whose transition is characterised by having a rotational quantum number of value J'' in the lower energy level. When $J'-J'' = -1$ then the wave-numbers of the lines are members of what is known as the P-branch. These wave-numbers may be expressed in terms of the formula:

$$\nu = \nu_0 + F_{v'}(J''-1) - F_{v''}(J'') = P(J'') \tag{1.32}$$

where $P(J'')$ is used to represent the wave-numbers of the lines in the P-branch. In a similar way the wave-numbers of the lines in the Q-branch where $J' = J'' = 0$ are given by:

$$\nu = \nu_0 + F_{v'}(J') - F_{v''}(J'') = Q(J'') \tag{1.33}$$

It is usual in equations (1.31), (1.32), and (1.33) to let $J'' = J$. Thus, the equations for the P-, Q-, and R-branches of a diatomic molecule are:

$$\nu = \nu_0 + F_{v'}(J-1) - F_{v''}(J) = P(J) \tag{1.34}$$

$$\nu = \nu_0 + F_{v'}(J) - F_{v''}(J) = Q(J) \tag{1.35}$$

$$\nu = \nu_0 + F_{v'}(J+1) - F_{v''}(J) = R(J) \tag{1.36}$$

Potential energy curves and electronic transitions

A diatomic molecule X—Y will now be considered where one nucleus is regarded as being fixed at the ordinate axis, and the other vibrates along the direction of the bond with respect to this. When the potential energy is plotted against the distance between the centre of the atoms, then at one particular separation (equilibrium distance) the potential energy is a minimum. If this nuclear separation is reduced to less than the equilibrium distance, then owing to interatomic repulsion the potential energy increases very rapidly. On the other hand, if the separation is continually increased from the equilibrium distance, the potential energy increases more gradually and eventually reaches a limiting value. At this point the amplitude of vibration has become very large, and the molecule dissociates. The plot of internuclear distance against the potential energy for the lowest electronic energy state (the so-called *ground state*) for a diatomic molecule is illustrated in Fig. 1.7. The limb AB of the potential energy curve represents the compression of the nuclei while BC represents that of the stretching motion. The value of r at the minimum of the curve is the equilibrium internuclear distance (r_e) and is the distance at which the attractive and repulsive forces balance. Throughout the compression and stretching motions illustrated in Fig. 1.3 the total vibrational energy is constant and equal to the sum of the kinetic and potential energies. These two forms of energy are continually interchanging, and, in fact:

$$\text{vibrational energy} = \text{potential energy} + \text{kinetic energy} \qquad (1.37)$$

At the position of equilibrium separation the potential energy is a minimum, while at the extremities of both the stretching and compression motions the

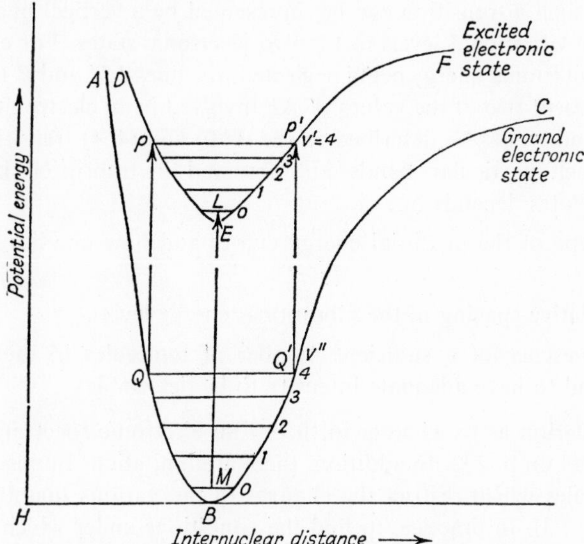

FIG. 1.7 Potential energy internuclear distance curves for a diatomic molecule in the ground and an excited electronic state. One nucleus is treated as being fixed at the ordinate axis, and the distance of the other nucleus is varied with respect to this along the abscissa. The (0, 0) and (4, 4) electronic transitions are indicated, no account being taken of rotational energy

kinetic energy is zero, since the nuclei are brought momentarily to rest and the potential energy must then be a maximum. A molecule may possess various amounts of quantised vibrational energy, and the permissible values are indicated by the horizontal lines intersecting the potential energy curve. Thus, the chosen lines are those where the kinetic energy is zero, and from equation (1.37) it then follows that the vibrational energy is equal to the potential energy. For simple harmonic motion the potential energy is given by $\frac{1}{2}kr^2$, where k is called the *force constant* (see p. 312). The motion, however, is never strictly a simple harmonic one. If it were, then the potential energy internuclear distance curve would have a parabolic shape. The nearest approach to this is in the lowest vibrational level.

If an electron within a diatomic molecule is excited, then the overall energy of the molecule is changed, and this requires a different potential energy curve for its representation. An example of this is given in Fig. 1.7 where *DEF* is the potential energy curve for the excited electronic state. The difference in electronic energy between the two minima is $E_e'-E_e''$. In the excited electronic state the molecule may have several possible quantised vibrational energy values which are represented by the horizontal lines which intersect the upper potential energy curve.

Usually an electronic transition is accompanied simultaneously by a vibrational energy change, and since there is a negligible change in the internuclear distance during the time of excitation (which is of the order of 10^{-16} sec), such a transition can be represented by a vertical line joining the appropriate vibrational levels in the two electronic states. For example, any change in rotational energy being neglected, the lines *LM* and *P′Q′* in Fig. 1.7 would represent two of the values of ΔE involved in an electronic absorption spectrum and would be described as the (0, 0) and (4, 4) transitions, respectively. Which particular bands are observed in transitions between two electronic states depends on:

(i) The shape of the potential energy curves and how one lies with respect to the other.

(ii) The relative spacing of the vibrational energy levels.

(iii) The presence of a sufficient number of molecules in the initial level for the band to have adequate intensity to be detectable.

The criterion as to whether in theory an electronic spectrum may occur is considered on p. 202. In addition, there are limitations imposed by certain selection rules which restrict the changes in the various quantum numbers (see Chapter 3). In practice, to find the conditions under which a particular electronic transition may be achieved is largely a matter of experience, intuition and experimental study. If it is desired to examine an emission spectrum, the major approaches would be either by some form of discharge or by the presence of the molecule (or radical) in a flame. If the energy required for the transition were high, as in, for example, the electronic transitions in the nitrogen molecule, then the transitions would not be observed by means of excitation in flames. In most discharges, however, a relatively much greater source of excitation energy is available, and electronic transitions in N_2 are readily produced.

In Fig 1.8 one of the potential energy curves (*DEF*) has no minimum. As a result an absorption electronic transition from the ground state of the molecule (potential energy curve *ABC*) to the unstable state *DEF* causes spontaneous dissociation of the molecule. Since the upper potential energy curve does not possess any quantised vibrational levels continuous absorption results, and the molecule dissociates into atoms which dispose of the energy in the kinetic form. In emission, some of the causes of continuous radiation result from (*a*) transition from an unstable state to a stable electronic state of a molecule, or (*b*) the combination of an electron with a positive ion to form a neutral atom or molecule, where the energy of recombination together with the kinetic energy of approach results in the emission of continuous radiation, or (*c*) the combination of two ions. A continuum normally extends over a reasonably wide region of the spectrum, and since, in general, it lacks characterising features, then it is often difficult to distinguish the emitter.

It will be noted from the asymmetry of the potential energy curves in Fig. 1.7 that the internuclear distance will vary from one vibrational energy state to the next. Hence, it follows from equation (1.11) that the moment of inertia varies with the vibrational quantum number v. In the analysis of microwave spectra only one value of B need be taken into account. For infra-red and electronic spectra $B_{v'}$ and $B_{v''}$ are usually required. One of the most important features in these three different types of spectra is the determination of the B-values by fitting the observed wave-numbers of the spectral lines to the appropriate formula involving B- and J-values, where the main object of the analysis is internuclear distance evaluation.

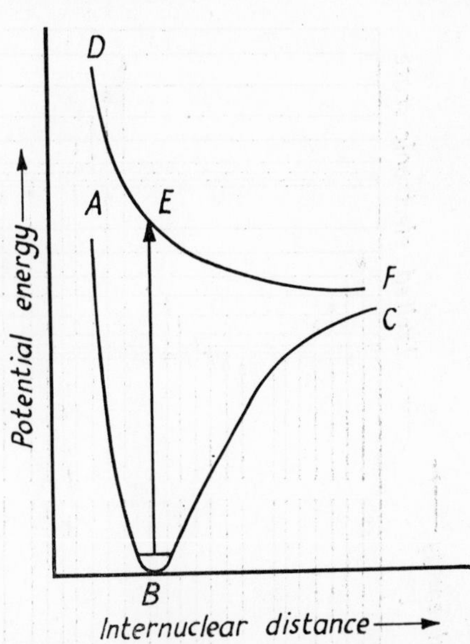

FIG. 1.8 Potential energy internuclear distance curves for a transition between which continuous radiation is being absorbed

Total energy plot and electronic transitions

In the treatment of potential energy curves the rotational energy was neglected, i.e. it was assumed that $J = 0$ for each vibrational level. The contribution of the rotational energy for each state with J greater than zero could be calculated, if the moment of inertia were known, by insertion of the appropriate J-value into equation (1.8). If this amount of rotational energy were added to the appropriate vibrational energy, then the total energy in the given vibrational state would be obtained. In Fig. 1.9 the total energy plots are made for the various rotational levels of the two vibrational energy states $v = 0$ and $v = 1$ for the ground and excited electronic states where the rotational quantum numbers are indicated on the right, and, the height of each line represents the sum of the vibrational and rotational energies. It must be emphasised that the vibrational energy is not now subdivided into potential and kinetic energies. The electronic transitions for the (0, 0), (1, 0), and (0, 1) bands have been inserted. The case treated is that of a diatomic molecule where the selection rule $\Delta J = \pm 1$ applies.

In this introduction we have mainly considered diatomic molecules which in the lowest vibrational level have only one vibrational frequency. In the case of polyatomic molecules there are frequently many possible modes

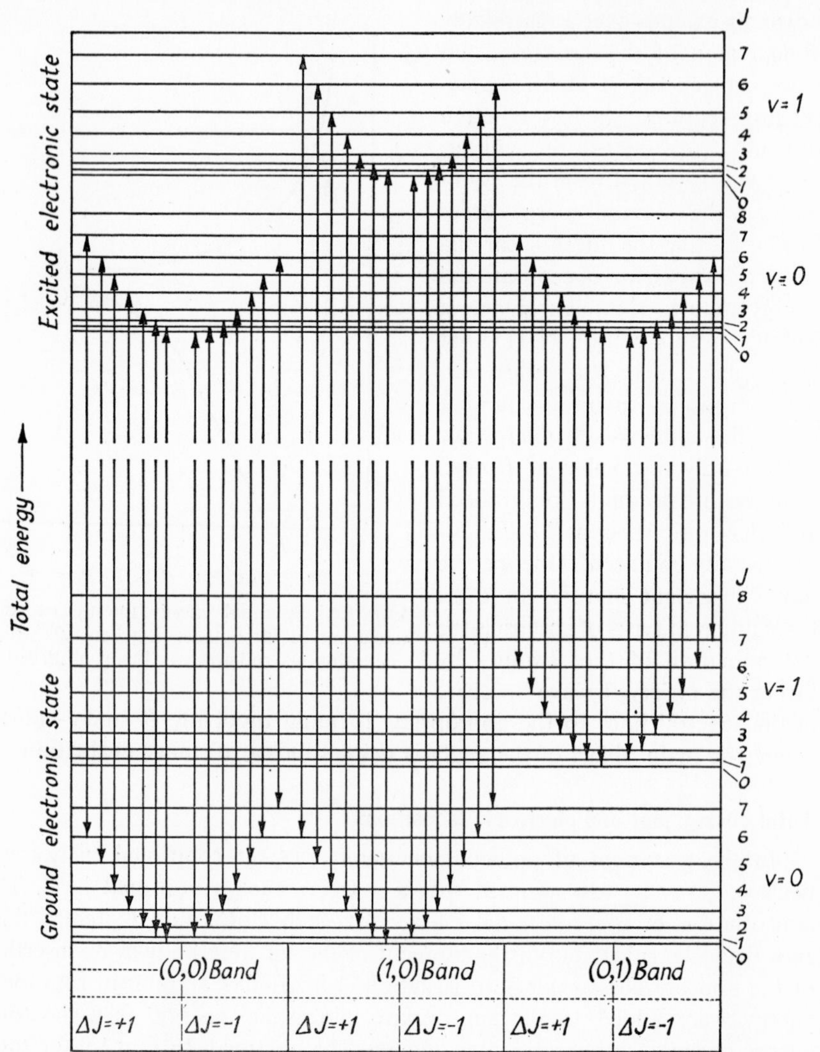

FIG. 1.9 Total energy plot for the ground and an excited electronic state. The electronic transitions for the (0, 0), (1, 0), and (0, 1) bands have been inserted. The case treated is that of a diatomic molecule where the selection rule $\Delta J = \pm 1$ is applicable

of vibration. For example benzene has twenty different fundamental vibrational frequencies.† It may perhaps be readily appreciated that when electronic absorption or emission of energy occurs in such a molecule, the resulting

† The meaning of the phrase "fundamental vibrational frequency" is dealt with on p. 92.

band system is extremely complex. In general, the most fundamental information, which results from the study of the rotational structure of a band, can be elucidated for only very simple molecules. For the majority of polyatomic molecules the rotational structure of the band cannot be resolved.

Three main types of study in the ultra-violet, visible, and infra-red regions have been:

(i) As a means of fingerprinting the molecule and as a subsequent means of qualitative analysis.

(ii) For quantitative analysis where the intensity of the spectral lines has been related to the concentration of the species concerned.

(iii) For the determination of the geometry of simple molecules.

Much of the qualitative analysis—especially in the ultra-violet and visible regions—is dependent on the intensities of the bands, and some intensity aspects will now be considered briefly.

Population of rotational and vibrational levels and band intensities

It will be observed in Fig. 1.5 that there is an appreciable variation in the intensity of the bands in the given band system of CN. The intensity of each of these bands is dependent on how highly populated each vibrational level is from which the transition takes place. Since this spectrogram is an emission one, then this means that the intensities are dependent on the population of the v' vibrational levels, that is those of the upper electronic state. The most intense bands involve the $v' = 0$ vibrational level. However, many other bands are obtained involving the $v' = 1, 2, 3 \ldots$ vibrational levels. A visual estimate of the relative intensities of some of these bands is given in Table 1.1; these estimates are based on an arbitrary scale of allotting the most intense band an intensity of 10 and then estimating the intensities of the others relative to this.

TABLE 1.1

The relative intensities and transitions in some of the violet system bands of CN

Wavelength (Å)	Intensity	Transition $v' \to v''$
4606.1	1	0 2
4578.0	2	1 3
4553.1	2	2 4
4216.0	9	0 1
4197.2	8	1 2
4181.0	7	2 3
3883.4	10	0 0
3871.4	9	1 1
3861.9	8	2 2

For a particular vibrational state (v') the number of molecules present in that state is proportional to the Boltzmann factor, $\exp -(E_{v'}/kT)$. $E_{v'}$ is the vibrational energy of the v' level, $\boldsymbol{k}$ is the Boltzmann constant, and T is the absolute temperature. The greater the value of v' the greater $E_{v'}$ and the very much less the value of $\exp(-E_{v'}/\boldsymbol{k}T)$. In fact, this term usually falls off very rapidly in value with increasing v' values. The distribution of the molecules in the v' levels in the case of an emission spectrum is dependent on the method employed for the excitation. For the emission spectra which result from flames, and also arc excitation, usually a fair range of v' values is found in the spectrum. In the case of an electronic or a rotation-vibration absorption spectrum carried out at room temperature, by far the larger number of molecules is in the $v'' = 0$ level initially and, thus, relatively intense $v' \leftarrow 0$ bands are to be expected. The $v' \leftarrow 1$, $v' \leftarrow 2$, $v' \leftarrow 3$ bands would be anticipated to be progressively less intense since the $v'' = 1, 2, 3$ levels are progressively less populated. However, by considerably increasing the temperature (e.g. a 1000°C) the number of molecules in the $v'' = 1, 2$ and 3 levels will be increased at the expense of those in the $v'' = 0$ level. However, even such a temperature increase would normally leave many more molecules in the $v'' = 0$ level than in the sum of all the other vibrational levels together.

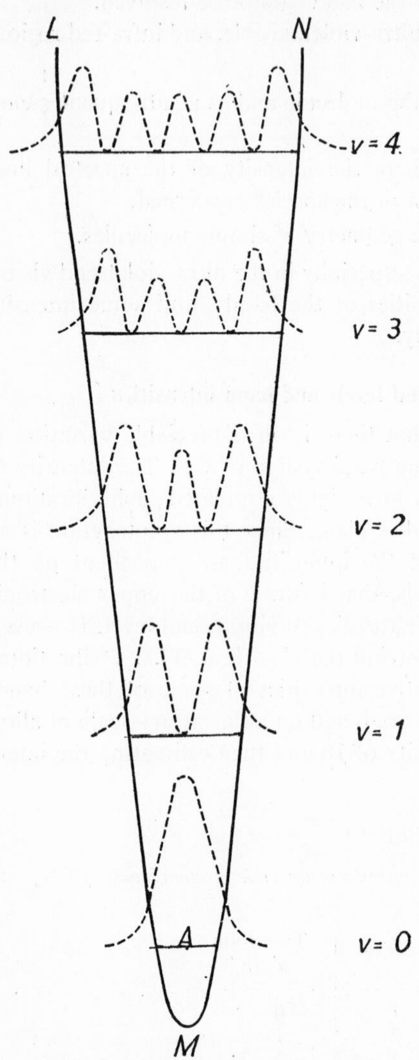

Fig. 1.10 Potential energy internuclear distance curve (*LMN*) where the first five vibrational levels are indicated by the full lines parallel to the abscissa. The ordinate plot (broken lines) is that of the probability density distribution for the particular vibrational level and this plot is independent of the scale on the potential energy axis

The intensity distribution of the bands in an electronic transition from a given set of vibrational levels may be largely accounted for on the basis of a theory developed by Condon and Franck. The two main assumptions of the theory are that:

(i) The time of an electronic transition (about 10^{-16} sec) is so very much smaller than that of the period of nuclear vibration (about 10^{-14} sec) that the internuclear distance does not alter during the electronic transition.

(ii) The most probable internuclear distance at which an electronic transition is likely to occur is that when the nuclei are in their extreme positions. These positions correspond with the internuclear distances at which the vibrational levels intersect the potential energy curve (see Fig. 1.7). The choice of two such positions for the transitions from a particular vibrational level is justified on the grounds that during the period of vibration each nucleus spends more time at these extreme positions where the turning point of the motion occurs.

The Franck-Condon type of theory, which was first put forward over thirty years ago, has now been slightly modified. From a wave-mechanic point of view the most probable internuclear distance in a particular vibrational level is given by the maxima in Fig. 1.10 where a quantity proportional to the most probable internuclear distance is plotted against internuclear distance, and this plot is indicated by means of the dotted lines. Thus, in the $v = 0$ level the most probable internuclear distance is not at the point of

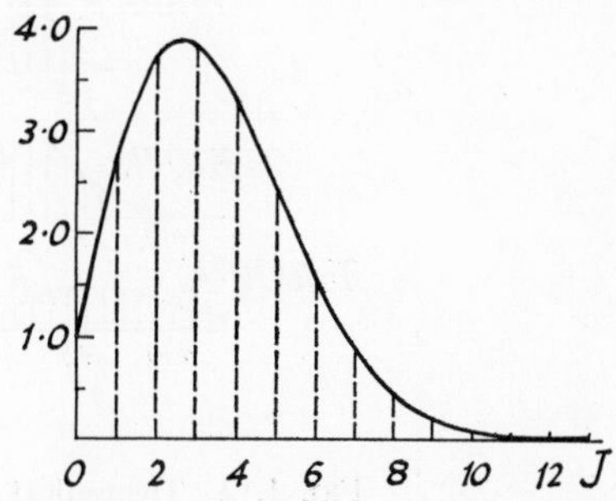

FIG. 1.11 Thermal distribution of the rotational levels for HCl in the ground state at 300°K. The curve represents the function $(2J+1) \exp(-BJ(J+1)hc)/kT$ as a function of J ($B = 10.44$ cm^{-1}). The broken lines (ordinate plot) serve to indicate the relative populations of the corresponding rotational levels. (*From G. Herzberg*,[2] 'Spectra of Diatomic Molecules', Vol. 1, *2nd ed.*, 1950, *D. Van Nostrand Co., Princeton, N.J.*)

intersection of the vibrational energy line with the potential energy curve but at the point A. That is, the majority of molecules have this internuclear distance. Thus, when an electronic transition occurs from this $v = 0$ level the majority of molecules concerned will have an internuclear distance of r_A. Hence, for such transitions it is more correct to represent the transition from the point A rather than from the points at which the vibrational energy level intersects the potential energy curve.

For the higher vibrational levels in a given electronic state the larger maxima are found at the extremities of the vibration. In this case the Franck-Condon theory as originally put forward is usually adequate (see, however, p. 203), and the electronic transitions may be largely accounted for by drawing two lines such as PQ and $P'Q'$ on Fig. 1.7 parallel to the ordinate axis to the point of intersection with the upper electronic potential energy curve. The simplest case is chosen in Fig. 1.7, where there is negligible alteration in the equilibrium internuclear distance on electronic excitation.

For a diatomic molecule in the lowest vibrational level (i.e. $v = 0$) the number of molecules (N_J) in the rotational level J may be shown to be proportional to:

$$(2J+1)\exp\left(-\frac{E_r}{kT}\right)$$

where for a rigid rotator:

$$E_r = J(J+1)\frac{h^2}{8\pi^2 I} \tag{1.38}$$

The relative populations for different J values in the case of HCl are given in Fig. 1.11.

However, for the higher vibrational levels:

$$N_J \alpha (2J+1)\exp\left(\frac{-E_v}{kT}\right)\exp\left(\frac{-E_r}{kT}\right)$$

and although the distribution of the molecules over the rotational levels is the same, the population of each particular rotational level is diminished by the factor $\exp(-E_v/kT)$.

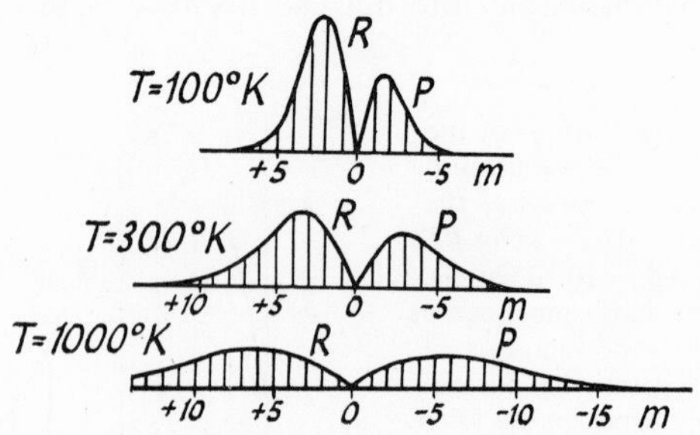

FIG. 1.12 Theoretical intensity distribution in a rotation-vibration band in absorption at 100°, 300°, and 1000°K for HCl where $B = 10.44$ cm^{-1}. The ordinate plot is of intensity while the abscissa is that of wave-number m; shorter wavelengths lie to the left in this figure. (*From G. Herzberg*,[2] 'Spectra of Diatomic Molecules', Vol. 1, 2*nd ed.*, 1950, *D. Van Nostrand Co., Princeton, N.J.*)

It may also be deduced that the intensity, I, of an absorption line of wave-number ν in a pure rotational change or a rotation-vibration change is given by:

$$I_{\text{abs}} = \frac{C_{\text{abs}}}{f_r}\nu(J'+J''+1)\exp\{-B''J''(J''+1)hc/kT\} \tag{1.39}$$

and in emission by:

$$I_{\text{em}} = \frac{C_{\text{em}}\nu^4}{f_r}(J'+J''+1)\exp\{-B'J'(J'+1)hc/kT\} \tag{1.40}$$

where C_{abs} and C_{em} may be regarded as constants. f_r is the rotational partition function (see p. 328). For a particular rotation-vibration band at a fixed temperature the factors $C_{abs}\nu/f_r$ and $C_{em}\nu^4/f_r$ are almost constant. Hence, the intensity distribution within the band is largely dependent on the factor $\exp(-E_r/kT)$, that is the intensity distribution of the rotational levels in the (i) lower vibrational state for absorption, and (ii) upper vibrational state for emission. Fig. 1.12 illustrates the theoretical intensity distribution for a rotation-vibration band of HCl in absorption. It may be observed that with increasing temperature the range of J values increases. It is interesting to note that the intensity of an emission line is dependent on ν^4, but the corresponding absorption line would depend only on ν. Thus, a low intensity rotation-vibration transition might be detectable in emission but not necessarily so in absorption.

The relative intensity distribution of the bands resulting from an electronic transition is dealt with on p. 202.

References

1. PEARSE, R. W. B. and GAYDON, A. G. *Identification of Molecular Spectra*. Chapman and Hall (London, 1950).
2. HERZBERG, G. *Spectra of Diatomic Molecules*. D. Van Nostrand (New York, 1950).

2

Instrumentation

THIS chapter describes the theoretical and practical aspects of two kinds of spectrographs termed the *prism* and *grating types*. The instruments considered will be mainly those employed in electronic spectra studies ranging from 2000 Å to about 1.8 μ, although the principles dealt with will, in the main, apply equally to the vacuum ultra-violet and infra-red regions. The spectrometers used in other regions will be considered in the appropriate chapters. Before the prism and grating spectrographs are described, it is useful to revise some of the basic theory of refraction and dispersion.

Theoretical aspects of prism instruments

Index of refraction

When monochromatic light passes through a transparent isotropic medium at constant temperature the ratio of the sine of the angle of incidence i to the sine of the angle of refraction r (see Fig. 2.1) is constant for that medium. This ratio is known as the *refractive index n*:

$$n = \sin i/\sin r \qquad (2.1)$$

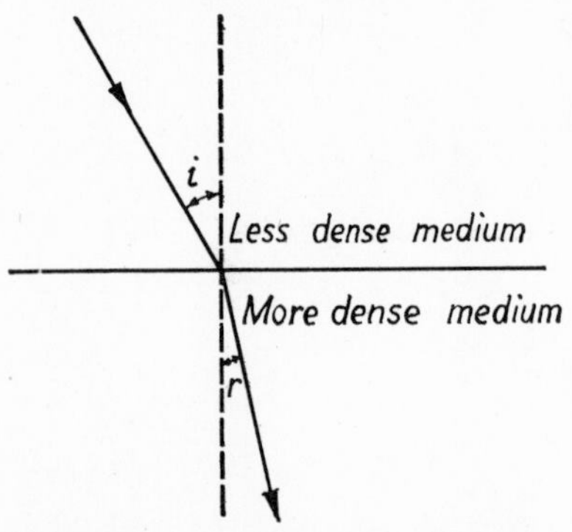

FIG. 2.1 Refraction of a ray on passing from a less to a more dense medium

In the wavelength region for which the medium is transparent the refractive index increases as the wavelength of the light decreases. A useful empirical relation between the refractive index n and the wavelength λ is given by the *Hartmann dispersion formula*:

$$n = n_0+c/(\lambda-\lambda_0) \qquad (2.2)$$

where n_0, c, and λ_0 are constants over a restricted wavelength range for the material of the medium. This formula is of use in obtaining an expression for (*a*) the angular dispersion of a prism, and (*b*) a formula employed in the determination of wavelengths of lines and bands.

Angle of minimum deviation

The best optical image in the case of a prism can be obtained if the prism is traversed by parallel light, and if the light rays pass through the prism parallel to its base, that is, with equal refraction at each surface. These conditions can be realised for only one wavelength and cannot be true simultaneously for a range of wavelengths passing through a prism spectrograph. In the construction of a prism instrument, however, an approximation to these conditions is made.

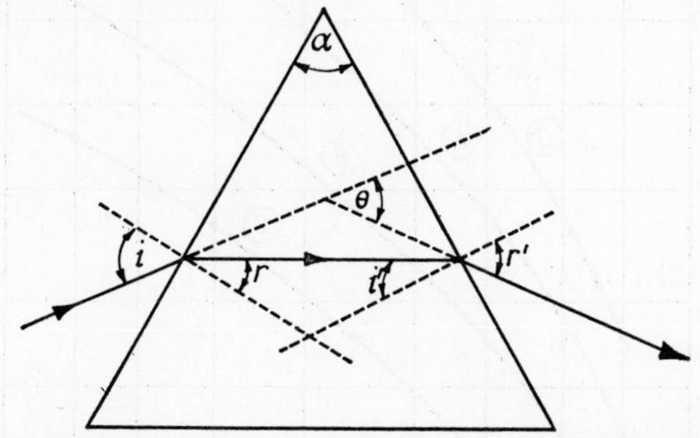

FIG. 2.2 Ray of light passing through a prism at minimum deviation

When the incident and emergent rays are symmetrically disposed with respect to the prism, that is, when $i = r'$ and $i' = r$ as in Fig. 2.2, the deviation θ is less than for any other angle of incidence i, and the prism is said to be set for minimum deviation.

Dispersion by a prism

The dispersion by a prism is expressed as the deviation $d\theta/d\lambda$ in units of radians per Ångström unit (rad/Å); this measures the angular separation of two light rays which differ in wavelength by an amount $d\lambda$. The value of $d\theta/d\lambda$ is not constant but depends on the wavelength and is greatest in the ultra-violet, and decreases with increasing wavelength. For the ray of minimum deviation it may readily be shown that:

$$n = \sin i/\sin r = \sin \tfrac{1}{2}(\alpha+\theta)/\sin \tfrac{1}{2}\alpha \qquad (2.3)$$

On differentiation of equation (2.3) we get:

$$\frac{dn}{d\theta} = \frac{\cos \frac{1}{2}(\alpha+\theta)}{2 \sin \frac{1}{2}\alpha} = \frac{\sqrt{1-\{\sin \frac{1}{2}(\alpha+\theta)\}^2}}{2 \sin \frac{1}{2}\alpha} \qquad (2.4)$$

and on substitution from equation (2.3) it follows that:

$$\frac{dn}{d\theta} = \frac{\sqrt{1-n^2 \sin^2 \frac{1}{2}\alpha}}{2 \sin \frac{1}{2}\alpha} \qquad (2.5)$$

If the Hartmann dispersion formula (equation (2.2)) is differentiated, then:

$$\frac{dn}{d\lambda} = -\frac{c}{(\lambda-\lambda_0)^2} \tag{2.6}$$

where $dn/d\lambda$ is the characteristic dispersion of the prism material at the wavelength λ.

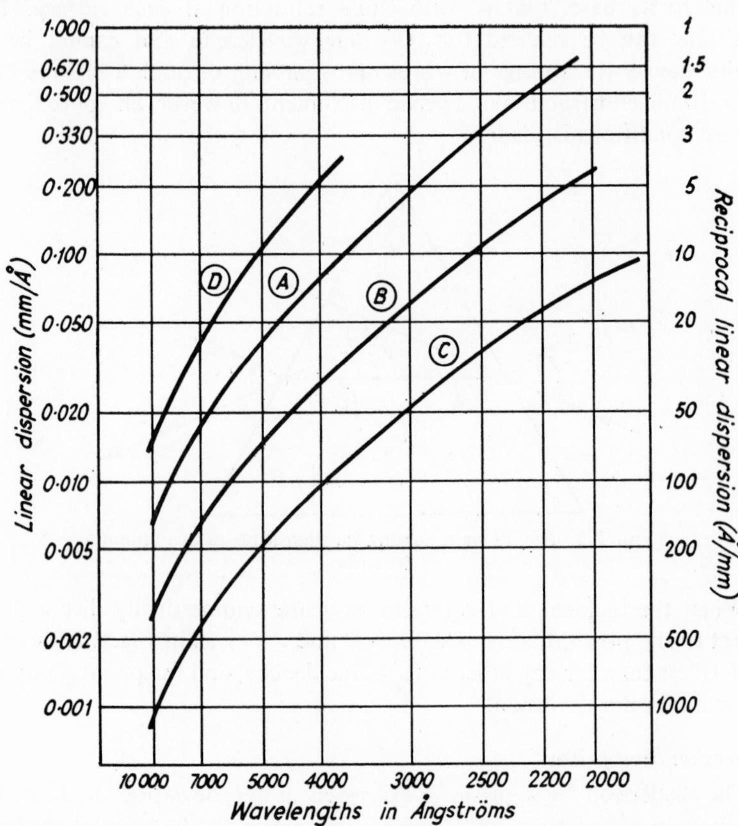

FIG. 2.3 Linear and reciprocal linear dispersion of four Hilger prism spectrographs, where A, B, C, and D are for the large, medium, small quartz and large glass spectrographs, respectively. (*Courtesy of Hilger and Watts Ltd.*)

The angular dispersion $d\theta/d\lambda$ may be written in the form:

$$\frac{d\theta}{d\lambda} = \frac{d\theta}{dn} \cdot \frac{dn}{d\lambda} \tag{2.7}$$

which on substitution for $d\theta/dn$ and $dn/d\lambda$ from equations (2.5) and (2.6) gives:

$$\frac{d\theta}{d\lambda} = \frac{-2c \sin \frac{1}{2}\alpha}{(\lambda-\lambda_0)^2\sqrt{1-n^2 \sin^2 \frac{1}{2}\alpha}} \tag{2.8}$$

Thus, the deviation of a ray of wavelength λ depends on the geometry of the prism and the prism material. It should be noted that the size of the prism does not enter into this expression for $d\theta/d\lambda$.

In practice, in the literature it is more usual to find dispersion described in terms of reciprocal linear dispersion in units of Å/mm of photographic plate rather than the angular dispersion of the prism in units of rad/Å. The reciprocal linear dispersion is defined as $d\lambda/dx$, where dx is the distance

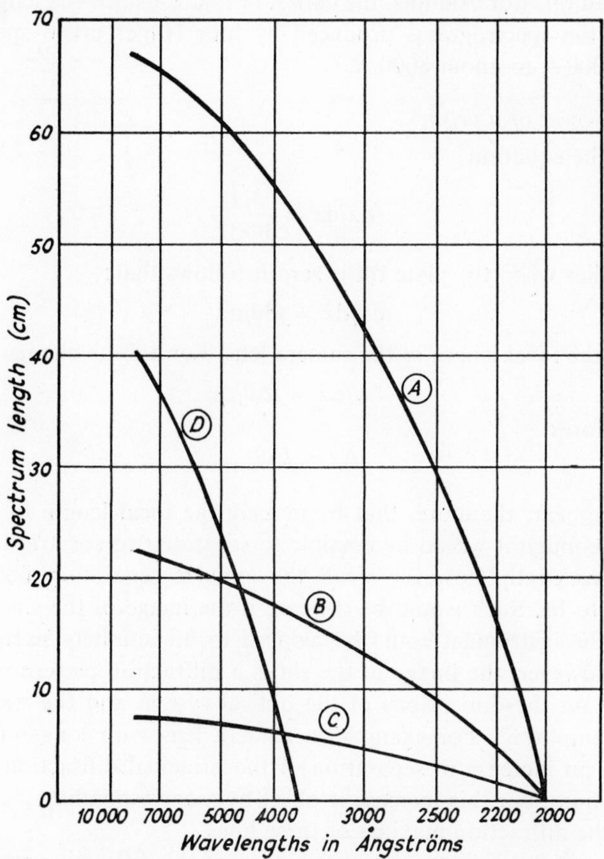

FIG. 2.4 Spectrum lengths of four Hilger prism spectrographs, where *A*, *B*, *C*, and *D* are for the large, medium, small quartz and large glass spectrographs, respectively. (*Courtesy of Hilger and Watts Ltd.*)

in millimetres on the photographic plate between rays with wavelengths λ and $(\lambda + d\lambda)$. When the plate tilt is zero the angular dispersion $d\theta/d\lambda$ is related to the reciprocal linear dispersion by the equation:

$$d\lambda/dx = \frac{1/f}{d\theta/d\lambda} \tag{2.9}$$

where f is the focal length of the (camera) lens bringing light to focus on the photographic plate of the spectrograph. For convenience the dispersion, both linear $dx/d\lambda$ (mm/Å) and reciprocal linear $d\lambda/dx$ (Å/mm), of a spectrograph may be presented in the form of a graph of dispersion plotted against wavelength. This is illustrated in Fig. 2.3 for the linear dispersion of four Hilger prism instruments. Alternatively, a useful graph is that which gives the plot of spectrum length in centimetres against wavelength in Ångström units, and from this graph the spectrum length between any two wavelengths may be read off. For example, the curves in Fig. 2.4 show the length in centimetres of the spectrograms produced by four Hilger prism spectrographs between 2000 Å to about 8000 Å.

Resolving power of a prism

From the equation

$$\mathrm{d}\lambda/\mathrm{d}x = \frac{1/f}{\mathrm{d}\theta/\mathrm{d}\lambda} \tag{2.10}$$

which applies when the plate tilt is zero it follows that:

$$\mathrm{d}x/\mathrm{d}\lambda = f\mathrm{d}\theta/\mathrm{d}\lambda \tag{2.11}$$

where f is the focal length of the camera lens. For a finite change

$$\Delta x/\Delta\lambda = f\Delta\theta/\Delta\lambda \tag{2.12}$$

and, therefore:

$$\Delta x = f\Delta\theta \tag{2.13}$$

It would appear, therefore, that by making the focal length of the camera lens large enough it would be possible to separate two spectral lines of very similar wavelength, however small the angular separation between them happened to be. Such would be the case if the image of the slit in the focal plane of the instrument could be reduced to an infinitely narrow line. In practice, however, the image of the slit is a diffraction pattern of finite size depending on the dimensions of the optical system and the wavelength of the light employed. For example, a camera lens with longer focal length will cause an increase in separation of the principal diffraction maxima of two close lines, but this increase is offset by a corresponding increase in the width of the diffraction maxima of these lines.

To appreciate the intensity distribution of the diffraction pattern an example will be considered using monochromatic light as source, and for the sake of simplicity the actual dispersing element will be omitted.

With reference to Fig. 2.5, if AB is the limiting aperture, the diffraction pattern will be that of this aperture and will depend on its size only, since λ and f are constants. AB may be regarded as a diaphragm which restricts the size of the bundle of rays, and in a spectrograph its position would be occupied by the dispersing system (a prism): for monochromatic light the diaphragm AB and the prism would produce the same effect.

In Fig. 2.5 monochromatic light passes through an infinitely narrow vertical slit at S, then falls on the collimating lens, L_1, which makes the light parallel and directs it on to AB. An image of AB is formed by the lens, L_2, in the focal plane PP' (plane in which the photographic plate is located in a spectrograph). When the wave-front from the aperture AB (Fig. 2.5) passes through the lens L_2 and is focused at P, no phase difference in the light is introduced, since by Fermat's principle the length of any path from the aperture AB is the same. Expressed in terms of the path lengths in Fig. 2.6 this becomes:

$$x+ny+z = x'+ny'+z' = x''+z'' = \text{constant} \tag{2.14}$$

where n is the refractive index of the lens material. Hence, at P the light waves arrive in phase, and their intensities add together and give a resultant intensity which is a maximum. In addition, according to the Huyghens principle

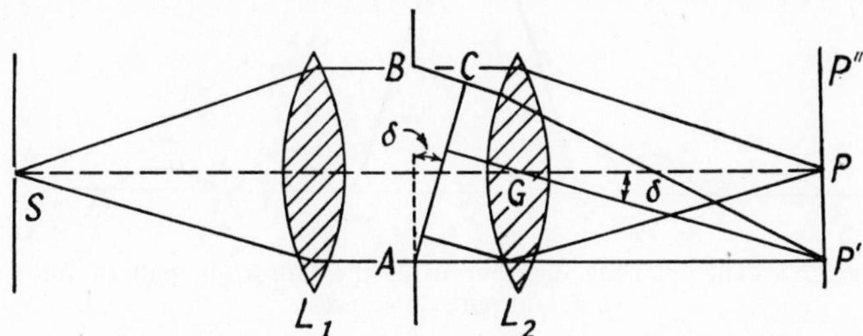

FIG. 2.5 Diffraction of a wave front by a rectangular aperture. (*After Sawyer*[1])

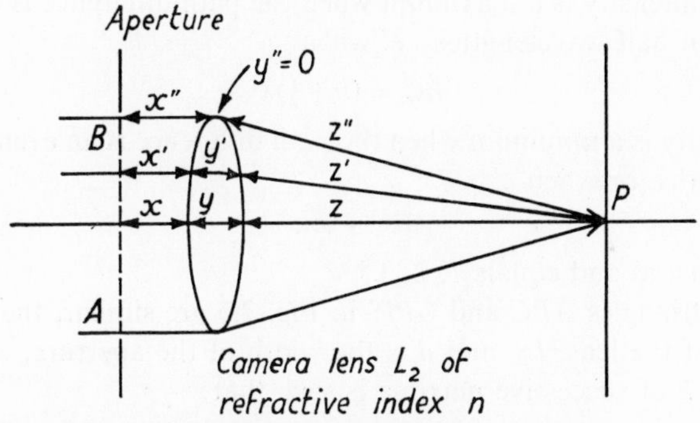

FIG. 2.6 Illustration of Fermat's principle

diffracted wave-fronts may spread in all directions; such a front brought to focus at P' will now be considered. It may be seen from Fig. 2.5 that the light passing through the upper half of the aperture (AB) must travel further than that passing through the lower half; the path difference between the rays passing through the bottom and top of the aperture is equal to the distance BC. As before the lens will not introduce any further phase shifts. If the path difference BC is equal to an even number of half wavelengths, then the intensity at a point such as P' will be a minimum, since for every point in the lower half of AC there will be a corresponding point in the upper half whose distance from P' differs by $\lambda/2$ and whose contributions at P' destructively interfere. Thus, the two rays would be exactly out of phase and would cancel each other out. If, on the other hand, the path difference BC is an odd number of half wavelengths, the intensity will give a maximum. For example, if

$BC = 3\lambda/2$, the bundles of light from AC may be considered to be divided into three equal parts where two of these parts will cancel each other out, but the third will produce a weak maximum. If $BC = 5\lambda/2$, the diffracted wave-front may be regarded as being divided into five parts, where disturbances due to two will destroy another two, while the fifth part will provide light for a weak maximum.

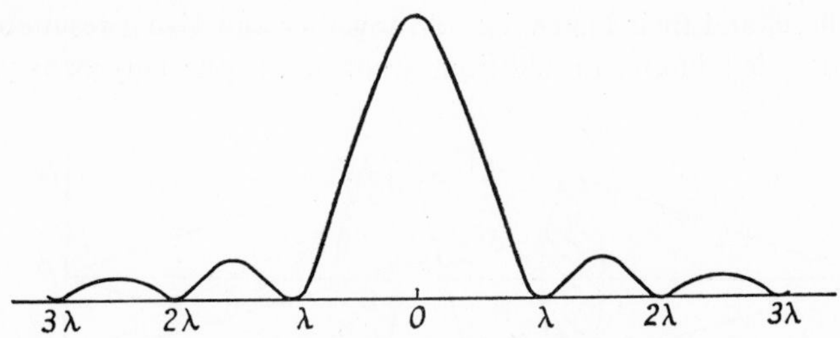

FIG. 2.7 The intensity distribution of the diffraction pattern for different path differences

The intensity distribution of the diffraction pattern for these different path differences, BC, is represented in Fig. 2.7. It may be seen from the figure that the light intensity is a maximum when the path difference is equal to an odd number of half wavelengths, i.e. when

$$BC = (n+\tfrac{1}{2})\lambda \tag{2.15}$$

and the intensity is a minimum when the path difference is an even number of half wavelengths, or when

$$BC = n\lambda \tag{2.16}$$

where n is integral and equals 1, 2, 3.†

Since the triangles ABC and GPP' in Fig. 2.5 are similar, then if f is the focal length of the lens, L_2, and d is the width of the aperture, AB, the distance x from P of successive maxima is such that:

$$\sin \delta = (n+\tfrac{1}{2})\lambda/d \tag{2.17}$$

or approximately for small values of δ:

$$x = (n+\tfrac{1}{2})f\lambda/d \tag{2.18}$$

while the distance of successive minima from P can likewise be shown to be:

$$x = nf\lambda/d \tag{2.19}$$

The most intense maximum is known as the zero order fringe or central maximum, and its width is $2f\lambda/d$.

If two wavelengths are present in the incident radiation, then two sets of diffraction patterns of the aperture result. If no dispersing element is present, then the zero-order fringes would be coincident since they do not depend on a path difference. However, when a prism is present in the light path, different wavelengths suffer differing dispersions, and the zero-order fringes

† This symbol should not be confused with the one for refractive index.

are not coincident. Should the wavelengths of two spectral lines be close together, the diffraction patterns of the images of the aperture will overlap as shown in Fig. 2.8 giving a resultant intensity indicated by the dotted line.

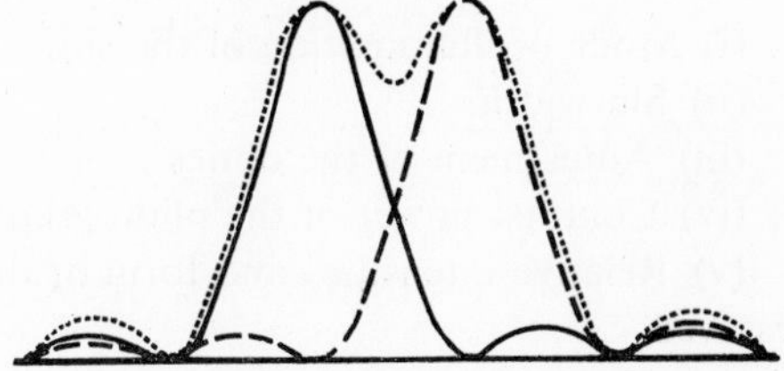

FIG. 2.8 Two overlapping diffraction patterns (full and broken lines) and their resultant intensity (dotted line). (*After Sawyer*[1])

Two overlapping lines may be recognized only if the two maxima appear as separate peaks with a distinct minimum between. A criterion was proposed by Lord Rayleigh by which it can be adjudged whether two lines of wavelengths λ and $(\lambda+d\lambda)$ are separated, that is resolved. The criterion is that two wavelengths λ and $(\lambda+d\lambda)$ can be regarded to be just resolved when the

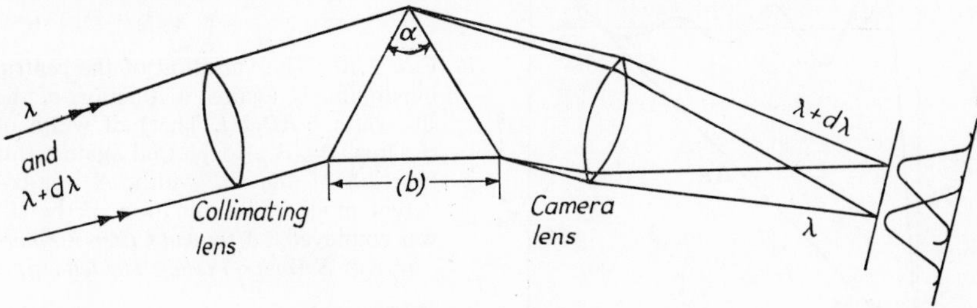

FIG. 2.9 Resolution of light by a prism

central maximum of the diffraction pattern of the line of wavelength λ falls on the first minimum of the diffraction pattern of the line of wavelength $(\lambda+d\lambda)$. This is the case represented in Fig. 2.8 where each of the lines has equal intensity. However, when the dip between the two central maxima is no longer recognizable, then the two lines remain unresolved. The ability of a spectrograph to separate two close lines of wavelength λ and $(\lambda+d\lambda)$ is called its resolving power R and is expressed as the ratio of the wavelength observed to the smallest difference between two wavelengths which can be distinguished as two lines. This ratio

$$R = \lambda/d\lambda \tag{2.20}$$

varies widely for different types of instruments. When the whole of the prism face is employed, the resolving power may readily be shown to be†

$$R = b \, . \, dn/d\lambda \tag{2.21}$$

where b is the length of the base of the prism (see Fig. 2.9) and $dn/d\lambda$ is the characteristic dispersion of the material of the prism. Should only a part of

† See for example Sawyer.[1]

the prism face be used, then b is the effective thickness and is the difference in thickness of the prism traversed by the two extreme rays.†

In practice the resolution achieved depends on several factors, and a few of the more important ones are the:

(i) Mode of illumination of the slit.

(ii) Slit width.

(iii) Adjustment of the optics.

(iv) Contrast power of the photographic plate.

(v) Relative intensities and form of the two adjacent spectral lines to be resolved.

Selection of most suitable slit width

In practice there is no absolute rule for the choice of slit width, a compromise having to be made as regards intensity and resolution. In the ideal case with an infinitely narrow slit width and no diffraction there would be

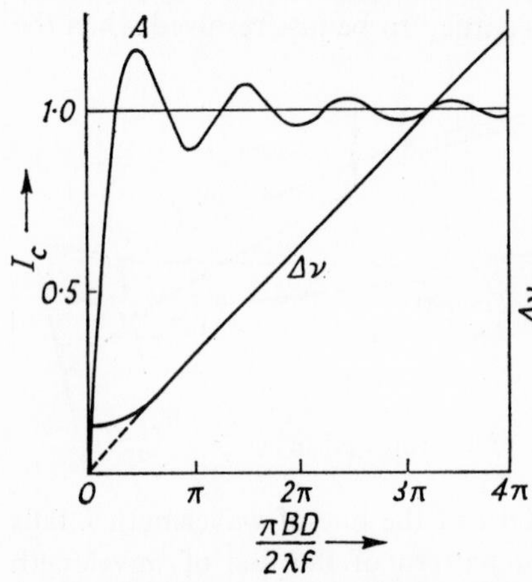

FIG. 2.10 The variation of the central maximum, I_c, against a function of the slit width, $\pi BD/2\lambda f$. The half width of the line, $\Delta\nu$, is also plotted against this function of the slit width. A non-coherent mode of illumination of the slit was employed. (*After van Cittert.*[2] *Courtesy of Springer-Verlag, Heidelberg*)

perfect resolution. However, when finite slit widths are employed and diffraction effects are considered, the resolving power is limited.

The dependence of the intensity of the central diffraction maximum I_c (in arbitrary units) on the slit width may be deduced from Fig. 2.10. Along the abscissa a function of the slit width is plotted and is $\pi BD/2\lambda f$, where B is the slit width, λ the wavelength employed, and f the focal length of the collimator lens of diameter D. It will be seen from the figure that if a very narrow slit is used and gradually increased, the intensity of the central maximum rises rapidly to a peak value. However, on further increase of the slit width beyond this peak value the intensity of the central maximum is modified only slightly. The half width of the absorption $\Delta\nu$ is also plotted in Fig. 2.10 where $\Delta\nu$ may be defined as half the width (in cm^{-1}) at the position where the intensity of the line falls from its maximum to one-half

† It is interesting to note that whereas the dispersive power of a prism instrument is independent of the prism size (apart, of course, from the angle α) the resolving power depends on the effective thickness of the prism traversed by the beam.

of that value. It follows directly from the figure that beyond the peak intensity A, the central maximum intensity value is altered only slightly when the slit width is increased, whereas the half-width of the line increases linearly with the slit width. From a spectroscopic viewpoint maximum resolution is required without a large increase in the exposure time, while the half width of the line should be a minimum. These criteria may best be achieved for point A in Fig. 2.10, where:

$$\pi BD/2\lambda f = \pi/2 \tag{2.22}$$

that is when the value of the slit width B is given by:

$$B = \lambda f/D \tag{2.23}$$

Such a slit width leads to a good central diffraction maximum with negligible loss of resolving power.

The case just considered was for a noncoherent mode of illumination and was evaluated by van Cittert.[2] He has also calculated the effect of employing a coherent mode of illumination where all the rays from the slit are in phase. In this case the maximum corresponding with point A in Fig. 2.10 occurs when $\pi BD/2\lambda f = \pi$. Thus, for a coherent mode of illumination the most desirable slit width is $2\lambda f/D$, that is double the width of the noncoherent case. In general, in spectroscopic work, a range of wavelength is involved, and the radiation is most likely to be a mixture of coherent and noncoherent modes of illumination. Thus, the most suitable slit width will range in value between $\lambda f/D$ and $2\lambda f/D$. In practice some value just less than $\lambda f/D$ may be tried as the slit width. The slit width is then gradually increased until the best condition is found. If the intensity of the illumination is observed on a white card on the far side of the slit, then when the best slit width is obtained, a sudden increase in brightness ensues. If the slit width is increased beyond this, then the brightness increases only very slowly. To discern the effect of slit width on resolution and spectral intensity a number of exposures have to be carried out at different slit widths. In fundamental research this is often worth while. In practice slit widths greater than the calculated value are often advantageous. This becomes desirable as a result of imperfections in the optical system. Two conditions which call for wide slit widths are:

(*a*) When the intensity of the incident radiation is very low, e.g., in some infra-red work.

(*b*) When high-speed recording is required, it might be permissible to sacrifice resolving power in favour of speed.

Photographic speed of spectrograph

The photographic speed of a spectrograph regulates the time required for a given amount of blackening of a photographic plate. It can be expressed in what is known as the *F-number* which is defined by:

$$F = f/D \tag{2.24}$$

where f and D are the focal length and diameter of the camera lens, respectively. The quantity $(D/f)^2$ determines the solid angle subtended at the focus of the camera lens by the aperture and is, therefore, a measure of the amount of light entering. A small *F*-number indicates a high speed, and to increase the focal length without also increasing the diameter of the camera lens means a reduction in the speed of the instrument. For Raman and other work involving weak sources speed is essential, and lenses with small *F*-numbers are used. However, dispersion is sacrificed with such instruments. In the Hilger large-aperture two-prism glass spectrograph (see Fig. 2.11) two interchangeable cameras are available, one for preliminary survey work with $F = 1.5$ giving a reciprocal linear dispersion of 64 Å/mm at 4358 Å and the second for more detailed examinations with $F = 5.7$ and a reciprocal linear dispersion of 16 Å/mm at 4358 Å.

Types of prism instruments

Medium quartz and glass spectrograph

A spectrograph which is adaptable to many kinds of work where speed and high dispersion are not required is the medium quartz and glass type of spectrograph. The instrument is able to take either glass or quartz refracting components, the latter having a greater range (2000 to 10 000 Å) than the former (3700 to 8000 Å). The length of the spectrum in the case of the quartz instrument is 22 cm, while the glass instrument has a spectrum length of 14 cm. The glass instrument has a greater angular dispersion than the quartz, giving, therefore, a smaller reciprocal linear dispersion (Å/mm). A medium quartz spectrograph is illustrated in Fig. 2.12.

Basically the instrument consists of a slit, collimating lens, prism, a two-component camera lens, and a photographic plate. The slit is a narrow vertical rectangular aperture through which the light to the spectrograph passes. Since the image of the slit after dispersion constitutes the spectral line, it is of importance that the slit edges should not only be straight and parallel to give a clean-cut image but also sharp to avoid reflections of light from the edges. On an instrument which is to be used for routine analysis a fixed slit width may be satisfactory.

For research work, however, and on instruments of high dispersion variable slits are provided so that the width can be adjusted to suit the type of work and the wavelength being used. The slits open bilaterally so that the centre of the spectral line is fixed for all slit widths. The width of the slit is varied by adjustment of a micrometer screw with a calibrated drum head.

The usual 60° prism, if constructed of quartz, requires to be made of two halves since quartz crystal is a doubly-refracting material and also possesses the property of rotating the plane of polarisation of plane-polarised light even if the beam is parallel with the optical axis. Quartz, however, occurs in two forms, rotating the plane of polarisation of the light in opposite senses. Thus, a 60° prism can be constructed of two 30° prisms, one from each variety of quartz, the second prism introducing a compensating rotatory effect.

The collimating lens renders light from the slit parallel and hence eliminates astigmatism in the prism system, while the camera lens brings to focus

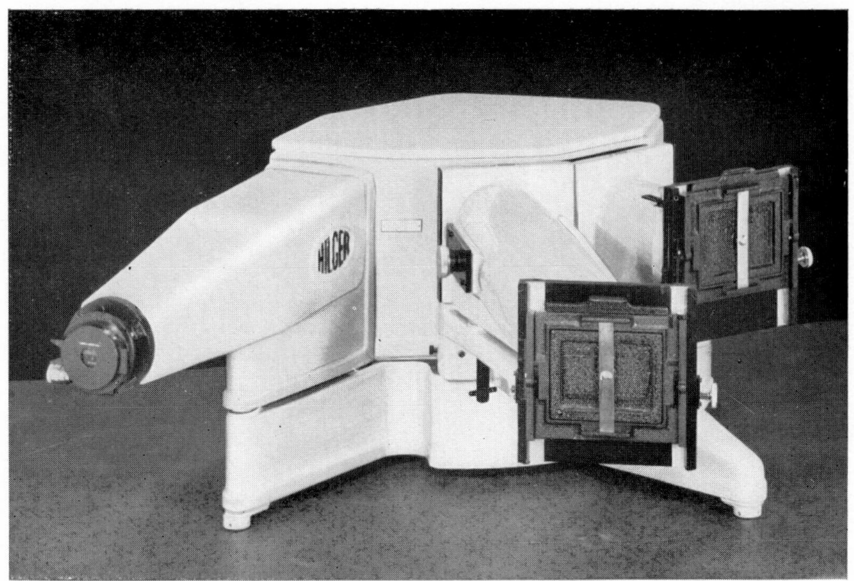

FIG. 2.11 Hilger two-prism glass spectrograph. (*Courtesy of Hilger and Watts Ltd.*)

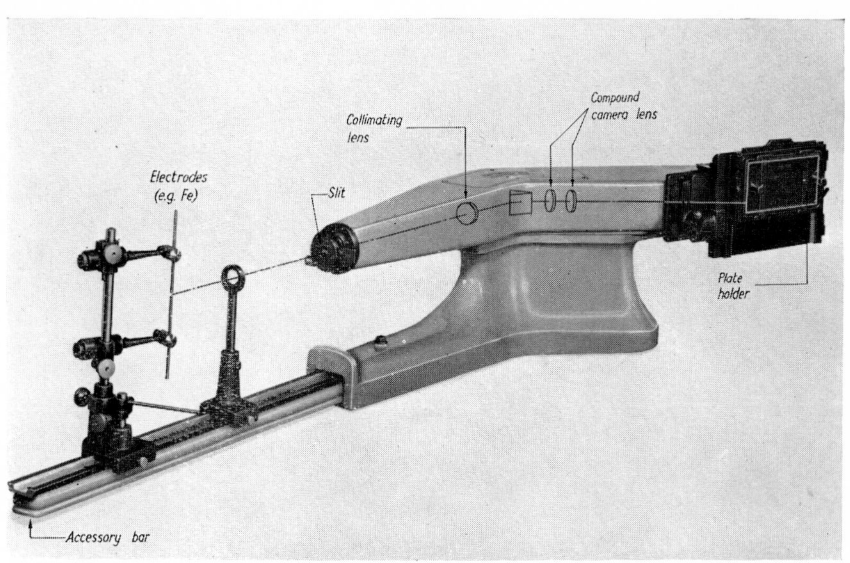

FIG. 2.12 Hilger medium quartz spectrograph showing the optical arrangement. (*Courtesy of Hilger and Watts Ltd.*)

[*To face page* 32

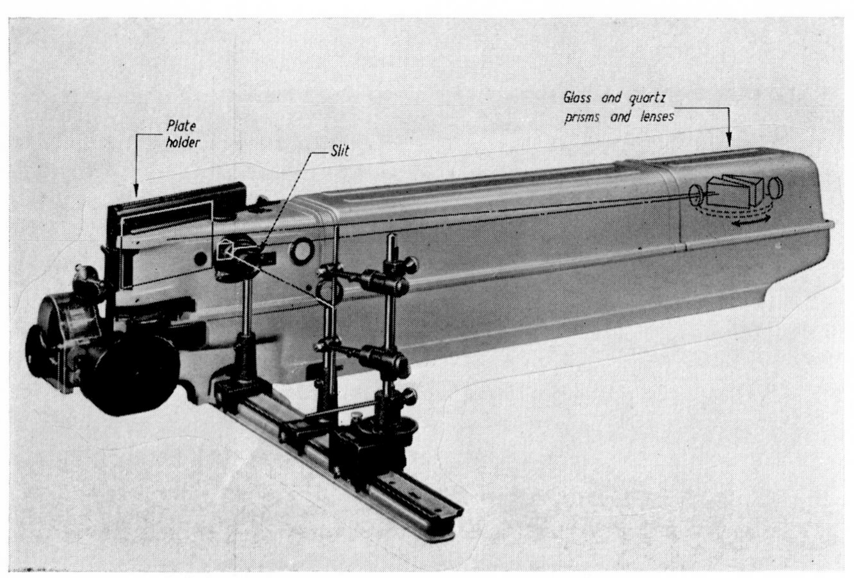

FIG. 2.13 Hilger large quartz and glass spectrograph showing optical arrangement. (*Courtesy of Hilger and Watts Ltd.*)

the beams of light of different wavelengths emerging from the prism at different angles. Images of the slit are produced in the focal plane, and in this position a photographic plate is fixed in a suitable plate holder to record the spectrum. The size of the photographic plate is 10 in. by 4 in. and several exposures may be taken on one and the same plate by vertical adjustment of the plate holder. Since the focal plane of the medium quartz instrument is flat, no adjustment of focus is necessary for any part of the spectrum. The medium quartz and glass spectrographs have built into them a wavelength (or if desired, a wave-number) scale which can be printed directly on to the photographic plate. The error in the wavelength reading may be of the order of 100 Å at 7000 Å and falls to 1 Å at 2200 Å. A much more accurate determination of wavelength which could be applied to a spectrogram obtained on a medium quartz spectrograph is described on p. 42.

Littrow spectrograph

When good dispersion is required the large quartz or glass spectrograph is available (see Fig. 2.13). The focal length of the camera lens of such an instrument is of the order of 170 cm. It can be appreciated that if the same

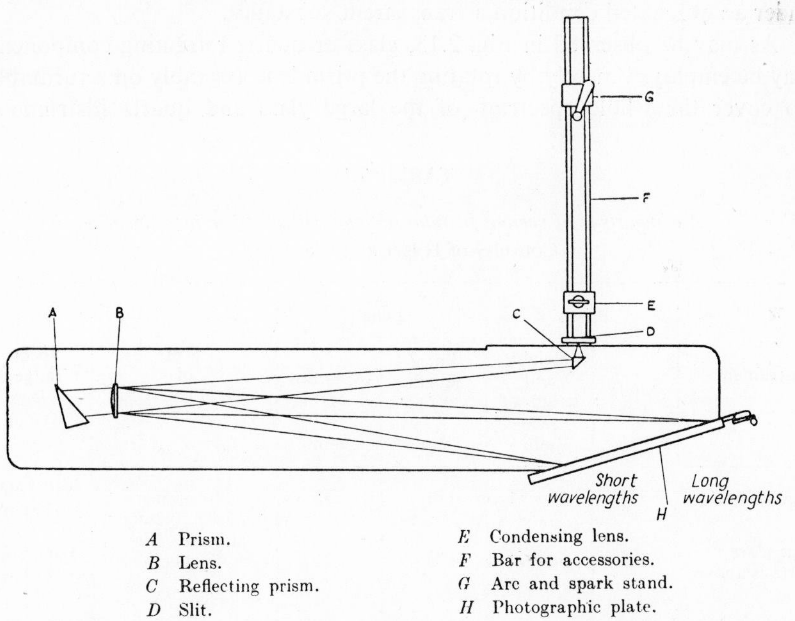

A	Prism.	*E*	Condensing lens.
B	Lens.	*F*	Bar for accessories.
C	Reflecting prism.	*G*	Arc and spark stand.
D	Slit.	*H*	Photographic plate.

FIG. 2.14 Light path of a typical large quartz spectrograph. (*Courtesy of Hilger and Watts Ltd.*)

construction were used for such an instrument as is employed for the medium type of spectrograph (focal length 60 cm), the length of the spectrograph would be considerably increased; to avoid this the so-called Littrow mounting is employed as is shown in Fig. 2.14. The range of the quartz instrument is from 1910 to 8000 Å, and the glass from 3700 to 12 000 Å, the spectrum lengths being 75 and 47 cm, respectively. A 10 in. by 4 in. photographic plate is used, as was the case with the medium type of instrument, although with the large quartz type of spectrograph three exposures are necessary to cover the whole spectral range. One of the attractive features of this large spectrograph with quartz optical components is that it gives good dispersion in the ultra-violet region. The dispersion of the glass assembly is greater than that of the quartz, and in the visible region the glass prism produces about three times the dispersion of the quartz prism.

The operation of the slit in the Littrow instrument is the same as that for the medium quartz or glass spectrograph. Light from the slit is reflected by a small 90° prism through a collimating lens to a 30° prism which is aluminised on its rear face so that the light is reflected. Thus, the light traverses the prism twice and is brought to a focus on a photographic plate by means of a lens which acts both as a collimating and a camera lens. These points are illustrated in Fig. 2.14.

Reflected light from the surface of the lens is more troublesome in this type of instrument than in the medium quartz type, though the reflection can be cut down materially by blooming the lens. Blooming consists of depositing under an evacuated condition a transparent substance.

As may be observed in Fig. 2.13, glass or quartz refracting components may be employed merely by rotating the prism lens assembly on a turntable. To cover the whole spectrum of the large glass and quartz instruments

TABLE 2.1

A comparison of various features of some Hilger prism instruments.
(Courtesy of Hilger and Watts Ltd.)

Instrument	Prism		Lens		Size of Plate	Spectrum range and length (x)
	Angle (α)	Height and length of face mm	Focal length (f) cm	Aperture (D) mm		
Large quartz	30°	56×94	170	75	10×4 in. 25.4×10.2 cm also 10×2 in. 9×24 cm	1910—8000 Å = 75 cm
Large glass quartz as above	26°	56×94	170	75		3700—12000 Å = 47 cm
Medium quartz Flat field	60°	41×65	60	51	10×4 in.	2000—10 000 Å = 22 cm
Medium glass	60°	41×65	60	51	10×4 in.	3700—8000 Å = 14 cm
Large aperture 2 prism glass	63°	86×164 86×130	13.2	89	$4\frac{1}{4}\times3\frac{1}{4}$ in. only	3900—8000 Å = 2.9 cm
Large aperture 2 prism glass	63°	86×164 86×130	45	101		3900—7000 Å = 10 cm

a change from one region to another requires rotation of the aluminised prism, re-focusing of the lens, and a change in the angle of tilt of the photographic plate. All these adjustments are made from the plate-holder end of the instrument by a single control. For the quartz instrument the wavelength range 1910 to 8000 Å is spread over 75 cm of photographic plate, and for a given setting any 25 cm may be selected. In addition, a millimetre scale is so mounted that it can be imposed on the spectrogram. The plate carrier can be vertically adjusted so that many exposures can be taken on one and the same plate. A comparison of various features of five Hilger prism instruments is given in Table 2.1.

The Littrow mounting is also employed in a modified form in infra-red spectrophotometers (see p. 71), its chief advantage being the double dispersion and resolution resulting from the beam traversing the prism twice. A typical arrangement is shown in Fig. 2.15 where light from an entrance slit S_1

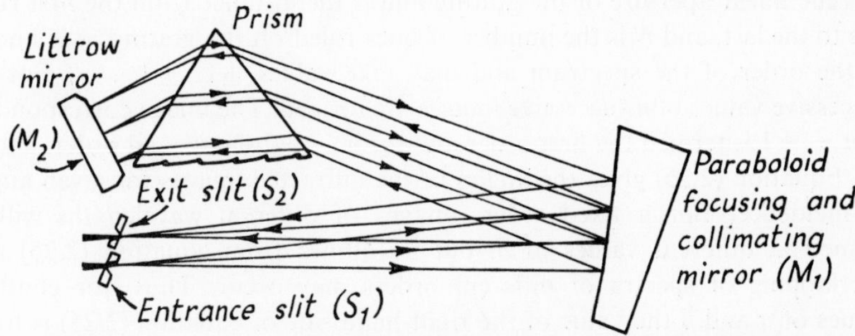

FIG. 2.15 Littrow mounting as employed in infra-red spectrophotometers

falls on to an off-axis parabolic collimating mirror M_1. The parallel rays pass through the prism and are reflected back through the prism by mirror M_2. The parabolic mirror M_1 acts also as a focusing mirror bringing the rays to focus at an exit slit S_2. To scan the complete spectrum it is necessary to rotate the mirror M_2 about a vertical axis.

Diffraction grating spectrographs

The diffraction grating may be employed instead of the prism as a dispersing element and has the following points to recommend its use:

(*a*) It may be used below 1200 Å and above 40 μ where no suitable transparent prism materials are available. In addition, gratings are frequently used in the region between 1200 Å and 40 μ, where it is desirable to have the features mentioned in (*b*) below.

(*b*) Generally a grating has a greater dispersion and resolving power than a prism.

(*c*) The grating yields a linear spectrum whereas a prismatic spectrum is non-linear. This is labour-saving when the wavelengths of a number of lines are to be measured.

Grating spectra

A diffraction grating may be regarded as being composed of a large number of parallel, equidistant and narrow slits side by side made by ruling lines on a suitable surface with a diamond point. The surface can either be transparent or opaque to the radiation used. In the former case the grating is a *transmission grating* and in the latter a *reflection grating*. The fundamental theory is the same for both types. A reflection grating is superior to a transmission grating, however, in that, if the lines are ruled on a concave mirror, then the need for employing focusing and collimating lenses can be eliminated.

If α is the angle of incidence of the light of wavelength λ on to the grating and β is the emergence angle, where both the angles are measured with respect to the normal, then the diffraction by the grating is taken into account by the formula:

$$\pm n\lambda = \frac{A}{N}[\sin\alpha + \sin\beta] \qquad (2.25)$$

A is the linear aperture of the grating and is the distance from the first ruled line to the last, and N is the number of lines ruled on the grating. n is known as the order of the spectrum and may take values ± 1, ± 2, . . . For the successive values of n successive images are formed. The image corresponding to $n = \pm 1$ is termed the first order and for $n = \pm 2$ the second order, and so on. Equation (2.25) gives the angles of the diffracted images for given angles of incidence. For a fixed order, images of different wavelengths will be formed at different values of β, but it follows from equation (2.25) that overlapping of spectra of different orders may occur. Thus, for constant values of α and β the value of the right-hand side of equation (2.25) is fixed, and, therefore $n\lambda =$ constant.

This constant value may be achieved for combinations such as the following:

$$n \,.\, \lambda \qquad 1 \,.\, \lambda \qquad 2 \,.\, \lambda/2 \qquad 3 \,.\, \lambda/3$$

For example, for a given value of β the spectra of 12 000 Å in the first order, 6000 Å in the second order, and 4000 Å in the third order would be observed at the same position on the photographic plate. It is frequently possible to separate these overlapping orders by:

(*a*) The use of a fore-prism which provides a narrow range of wavelength and acts as a monochromator for the grating (see p. 74).

(*b*) The use of photographic plates with limited spectral sensitivity.

(*c*) The use of certain cut-off filters which though transparent to the desired wavelengths are opaque to the sub-multiples of these wavelengths. Examples of such filters used in the infra-red region are thin films of PbS, Ag_2S, and Te deposited on a material which is by itself transparent. Semiconductor filters such as Si, Ge, indium arsenide and antimonide provide a very effective discrimination against visible and short wave infra-red radiation. Subsequent to optical blooming transmission at the peak wavelengths (2μ for Si, 3μ for Ge, 5μ for indium arsenide and 10μ for indium antimonide) is between 70-90 %. A second most promising type of filter is made from the coloured alkali halide crystals.[3]

Equation (2.25) holds for both transmission and reflection gratings; the positive sign on the left-hand side applies when the incident and diffracted rays are on the same side of the grating normal and the negative sign when the rays are on opposite sides of the normal.

Dispersion by a grating

Since

$$n\lambda = \frac{A}{N}[\sin\alpha + \sin\beta] \tag{2.26}$$

and if α is arranged to be constant, then it follows that the dispersive power of the grating is given by:

$$\mathrm{d}\beta/\mathrm{d}\lambda = nN/A\cos\beta \tag{2.27}$$

Thus, the dispersive power varies directly with the order and also with the number of grating lines per unit width of grating (N/A).

If the spectrum is viewed normal to the grating, $\beta = 0$, $\cos\beta = 1$, and

$$\mathrm{d}\beta/\mathrm{d}\lambda = \frac{nN}{A} = \text{constant} \tag{2·28}$$

for a given order and grating, and the dispersion has a minimum value. For this type of spectrum it follows from equation (2.28) that $\Delta\beta$ is approximately proportional to $\Delta\lambda$ and that the wavelength is a linear function of the angle of emergence. In addition, it also follows from equation (2.28) that for a spectrogram observed at small values of β the dispersive power is constant.

Resolving power of a grating

The resolving power of a grating may be shown to be:†

$$R = \lambda/\mathrm{d}\lambda = nN \tag{2.29}$$

where n is the order and N the number of lines in the ruled surface. Thus, to resolve, for example, the sodium D-lines at an average wavelength of 5893 Å with $\Delta\lambda = 6$ Å the resolving power required would be:

$$\lambda/\Delta\lambda = 5893/6 = \text{approximately } 1000$$

Hence a grating with 1000 ruled lines would be adequate to resolve the sodium D-lines in the first order. It is interesting to note that it follows from equation (2.29) that the resolving power of a grating is independent of the wavelength or the spacing of the lines in the grating.

Light distribution in a grating spectrum

In an ideal grating consisting of alternate equidistant opaque and transparent strips the distribution of light should be uniform on each side of the normal to the grating, and the intensity of successive orders should decrease in a regular manner. Such, however, is not the case, since the rulings have in addition to finite width a definite shape, usually taking the form of a flat trough, the sides of which make unequal angles with the vertical. This results

† See, for example, Sawyer[1], p. 124.

in an irregular distribution of light on the two sides of the normal and also within the orders on one given side. The efficiency of a grating ruled in the ordinary manner with a diamond point cannot be predicted but must be determined experimentally.

It has already been indicated that one disadvantage of the diffraction grating is that it disperses the incident energy over a large number of orders. This may be overcome in the visible region by increasing the fineness of the groove spacing. As the wavelength being studied becomes longer, however, it is desirable to use coarser gratings; for example in the infra-red, gratings are used ranging from about 15 000 lines/in. down to as low as 25 lines/in.

This waste of energy by diffraction into a variety of orders can be serious when, for example, in the infra-red the total amount of energy is small in any case. In the production of modern gratings this problem can to some extent be overcome by shaping the tip of the ruling diamond so that the contours of the grooves are such as to concentrate the diffracted energy into a definite direction. This is called *blazing the grating*, and the angle the groove makes with the vertical is known as the *blaze angle.* The effect may be illustrated by considering a plane reflection grating having 2400 lines/in. and a ruled area of 4×3 in. with a blaze angle of 29° which gives a first-order concentration at 10 μ. In addition, such a grating would be most efficient at wavelengths of from 5 to 6 μ in the second order, 3.3 μ in the third order, and so on. Fig. 2.16 demonstrates this by the plot of spectral slit width

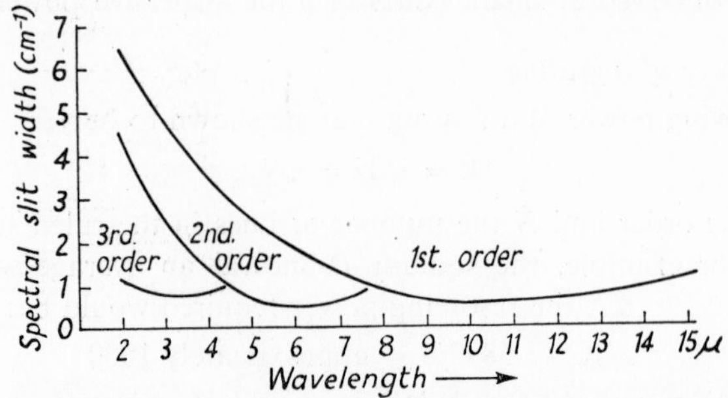

FIG. 2.16 Plot of spectral slit width against the wavelength for three orders of a plane diffraction grating. (*After Sayce and Jackson.*[4] *Courtesy of the Institute of Petroleum, London*)

(in cm^{-1} units) against the wavelength (in μ), where the criterion for the choice of order is that the best resolution is obtained for small slit widths. Such a grating could also be used at wavelengths between 2 to 4.3 μ in the third order, 4.3 to 7.6 μ in the second order, and 7.6 to 15 μ and beyond in the first order. The spectrograms of water vapour obtained from such a blazed grating in the range 2.8 to 2.5 μ in the first, second and third order are illustrated in Fig. 2.17. This figure shows quite clearly that the best resolution is obtained in the third order in this wavelength range.

Grating ghosts

A perfect grating should have grooves which are:

(*a*) Straight.

(*b*) Parallel to each other.

(*c*) Equidistant across the whole of the ruled surface.

(*d*) Identical in shape and depth.

The results of deviations from these conditions will lead to phase variations of the reunited beams from different grooves. Spacing errors are much more troublesome than those arising from the lack of lineality and parallelism of

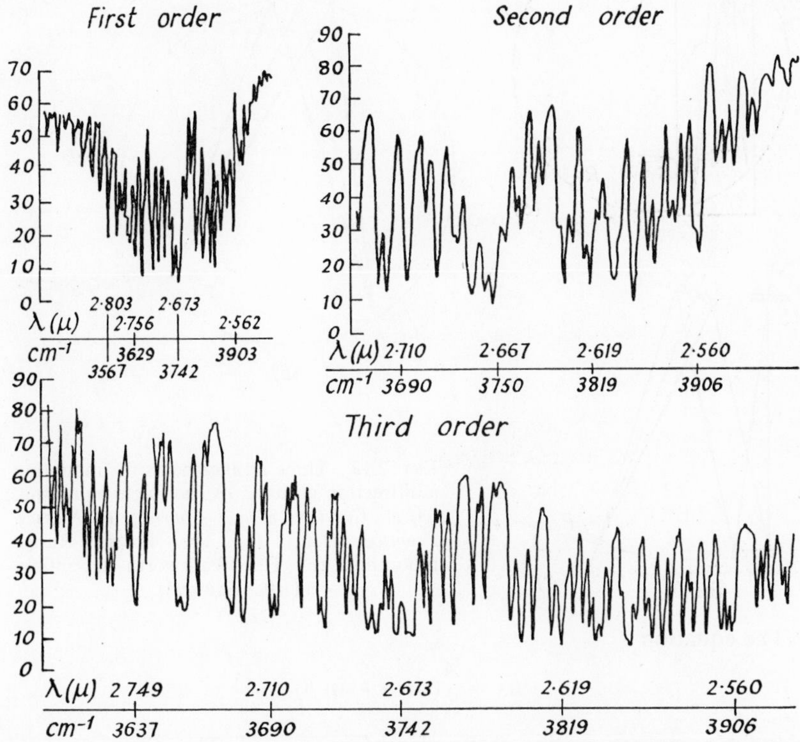

FIG. 2.17 The infra-red spectrum of atmospheric water vapour between 2.85 and 2.53 μ in the first, second, and third orders. (*After Sayce and Jackson.*[4] *Courtesy of the Institute of Petroleum, London*)

the grooves, this being particularly true if the spacing errors are systematic, since the effect is cumulative. These periodic spacing errors which give rise to false lines in the spectrum were investigated by Rowland and are known as *Rowland Ghosts*. They occur close to the parent line and are symmetrically placed with respect to it. The intensities of the ghost lines are usually much less than the intensity of the parent line and generally may be identified as their wavelengths are calculable. Another type of ghost, the *Lyman ghost*, also occurs. These are thought to be due to the superposition of two periodic ruling errors. They occur in good gratings with low intensity at considerable distances from the parent line and are less readily detected than Rowland ghosts.

Grating mountings

A grating may be mounted in a variety of ways three of which are shown in Figs. 2.18(*a*), 2.18(*b*), and 2.18(*c*).

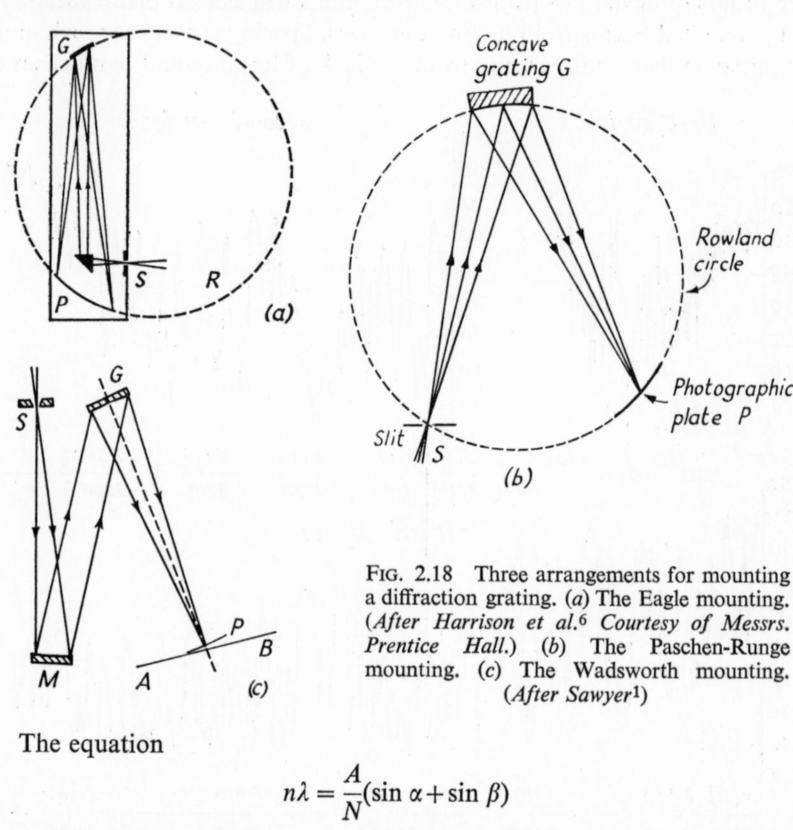

FIG. 2.18 Three arrangements for mounting a diffraction grating. (*a*) The Eagle mounting. (*After Harrison et al.*[6] *Courtesy of Messrs. Prentice Hall.*) (*b*) The Paschen-Runge mounting. (*c*) The Wadsworth mounting. (*After Sawyer*[1])

The equation

$$n\lambda = \frac{A}{N}(\sin \alpha + \sin \beta)$$

holds for a concave grating as Rowland first showed. The slit, grating, and diffracted spectrum all lie on a circle, the *Rowland circle,* whose diameter is equal to the radius of curvature of the concave grating. Both the Eagle and Paschen–Runge mountings are partly built on the Rowland circle principle while the Wadsworth arrangement is rather different. Details of each of these mountings will be briefly considered.

Eagle mounting

The Eagle mounting is similar to the Littrow mounting of a prism in that the slit, *S*, and photographic plate *P* are mounted close together as in Fig. 2.18(*a*). The grating, *G*, and the photographic plate, but not the slit in this case, lie on the Rowland circle, *R*. To change the spectral region it is necessary to rotate the grating about its vertical axis, change the distance between the grating and plate holder, and also to rotate the plate holder about the slit. These operations are usually coupled together and motor-driven, the wavelength range being read on a wavelength drum. One such instrument employs a grating with a radius of curvature of 3 m and has a reciprocal linear dispersion of 5.6 Å/mm in the first order. The grating has 15 000 lines/in. and a 4 in. ruled surface.

The Eagle mounting though very compact has a certain amount of astigmatism associated with it and requires very precise mechanical parts for its operation in order to achieve the highest resolving power of the grating.

Paschen–Runge mounting

A very popular mounting for large concave gratings is the Paschen–Runge one. In this case the slit, grating, and plate holder lie on the Rowland circle. One feature peculiar to this mounting is the arrangement for placing photographic plates along a large part of the Rowland circle enabling a wide spectral range to be simultaneously photographed. One minor disadvantage is the non-linear dispersion which results when operating away from the grating normal.

Wadsworth mounting

The advantage of the mounting is that it yields a stigmatic image, the beam being collimated by a concave mirror, M, before it strikes the grating, G, as indicated in Fig. 2.18(c). The plate holder, P, is mounted normal to the grating to cut down astigmatism and spherical aberration. As the grating is rotated to scan the spectrum the distance from the grating to plate holder, tilt of plate holder, and its curvature must be adjusted for each setting. The motion of the plate holder relative to the grating is automatically controlled by a cam to execute a parabolic path along AB. One instrument using this mounting has a grating with a radius of curvature of 21 ft with 15 000 lines/in.; this gives a reciprocal linear dispersion of 5 Å/mm in the first order. The Wadsworth mounting has been adapted to plane gratings. A concave mirror is arranged to reflect the radiation on to a plane transmission grating, and the radiation passes through and converges to a focus on a photographic plate.

Automatic recording spectrographs

Between 10 Å and 1.3 μ the method of recording the spectrum is by means of a photographic plate.† However, one recent development has been to replace this plate by a photomultiplier assembly, so making the spectrograph a direct reading instrument. The output from the photomultiplier tube is fed to a microammeter or a pen recorder.

† At greater wavelengths than 1.8 μ this is not possible since no emulsion has been made sensitive to longer wavelengths.

Wavelength measurement

Once the desired spectrum has been obtained it is frequently required to determine the exact wavelengths of lines or band heads. The position of these is determined with respect to the positions of lines of an element whose exact wavelengths are known.

The measurement of the relative positions of the lines or bands on the plate is carried out by means of a travelling microscope under which the plate is mounted on a movable carriage. This carriage can be moved backwards or forwards by means of a screw coupled to a drum normally calibrated in divisions corresponding to 0.01 mm of travel, while an attached vernier permits estimations to 0.001 mm. The determination of wavelength is much simpler for a spectrogram resulting from a grating instrument since the position of lines on the plate has a linear dependence on wavelength. This enables linear interpolation between standard reference lines to be made. With prism spectrographs, however, there is such variation in dispersion for different wavelengths that it is necessary to have a number of standard comparison lines fairly closely dispersed between the lines whose wavelengths are to be determined and to employ a non-linear dispersion formula. For this non-linear interpolation the Hartmann formula can be used over a restricted wavelength range. Hartmann showed that the dispersion of a prism instrument could be represented over small wavelength ranges to a fair degree of approximation by the expression:

$$\lambda = \lambda_0 + \frac{c}{n - n_0} \tag{2.30}$$

λ is an unknown wavelength, λ_0 a constant having the dimensions of wavelength, c a constant valid for a range of wavelengths in the immediate neighbourhood of the unknown line, n the index of refraction of the prism material at the wavelength λ, and n_0 is a further constant. A more convenient expression of the Hartmann formula (equation 2.30) for the purpose of wavelength calculation is:

$$\lambda = \lambda_0 + \frac{C}{d_0 - d} \tag{2.31}$$

where d_0 is a constant and d the measured distance on the plate from an arbitrary point in the spectrum to the line of unknown wavelength.

Equation (2.31) has three unknown constants λ_0, C, and d_0. These may be determined if the separations d_1, d_2, and d_3 of three lines of known wavelength λ_1, λ_2, and λ_3 respectively are measured with a travelling microscope. The set of three independent equations:

$$\lambda_1 = \lambda_0 + C/(d_0 - d_1) \tag{2.32}$$

$$\lambda_2 = \lambda_0 + C/(d_0 - d_2) \tag{2.33}$$

$$\lambda_3 = \lambda_0 + C/(d_0 - d_3) \tag{2.34}$$

is then solved simultaneously for the three unknown parameters. The arbitrary (fiducial) point in the spectrum referred to earlier, if convenient, may be located on one of the three lines of known wavelength. Hartmann showed that, while d_0 depends on the position of the fiducial mark C on the selected range and region of the spectrograph, λ_0 is a constant of the spectrograph and should always have the same value for a given instrument. Actually since the Hartmann formula is only an approximation, λ_0 will vary slightly with the chosen spectral range. From a knowledge of the three parameters λ_0, C, and d_0 unknown wavelengths may be calculated from equation (2.31), if the distances (d) of these wavelengths are measured from the same fiducial point as previously employed. For reasonable accuracy the three lines of known wavelength should lie close together, and preferably the lines, band heads or band origins, whose wavelengths are being determined, should lie within their range.

The known lines associated with the original measurement could be members of the iron spectrum which was photographed on the same plate as the unknown spectrum. In Fig. 7.3 a spectrogram with a calibration iron spectrum is given. From charts of the iron spectrum it should be possible to choose three convenient lines for the determination.†

If the wavelengths of standard lines other than those used to calculate the constants in the Hartmann equation are evaluated and these compared with the theoretical values, it will be found that there is a periodic error throughout the spectrum. This error is due to the approximate nature of the Hartmann formula. It is necessary, then, to correct the measured values, and this can be done with the aid of a correction curve. The curve is obtained

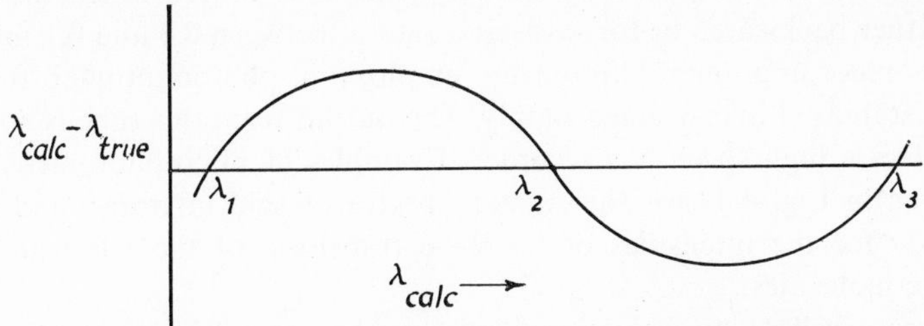

FIG. 2.19 Correction curve for wavelength determination

by calculating a large number of standard wavelengths for the calibration lines and plotting the difference between the wavelengths calculated from the measurements and that of the true wavelength as taken from the tables against the calculated wavelengths. Each of the calculated wavelengths is then converted into a true wavelength by means of this correction curve. Such a curve is shown in Fig. 2.19. When a corrected value of the wavelength in air has been obtained it is desirable for theoretical work to convert this value to wavelength *in vacuo* (λ_{vac}) by means of tables.

For most accurate wavelength determination it is desirable that the lines or band heads should be sharp and well defined. In general, lines may be

† Recently thorium has been employed as a standard since this element has many more lines uniformly spaced.

determined to a greater accuracy than a few-tenths of an Ångström unit by means of a prism spectrograph. With a large diffraction grating, though, accuracies of a few-thousandths of an Ångström unit can be achieved, while for interferometer measurements on sharp lines an accuracy of 0.0001 Å or even greater can be obtained.

Microphotometers

Both manual and recording microphotometers are available for density measurements the basic principles of each being similar. We shall now briefly consider the principal features of these instruments.

The image of a battery-operated line filament lamp is focused on the spectrum plate by means of a microscope objective. An enlargement of the image of the line is then projected on to a slit placed in front of a barrier-type photocell or a photomultiplier tube.

The spectrum plate, emulsion side up, rests in guides on a stage which by means of a fine screw can accurately traverse a distance up to approximately 20 mm.This movement can be either hand-or motor-driven.

In the manual type of instrument the photocell is connected to a sensitive galvanometer. The difference between the readings of the galvanometer when light is excluded from the photocell and that when a particular spectral line is in position gives the intensity of light transmitted by that line.

When a spectrum plate is to be scanned a motor-driven stage is convenient, since then full attention can be given to the galvanometer. This scanning is achieved by means of a synchronous motor which moves the plate either backwards or forwards at a rate of between 0.3 and 0.1 mm/min.

The recording microphotometer employs a photomultiplier tube fed from a stabilised high-voltage supply. The output from this tube is amplified and drives a high speed pen recorder. Examples of microphotometer traces are given in Fig. 4.49 for the Raman spectra of acid mixtures, and also in Fig. 6.2*c* for the intensities of the 2→6 transition of the ^{11}BO and ^{10}BO isotopic molecules.

Three excellent books are available on the practical aspects of spectroscopy, one by Sawyer,[1] one by Strouts, Gilfillan and Wilson[5] and the third by Harrison, Lord and Loofbourow.[6]

References

1. SAWYER, R. A. *Experimental Spectroscopy*. Chapman and Hall (London, 1954).
2. VAN CITTERT, P. H. *Z. Phys.* **65** (1930), 547; **69** (1931), 298.
3. BURNS, W. G. and GAUNT, J. *Molecular Spectroscopy. Institute of Petroleum Conference*, 1955, p. 66.
4. SAYCE, L. A. and JACKSON, A. *Molecular Spectroscopy. Institute of Petroleum Conference*, 1955, p. 54.
5. STROUTS, C. R. N., GILFILLAN, J. H. and WILSON, H. N. *Analytical Chemistry*, Vol. 2, Oxford University Press (London, 1955).
6. HARRISON, G. R., LORD, R. C. and LOOFBOUROW, J. R. *Practical Spectroscopy*. Prentice-Hall (New York, 1948).

3

Molecular quantum numbers of diatomic molecules

Formation of molecular quantum numbers

IN the study of atomic spectra it was necessary to introduce the principal quantum number (n), the azimuthal quantum number (l), the electron and nuclear spin quantum numbers (s and I, respectively) or some combination of these. In addition, to account for the behaviour of the spectral lines of atoms in the presence of various electric or magnetic fields further quantum numbers were required.

When two atoms combine to give a diatomic molecule, these quantum numbers may be related to a new set of quantum numbers which characterise the electronic energy states of the molecule. In some respects diatomic molecules behave like atoms (see Vol. 1), and their energy distribution seems to follow a reasonably similar type of pattern. This is strikingly illustrated by comparing the electron states of the molecules with those of the atoms containing the same number of electrons. This comparison may be observed in Fig. 3.1. The main way in which they differ results from the presence of two nuclei; these produce a cylindrically symmetrical force field about the internuclear axis.

In an atom $l_1, l_2, l_3 \dots$ couple together to give L, while $s_1, s_2, s_3 \dots$ give a resultant electron spin quantum number S. The resultant orbit angular momentum is then $\sqrt{L(L+1)}\boldsymbol{h}/2\pi$, and the resultant electron spin angular momentum $\sqrt{S(S+1)}\boldsymbol{h}/2\pi$. When an atom characterised by $\sqrt{L_1(L_1+1)}\boldsymbol{h}/2\pi$ and $\sqrt{S_1(S_1+1)}\boldsymbol{h}/2\pi$ combines with another characterised by $\sqrt{L_2(L_2+1)}\boldsymbol{h}/2\pi$ and $\sqrt{S_2(S_2+1)}\boldsymbol{h}/2\pi$ the possible values of L and S for the molecule are given by:

$$L = L_1+L_2,\ L_1+L_2-1,\ \dots\ |L_1-L_2| \tag{3.1}$$

$$S = S_1+S_2,\ S_1+S_2-1,\ \dots\ |S_1-S_2| \tag{3.2}$$

An atom, however, unlike a diatomic molecule has a spherically-symmetrical force field. In a diatomic molecule, however, there is a strong electric field along the internuclear axis due to the electrostatic field of the two nuclei. The result is that the orbit and spin orbit angular momenta are uncoupled in this cylindrically-symmetrical force field. The effect is that the corresponding $L^{\star}h/2\pi$ and $S^{\star}h/2\pi$ vectors for the resultant orbit and total spin

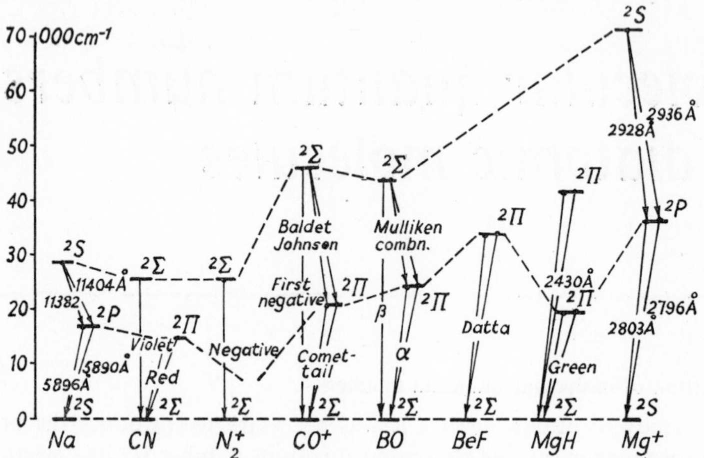

FIG. 3.1 Electronic energy levels of 13-electron molecules compared with those of Na and Mg^+. Corresponding levels are connected by broken lines, and observed lines and band systems are indicated by arrows. The names used to characterise some of the electronic transitions are also given. (*Courtesy of Dr. W. Jevons,*[2] *and the Council of the Physical Society, London*)

angular momentum, respectively,† precess independently about the internuclear axis,‡ and $L^{\star}h/2\pi$ has a constant component in that direction of $M_L h/2\pi$ where $M_L = L, L-1 \ldots -L$. In an electric field if the direction of motion of all the electrons is reversed, the energy of the molecule remains unchanged, although the positive M_L value is changed into a negative one. It follows, therefore, that only states with different M_L values possess different energies. These different energy states are characterised by a quantum number Λ which defines the constant component of the resultant orbital angular momentum $(\sqrt{L(L+1)}h/2\pi)$ for each energy state along the internuclear axis where Λ may take the values 0, 1, 2, 3, . . . L.§ The precession

† The shorthand representation of the form $X^{\star}h/2\pi$ will be used for $\sqrt{X(X+1)}h/2\pi$, where X may be L, S, J or K.

‡ Whether $L^{\star}h/2\pi$ and $S^{\star}h/2\pi$ are uncoupled depends on the strength of the internal electric field. The latter is dependent on the internuclear distance, and when this is relatively large, then the electric field becomes too weak to uncouple $L^{\star}h/2\pi$ and $S^{\star}h/2\pi$, and they form a common resultant vector. This is dealt with later under Hund's case (*c*). The treatment given here for the uncoupling of $L^{\star}h/2\pi$ and $S^{\star}h/2\pi$ corresponds with Hund's case (*a*).

§ This type of classification applies not only to diatomic molecules but to linear polyatomic molecules as well. In both cases the electric field is cylindrically symmetrical about the axis through the nuclei. For more complex molecules the electronic states are classified on the basis of symmetry properties in terms of group theory.

of the resultant orbit angular momentum about the internuclear axis is illustrated in Fig. 3.2(*a*).

The actual value of Λ is a measure of the number of units of angular momentum (in $h/2\pi$ units) resulting from projecting the electron orbit angular momentum along the internuclear axis. This component, $\Lambda h/2\pi$, along the axis always remains defined, whereas $L^\star h/2\pi$ itself frequently is not.

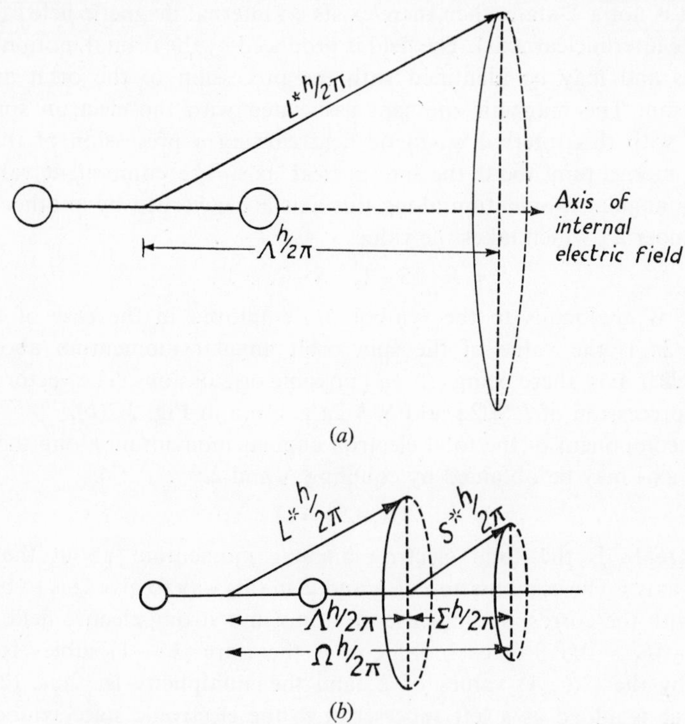

FIG. 3.2 (*a*) Precession of the resultant orbital angular momentum about the internuclear axis of a diatomic molecule. (*b*) Vector model for the precession of $L^\star h/2\pi$ and $S^\star h/2\pi$ in a diatomic molecule

The electronic states of diatomic molecules are characterised by:

$$\Lambda = 0, \quad 1, \quad 2,$$

and are called a Σ-state, Π-state, and Δ-state, respectively. This is a parallel classification to that employed for atoms where when

$$L = 0, \quad 1, \quad 2$$

these are termed *S*-, *P*- and *D*-states, respectively.

The effect of electron spin cannot be neglected when attempting to define a molecular electronic state by means of quantum numbers; the total electron spin quantum number *S* must be taken into account. Each electron has a spin of $\pm\frac{1}{2}$ from which the resultant spin of the individual atoms may be evaluated.

If S_1 and S_2 are the resultant spins in the separate atoms, then the possible values for the resultant electronic spin, S, of the molecule are given by:

$$S = S_1+S_2, \quad S_1+S_2-1, \; . \; . \; . \; |S_1-S_2| \tag{3.3}$$

The value of S may be integral or half-integral, depending on whether the total number of electrons is even or odd. If the component of the electron orbit angular momentum ($L^*\boldsymbol{h}/2\pi$) along the internuclear axis is not zero, that is it is not a Σ-state, then there exists an internal magnetic field† (acting along the internuclear axis). The field is produced by the orbital motion of the electrons and may be identified with the precession of the orbit angular momentum. The magnetic moment associated with the electron spin can interact with this internal magnetic field causing a precession of the spin angular momentum about the internuclear axis. The component values of this spin angular momentum along this axis are governed by another quantum number $\mathit{\Sigma}$‡ which takes the values:

$$\mathit{\Sigma} = S, \quad S-1, \quad S-2, \; . \; . \; . \; -S \tag{3.4}$$

Thus, $\mathit{\Sigma}$ is analogous to the symbol M_S employed in the case of atoms, and $\mathit{\Sigma}\boldsymbol{h}/2\pi$ is the value of the spin orbit angular momentum about the internuclear axis, there being $(2S+1)$ possible orientations. The vector model for the precession of $L^\star\boldsymbol{h}/2\pi$ and $S^\star\boldsymbol{h}/2\pi$ is given in Fig. 3.2(*b*).

The component of the total electron angular momentum along the internuclear axis may be obtained by coupling Λ and $\mathit{\Sigma}$:

$$|\Lambda+\mathit{\Sigma}| = \Omega \tag{3.5}$$

where $\Omega\boldsymbol{h}/2\pi$ is the total electron angular momentum about the internuclear axis.§ The combination of Λ and $\mathit{\Sigma}$ in this way to give Ω is to be compared with the corresponding case of atoms in a strong electric field, where $|M_L|+M_S = M_J$. For each value of Λ there are $(2S+1)$ sublevels determined by the $(2S+1)$ values of $\mathit{\Sigma}$, and the multiplicity is, thus, $(2S+1)$; this value is added as a left superscript to the electronic state symbol. For example, a state for which Λ is equal to 1 having a spin of 1 would be $^3\Pi$-state. The value of Ω is indicated as a right subscript to the main symbol; in this case $\mathit{\Sigma} = 1$, 0 and -1, and $\Omega = 1+\mathit{\Sigma}$ and has $2\times1+1$ values which are 2, 1, and 0. The three different electronic energy states for the molecule in this quantum condition would thus be $^3\Pi_2$, $^3\Pi_1$, and $^3\Pi_0$, and would be represented by three different potential energy curves.

† The magnetic moment of the spinning electron cannot interact directly with the internuclear electric field as does the induced electric dipole moment associated with resultant orbit angular momentum vector. The latter is governed by the torque exerted by the electric field which causes it to precess about the internuclear axis and to have quantised components along this axis.

‡ This is the sloping Greek capital $\mathit{\Sigma}$, and it is necessary not to mistake this for the upright symbol Σ which is used to represent a molecular state of $\mathit{\Lambda} = 0$.

§ This is really Hund's case (*a*) (see later). In case (*b*) the angular momentum along the internuclear axis is $\mathit{\Lambda}\boldsymbol{h}/2\pi(= \mathit{\Omega}\boldsymbol{h}/2\pi)$ while in case (*c*) $L^\star\boldsymbol{h}/2\pi$ and $S^\star\boldsymbol{h}/2\pi$ remain coupled, and it is the presence of their resultant vector which gives the value of $\mathit{\Omega}\boldsymbol{h}/2\pi$. Thus, for cases (*a*), (*b*), and (*c*) of Hund's coupling the angular momentum along the internuclear axis in each case may be regarded as being $\mathit{\Omega}\boldsymbol{h}/2\pi$.

The splitting of the energy levels in a multiplet state may be related to the values of the quantum numbers Λ and Σ. For example, the electronic energy of term value T_e of a multiplet term is given approximately by:

$$T_e = T_0 + A\Lambda\Sigma$$

where T_0 is the term value when $\Sigma = 0$. A is known as the *coupling constant* and fixes the magnitude of the multiplet splitting; its value increases rapidly with the size of the atoms as does the multiplet splitting $(T_e - T_0)$.

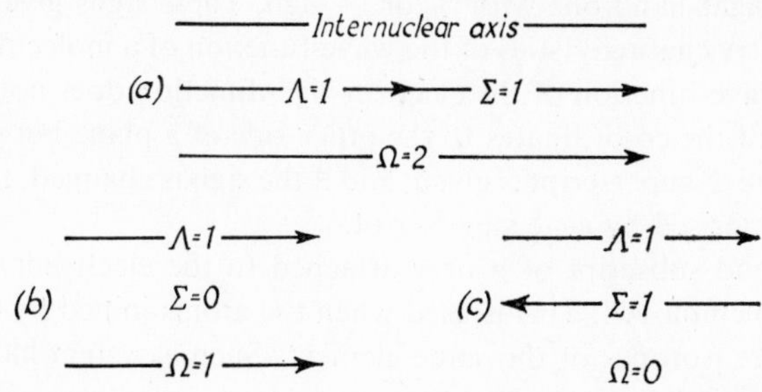

FIG. 3.3 Vector diagram of (*a*) $^3\Pi_2$ (*b*) $^3\Pi_1$ and (*c*) $^3\Pi_0$ states

The relative orientations of the vectors Λ and Σ in the $^3\Pi_2$, $^3\Pi_1$ and $^3\Pi_0$ states are illustrated in Fig. 3.3, and neglecting all considerations of rotational and vibrational levels the corresponding three electronic states may be represented as in Fig. 3.4.

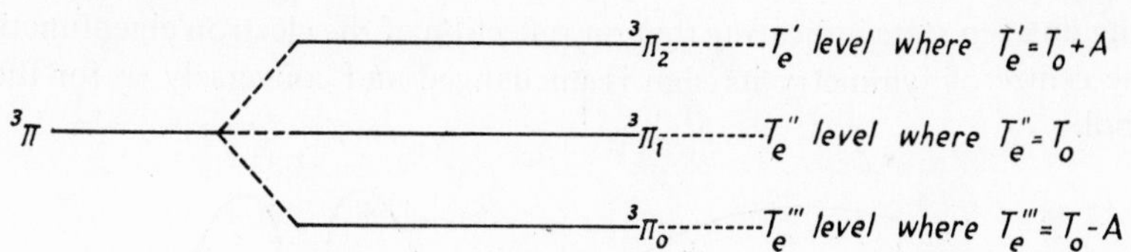

FIG. 3.4 Energy level diagram of a $^3\Pi$-state

The coupling constant A is constant for a given multiplet term. A coupling constant may have a positive or negative value, and in the case in Fig. 3.4, if A had been negative, then the $^3\Pi_2$ level would interchange places with the $^3\Pi_0$ level.

When $\Lambda = 0$, this means that the component of the resultant electron orbit angular momentum along the internuclear axis is zero; hence, the magnetic field along this line will also be zero and no splitting of the energy levels will occur. For example, if $\Lambda = 0$ and $S = 2$ this would be represented by a $^5\Sigma$-state, but there would be no splitting of this electronic energy state. This is in harmony with putting $\Lambda = 0$ in the formula $T_e = T_0 + A\Lambda\Sigma$, whence $T_e = T_0$. Thus, superficially the superscript symbol may seem somewhat misleading. However, even for Σ-states a small amount of splitting of the electron states may occur when $(2S+1) > 1$ provided the molecule is rotating. This type of splitting results from interaction of the magnetic moment due to electron spin with the magnetic field due to molecular rotation.† As regards molecules in other than Σ-states (e.g. Π and Δ) the full splitting of the electronic energy levels required by $(2S+1)$ generally seems to occur.

'Scripts' giving information on the wave-function symmetry of diatomic molecules

Another superscript is used in addition to the one denoting multiplicity and this is a right-hand one with + or — sign. These signs give information on the symmetry characteristics of the wave-function of a molecular electronic state. If the wave-function of the electron eigenfunction does not change sign on reflection of the co-ordinates to the other side of a plane between the two nuclei, then the + superscript is given, and if the sign is changed, the electronic state is characterised by a — superscript.

A right-hand subscript of *g* or *u* attached to the electronic energy state symbol is also employed. This is used when the atoms joined by the bond are identical or are isotopes of the same element. Such a system has a centre of symmetry.

If the co-ordinates of all the electrons x_i, y_i, z_i are replaced by $-x_i$, $-y_i$ and $-z_i$, then provided the electron eigenfunction remains unaltered in sign by this reflection through the centre of symmetry, the subscript *g* is attached. If the sign of the wave-function changes, a subscript *u* is employed. The *g* symbol is derived from the German *gerade* denoting even and *u* from *ungerade* meaning odd. Thus, a molecule characterised by the symbol *g* is regarded as having an even state indicating that on reflection of the electron eigenfunction at the centre of symmetry its sign is unchanged and conversely so for the *u* symbol.

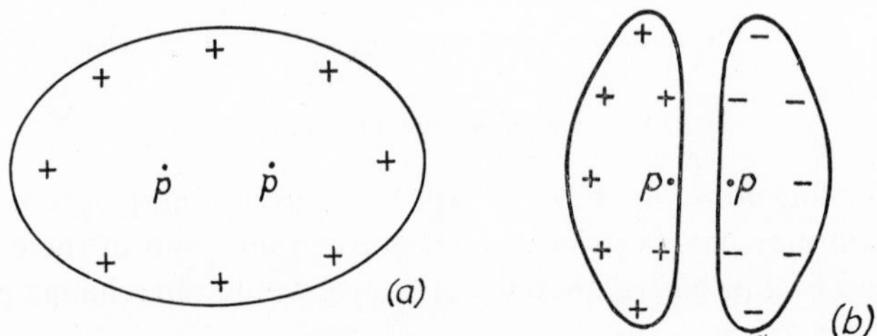

FIG. 3.5 (*a*) A bonding orbital, e.g. a $^2\Sigma_g^+$-state (*b*) An anti-bonding orbital, e.g. a $^2\Sigma_u^+$-state

As an example of the use of + and — symmetry and *g* and *u*, the molecular orbit of the H_2^+ will now be considered. The bonding orbit is shown in Fig. 3.5(*a*) and the non-bonding orbit in Fig. 3.5(*b*). The positive and negative signs inside the boundary indicate that the wave-function ψ is positive and negative, respectively, in that region, while the *p* represents a proton. If a

† This magnetic field is produced by the rotation of the nuclei as a pair about a common centre of gravity, and consequently a perpendicular magnetic field is produced in the direction of the vector representing the nuclear angular momentum.

plane is placed through the two protons, then on either side of the plane the wave-function does not change sign on reflection through the plane, hence, a + sign is attached as a superscript to the term symbol. If a straight line is drawn between the centres of the two protons, then the mid-point would be the centre of symmetry, and if this is made the origin of the co-ordinates (x, y, z) it follows from Fig. 3.5(*a*) that on replacement of these co-ordinates by $(-x, -y, -z)$ the wave-function will still be positive; hence, the symbol g is used for this case. In Fig. 3.5(*b*), however, by a similar procedure the wave-function would be negative; hence, for this case, the symbol u would be employed. As there is only one electron, the multiplicity must be $2\times\frac{1}{2}+1 = 2$, and this is added as the left-hand superscript; hence, the bonding orbital is described by ${}^2\Sigma_g^+$ but the anti-bonding orbital by ${}^2\Sigma_u^+$.

Correlation between atomic and molecular states

A further link between atomic and molecular spectra is that various rules have been evolved as to which possible molecular electronic states may result from the combination of two atoms in known electronic states to form a diatomic molecule. These rules emerge from quantum mechanics where only certain multiplicities and molecular states are permissible from the combination of any two atomic states. For instance a few of the examples on how atomic and molecular multiplicities may be related are given in Table 3.1.

TABLE 3.1

Feasible molecular multiplicities resulting from the combination of two atoms of known multiplicity

Atomic multiplicity	Resulting molecular multiplicity
singlet+singlet	singlet
singlet+doublet	doublet
doublet+doublet	singlet or triplet
triplet+triplet	singlet or triplet or quintet

In Table 3.2 the molecular electronic states which may result from combining two atomic states of known multiplicity to form a symmetrical diatomic molecule are given. Once, however, *P*- and *D*-states are considered, the number of feasible resulting molecular states considerably increases.

TABLE 3.2

Feasible molecular states of a symmetrical diatomic molecule resulting from the combination of known atomic states

Atomic states	Resulting molecular state
${}^1S+{}^1S$	${}^1\Sigma_g^+$
${}^2S+{}^2S$	${}^1\Sigma_g^+$ or ${}^3\Sigma_u^+$
${}^3S+{}^3S$	${}^1\Sigma_g^+$ or ${}^3\Sigma_u^+$, or ${}^5\Sigma_g^+$

For example, the combination of two atoms in a ^1P-state may result in $^1\Sigma_g^+$, $^1\Sigma_u^-$, $^1\Pi_g$, $^1\Pi_u$, $^1\Delta_g$ states, while $^1D + ^1D$ may give nine different molecular states.

Coupling of angular momenta

So far we have considered the rotation of a diatomic molecule with respect to the rotation of the nuclei only. However, this rotation and the rotational energy equation may be influenced by the motion of the electrons. We shall now consider the effect of one on the other and the quantum numbers which characterise the rotational levels in the various types of electronic states.

A molecule has four different sources of angular momenta which are due to (i) the motion of the electron in the orbit, (ii) electron spin, (iii) one or both of the nuclei spinning, and (iv) the rotation of the nuclei as a unit (nuclear rotation). The nuclear-spin angular momentum is often neglected, and the total angular momentum of the molecule may then be regarded as the resultant angular momentum obtained by combining the other three types of angular momenta.

In nearly all diatomic molecules in their ground state the electron spins are paired,† and the electron spin angular momentum $S^\star \boldsymbol{h}/2\pi$ is zero. Furthermore, the orbit angular momentum $L^\star \boldsymbol{h}/2\pi$ of the electrons is also usually zero. Thus, such molecules have a $^1\Sigma$ ground state. If the nuclear spin is neglected, then the only other source of angular momentum of the molecule is that due to nuclear rotation, and the rotational energy equation for such a case was considered on p. 6.

For free radicals, and certain electronically-excited molecules, however, there would be more than one source of angular momentum. Hund was the first to show how these different sources of angular momenta could be coupled together to give a resultant angular momentum. He considered five different cases, known as Hund's cases (*a*), (*b*), (*c*), (*d*) and (*e*), in which the resultant angular momentum could be formed.

To appreciate Hund's coupling cases it is necessary to realise that both internal electric and magnetic fields can act along the internuclear axis. The electric field results from the electrostatic field due to the two nuclei. This electric field causes an induced electric dipole to be set up in the molecule which can interact with the electric field and make the orbit angular momentum precess about its axis. Furthermore, as a result of the precession of this orbit angular momentum a magnetic field is set up along the internuclear axis. In addition to these fields a further magnetic field may arise because of the rotation of the nuclei as a pair about their common centre of gravity. This magnetic field acts in the direction of the nuclear angular momentum vector, that is perpendicular to the internuclear axis. For cases where $\Lambda > 0$ and $S > 0$ the interaction between the nuclear angular momentum and the orbit and spin angular momenta of the electrons occurs magnetically.

† The O_2 and NO molecules are exceptions.

For each of Hund's cases an equation may be obtained for the rotational energy of the molecule in terms of quantum numbers. All the five cases of Hund are either limiting or extreme cases, and many intermediate cases are found in practice. In general, cases (*a*) and (*b*) may be looked upon as the normal coupling cases; these together with case (*c*) will now be considered.

Hund's case (*a*)

This applies to diatomic molecules where the internuclear distance is small enough for there to be a sufficiently strong electric field (resulting from the electrostatic field of the two nuclei) along the internuclear axis to prevent $L^\star \boldsymbol{h}/2\pi$ and $S^\star \boldsymbol{h}/2\pi$ from directly coupling. The electric dipole moment (associated with $L^\star \boldsymbol{h}/2\pi$) induced by this electric field then interacts with the electric field and $L^\star \boldsymbol{h}/2\pi$ is caused to precess about the internuclear axis and has an angular momentum $\Lambda \boldsymbol{h}/2\pi$ in the direction of the internuclear axis. The precession of $L^\star \boldsymbol{h}/2\pi$ sets up a strong magnetic field along the internuclear axis, which enables the magnetic dipole associated with the electron spin vector to interact, and $S^\star \boldsymbol{h}/2\pi$ is also caused to precess about the internuclear axis. The magnetic interaction of the $S^\star \boldsymbol{h}/2\pi$ and $\Lambda \boldsymbol{h}/2\pi$ vectors is strong. This results in the $S^\star \boldsymbol{h}/2\pi$ vector being strongly coupled to the magnetic field along the internuclear axis so that its axial component $\Sigma \boldsymbol{h}/2\pi$ is quantised. It follows, therefore, that the total angular momentum quantum number Ω along the internuclear axis is given by:

$$\Lambda + \Sigma = \Omega$$

where $\Omega \boldsymbol{h}/2\pi$ is the total electron angular momentum along the internuclear axis.

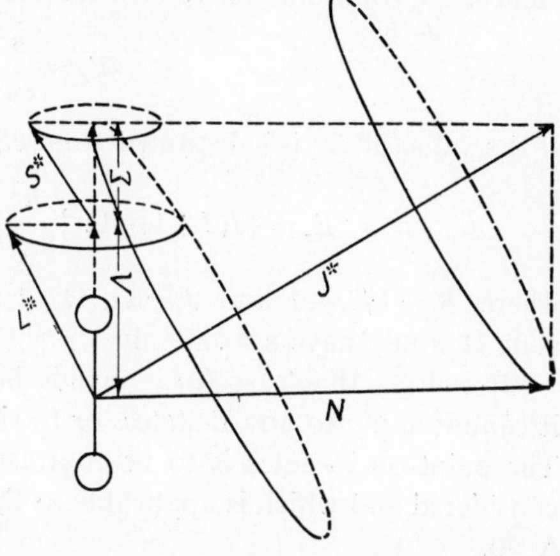

FIG. 3.6 Vector diagram for Hund's case (*a*) L^*, S^*, Λ, Σ, J^*, and N are each in $\boldsymbol{h}/2\pi$units

The precession of $L^\star \boldsymbol{h}/2\pi$ and $S^\star \boldsymbol{h}/2\pi$ is shown in Fig. 3.6, and their components $\Lambda \boldsymbol{h}/2\pi$ and $\Sigma \boldsymbol{h}/2\pi$, respectively, along the internuclear axis are indicated. The total electron angular momentum about the internuclear axis is well defined. The nuclei in the rigid diatomic molecule may be regarded as rotating as a whole about an axis perpendicular to the internuclear axis and having an angular momentum of rotation $N\boldsymbol{h}/2\pi$ which will act perpendicular to the centre of gravity of the molecule. If the interaction between $N\boldsymbol{h}/2\pi$ and $\Omega \boldsymbol{h}/2\pi$ is very weak, then these two angular momenta may be combined vectorially to form a resultant angular momentum:

$$\sqrt{J(J+1)}\frac{\boldsymbol{h}}{2\pi}$$

where $J = \Omega, \Omega+1, \Omega+2 \ldots$

The precession of various vectors is given in Fig. 3.6, where the vector parallelogram formed from $\Omega h/2\pi$ and $Nh/2\pi$ has been completed with the broken lines, and the resultant total angular momentum is represented by the diagonal. The coupling vectors $\Omega h/2\pi$ and $Nh/2\pi$ precess about the axis of the resultant total angular momentum.

N is related to Ω and J by the equation:

$$N = \sqrt{J(J+1)-\Omega^2} \tag{3.6}$$

From classical theory the rotational energy of a rigid diatomic molecule may be expressed in terms of its angular momentum (P) and its moment of inertia (I) by the equation:

$$E_r = \frac{1}{2}\frac{P^2}{I} \tag{3.7}$$

For the rotation of the molecule (nuclei) as a whole:

$$P = N\frac{h}{2\pi} \tag{3.8}$$

Hence, the rotational energy (in ergs) is given by:

$$E_r = \frac{h^2}{8\pi^2 I}N^2 \tag{3.9}$$

If the value of N^2 is substituted from equation 3.6 into 3.9, then:

$$E_r = \{J(J+1)-\Omega^2\}\frac{h^2}{8\pi^2 I} = \{J(J+1)-\Omega^2\}Bhc \tag{3.10}$$

where $B = h/8\pi^2 cI$ and $J = \Omega$, $\Omega+1$, $\Omega+2$, etc. For a given electronic state Ω would have a fixed value.

It follows that case (a) demands both $\Lambda>0$ and $S>0$, and, therefore, it cannot apply to any Σ-states, or to singlet states (i.e. $S = 0$) of any kind. The point on Σ-states is to be contrasted with case (b) which will now be considered and which is applicable to Σ, and also to some other states where $\Lambda>0$.

Hund's case (b)

Again as with case (a) the internuclear distance is small enough for there to be a sufficiently strong electric field along the internuclear axis to prevent $L^{\star}h/2\pi$ and $S^{\star}h/2\pi$ from directly coupling. $L^{\star}h/2\pi$ again precesses about this electric field acting along the internuclear axis. However, case (b) differs from case (a) in that the magnetic field associated with this precession is so weak that the interaction between $\Lambda h/2\pi$ and $S^{\star}h/2\pi$ is negligible compared with that due to the interaction of the molecular rotation angular momentum ($Nh/2\pi$) and $\Lambda h/2\pi$. $\Lambda h/2\pi$ then combines directly with the nuclear angular momentum ($Nh/2\pi$) to give a resultant angular momentum, $K^{\star}h/2\pi$, where the rotational quantum number K takes the values Λ, $\Lambda+1$, $\Lambda+2$, etc. $K^{\star}h/2\pi$ is known as the total angular momentum apart from spin. The coupling occurs through the magnetic fields produced by the rotating nuclei and that of the orbital angular momentum, and $\Lambda h/2\pi$ and $Nh/2\pi$ precess around $K^{\star}h/2\pi$. The electron spin vector $S^{\star}h/2\pi$ couples with $K^{\star}h/2\pi$ to give a resultant $J^{\star}h/2\pi$ which is the total angular momentum including electron spin.† The values which J may take for a given value of K are obtained by the rules of vector addition:

$$J = (K+S), (K+S-1) \; . \; . \; . \; |K-S| \tag{3.11}$$

Apart from when $K<S$ each rotational level with a particular K-value has $2S+1$ components. Since

$$K = \Lambda, \Lambda+1, \Lambda+2, \; . \; . \; .$$

and Λ may have only the values 0, 1, 2, . . . it follows that K may take only integral values. In addition, since S may have integer or half-integer values according to whether there is an even or odd number, respectively, of electrons in the molecule, then it may be seen from equation (3.11) that J is half-integral when the number of electrons is odd and integral for an even number. In Fig. 3.7 the rotational levels of a $^2\Sigma$-state may be observed where for such a state $\Lambda = 0$ and $S = \frac{1}{2}$, and the relation between the J- and K-values is indicated in the figure.

FIG. 3.7 Rotational energy levels of a vibrational level in a $^2\Sigma$-state

The precession of the various vectors is represented in Fig. 3.8(i), and the formation of the total angular momentum vector $J^{\star}h/2\pi$ from $K^{\star}h/2\pi$ and $S^{\star}h/2\pi$ is indicated. Both $K^{\star}h/2\pi$ and $S^{\star}h/2\pi$ precess around $J^{\star}h/2\pi$. The value of N is:

$$N = \sqrt{K(K+1)-\Lambda^2} \tag{3.12}$$

and the rotational energy equation is given approximately by:

$$E_r = \{K(K+1)-\Lambda^2\}Bhc \tag{3.13}$$

where $K = \Lambda$, $\Lambda+1$, $\Lambda+2$. . . . Hund's case (*b*) applies to molecules in Σ-states, since when $\Lambda = 0$ there is no internuclear magnetic field to make $S^{\star}h/2\pi$ precess around it. Nearly all diatomic molecules have a Σ ground state. In addition, case (*b*) may also apply to states where $\Lambda = 1, 2, 3$ . . . , if the internuclear magnetic field is sufficiently weak.

† For this case, since $S^{\star}h/2\pi$ is not coupled to the internuclear axis it follows that the quantum number Σ does not exist.

Hund's case (*c*)

When the internuclear distance is sufficiently large then the electric field along the internuclear axis may be inadequate to destroy the coupling between the orbit and spin angular momenta. This corresponds with Hund's case (*c*) where the orbit and spin angular momenta couple to give a resultant

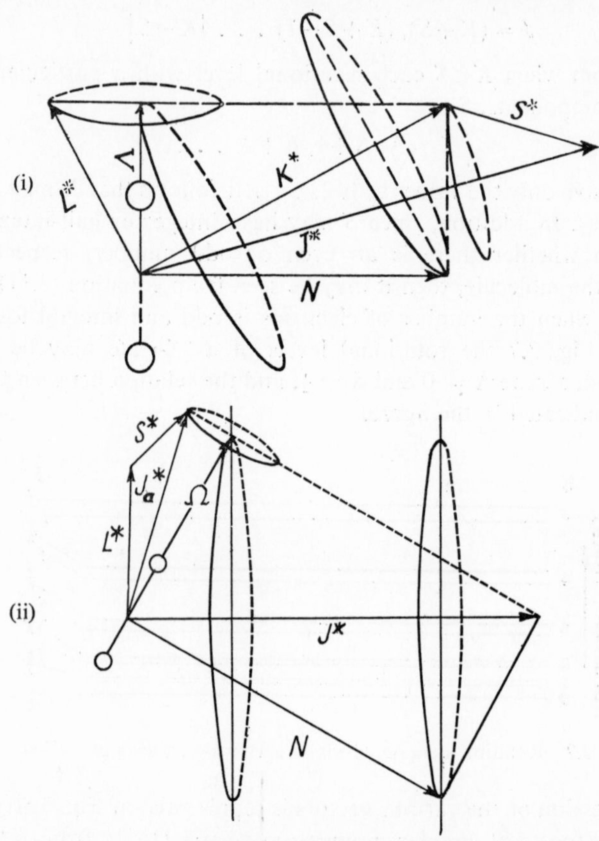

FIG. 3.8 (i) Coupling and precession of the vectors in Hund's case (*b*). (ii) Coupling and precession of the vectors in Hund's case (*c*)

angular momentum $\sqrt{J_a(J_a+1)}\boldsymbol{h}/2\pi$ which precesses about the internuclear electric field, while the $L^{\star}\boldsymbol{h}/2\pi$ and $S^{\star}\boldsymbol{h}/2\pi$ vectors precess about the axis of $J_a^{\star}\boldsymbol{h}/2\pi$. The symbol J_a is employed to indicate its relationship to the J employed in atomic spectra which is also formed from coupling L and S.

The component of $\sqrt{J_a(J_a+1)}\boldsymbol{h}/2\pi$ along the internuclear is $\Omega\boldsymbol{h}/2\pi$ where Ω takes the values:

$$J_a, J_a-1, \ldots \tfrac{1}{2} \text{ or } 0$$

The $\Omega\boldsymbol{h}/2\pi$ and $N\boldsymbol{h}/2\pi$ vectors then combine to give the resultant $\sqrt{J(J+1)}\boldsymbol{h}/2\pi$ and precess about it. These points may be observed in Fig. 3.8(ii). It should be noted that for case (*c*) Λ has no meaning, and hence the symbols Σ, Π, and Δ cannot be employed to represent such states.

On comparison of Fig. 3.6 and 3.8(ii) it follows that in Hund's case (*c*) N must be related to Ω and J by the same equation as that given for case (*a*), that is equation (3.6). In addition, the same rotational energy equation, that is equation (3.10), must apply to both these cases.

It is necessary to reconcile the equations (3.10) and (3.13) with the one already quoted (p. 6) for the rotational energy of a rigid molecule, that is with:

$$E_r = J(J+1)Bhc. \tag{3.14}$$

As already indicated nearly all diatomic molecules are in a $^1\Sigma$ ground state, that is a singlet, and for such a state $J \equiv K$. The resultant electron spin (S) and the resultant orbit angular momentum component $\Lambda h/2\pi$ of the electrons are both zero, and, hence, so is Ω; therefore, equations (3.10) and (3.13) reduce to (3.14), and the total angular momentum of the molecule may be attributed solely to the rotation of the rigid molecule. Since $\Lambda = 0$ and $\Omega = 0$ for a $^1\Sigma$ state, then $J = 0, 1, 2, 3$, which again were the ones previously quoted.

In an electronic transition from a detailed analysis of the rotational structure of the bands the values of Ω, Λ, and the multiplicity are allotted, and the two electronic states involved in the transition are identified.

One of the most helpful factors in this type of analysis is to note which lines are missing from the bands in the electronic spectrum and to relate them to the particular rotational energy levels involved. In Hund's coupling case (*a*) J takes the values Ω, $\Omega+1$, $\Omega+2$, etc., and if $\Omega>0$, then there will be at least one "missing" rotational energy level. In the case considered on p. 48 where $\Lambda = 1$ and $S = 1$, there were three sub-electronic states $^3\Pi_0$, $^3\Pi_1$, and $^3\Pi_2$ where $\Omega = 0, 1$, and 2, respectively. For the sub-state $^3\Pi_1$ there will be one missing rotational level, the $J = 0$ level, while for the sub-state $^3\Pi_2$ the $J = 0$ and the $J = 1$ levels would be absent. Thus, knowledge of which rotational levels are absent assists in inferring the types of molecular states between which the electronic transitions are taking place.

Selection rules of diatomic molecules

General

As is typical of spectra, selection rules limit the possible transitions—for both absorption and emission—between the various electronic states, and for a diatomic molecule some of these are:

$$\Delta\Lambda = 0, \pm 1 \tag{3.15}$$

$$\Delta S = 0 \quad \dagger \tag{3.16}$$

$$\Delta\Sigma = 0 \tag{3.17}$$

$$\Delta\Omega = 0, \pm 1 \quad \ddagger \tag{3.18}$$

† Although transitions between states of different multiplicity are forbidden (i.e. $\Delta S = 0$), in practice the rule is sometimes violated as in the case of the Cameron bands of CO which are attributed to a $^3\Pi - {}^1\Sigma^+$ transition. Usually, however, whenever the ΔS selection rule is violated $\Delta S = \pm 1$.

‡ Equations 3.15 and 3.16 apply only to Hund's case "*a*" and "*b*"; 3.17 requires that both electronic states belong to case "*a*", and 3.18 to case "*c*".

Thus, in theory transitions such as:

$$^2\Delta_{5/2}\leftrightarrow{}^2\Pi_{3/2},\quad {}^2\Delta_{3/2}\leftrightarrow{}^2\Pi_{1/2}$$

would be permissible whereas the transitions:

$$^3\Delta_{3}\leftrightarrow{}^2\Pi_{1/2},\quad {}^2\Delta_{5/2}\leftrightarrow{}^2\Pi_{1/2}$$

would be forbidden.

For transitions between Σ^+- and Σ^--states the selection rules are:

$$\Sigma^+\leftrightarrow\Sigma^+,\quad \Sigma^-\leftrightarrow\Sigma^-\quad \text{but}\quad \Sigma^+\not\leftrightarrow\Sigma^-$$

where the sign $\not\leftrightarrow$ indicates that the transition is forbidden. For a symmetrical diatomic molecule further restrictions are $g\rightarrow u$, $u\rightarrow g$, but $g\not\rightarrow g$ and $u\not\rightarrow u$. In addition to this there are further selection rules which govern the fine structure of the individual bands. The selection rules for the rotational quantum number are governed by whichever of Hund's coupling cases is concerned:

(i) for case (*a*): $\Delta J = 0, \pm 1$ (3.19)

although the $\Delta J = 0$ is forbidden when $\Omega = 0$ in both electronic states.

(ii) for case (*b*): $\Delta K = 0, \pm 1$ (3.20)

where $\Delta K = 0$ is forbidden for a $\Sigma - \Sigma$ transition.

Additional selection rules which determine the fine structure are considered on p. 61.

In order to gain some indication of the complexity of the electronic-energy states of diatomic molecules and the possible electronic transitions involved, together with application of the selection rules, one example will now be considered. Fig. 3.9 is the energy-level diagram for the N_2 molecule where the heavy (full) horizontal lines represent some of the several detected electronic states. The short thin lines indicate the vibrational levels relating to a particular electronic state.

The $X^1\Sigma_g^+$ is the ground electronic state and transitions may occur to this from some of the excited states. In addition, transitions occur between the excited electronic states. Two particularly well-known emission transitions to spectroscopists are the first and second positive nitrogen bands which correspond to the $B^3\Pi_g\rightarrow A^3\Sigma_u^+$, $C^3\Pi_u\rightarrow B^3\Pi_g$ transitions. These satisfy the selection rules

$$\Delta\Lambda = 0, +1,\quad \Delta S = 0\quad \text{and}\quad u\leftrightarrow g$$

and are, therefore, permitted transitions. The Vegard-Kaplan bands, however, which are also experimentally observed, correspond with the forbidden transition $A^3\Sigma_u^+\rightarrow X^1\Sigma_g^+$. A number of electronic transitions are indicated in the figure, and the names allotted to the main ones are given. It will be observed that the lowest lying triplet state is designated by the symbol *A* placed in front of its energy state symbol and the two succeeding triplet levels in order of increasing energy by *B* and *C*.

On the extreme right of the diagram the atomic states of the dissociation products of some of the molecular states are given of the N_2^+ ion and N_2 molecule, and these are indicated by broken horizontal lines. It will be seen that the atomic states of the dissociation products are ^4S, ^2D and ^2P; these correspond with the three lowest energy states of the nitrogen atom. The ^2D lies 2.383 eV above the ^4S state which is the ground state, while the ^2P lies 3.574 eV above it. In Fig. 3.9 two ionisation limits are indicated by means of the heavy broken horizontal lines across the whole of the figure, and these correspond to the two states $^2\Sigma_g^+$ and $^2\Sigma_u^+$ of the ionised nitrogen molecule (i.e. N_2^+).

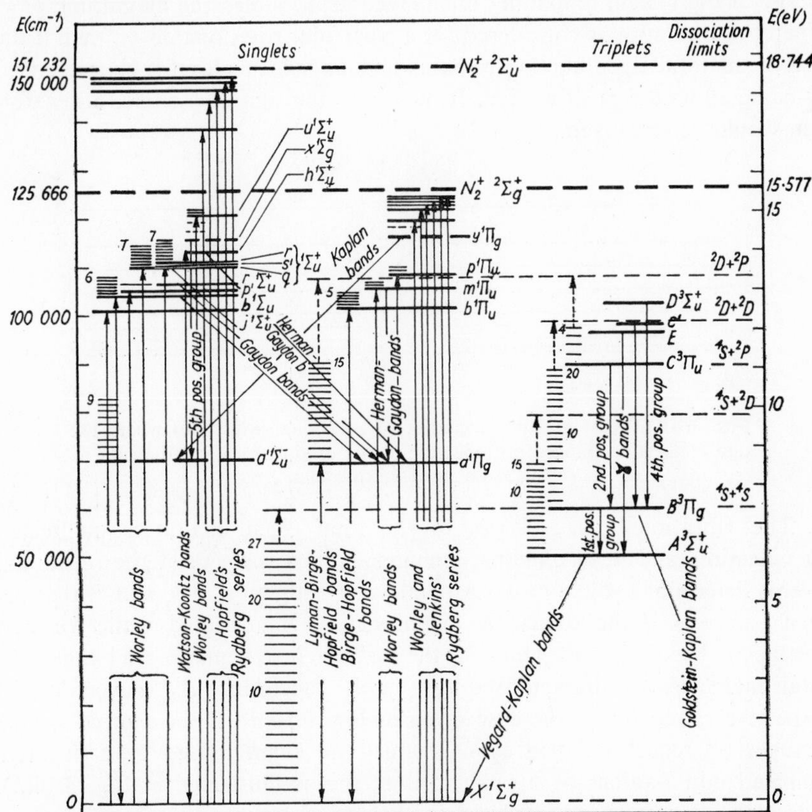

FIG. 3.9 Energy level diagram and electronic transitions of the N_2 molecule. The heavy (full) horizontal lines give the electronic states; the shorter thinner lines give the vibrational levels in each of them. The broken horizontal lines indicate dissociation limits. (*From G. Herzberg*,[1] 'Spectra of Diatomic Molecules', Vol. 1, *2nd ed.*, 1950, *D. Van Nostrand Co., Princeton, N.J.*)

Symmetry properties of rotational levels and their selection rules

The total eigenfunction ψ of a diatomic molecule is given to a first approximation by:

$$\psi = \psi_e \frac{1}{r} \psi_v \psi_r$$

where r is the internuclear distance and ψ_e, ψ_v and ψ_r are, respectively, the electronic, vibrational and rotational eigenfunctions. The rotational levels of a diatomic molecule may be classified as being either positive (+) or negative (—) according to the behaviour of ψ on reflection at the origin of the co-ordinates. The reflection applies to all the particles within the molecule including the nuclei, although the rotational and vibrational eigenfunctions depend solely on the co-ordinates of the nuclei. Reflection at the origin is achieved by replacing the co-ordinates (x, y, z) by $(-x, -y, -z)$, the potential energy of the system remaining unchanged as does also the magnitude of ψ. When this operation is considered for a particular rotational level, then if the sign of the total eigenfunction remains unchanged, this level is characterised by being allotted a positive sign. If, however, the sign of ψ alters, a negative sign would be employed.

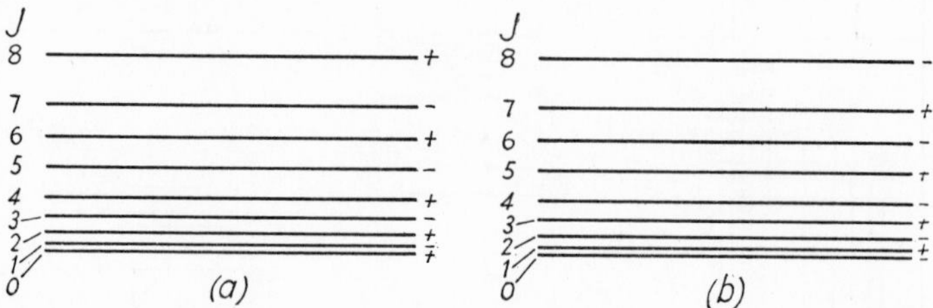

FIG. 3.10 The symmetry properties of rotational levels: (*a*) where the sign of ψ_e is unchanged on reflection at the origin; (*b*) where the sign of ψ_e is changed on reflection

The vibrational part, $(1/r)\psi_v$ of the total eigenfunction is unaffected by reflection, and if ψ_e remains unchanged, then the sign of the rotational level is determined solely by ψ_r. A detailed investigation of ψ_r shows that for even values of J the rotational eigenfunction is unaltered while for odd J-values ψ_r becomes $-\psi_r$. Thus, for the case where ψ_e remains unchanged the rotational levels are characterised by + and — according as J is even or odd, respectively, and this is the case given in Fig. 3.10(*a*). If the sign of ψ_e also changes on reflection, then even J-values are characterised by a negative sign and odd J-values by a positive one; this is illustrated in Fig. 3.10(*b*). Before the sign of ψ_e is considered further it is necessary to appreciate what is meant by inversion. Inversion may be achieved by the following operations: (*a*) rotation of the molecule through 180° about an axis which is perpendicular to the internuclear axis, then (*b*) reflection of the particles across the plane passing through the internuclear axis and perpendicular to the rotational axis. Only (*b*) could affect the sign of ψ_e. If these ideas are applied to Σ^+-and Σ^--states, it follows from previous considerations (see p. 51) that the sign of ψ_e would be unaltered for a Σ^+-state but would change for a Σ^--state. Thus, for Σ^+-states the $J = 0, 2, 4 \ldots$ rotational levels are characterised by a positive sign. The $J = 1, 3, 5 \ldots$ levels, however, would have a negative sign.

Rotation-vibration and electronic changes are governed by the selection rule

$$+ \leftrightarrow -$$

that is, positive levels combine only with negative. Transitions of the type

$+\leftrightarrow+$, $-\leftrightarrow-$ are forbidden for these types of changes but allowed for Raman spectra in which the $+\leftrightarrow-$ transitions are forbidden. These selection rules are given in Table 3.3 together with those for J and a and s (see below).

TABLE 3.3

Selection rules for infra-red, Raman, and electronic transitions

Infra-red rotation-vibration		Raman rotation-vibration		Electronic	
Rotator with $\Lambda = 0$	Rotator with $\Lambda \neq 0$	Rotator with $\Lambda = 0$	Rotator with $\Lambda \neq 0$	Case where $\Lambda' = \Lambda'' = 0$ e.g. $^1\Sigma - {}^1\Sigma$	Case where either Λ' or $\Lambda'' \neq 0$ e.g. $^1\Pi - {}^1\Sigma$
$\Delta J = \pm 1$	$\Delta J = 0, \pm 1$	$\Delta J = 0, \pm 2$	$\Delta J = 0, \pm 1, \pm 2$	$\Delta J = \pm 1$	$\Delta J = 0, \pm 1$
$+\longleftrightarrow-$	$+\longleftrightarrow-$	$+\longleftrightarrow+$ $-\longleftrightarrow-$	$+\longleftrightarrow+$ $-\longleftrightarrow-$	$+\longleftrightarrow-$	$+\longleftrightarrow-$
$a\longleftrightarrow a$	$a\longleftrightarrow a$	$a\longleftrightarrow a$	$a\longleftrightarrow a$	$a\longleftrightarrow a$	$a\longleftrightarrow a$
$s\longleftrightarrow s$	$s\longleftrightarrow s$	$s\longleftrightarrow s$	$s\longleftrightarrow s$	$s\longleftrightarrow s$	$s\longleftrightarrow s$

Symmetric and antisymmetric selection rules for the rotational levels of homonuclear molecules

For a homonuclear diatomic molecule, such as $^1H_2$, $^{16}O_2$, $^{14}N_2$, etc., the rotational levels are characterised in addition to + and − by s (symmetric) and a (antisymmetric). When an exchange of the positions of the nuclei in the molecule leaves the total eigenfunction unchanged the rotational levels are said to be symmetric, while if ψ changes sign the rotational levels are classified as antisymmetric. For a given electronic state of the molecule either

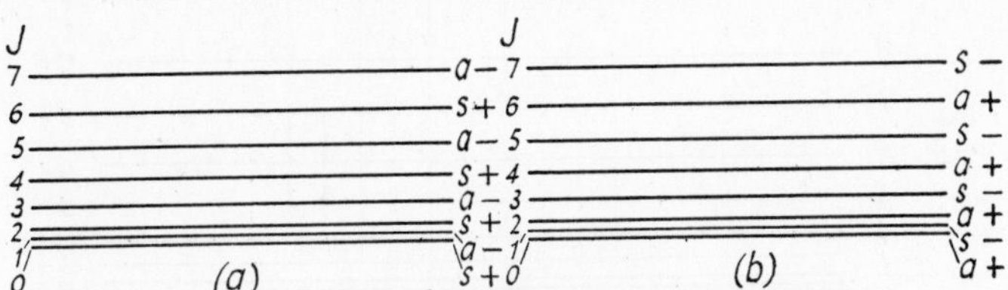

FIG. 3.11 Symmetry properties of rotational levels of homonuclear molecules: (*a*) where the positive levels and negative levels are symmetric and antisymmetric, respectively; (*b*) where the negative and positive levels are symmetric and antisymmetric, respectively

the positive rotational levels are all symmetric and the negative all antisymmetric or conversely these relations are reversed. Both of these possibilities are shown in Fig. 3.11(*a*) and (*b*). Whether (*a*) or (*b*) applies in a particular example depends on whether the nuclei in question obey the Bose-Einstein or the Fermi-Dirac statistics,[1] but this will not be considered further.

If the possibility of nuclear spin is neglected, a rigid selection rule operates for absorption or emission of radiation between symmetric and antisymmetric levels and is:

$$s\leftrightarrow s, \quad a\leftrightarrow a, \quad a \not\longleftrightarrow s$$

This with other selection rules is given in Table 3.3.

If all the molecules of a given type were in symmetric states at some given time, and providing the nuclei of these molecules did not possess a nuclear spin, then since the selection rule prohibits intercombinations between symmetric and antisymmetric states, the molecules would always remain in a symmetric state. In addition, if this were so, every second line would be missing from the electronic band spectrum of that species. In Fig. 3.12 some of the transitions between the ${}^1\Sigma_g^+$ and the ${}^1\Sigma_u^+$ electronic states are given.

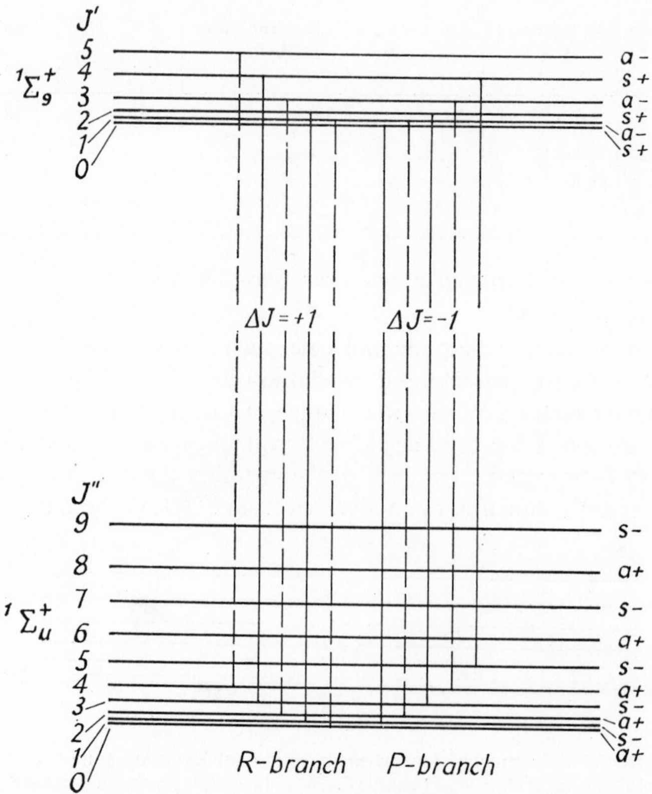

FIG. 3.12 Transitions between the ${}^1\Sigma_g^+$ and ${}^1\Sigma_u^+$ electronic states where the full lines indicate $s \leftrightarrow s$ transitions and the broken lines $a \leftrightarrow a$ transitions

The rotational levels have been characterised by + and − and also by symmetric (s) and antisymmetric (a). The selection rule for rotational transitions between such electronic states is $\Delta J = \pm 1$; transitions between antisymmetric states have been indicated by broken lines and those between symmetric states by full lines. It will be observed from Fig. 3.12 that if, in fact, all the molecules were in either symmetric or antisymmetric states, then either the transitions indicated by broken lines or those by the full lines would be absent, respectively, from the electronic band spectrum. This

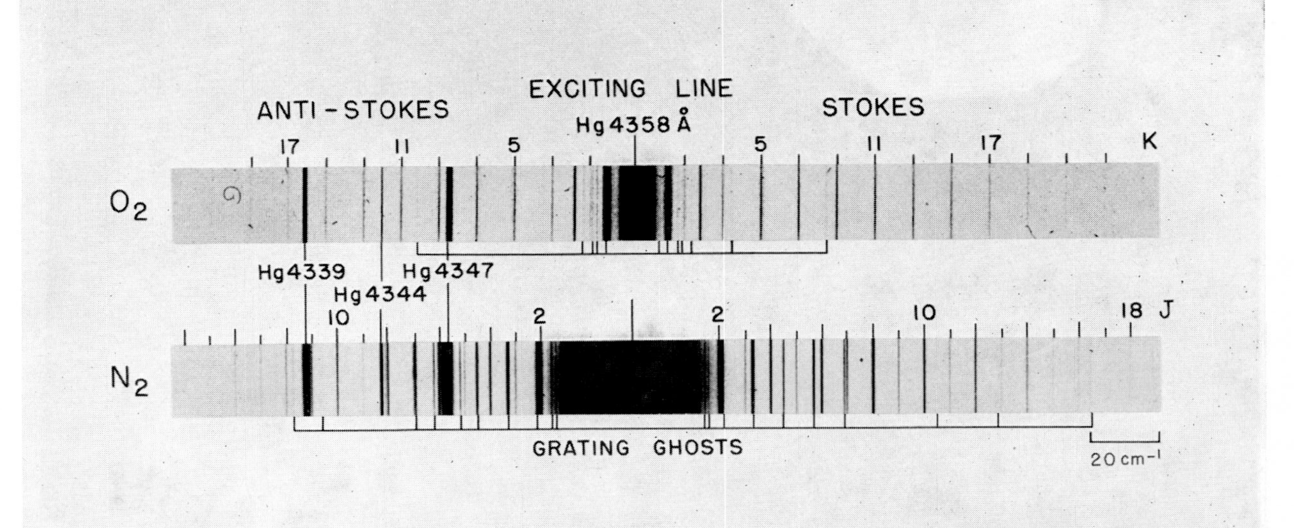

FIG. 3.13 Rotational Raman spectra (see Chapter 4) of the O_2 and N_2 molecules. In the case of the O_2 spectrum the rotational quantum number K values (Hund's case b) are given on the upper edge of the spectrogram. It will be noted that only rotational lines with odd K values are observed. The N_2 spectrum consists of widely spaced lines exhibiting the intensity alternation which are strong when J is even and weak when J is odd. The nuclear spin of nitrogen is 1. Grating ghosts are explained in Chapter 2.

(*Courtesy of Dr. B. P. Stoicheff*[3])

[*To face page* 62

absence of every second line in the band spectrum has been observed for several homonuclear diatomic molecules including $^{16}O_2$, (see Chapter 5) and $^{12}C_2$. If, however, the symmetry of such molecules is destroyed by isotopic substitution, then the question of symmetric and antisymmetric rotational levels does not arise, and all the rotational lines are observed.

For a homonuclear diatomic species in which the nuclei spin the band spectrum is characterised by alternately strong and weak rotational line intensities. The explanation of this intensity alternation was first given by Hund and depends upon the fact that the selection rule prohibiting the combination of symmetric and antisymmetric states is no longer rigid. The result of this is that both symmetric and antisymmetric term systems can appear but do so with different statistical weights.

The pure rotational Raman spectra of $^{16}O_2$ and $^{14}N_2$ given in Fig. 3.13 illustrate in the case of $^{16}O_2$ the absence of every second rotational line and for $^{14}N_2$ the alternately strong and weak rotational line intensities.[3]

Λ doubling

It was assumed in the treatment of Hund's cases (*a*) and (*b*) that the interaction between the angular momentum ($N\boldsymbol{h}/2\pi$) due to the rotation of the nuclei as a whole in the rigid diatomic molecule and that of the orbit angular momentum ($\sqrt{L(L+1)}\boldsymbol{h}/2\pi$) could be neglected. This is only strictly exact when the component of the orbital angular momentum about the internuclear axis is zero, that is when $\Lambda = 0$, and this is the case of a Σ electronic state. For Π, Δ . . . electronic states where $\Lambda \neq 0$, when the molecule is rotating (i.e. $J \neq 0$), splitting of each rotational level occurs into two components. For very low J-values the splitting is negligible and may not necessarily be detectable, but as the speed of rotation increases (i.e. for higher J-values) the splitting may be detected in the electronic spectrum of the molecule. However, the splitting of the rotational levels is usually only of the order of 1 cm^{-1} or less, and for the simplest cases the splitting increases as a simple function of J. For example, for a $^1\Pi$ electronic state the splitting is approximately proportional to $J(J+1)$ and for a $^1\Delta$-state to $J^2(J+1)^2$.

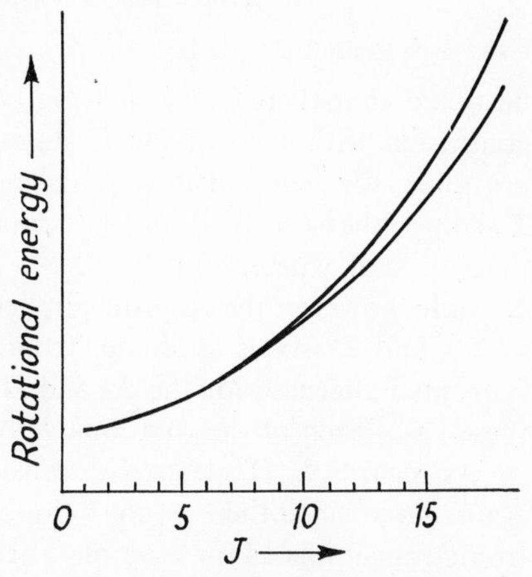

FIG. 3.14 Λ doubling in a $^1\Pi$-state. The doublet splitting is exaggerated

This small splitting of the rotational energy levels which is produced by the interaction of the electron orbit angular momentum with the rotation of the molecule as a whole is termed Λ doubling. It applies to all molecules where $\Lambda > 0$. The Λ doubling for a $^1\Pi$-state may be observed in Fig. 3.14

where the rotational energy is plotted against J. It will be noted that the splitting is negligible at low J-values. At the higher J-values, however, for each value of J, two values of the rotational energy may be observed.

In Fig. 3.15 the rotational energy levels for the electronic states $^1\Sigma^+$, $^1\Sigma^-$, $^1\Pi$, $^1\Delta$, $^1\Sigma_g^+$, $^1\Sigma_u^-$, $^1\Pi_g$, and $^1\Pi_u$ are given. The J-values are indicated on the figure together with the symmetry properties of each rotational level. It will

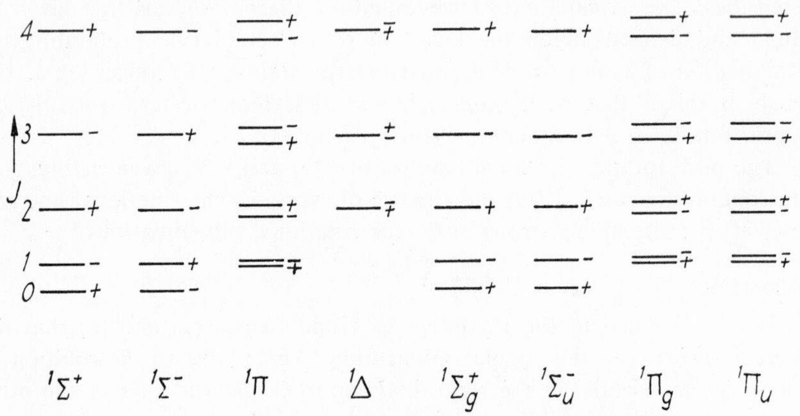

FIG. 3.15 Classification of some of the lower rotational energy levels in the electronic states of some homonuclear and heteronuclear molecules. (*Courtesy of Dr. W. Jevons* [2] *and the Council of the Physical Society*)

be noted that there is no splitting of the Σ rotational levels. This is to be contrasted with each of the Π-states. The $^1\Sigma^+$-, $^1\Sigma^-$-, $^1\Pi_g$- and $^1\Delta_u$-states are those for heteronuclear molecules. It was indicated on p. 60 that for Σ^+-states the $J = 0, 2, 4 \ldots$ rotational levels are characterised by a positive sign whereas the $1, 3, 5 \ldots$ levels have a negative sign. For a Σ^--state, however, the opposite applies. Thus, the signs of the rotational levels in Σ^+- and Σ^--states alternate. It may be seen also from Fig. 3.15 that the signs also alternate for the Δ- and Π-states as well, although in addition in these cases each of the rotational sub-levels is of oppposite sign.

As regards $\Sigma - \Sigma$ electronic transitions the position as outlined on p. 62 is unaltered since there is no Λ doubling. However, for other types of electronic transitions as for example a $^1\Pi_u - {}^1\Sigma_g^+$ the Λ doubling has to be taken into account. This is illustrated in Fig. 3.16 for a homonuclear diatomic molecule, where the transitions may be accounted for in terms of the selection rules:

$$\Delta J = 0, \ \pm 1; \ + \leftrightarrow -$$

In addition, the selection rules $a \leftrightarrow a$ and $s \leftrightarrow s$ apply although these symbols have not been inserted in the figure. If the transitions were a $^1\Pi - {}^1\Sigma^+$ for a heteronuclear molecule, then the a and s symbols would not apply although the transitions would still be those indicated in the figure.

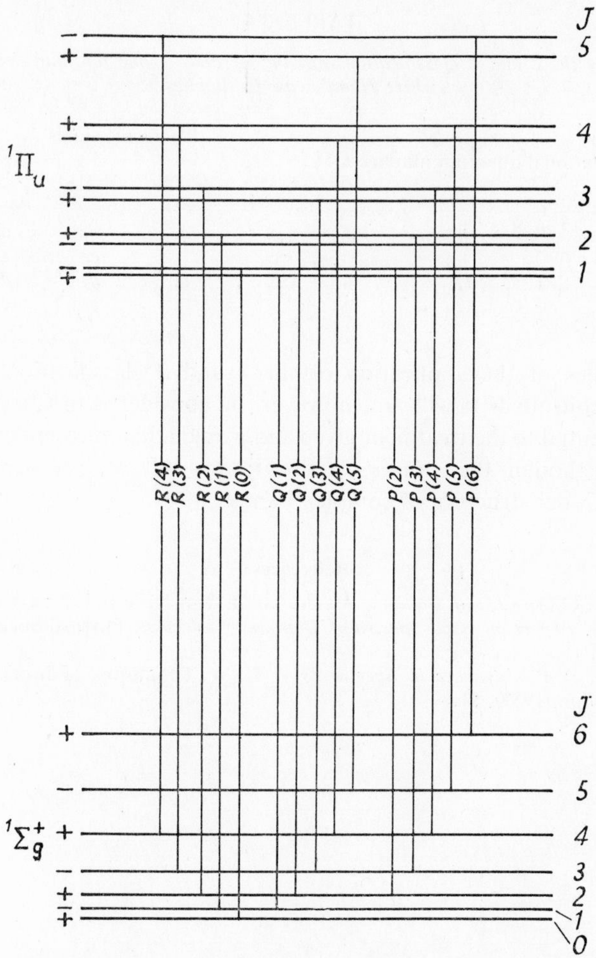

FIG. 3.16 $^1\Pi_u - {}^1\Sigma_g^+$ electronic transition where Λ doubling has been taken into account

c and *d* classification of rotational levels

In addition to the + and − classification, the letters *c* and *d* are employed to distinguish the components resulting from Λ type doubling of the rotational levels in electronic states with $\Lambda > 0$, which fall in or between Hund's cases (*a*) and (*b*). For a $^1\Pi$-state *c* and *d* characterise, respectively, the same set of rotational sub-states as + and −. For a $^2\Pi_{1/2}$-state, however, the reverse correspondence would be the case. The *c* and *d* classification was evolved before the theory was sufficiently developed to give the + and − one, but a definite relationship exists between the two systems. The subscripts *c* and *d* are allotted on the basis of transition properties as made from the observed band structure itself. The assignment of *c* and *d* to four singlet electronic states for Hund's case (*b*) is given in Table 3.4 and is compared with the corresponding + and − classification.

TABLE 3.4

Comparison of the c *and* d *classification with the* + *and* − *one for four electronic states where Hund's case* (b) *applies*

Rotational quantum number K	Electronic states			
	$^1\Sigma^+$	$^1\Sigma^-$	$^1\Pi$	$^1\Delta$
0, 2, 4, 6, . . .	$c,+$	$d,-$	$d,+$ $c,-$	$d,-$ $c,+$
1, 3, 5, 7, . . .	$c,-$	$d,+$	$d,-$ $c,+$	$d,+$ $c,-$

For examples of the application of the *c* and *d* classification Herzberg[1] should be consulted. It will not, however, be considered in Chapter 5 since it is not essential to the treatment given and would add a further complication. In practice, though, the *c* and *d* classification is still retained in the analysis of the rotational structure of complex bands.

References

1. HERZBERG, G. *Spectra of Diatomic Molecules.* D. Van Nostrand (New York, 1950).
2. JEVONS, W. *Report on Band Spectra of Diatomic Molecules.* Physical Society (London, 1932).
3. STOICHEFF, B. P. *Advances in Spectroscopy.* H. W. Thompson, (Editor). *Interscience* (London, 1959), 91.

4

Infra-red and Raman spectra

Introduction to infra-red and Raman spectra

THE infra-red and Raman methods in general yield similar types of information. They both provide a means of studying pure rotational, pure vibrational, and rotation-vibration energy changes in the ground state of simple and even complex molecules; however, for complex molecules the type of information which may be derived is limited. The mechanism by which these two methods accomplish the changes differs considerably. Infra-red spectra are principally concerned with the absorption of energy from a continuum (where the absorption occurs somewhere in the region 0.75 μ to 1 mm) or more recently with the study of emission spectra of wavelengths emitted somewhere in this region. Raman spectra, however, function by an entirely different mechanism and depend on the collision of incident light quanta with the molecule, where the molecule is induced to undergo a pure rotational, or a vibrational, or a rotation-vibration change. The corresponding emergent light quantum is altered by this amount. Thus, the effect of the incident radiation is to perturb the molecule so that it undergoes one of these transitions. The incident light employed is normally monochromatic and lies in the visible or the ultra-violet region (see p. 144). When both the Raman and infra-red methods can be used to study a particular energy change within the molecule, both yield the same or similar results. Not only does the mechanism by which the change is accomplished differ, but the criterion as to whether a particular transition may occur in the infra-red or Raman depends on widely different principles. For example, the occurrence of a vibrational transition in the infra-red region is dependent on a change of the electric dipole moment during the particular vibration. The Raman criterion, however, depends on a change in the polarisability during the vibration. In addition, the intensity of the infra-red spectrum is dependent on the magnitude of the dipole moment change, whereas the Raman intensity is related to how readily polarisable the vibrating atoms and their bonds are.

The infra-red and Raman approaches can be used to study gases, liquids and solids. Both these methods have been applied to a wide variety of problem and both have yielded desirable knowledge such as internuclear distances and vibrational frequencies. They have also been useful in the determination, by the statistical method, of thermodynamic quantities such as entropy and heat capacity; these have been calculated from the spectral moments of inertia and vibrational frequency data. The infra-red approach has been much the more prolific method so far in determining moments of inertia and internuclear distances of simple molecules, although the Raman method is now developing in this direction.

The vibrational frequencies obtained by these methods have been extensively used to fingerprint certain groups in different molecules, but more fundamental than this has been the use of vibrational frequencies in force constant work and in structural determinations. In fact, the latter has been a major line of investigation for both techniques.

For an unsymmetrical molecule every fundamental vibration is concerned with a change of electric dipole moment and, therefore, satisfies the criterion for absorption in the infra-red; in such a molecule there is also a change in polarisability during the vibration, and, therefore, a Raman spectrum is also produced. Thus, either method could be employed to obtain vibrational frequencies. For molecules with a centre of symmetry, though, e.g. CO_2, CS_2, C_2H_2, and CH_4, the fundamental frequencies (see p. 175) which appear in the Raman do not appear in the infra-red and vice versa; the two methods are then complementary.

Chapter 4 is concerned mainly with outlining the different types of problems studied by each method. The procedure adopted has been to divide the chapter into three sections:

(A) Infra-red spectra.

(B) Raman spectra.

(C) Correlation of infra-red and Raman spectra.

This division is one of convenience, and it must not necessarily be supposed that the points common to the Raman and infra-red methods are to be found only under Section (C). In fact, some of the problems studied by the infra-red method in Section (A) could well be studied by the Raman or even by both together. In a way Section (C) is an attempt to stress that the methods often work hand in hand. This is especially true for the vibrational studies of polyatomic molecules.

(A) INFRA-RED SPECTROSCOPY

Experimental infra-red technique

Introduction

For practical purposes the infra-red region has often been quoted as ranging from wavelengths of 0.75 to $\sim 100\ \mu$, but now has been extended to

1 mm.† The experimental infra-red approach may be subdivided into three types: (*a*) the photographic infra-red, (*b*) the prism infra-red, and (*c*) the grating infra-red.

The photographic infra-red extends from 0.75 μ to 1.3 μ. In this region types of spectrograph are used similar to those employed in the ultra-violet and visible regions (see p. 34). At wavelengths greater than about 1.3 μ the emulsions employed on the photographic plate lose their sensitivity. The range may be extended to about 3.0 μ by replacement of the photographic plate by a lead sulphide cell.‡ The amount of work done in the region 0.75 to 3.0 μ by these techniques is rather limited. In fact, this region corresponds with extremely high vibrational frequencies and is used mainly in the study of vibrational changes involving hydrogen atoms (e.g. the C—H vibrational frequency) and overtone and combination frequencies (see p. 94).

The majority of near infra-red spectrophotometers have in the past been based on prisms. Grating instruments were used especially for problems where resolution of the rotation-vibration structure was essential. However, with the recent introduction of inexpensive diffraction gratings with their definite advantages, the trend in modern infra-red spectrophotometers is towards the grating instrument. The wavelengths at which prism instruments can function is determined by the availability of suitable materials transparent to the wavelengths being studied. For example, if a rock salt prism is used as the dispersing element, then wavelengths up to ~15 μ could be studied, whereas, if KBr is used the limit would be about 25 μ. The useful range of some materials is given in Table 4.1.

TABLE 4.1

Transmission range of some window and prism materials

Material	Transmission range
Glass	up to 2.5 μ
Quartz	up to 3.5 μ
LiF	up to 6 μ
CaF_2	2 to 8.5 μ
NaCl (rock salt)	up to 15 μ
KBr	up to 25 μ
CsBr	15 to 40 μ
CsI	15 to 50 μ

The experimental arrangement is shown in block diagram form in Fig. 4.1 and the various components forming the spectrophotometer will now be considered.

† Since the infra-red and the microwave regions have now overlapped the whole of the electromagnetic spectrum is covered from the vacuum ultra-violet to radio frequencies.

‡ A lead sulphide cell is a form of photoconductive cell. It consists of a thin film (10^{-4}–10^{-5} cm) of PbS chemically precipitated on glass or by sublimation of the PbS on the glass *in vacuo*. The lead sulphide cell is much more sensitive than thermocouples and has a very short response time. The PbS cell provides very good resolution and allows fast scanning of the spectrum in the near infra-red region.

To study infra-red absorption spectra the source must emit a continuous spectrum of radiation which should approximate to that of a black body.† To cover the necessary range of from 0.75 μ to 1000 μ no one emitter would be sufficient. The two sources in most general use are the Nernst glower and the Globar, but in addition a quartz high-pressure mercury arc is useful beyond 50 μ. For the photographic infra-red a tungsten filament lamp may be used provided the envelope is transparent to the region studied.

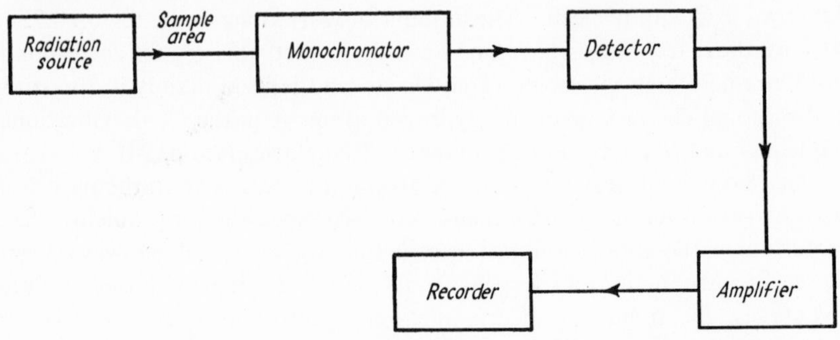

FIG. 4.1 Block diagram of major units in an infra-red spectrophotometer

The Nernst glower consists of 90 parts zirconium oxide, 7 parts yttrium oxide, and 3 parts erbium oxide held together by a binder into a rod of ~3 mm by 2 cm. The filament is maintained at incandescence by electrical means and run at temperatures above 1500°C. Since the Nernst glower has a negative coefficient of resistance, that is its resistance decreases with increasing temperature, it must be run in series with a number of ballast lamps acting as stabilisers.

The Globar is a rod of silicon carbide which has its ends silver coated to obtain good electrical contact. The rod is mounted in cups spring-loaded at one end and the voltage across it is regulated in order to achieve a constant radiation source.

At wavelengths less than 10 μ the Nernst glower has the advantage of working at a low power consumption but still having a high intensity. The Globar is most suited to wavelengths greater than ~10 μ, and both may be used even up to ~50 μ although the energy available in that region is rather low. In ordinary infra-red spectrophotometers the Nernst glower is preferred. However, for single beam spectrophotometers (see later) the Globar is normally employed since it gives a much steadier source intensity; variations in intensity in such an instrument would be most undesirable.

All infra-red spectrophotometers use mirror optics; glass because of its opacity would be unsuitable to employ as a lens material. Fortunately, the reflection from most metallic surfaces is generally very good in the infra-red region, and consequently front surface mirrors are employed instead of lenses. This use of mirrors is mainly responsible for the various features

† A black body is one which absorbs all the radiant energy directed on to it.

which characterise infra-red instruments. Although no general rules can be made governing the optical arrangements, the older instruments generally use the Wadsworth mounting, while the more modern types invariably employ the Littrow (see p. 35).

Some of the chief materials used for prisms and windows of cells with their useful transmission limits are listed in Table 4.1.

The most common window and prism materials are rock salt and KBr, and the upper wavelengths at which the spectrophotometer can be used are fixed at 15 and 25 μ, respectively. For most routine work rock salt is sufficient.

Single and double beam spectrophotometers

Two types of instruments are available, namely the single and double beam; in the double beam instrument the radiation from the source is split into two exactly equivalent beams, one of which passes through the sample

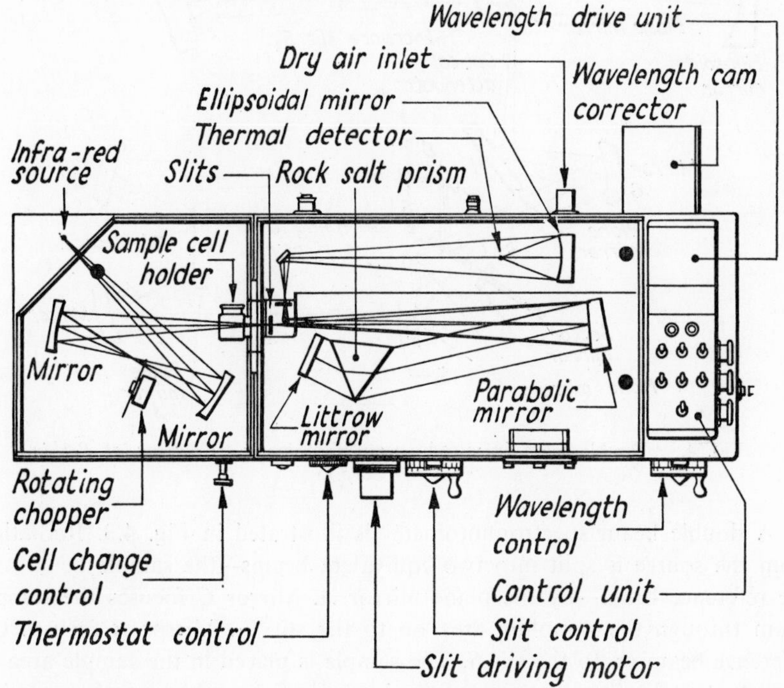

FIG. 4.2 Typical single-beam infra-red spectrophotometer. (*Courtesy of Grubb Parsons and Co. Ltd.*)

whilst the second beam traverses a reference cell. The single beam instrument functions with one beam only, and the optical arrangement is essentially that described under the heading of Littrow mounting (see p. 35). The Grubb–Parsons single beam spectrophotometer is illustrated in Fig. 4.2. In this instrument radiation from the source is rendered intermittent by the rotating chopper (the object of which is explained on p. 76) and is brought to a focus on the entrance slit of the monochromator. The main function of the monochromator is to provide a means of isolating narrow bands of wavelengths. The sample cell holder is located in the path of the beam just in front of the entrance slits of the monochromator. The light is then collimated by a parabolic mirror on to the prism where it is refracted twice, and a narrow range of wavelengths is selected by adjustment of the Littrow mirror. The dispersed beam is focused by mirrors on to the exit slit and is then focused by an ellipsiodal mirror on to a thermal detector. This thermal detector converts the radiant energy into measurable electrical energy.

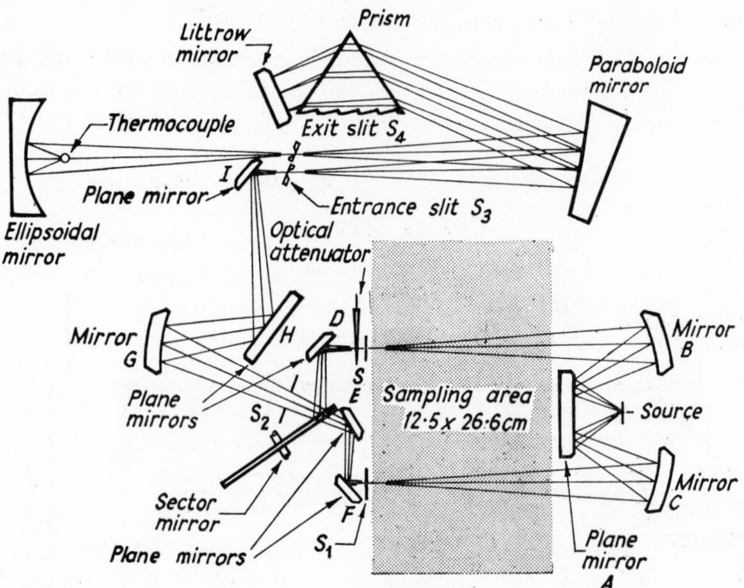

FIG. 4.3 Double-beam infra-red spectrophotometer. (*Courtesy of Perkin Elmer Corp.*)

A double beam spectrophotometer is illustrated in Fig. 4.3. Radiation from the source is split into two equivalent beams—the sample beam and the reference beam—by the plane mirror *A*. Mirror *C* focuses the sample beam through the sampling area on to the slit S_1. Mirror *B* focuses the reference beam on to the slit *S*. The sample is placed in the sample area as close to the slit S_1 as possible. Sample and reference beams, after passing through the sampling area, are recombined by a semi-circular sector mirror which rotates at 13 c/s. The orientation of the sector mirror is fixed with respect to the three plane mirrors *D*, *E*, and *F* so that it alternately reflects the reference beam and passes the sample beam through the aperture stop S_2. The aperture stop ensures that both beams are the same size and will thus be able to follow identical paths through the remainder of the system. The signal beam, which now consists of alternate pulses of sample and reference radiation, is focused by the mirror *G* and reflected by plane mirrors *H* and *I* through the entrance slit of the monochromator S_3 (this slit is at the focal point of the mirror *G*). On leaving the slit S_3 the beam diverges until the off-axis paraboloid mirror reflects it as collimated light on to the prism. At the prism the component wavelengths are dispersed and reflected by the Littrow mirror back into the prism, where further dispersion takes place. The dispersed radiation is then focused on the plane of the exit slit S_4 by the paraboloid. The particular wavelengths which emerge from the slit strike the ellipsoidal mirror which focuses them on the thermocouple.

If the energy in both sample and reference beams is equal, a direct voltage is produced at the thermocouple which is not amplified by the A.C. amplifier of the instrument. When the sample absorbs radiation at characteristic wavelengths, the intensity of the sample beam is reduced. This results in an intermittent signal at the detector which is converted to an alternating voltage and then amplified by the 13-c/s amplifier. The amplified signal is used to drive a servo motor which moves the optical wedge (or optical attenuator) into or out of the reference beam to equalise the beam intensities. The position of the wedge is, thus, a measure of the intensity difference in the sample and reference beams, and is a measure of the transmittance of the sample. Since a recorder pen is coupled directly to the wedge, its movements are a record of transmittance.

The spectrum is scanned by rotation of the Littrow mirror about a vertical axis by means of a micrometer screw. Having been previously calibrated the setting of the screw corresponds with a definite wavelength (see later).

The advantages of the double over the single beam instrument are:

(*a*) The single beam instrument gives an arbitrary trace from which the absorption must be calculated at each wavelength by comparison with the background trace obtained when the substance whose absorption spectrum is required is no longer in the beam. The double beam, however, gives the percentage transmission immediately.

(*b*) The absorption of water vapour and carbon dioxide in the atmosphere is automatically compensated for by the double beam and hence should be absent from the final trace. There are drawbacks to the more refined double beam instrument, but these are mainly technical difficulties, such as optical adjustment for equality of the two beams, amplification of signal, difficulties in detection, and also the noise level due to extraneous, random, internal and external currents not connected with that being measured. However it must be emphasized that, in general, both methods ultimately give the same result.

Double passing of prism spectrophotometers

The conventional monochromator suffers from two disadvantages: (*a*) the limited resolution due to the size and quality of the prism, (*b*) an impure spectrum resulting from scattered radiation. Much better resolution and almost complete elimination of scattered radiation can be obtained by making the radiation pass through the monochromator twice. This principle of double passing was introduced by Walsh[1, 2] and can be applied to both prism and grating instruments.

Since the radiation traverses the prism four times (it passes twice in the ordinary Littrow mounting) the second pass radiation has twice the dispersion of the first pass. Theoretically also the resolving power of the second pass radiation is twice that of the first pass, since the effective length of the prism base is doubled.

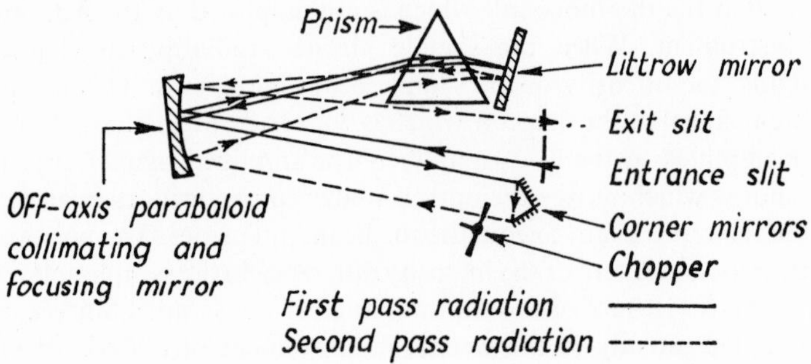

FIG. 4.4 Double passing technique employed in prism spectrophotometers. (*Courtesy of Dr. A. Walsh*[2] *and the Editor of 'Nature'*)

The manner in which a second passing is achieved may be observed in Fig. 4.4. Light from the source passing through the entrance slit is collimated by an off-axis paraboloid mirror on to the prism, and is reflected by the Littrow mirror. The beam is then focused by the paraboloid on to the corner mirrors and becomes so displaced that it passes through the system a second time (shown by dotted lines in Fig. 4.4) and is eventually brought to a focus on the exit slit.

For a given setting of the Littrow mirror some first pass radiation (always of longer wavelength) must also travel through the exit slit along with the second pass radiation. In order to differentiate between first and second pass radiation only the second pass beam is chopped (see Fig. 4.4), and hence it alone produces a fluctuating output at the detector. Since the amplifier is an A.C. amplifier tuned to the frequency of the chopper, only second pass radiation is amplified. The steady direct first pass radiation and any constant scattered radiation produces no signal from the amplifier.

Grating spectrophotometer

For higher resolving power the grating instrument may be employed. It was explained in Chapter 2 that the difficulty in designing a grating instrument was due to the elimination of overlapping orders. To this purpose the modern infra-red grating spectrophotometer uses a prism monochromator placed either before or after the grating.[3] In Fig. 4.5 a grating monochromator is shown which employs a single grating for the 2–15 μ range. The grating has 2400 lines/in. and is blazed to give maximum energy at $\sim 9\ \mu$ in the first order. The range 2–15 μ is covered in four orders as follows:

2–2.5 μ	fourth order
2.5–3.75 μ	third order
3.5–5 μ	second order
5–15 μ	first order

In the monochromator two interchangeable prisms are used: one of CaF_2 for use in the second, third, and fourth orders, and one of KBr for the first-order region. The prisms are mounted on a rotating table so that either can be selected at will.

The source unit which is a Nernst glower with its associated mirrors and chopper is not shown in Fig. 4.5, but is the same as that employed in the single beam instrument of Fig. 4.2. This source unit is so positioned to the left of the monochromator that the radiation passes through the entrance slit as illustrated. The sampling area is the same as in Fig. 4.2.

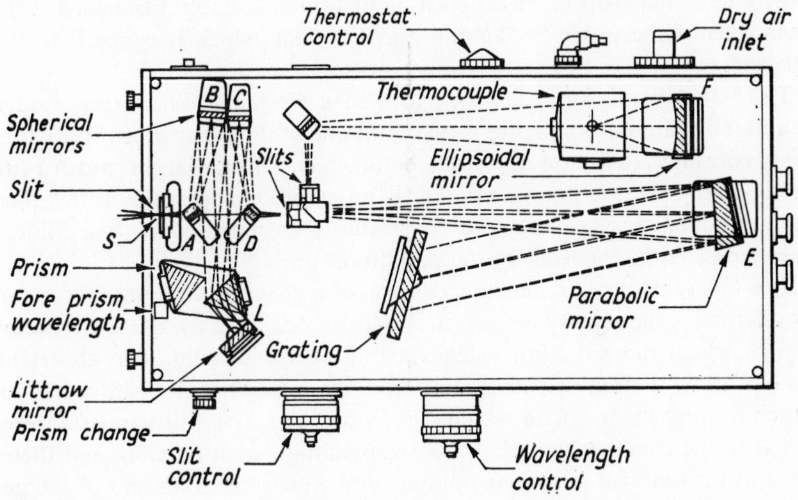

FIG. 4.5 Grating infra-red spectrophotometer. (*Courtesy of Grubb Parsons and Co. Ltd.*)

After passing through the entrance slit of the monochromator the radiation is reflected by a mirror *A* on to a spherical mirror *B* which collimates the light on to the prism. The beam suffers two refractions at the prism, and by rotation of the Littrow mirror *L* a narrow range of wavelengths can be selected. The beam is reflected by the spherical mirror *C* on to the plane mirror *D* from which it passes through a further set of slits and is collimated by a parabolic mirror *E* on to the grating. The now greatly dispersed beam is reflected from the grating surface and brought to a focus on the exit slits, from which the beam is again focused by the ellipsoidal mirror *F* on to the thermocouple which functions as detector.

Detectors

The main types of detectors for use in the infra-red, are, (*a*) the vacuum thermocouple, (*b*) the bolometer, and (*c*) the detector Golay. The most desirable features of detectors are the closeness to which they approach the behaviour of a black body, high sensitivity, high speed and robustness.

The thermocouple most commonly used is constructed from pure bismuth wire soldered to another wire which is an alloy of 95 per cent Bi and 5 per cent Sn. The wire used is about 3 mm long with a diameter of 25 μ. Since this is too small for use with a spectrophotometer, a receiving element of blackened gold foil about 0.5 μ thick and 0.2×2 mm in area is soldered to the junction of the thermocouple. The couple is mounted in a tube which has a suitably transparent window and evacuated to a pressure of 10^{-4} mm of mercury. The evacuation reduces thermal losses, but it unfortunately also decreases the speed of response.

Vacuum bolometers have sometimes been employed due to their low response time, which is of the order of a few milliseconds. The bolometer consists of a fine strip of metal such as platinum, suitably blackened, with dimensions of the order 5×0.5 mm and 1 μ thick which is exposed to the radiation.

The bolometer is placed in one arm of a modified Wheatstone bridge circuit, and a similar bolometer is placed in one of the other arms. Radiation is only permitted to fall on one of the bolometers. This radiation causes a rise in temperature on the bolometer and its resistance changes, the bridge then becoming unbalanced. The radiation produces a voltage which has a linear dependence on the intensity of the radiation.

The Golay pneumatic detector consists of a chamber containing a gas of low thermal conductivity which is sealed at one end by a KBr window through which the radiation reaches a thin absorbing film. The absorbing film has a low thermal capacity and responds readily to infra-red radiation, in turn heating the gas with which it is in contact. A rise in temperature of the gas in the chamber produces a corresponding rise in pressure and therefore a distortion of a mirror membrane with which the other end of the gas chamber is sealed. An alternating radiation signal (e.g. 10 c/s) will therefore produce a corresponding deformation of the mirror membrane at 10 c/s which, by a suitable optical system and a photocell, can be converted into an alternating voltage.

Amplifiers

The function of these detectors is to receive the radiant energy and convert it into measurable electrical energy. The resistance of thermocouples and bolometers is small, and amplification of the output is rather difficult. Since it is easier to build a stable high gain A.C. amplifier, the method of amplification in modern instruments is as follows. The incident radiation is first chopped by a rotating sector at a rate of $\sim$10–15 times per sec. The resulting energy passes through the system and eventually falls on to the thermosensitive element and produces a pulsating output. This output is fed to an A.C. amplifier via a transformer and then to a pen recorder. Any continuous energy falling on the detector will produce a D.C. output and will not be amplified. This tends to eliminate errors from stray radiation and is a feature of the double beam instrument described on p. 72. If the sample and reference beams are of the same energy, that is no absorption by the sample has taken place, then a D.C. voltage is produced by the thermocouple which is not amplified by the A.C. amplifier of the instrument. Only when the intensity of the sample beam is less than that of the reference beam is an unequal (pulsating) signal produced at the detector.

Calibration of spectrophotometer

The spectrophotometer is calibrated by employing substances whose exact absorption wavelengths are known. The position of the micrometer screw controlling the Littrow mirror orientation is recorded for each peak absorption wavelength. The value of each peak wavelength is then plotted against the corresponding micrometer setting. By employing different substances a curve may be constructed to cover the wavelength region over

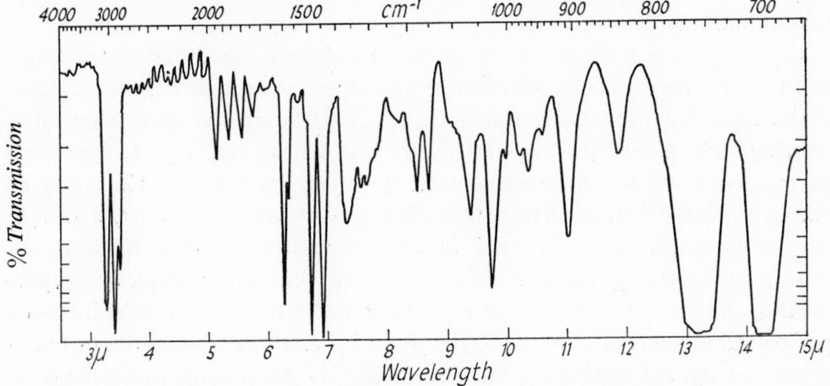

FIG. 4.6 Infra-red spectrum of polystyrene film. (*Courtesy of Perkin Elmer Corp.*)

which the spectrophotometer operates. Naturally, it is essential to use only materials whose absorption bands have been precisely measured. It is desirable to have absorption bands which are sharp, easily recognised, and found at frequent intervals throughout the range of the spectrophotometer. Some of the substances which best fulfil these requirements are listed below:

Mercury arc	0.5 to 1.5 μ
Water vapour	5.0 to 7.0 μ
Ammonia	8.0 to 14 μ
Methyl alcohol	12 to 24 μ

Carbon dioxide has two useful bands at 4.235 μ and 13.875 μ for calibration purposes. A thin film of polystyrene has a number of sharp absorption bands whose wavelengths are accurately known. The infra-red spectrum of a solid film of polystyrene is shown in Fig. 4.6, where the minima indicate the wavelengths at positions of maximum absorption. The intensities recorded by one instrument cannot, in general, be used with quantitative accuracy on another instrument. In fact, the intensity concentration curves obtained on one infra-red spectrophotometer cannot with safety be employed in conjunction with another spectrophotometer.† Thus, such data extracted from the literature must be completely re-standardised for each instrument. Even to obtain consistent results from a given instrument it must be used under the same conditions of resolving power. This means that the slit widths should be constant at a given wavelength. The difficulties of non-repeatability of intensities show signs of being overcome by the use of high resolution instruments (see p. 136).

Infra-red spectrogram

There is as yet no definite convention regulating the quantities plotted on the two axes, and the following procedures exist:

(i) The wavelength or wave-number (or occasionally frequency) is plotted against some quantity expressing absorption. In analytical work the wavelength has been used, whereas in research (e.g. structural determinations) wave-number is a more fundamental and useful unit.

(ii) If I_0 is the intensity of the infra-red radiation and I that of the emergent light at the particular wavelength concerned, then either the percentage of the infra-red light transmitted, that is $100I/I_0$, or the percentage of it absorbed, $100(I_0-I)/I_0$ or less likely, optical density, i.e. $\log_{10}I_0/I$, or even the molecular extinction coefficient, i.e. $(1/cl)\log_{10}I_0/I$ (see p. 129), may be plotted along the ordinate axis, where c is the molar concentration (g-moles/l.) and l is the length (cm) of the cell through which the radiation travels.

For choice the optical density is preferable since this is directly proportional to the concentration of the absorbing material. Nearly all the infra-red spectrophotometers are limited to the plot of percentage absorption or transmission or optical density. In the case where the percentage transmission is plotted the wavelengths of maximum absorption are indicated by the minima in the curve, while if the percentage absorption is plotted, then the maxima actually represent the maximum absorption.

Preparation and examination of samples

The infra-red technique can be used to study the gaseous, liquid, and solid states of a substance or a mixture. However, many substances have not sufficient vapour pressure to be examined in the gaseous phase, and in this case the material may either be examined as a crystalline solid, or in the liquid phase. Such a substance is usually examined as a solution or as a paste made by mixing the substance with a mineral oil. The cell in Fig. 4.7(*a*) is suitable for the examination of pastes. Since the infra-red absorption bands of most liquids and solids are quite intense, the thickness of samples

† This is to be contrasted with ultra-violet and visible spectroscopy, where no such problem exists.

(*a*)

(*b*)

(*c*)

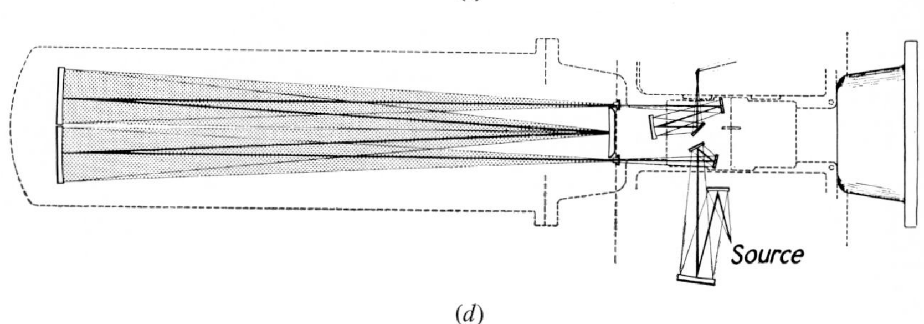

(*d*)

FIG. 4.7 Infra-red sample cells: (*a*) demountable cell, (*b*) variable space cell, (*c*) gas cell, (*d*) long path cell. (*Courtesy of Perkin Elmer Corp.*)

[*To face page* 78

employed is generally quite small, and the cell width is usually between 0.1 mm and 20 μ, though for overtones (see p. 94) in the 0.75–1.5 μ range cells up to 1 cm wide are employed. An accurately adjustable cell for the study of liquids may be seen in Fig. 4.7(*b*).

Gases are easily handled in the infra-red region since the concentration may readily be controlled by varying the pressure. Usually long sample cells ranging from one centimetre to several metres in length are used. A typical cell for examining gases is shown in Fig. 4.7(*c*). Attached to this cell is an apparatus for manipulating the gas and a pressure-measuring device. The cells must have windows constructed from material which is freely transparent in the part of the infra-red region chosen for investigation. Unfortunately, these materials are readily attacked by many substances (for example NaCl windows are attacked by moisture), and it is difficult, therefore, to construct cells which have a reproducible thickness.

In quantitative work it is very important to know the cell thickness accurately if precise values of extinction coefficients are to be calculated. An accurate value of the cell thickness may be obtained by means of an interference method, where the empty cell is calibrated by observing the interference fringe pattern in the infra-red region.[4]

As already indicated, absorption cells in the infra-red generally have windows of rock salt and other alkali halides. These windows require polishing, and, although the surface need not be as true as the surfaces used at shorter wavelengths, it may be necessary in the case of a thin cell for the surface to have a high degree of optical flatness to the extent of 10^{-4} mm. Frequent re-polishing of these windows is also necessary owing to surface deterioration brought about by moisture.

Pure liquids and solutions are examined in cells, where the space between the windows of which is either determined by Pb or Cu spacers, as in the demountable cell in Fig. 4.7(*a*), or by a micrometer screw arrangement, as in the variable space cell in Fig. 4.7(*b*). Special compact multiple reflection cells[5] are available with a path length of up to 10 m, and for gaseous samples these cells are designed for work between very low pressures and 10 atm. One such long path cell is illustrated in Fig. 4.7(*d*). For the study of change of spectrum with state of aggregation, or for solids for which no suitable solvent is known, absorption cells of the spacer type[6] have been adapted to work between 20–200°C. The examination of solids may be made in one of several ways, some of which are given below.

Mull technique. The finely-ground solid is wetted with a suitable liquid which has only a few absorption bands in the infra-red. Nujol and hexachlorobutadiene have been widely used for this purpose. The suspension is then placed between two NaCl plates. The function of the liquid is to surround the particles of solid with a medium of high refractive index and so reduce light scatterings. If Nujol is employed, it absorbs at approximately 3.5 μ, 6.9 μ, and 7.3 μ, but apart from this does not further interfere with the absorption spectrum of the sample. This CH absorption may be overcome if fluorocarbon is used. Together Nujol and fluorocarbon serve to cover the main spectral range.

Evaporation. A solution or a suspension of a solid is made, and a film of this solid is formed on a suitable transparent plate by evaporation of the solvent. The plate may be of NaCl for non-aqueous solutions, while AgCl is useful for solutions where water is the solvent.

Melting. Examination of molten solids has already been referred to. Alternatively, a solid may be melted between two NaCl plates and then cooled, the resulting crystalline film showing little or no scatter.

Pressed disk technique[7]. The substance whose spectrum is required is ground up with 200 times its weight of powdered KBr and the mixture is compressed (pressures of 25 tons/in.^{2} and upwards are used) under vacuum to form a clear transparent disk. The advantages of this method over the 'mull' method are that:

(*a*) It gives a distribution of particles in the suspending medium, and a smaller particle size is possible.

(*b*) It reduces scatter and sharpens the absorption bands which show more detail.

(*c*) It is possible to store the sample for future reference.

It is not limited to KBr. Most alkali halides and many other substances can be used.

However, unless great care is taken the KBr disks exhibit bands due to the absorption of water. In addition, a serious disadvantage is that the electric field of the positive and negative ions modifies the spectrum.

Choice of solvents

A considerable amount of work is done in solution, and the selection of a suitable solvent is governed by the factors: (*a*) that the solvent should not exhibit absorption within the wavelength range investigated; and (*b*) it should not appreciably interact with the dissolved substance (e.g. hydrogen bonding or complex formation).

Water absorbs strongly at wavelengths greater than about 2.7 μ except for 3.4–5.7 μ and 6.3–10.7 μ, though even here it is essential to work with very thin cells. One of the best solvents is CCl_4. CS_2 is also a good solvent but being volatile is difficult to handle in ordinary absorption cells. A few solvents and the range in which they are transparent are given in Table 4.2. Other useful solvents include benzene, chloroform, dioxane, acetonitrile, nitromethane, pyridine, acetone, tetrachloro-ethylene, dibromo- and tribromo-methane.

For polymers (e.g. nylon), no suitable solvents are available although molten $SbCl_3$ has been employed to dissolve the polypeptides. However, if the material has a reasonably low melting point, the high temperature absorption cell could be used and the substance investigated in the molten state. A further possibility is to examine a very thin film of the substance, the film being cut by means of a microtome.

TABLE 4.2

Some solvents and their useful transmission limits

Solvent	Spectral range (cm^{-1})	(μ)
Carbon disulphide	500–800	20–12.5
	900–1400	11.1–7
	1600–2000	6.2–5.0
	2400–3200	4.1–3.1
Carbon tetrachloride	500–700	20–14.3
	1000–1200	10.0–8.3
	1300–1500	7.7–6.6
	1600–3200	6.2–3.1
Cyclohexane	500–800	20–12.5
	1500–2000	6.6–5.0

Pure rotational spectra of diatomic molecules

Initially the study of pure rotational energy changes in the far infra-red region was of great interest. However, the results from this type of spectra are now neither extensive nor of great theoretical interest for the following reasons:

(*a*) The spectra lie in the far infra-red region and are difficult to investigate experimentally.

(*b*) Although the moment of inertia of the absorbing molecule may be obtained from the frequency separation of the pure rotational lines, it is generally available from rotation-vibration bands observed at shorter wavelengths or from microwave spectra.

(*c*) Other fundamental information which results from rotation-vibration bands cannot be obtained from pure rotational bands.

However, occasionally the vibrational spectrum is complicated by rotation-vibration interaction, and also there may be several vibrational frequencies superimposed. In such cases analysis of the bands may be very difficult, and pure rotational spectra become of importance since they furnish a source of independent data.

The possible energy levels of a diatomic rigid rotator are given by:

$$E_r = \frac{\boldsymbol{h}^2}{8\pi^2 I} \cdot J(J+1) = \boldsymbol{h}cBJ(J+1) \tag{4.1}$$

where B is the rotational constant and is related to the moment of inertia by:

$$B = \boldsymbol{h}/8\pi^2 cI \tag{4.2}$$

J is the rotational quantum number of the molecule and governs the angular momentum which has the value of $\sqrt{J(J+1)}\boldsymbol{h}/2\pi$. Only if the diatomic molecule has a permanent dipole moment can it interact with the infra-red radiation and have a pure rotational infra-red spectrum. All heteronuclear diatomic molecules have a permanent electric dipole moment, and hence if a suitable continuous radiation is supplied, the appropriate frequency may be absorbed, and a rotational energy change may take place. The wave-number of the absorbed radiation ν is given by:

$$\nu = F(J') - F(J'') \tag{4.3}$$

where $F(J')$ is the rotational term value in the J' rotational level and

$$F(J') = \frac{E'_r}{hc} \tag{4.4}$$

(see p. 10). Hence, on substitution for E'_r and E''_r from equation (4.1) we get:

$$\nu = BJ'(J'+1) - BJ''(J''+1) \tag{4.5}$$

The selection rule for changes of J is that $J' - J'' = +1$ for an absorption transition. On substitution for J' in equation (4.5) we obtain

$$\nu = 2B(J''+1) \quad J'' = 0,\ 1,\ 2,\ 3,\ \ldots \tag{4.6}$$

The spectrum of a rigid rotator, therefore, consists of a series of equidistant lines separated from one another by $2B$ cm^{-1}. The first rotational line ($1 \leftarrow 0$) is to be found at $2B$, that is at $h/4\pi^2 cI$ cm^{-1}. The region in which the pure rotational spectrum occurs is, thus, fixed by the value of its moment of inertia.

The concept of a diatomic molecule (or any other molecule) as a rigid rotator is inadequate, since the nuclei must vibrate. A more accurate expression for the rotational energy levels of such a molecule is given by:

$$E_r = hcBJ(J+1) - hcDJ^2(J+1)^2 = hcF(J) \tag{4.7}$$

The term $hcDJ^2(J+1)^2$ is only of small magnitude and takes into account the centrifugal distortion in the molecule. D is a second rotational constant and always has a positive value dependent on the vibrational frequency (ω) of the molecule. D can be related to ω by equation (4.8):

$$D = 4B^3/\omega^2\dagger \tag{4.8}$$

For the transition $J' - J'' = +1$ the frequency of the absorbed radiation is given by:

$$\nu = F(J') - F(J'') \tag{4.9}$$

and on substitution from equation (4.7) we get:

$$\nu = \{2B(J''+1) - 4D(J''+1)^3\} \tag{4.10}$$

The frequency spacing between successive rotational lines as based on equation (4.10) is no longer constant but decreases slightly as J increases.

The first infra-red study of the pure rotational spectra of the hydrogen halides was made by Czerny[8] in 1925. He observed most of the rotational lines of HCl, HF, and HI in the 40 μ to 125 μ region. The first five rotational lines of HCl were observed in 1950 by McCubbin and Sinton,[9] the line corresponding to the $J' \leftarrow J''$ transition of $1 \leftarrow 0$ being located at approximately 500 μ.

† In the derivation of this equation it is assumed that during the vibration the harmonic oscillator model holds.

The heavier molecules DCl, DBr, and DI have also been studied, although the lowest rotational transitions in these molecules which are at longer wavelengths have not been observed.

Czerny found for HCl that the wave-numbers of the rotational lines could be fitted to the equation:

$$\nu = 20.794(J''+1) - 0.00164(J''+1)^3 \tag{4.11}$$

On comparison of the coefficients of the linear term in equations (4.11) and (4.10) the rotational constant B is found to equal 10.397 cm^{-1}. Since

$$B = h/8\pi^2 cI \tag{4.12}$$

the moment of inertia of HCl may be calculated to be 2.72×10^{-40} g-cm^2. In addition, since:

$$I = \frac{m_1 m_2}{m_1 + m_2} r^2 = \mu r^2 \tag{4.13}$$

where the reduced mass μ of HCl is 1.63×10^{-24} g the internuclear distance $r_{\text{H—Cl}}$ is found to be 1.29×10^{-8} cm. On comparison of the coefficients of the term in $(J''+1)^3$ we find

$$4D = 0.00164 \quad \text{and} \quad D = 4.1\ 10^{-4}\ \text{cm}^{-1} \tag{4.14}$$

By the use of equation (4.8) an approximate value of ω, the vibrational frequency of the HCl molecule, can be estimated, although the value of ω is best evaluated from electronic band spectra.

Hydrogen bromide has been studied by Hausler and Oetjen,[10] and the spectrogram they obtained is shown in Fig. 4.8. The HBr contained HCl as an impurity, and the spectrogram gives absorption lines for each molecule.

TABLE 4.3

The observed wave-numbers for some $J' \leftarrow J''$ pure rotational transitions in gaseous HCl *and* HBr

HCl			HBr		
J'	J''	ν observed (cm^{-1})	J'	J''	ν observed (cm^{-1})
5	4	104.13	6	5	99.87
6	5	124.73	7	6	116.48
7	6	145.37	8	7	132.88
8	7	165.89	9	8	149.30
9	8	186.23	10	9	165.69
			11	10	181.78
			12	11	198.13

The HCl rotational transitions are indicated by arrows below the curve and those of the HBr molecule by arrows above the curve. The approximate equal spacing of each set of lines may be observed. The J' and J'' values with the appropriate wave-numbers corresponding to the transitions are given in Table 4.3.

Palik[11] observed the pure rotational spectrum of DBr, HI, and DI in the 45 to 170 μ region. He found that an equation of the type (4.10) fitted the wave-numbers of the observed lines.

As yet pure rotational work in the far infra-red region has been very limited, and, indeed, is restricted to molecules with small moments of inertia. However, as may be seen in Vol. 1, the microwave technique is admirably suited to the study of most pure rotational changes in heteronuclear diatomic molecules.

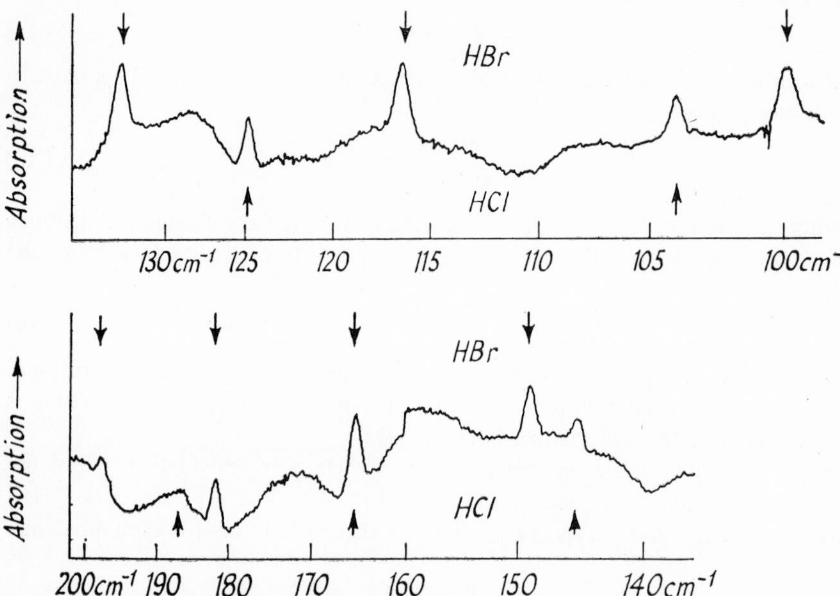

FIG. 4.8 Far infra-red pure rotational spectrum of gaseous HCl and HBr. (*After Hausler and Oetjen.*[10] *Courtesy of 'The Journal of Chemical Physics'*)

Pure rotational spectra of polyatomic molecules

For molecules with small moments of inertia such as NH_3 and H_2O the pure rotational spectrum lies almost entirely on the short wavelength side of 100 μ. Normally for heavier molecules the pure rotational spectrum may be found on the longer wavelength side of 100 μ. For convenience polyatomic molecules may be divided into four groups according to the values of their three principal moments of inertia.

Linear molecules

As was the case for diatomic molecules, linear polyatomic molecules have two of the principal moments of inertia equal and the other equal to zero. The rotational energy levels of a linear molecule are given by the same formula as for diatomic molecules, i.e. equation (4.7).

Up to the present time little work has been reported on the infra-red rotational spectrum of linear molecules. One of the reasons for this can be appreciated if the values of B and D are substituted into equation (4.10) and the positions of the rotational lines calculated. From rotation-vibration spectra the values $B = 1.48$ and $D = 3.63 \times 10^{-6}$ cm^{-1} are obtained for HCN. Thus:

(*a*) For the first rotational line, that is for the $J' \leftarrow J''$ transition of $1 \leftarrow 0$:

$$\nu_{1\leftarrow 0} = 2 \times 1{\cdot}48 - 4 \times 3{\cdot}63 \times 10^{-6} \text{ cm}^{-1} \quad (4.15)$$

$$\nu_{1\leftarrow 0} = 2{\cdot}96 \text{ cm}^{-1} = 3380\ \mu \quad (4.16)$$

(*b*) For the twenty-second rotational line, that is for the transition $J' \leftarrow J''$ of $22 \leftarrow 21$

$$\nu_{22\leftarrow 21} = 2 \times 1{\cdot}48 \times 22 - 4 \times 3{\cdot}63 \times 10^{-6} \times 22^3 \text{ cm}^{-1} \quad (4.17)$$

$$\nu_{22\leftarrow 21} = 64{\cdot}92 \text{ cm}^{-1} = 154\ \mu \quad (4.18)$$

Thus, in the case of HCN the pure rotational spectrum lies in the extreme part of the far infra-red region. It is typical of linear molecules that their pure rotational spectrum lies either in this extreme part of the infra-red or beyond this in the microwave region.

Spherical-top molecules

A molecule may have three principal moments of inertia I_A, I_B, and I_C where these values are taken about three perpendicular axes. A spherical-top molecule is one for which $I_A = I_B = I_C$ such as CCl_4 or SF_6. Such molecules can have no pure rotational infra-red spectrum since their permanent dipole moment is zero. In theory it is possible that there might be a molecule such as $C(WXYZ)$ where $I_A = I_B = I_C$ which has a permanent electric dipole moment; this type of molecule is known as an accidental spherical-top molecule and would have a pure rotational infra-red spectrum.

Symmetric-top molecules

The molecules examined have been mainly of the pyramidal type, such as NH_3 and PCl_3, or of the tetrahedral type, such as in CH_3Cl and $CHCl_3$, where $I_B = I_C \neq I_A$, and none of these values is zero. For tetrahedral and pyramidal molecules I_A is the moment of inertia along the main axis of symmetry (the z-axis), and this axis of highest symmetry is termed the *figure axis*. I_B and I_C are the moments of inertia about the other two mutually orthogonal axes. Fig. 4.9 shows the axes chosen for the analysis of the rotation of the symmetric-top molecule CH_3Cl, where the main electric dipole (C—Cl) lies along the molecular axis of symmetry. The z-axis was selected along the internuclear line of the carbon chlorine atoms because of the resulting CH_3 group symmetry about this axis. The other two axes were then placed perpendicular to the z-axis through the centre of mass of the molecule. I_A is always chosen so that its moment of inertia is less than that of I_C, and if the axis of I_A lies along the highest symmetry axis, this type of molecule is termed a *prolate symmetric-top*. Thus, the CH_3Cl molecule which has just been considered is a prolate symmetric-top. However, if the axis of the greater moment of inertia I_C (where $I_A = I_B < I_C$) lies along the symmetry axis as in the plane symmetrical structure of BCl_3, then the molecule is termed an *oblate symmetric-top*. In general, we shall consider only the case of a prolate symmetric-top, and the equations given will apply to this type.

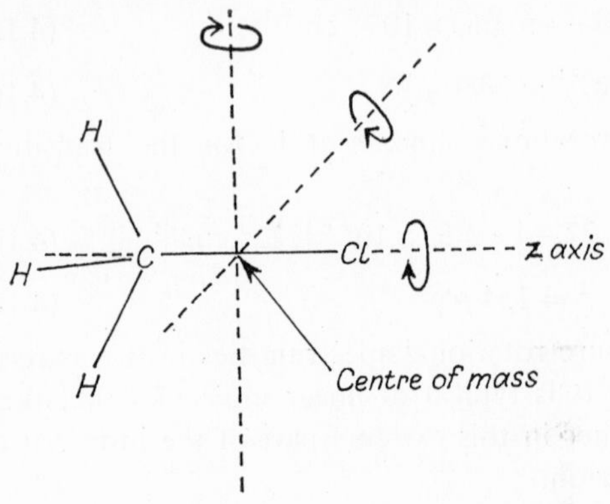

FIG. 4.9 Rotation of a prolate symmetric-top molecule about the three principal axes.

The symmetric-top type of molecule has a permanent electric dipole moment and hence satisfies the criterion for a pure rotational infra-red spectrum. The energy levels of a symmetric-top molecule are given by the equation:

$$E_r = \frac{h^2}{8\pi^2 I_B} \cdot J(J+1) + \frac{h^2}{8\pi^2}\left\{\frac{1}{I_A} - \frac{1}{I_B}\right\}K^2 = hcF(J, K) \qquad (4.19)$$

where K is the quantum number which governs the component of the angular momentum about the symmetry axis.† The selection rules to be applied are:

$$\Delta J = 0, \ \pm 1 \quad \text{and} \quad \Delta K = 0$$

The quantum number K cannot be greater than J, and J takes the values:

$$J = K, \ K+1, \ K+2, \ \ldots$$

Equation (4.19) is for a rigid symmetric-top molecule. For a non-rigid molecule Slawsky and Dennison[12] give the following equation for the rotational energy levels:

$$E_r = \frac{h^2}{8\pi^2 I_B} \cdot J(J+1) + \frac{h^2}{8\pi^2}\left\{\frac{1}{I_A} - \frac{1}{I_B}\right\}K^2 - hcD_J \cdot J^2(J+1)^2 - hcD_{JK} \cdot J(J+1)K^2 - hcD_K \cdot K^4 \qquad (4.20)$$

where the terms involving the constants D_J, D_K, D_{JK} take into account the centrifugal stretching in the molecule; these terms are normally very small.

† This is the equation for a prolate symmetric-top molecule such as CH_3Cl where $I_A < I_B = I_C$, but for an oblate symmetric-top molecule such as BCl_3 where $I_A = I_B < I_C$ the equation becomes:

$$E_r = \frac{h^2}{8\pi^2 I_B} \cdot J(J+1) + \frac{h^2}{8\pi^2}\left\{\frac{1}{I_C} - \frac{1}{I_B}\right\}K^2$$

The D_J term comes about owing to the stretching from the end-over-end rotation of the molecule, whereas the D_K term results from the distortion caused by the rotation about the symmetry axis. The D_{JK} term may be identified with the interaction between these two types of motion. In all but the most accurate measurements equation (4.19) is usually sufficient.

For a change in J of $+1$, that is an absorption transition, and for $K'-K''=0$, the wave-numbers of the rotational lines, as based on equation (4.19), are given by:

$$\nu = F(J',\ K')-F(J'',\ K'') \tag{4.21}$$

$$\nu = 2B(J''+1) \tag{4.22}$$

while if the centrifugal stretching is taken into account, then from equation (4.20):

$$\nu = 2B(J''+1)-2D_{JK}(J''+1)K^2-4D_J(J''+1)^3 \tag{4.23}$$

The experimental observations on symmetric-top molecules are somewhat limited. Measurements have been made, however, on NH_3, ND_3, and PH_3.

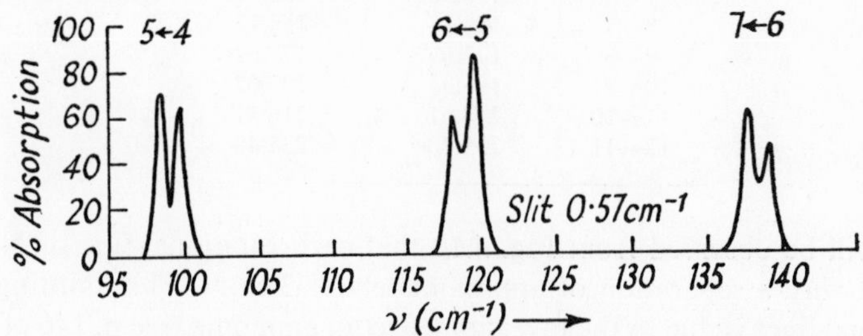

FIG. 4.10 Far infra-red pure rotational spectrum of gaseous NH_3. The absorbing path was 1 cm. and the gas pressure for the transitions 5←4, 6←5, and 7←6 was 8 cm, 10 cm, and 7.3 cm, respectively. (*After Wright and Randall.*[13] *Courtesy of 'The Physical Review'*)

Wright and Randall[13] have studied the rotational lines of NH_3. The far infra-red pure rotational absorption transitions corresponding to the following changes $J' \leftarrow J''$ of 5←4, 6←5 and 7←6 at wave-numbers of 99.20, 118.92 and 138.50 cm^{-1}, respectively, are shown in Fig. 4.10. Barnes[14] was able to fit the wave-numbers of the rotational lines to the equation (4.24):

$$\nu = 19.880(J''+1)-0.00176(J''+1)^3 \tag{4.24}$$

Thus, in this case the D_{JK} term was considered negligible. A comparison of the wave-numbers as calculated from equation (4.24) with the observed values is made in Table 4.4.

On comparison of the coefficients of $(J''+1)$ in equations (4.24) and (4.23) where the D_{JK} term in equation (4.23) is neglected, the value of B is obtained. From this, I_B the moment of inertia perpendicular to the symmetry axis was calculated to be 2.815×10^{-40} g-cm^2.

In a later work Foley and Randall[15] were able to resolve some of the rotational lines of NH_3 with high J values into component lines with different K. The transitions studied were the $J' \leftarrow J''$ of $11 \leftarrow 10$, $12 \leftarrow 11$, $13 \leftarrow 12$, $14 \leftarrow 13$, and $15 \leftarrow 14$ rotational changes and the equation:

$$\nu = 19.89(J''+1)+0.00279(J''+1)K^2-0.00294(J''+1)^3 \qquad (4.25)$$

was found to fit these lines. Equation (4.25) is of the same type as equation (4.23), and in this case the D_{JK} term has been included in the analysis.

TABLE 4.4

Observed and calculated wave-numbers for some $J' \leftarrow J''$ pure rotation transitions in gaseous NH_3

J' J''	Observed ν (cm^{-1})	Calculated ν (cm^{-1})
$3 \leftarrow 2$	59.36	59.59
$4 \leftarrow 3$	79.32	79.40
$5 \leftarrow 4$	99.20	99.17
$6 \leftarrow 5$	118.92	118.89
$7 \leftarrow 6$	138.50	138.54
$8 \leftarrow 7$	158.33	158.12
$9 \leftarrow 8$	177.69	177.62
$10 \leftarrow 9$	196.93	197.02
$11 \leftarrow 10$	216.61	216.31
$12 \leftarrow 11$	235.40	235.48

It will be observed from Fig. 4.10 that each rotational line of NH_3 is a doublet with a separation of approximately 1.33 cm^{-1}. This splitting of the rotational lines is due to the inversion effect in ammonia (see p. 146 of Vol.1). The N atom can lie above or below the plane of the H atoms with only a small potential energy barrier opposing the inversion. The result is that each level splits into two levels each characterised by the same J value. The first five pure rotational lines of NH_3 have now been observed by McCubbin and Sinton.[9]

Barnes[14] has studied the ND_3 molecule. For the eleven transitions whose J' values range from 8 to 18 the absorption spectrum† is shown in Fig. 4.11, where the $18 \leftarrow 17$ transition is to be found at the lowest wavelength and the $8 \leftarrow 7$ at the highest wavelength. The rotational lines resulting from these transitions were fitted to the equation:

$$\nu = 10.26(J''+1)-0.00045(J''+1)^3 \qquad (4.26)$$

where $J'-J'' = +1$.

On comparison of the coefficients of the $(J''+1)$ terms in equations (4.23) and (4.26) the value of B is obtained, and then the moment of inertia about the axes perpendicular to the symmetry axis is calculated to be 5.457×10^{-40} g-cm^2.

† In this case since transmission and not absorption is plotted as the ordinate axis, the minima represent maximum absorption.

Asymmetric-top molecules

These are molecules such that $I_A \neq I_B \neq I_C$ and none of these principal moments of inertia is zero. Although the great majority of polyatomic molecules fall into this class, the only molecules whose pure rotational infra-red spectra have been investigated in any detail are H_2O and D_2O. Randall *et al.*[16a] and Fuson *et al.*[16b] have measured the spectra of H_2O and D_2O with great accuracy and very good resolution. Their results, however, are far too complex to be dealt with here.

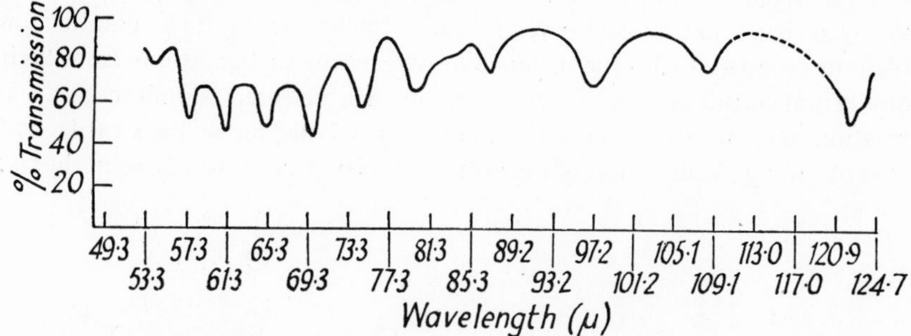

FIG. 4.11 Pure rotational spectrum of gaseous ND_3 with J' values from 8 to 18 where the first minimum value corresponds with $J' = 18$. (*After Barnes.*[14] *Courtesy of 'The Physical Review'*)

Molecular vibrations

The atoms in a molecule are never stationary, whatever the temperature. In fact, even in a solid near the absolute zero temperature the atoms are in constant oscillation about an equilibrium position. However, the amplitude of the oscillation of the atom is only of the order 10^{-9} to 10^{-10} cm, while their vibrational frequencies are of the order of infra-red radiation.

If there are N uncombined atoms free to move in three dimensions, then the system would have $3N$ translational degrees of freedom. However, if these atoms are contained in one molecule, there are still $3N$ degrees of freedom of which three degrees are for the translation of the centre of gravity of the molecule, and for a non-linear molecule three degrees for the rotation of the whole which may be resolved about three perpendicular axes. If it is assumed there are only three types of motion, then:

$$\text{translational}+\text{vibrational}+\text{rotational degrees of freedom} = 3N \quad (4.27)$$

$$\text{i.e. the vibrational degrees of freedom} = 3N-6\dagger \quad (4.28)$$

For a linear molecule such as Cl_2, CO_2, or C_2H_2 if the molecule is placed along the z-axis (see p. 86) then it has only finite moments of inertia about the other two axes, and hence there are only two degrees of rotational freedom. Thus, the number of vibrational degrees of freedom would now become $3N-5$.

† These values are the number of fundamental vibrational frequencies of the molecule; that is the number of different 'normal' modes of vibration (see p. 90). In practice, because of degeneracy the number of fundamental vibrational frequencies which may be measured is often smaller than this.

To gain some appreciation of the type of vibration which may result from the atoms in a molecule consider a molecular model, where the nuclei may be visualised as balls and the forces acting between them are represented by spiral springs. It is assumed that the major restoring forces lie along the valence bonds and that the restoring force, for small displacements, would obey Hooke's law. The model chosen is benzene where the carbon balls are twelve times heavier than the hydrogen ones. The springs connecting the carbon–hydrogen balls are now slightly stretched by moving each of the six pairs of weights along the direction of the carbon–hydrogen bonds. The hydrogen balls are moved twelve times further from their equilibrium positions compared with the distance moved by the carbon atoms from their equilibrium positions. When the weights are released simultaneously a vibration sets in where the carbon–hydrogen balls move backwards and forwards along the direction of the bond connecting carbon-hydrogen, that is:

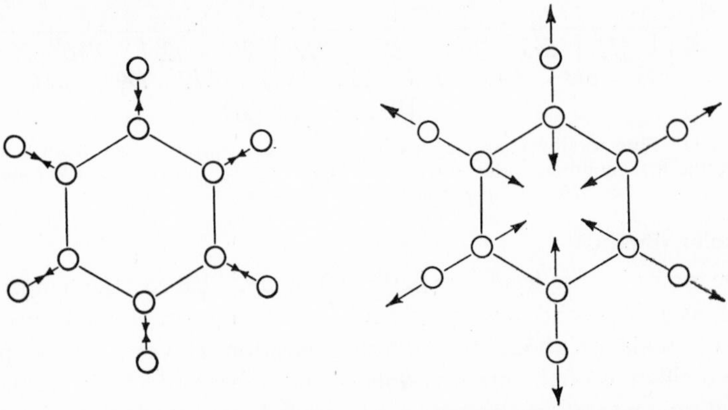

The motion continues along these carbon–hydrogen directions, and the centre of gravity of the system does not alter. This type of vibration is known as the *symmetrical stretching mode* of benzene. Altogether there are theoretically $3N-6 = 30$ normal modes of vibration of the benzene molecule. A normal mode of vibration is one where, in the absence of other normal modes, each nucleus executes simple harmonic oscillations in a straight line about its equilibrium position. All the nuclei move with the same frequency and are in phase, and the centre of gravity of the molecule remains unaltered. Each normal mode of vibration is treated as the simple harmonic oscillation of what is termed a *normal co-ordinate*. The normal co-ordinate is constructed so that it expresses all the individual displacements of the nuclei involved. An application of normal co-ordinates may be seen on p. 140. In practice it is only possible to observe twenty of the normal modes of vibration of the benzene molecule. In fact, ten of the thirty theoretically possible modes are degenerate. The twenty normal modes of vibration of the benzene molecule are given in Fig. 4.12. A number of these benzene vibrational modes may be analysed by the ball-like nuclei and spring model. Another model may be visualised in which the six carbon balls were displaced slightly above the plane of the ring while the six hydrogen balls were pulled twelve times their displacement below the plane. Then, if all twelve balls were released simultaneously, the resulting motion would be:

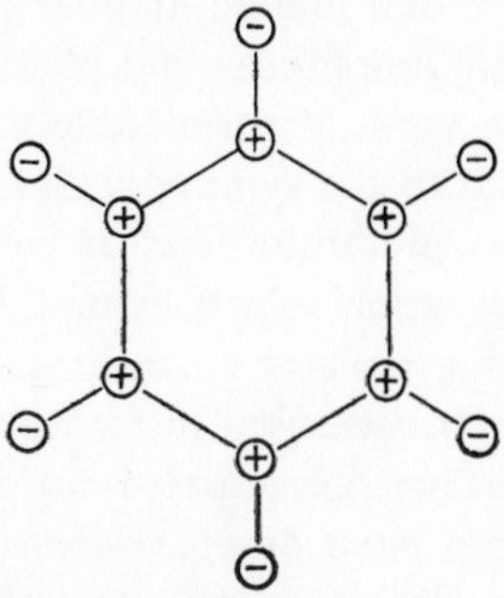

where the positive and negative signs indicate displacements in opposite directions out of the plane of the benzene ring.

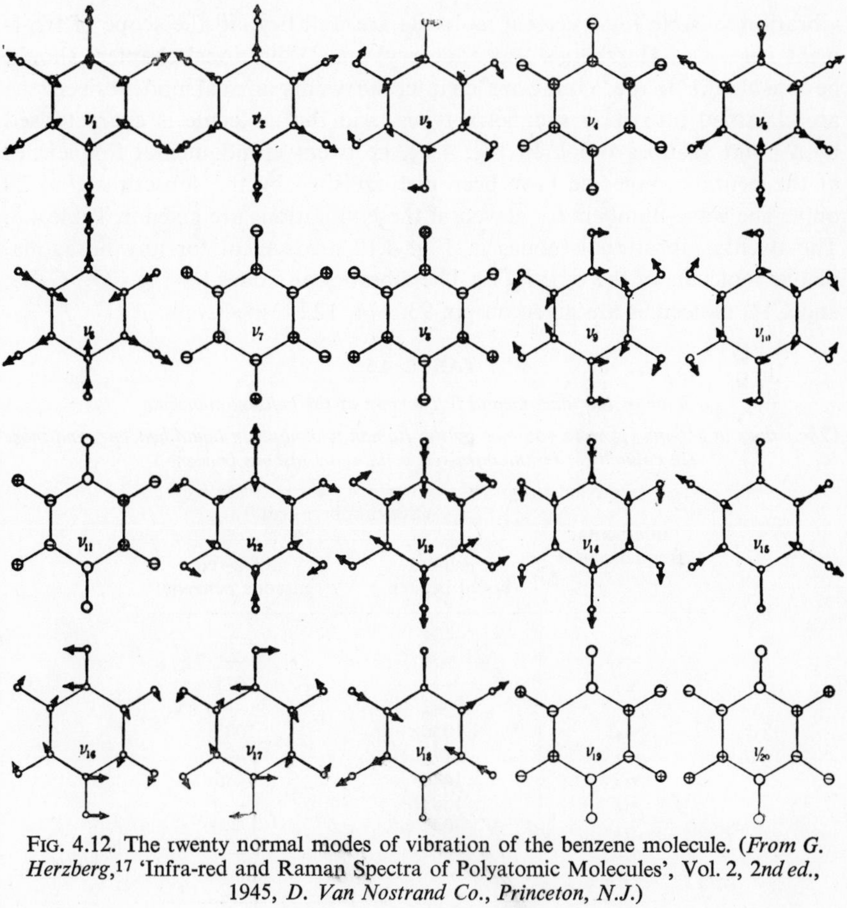

FIG. 4.12. The twenty normal modes of vibration of the benzene molecule. (*From G. Herzberg*,[17] 'Infra-red and Raman Spectra of Polyatomic Molecules', Vol. 2, 2*nd ed.*, 1945, *D. Van Nostrand Co., Princeton, N.J.*)

In general, if the nuclei were slightly displaced from their equilibrium position and then simultaneously released, the ensuing vibration would have a complex form. The resulting vibration from the displacement could be analysed as a superposition of a limited number of normal vibrations which would have mostly different amplitudes and phases.

To appreciate fully the types of permissible normal modes of vibrations consideration must be paid to the symmetry elements of the vibration. For example, reflection of the equilibrium nuclear configuration in a plane may produce a nuclear configuration which cannot be distinguished from the original. A number of such symmetry operations are performed on the molecule, and the molecule is characterised in terms of these. When a complete set of symmetry operations has been carried out on the molecule it is identified by what is known as a *point group symbol.* This indicates the type of symmetry to which the nuclear equilibrium configuration belongs. In fact, the symmetry of the molecule determines the potential energy field experienced by the nuclei and hence fixes the symmetry types of the normal vibrational modes. However, symmetry considerations and the analysis of the types of vibration feasible for a certain molecule are well beyond the scope of treatment here, and Herzberg's 'Introductory' and 'Vibrations' chapters should be consulted.[17] In the 'Vibrations' chapter the twenty normal modes of benzene are classified into their symmetry types, and the molecule is characterised by a point group symbol. In Fig. 4.12 the twenty fundamental frequencies of the benzene molecule have been distinguished by the subscripts 1 to 20 on v. The wave-numbers for eleven of these vibrations are given in Table 4.5. The twenty vibrational modes in Fig. 4.12 are typical for any hexagonal planar molecule of the type X_6Y_6. The vibrational modes for the CO_2, C_2H_2, and CH_4 molecules are given on pp. 93, 174, 122 respectively.

TABLE 4.5

Some of the fundamental frequencies of the benzene molecule

(*The values in column* (2) *were obtained by the Raman technique on liquid benzene, and those in column* (3) *by the infra-red method on gaseous benzene.*)

Fundamental frequencies	Wave-numbers (cm^{-1})	
	Raman (liquid benzene)	Infra-red (gaseous benzene)
ν_{20}	404	—
ν_{18}	606	—
ν_{4}	—	671
ν_{2}	992	—
ν_{14}	1030	1037
ν_{17}	1178	—
ν_{13}	1478	1485
ν_{16}	1585	—
ν_{15}	3047	—
ν_{1}	3062	—
ν_{12}	—	3099

The frequencies of vibration of the atoms in molecules are of the same magnitude as that of infra-red radiation. Provided the criterion for infra-red absorption is satisfied for a particular vibration, then infra-red radiation is capable of interacting with the vibrating nuclei and of increasing their vibrational energy.

Absorption of vibrational energy in the infra-red region

Criterion for an infra-red vibrational spectrum

The criterion for the absorption or emission of vibrational energy by a molecule in the infra-red region is that a change of electric dipole moment must occur during the vibration, that is the vibration should produce temporary displacement of the electrical centre of gravity.

For a diatomic molecule there is only one vibrational mode because $3N-5 = 3\times2-5 = 1$. The X→—←X type is normally inactive in the infra-red region where owing to the electrical symmetry throughout the vibration there is never a resultant electric dipole moment. However, for X→—←Y owing to the compression of charge during the vibration and differing polarisabilities of the electrons in the atoms X and Y a change in dipole moment occurs during the vibration, and diatomic molecules of this type exhibit an infra-red spectrum.

In the case of a linear triatomic molecule such as carbon dioxide there are in theory four ($3N-5$) fundamental vibrational modes. These vibrational modes may be represented diagrammatically as follows:

(*a*) ←O—C—O→ this is a symmetrical frequency† of value ν_1;

(*b*) O—C—O (↑ on C; ↓ on each O) this is a deformation frequency of value ν_2 where during the vibration the molecule ceases to be exactly linear;

(*c*) ←O—C→—←O This is an antisymmetrical frequency of value ν_3.

The remaining fundamental vibration is accounted for by the fact that the ν_2 mode is doubly degenerate; that is, if (*b*) were rotated through 90° out of the plane of the paper the corresponding vibration would have the same frequency ν_2. Thus, the anticipated four frequencies may be explained.

To decide which of these vibrations may appear in the infra-red region the criterion that a change of dipole moment must occur during the vibration is applied. For example:

(i) In vibration (*b*) the molecule is initially linear but during the vibration it becomes:

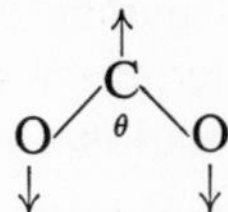

† This is sometimes written O→C←O and in each of these figures indicating motion of atoms by arrows, providing all the arrows are reversed, the same vibrational frequency is represented. Thus, ←O—C—O→ indicates that the oxygen nuclei are moving outwards while O→C←O implies that they are moving inwards, and the vibration itself goes on continuously with the same frequency ν_1.

This has a resultant dipole moment of $2\mu_{CO} \cos \theta/2$, where μ_{CO} is the bond moment of one CO link. Hence, the dipole moment varies from O through all the $2\,\mu_{CO} \cos \theta/2$ values and, therefore, the criterion for the appearance of an infra-red spectrum is satisfied.

(ii) In the case of vibration (*a*) owing to the symmetry the molecule never has a resultant dipole moment throughout the vibration because the changes in the bond moments always cancel on vector addition, and, therefore, no infra-red spectrum would be anticipated.

(iii) For the vibration (*c*) during the vibration there is an unequal change in charge on the left-hand side of the carbon compared with that on the right. A resultant dipole moment change occurs, and the molecule becomes active to the infra-red radiation. It must be stressed that when the asymmetric vibration ν_3 alters its vibrational energy by the absorption of the particular frequency ν_3 then all the three nuclei are simultaneously involved. The same, of course, holds for ν_2. The motion of a particular fundamental vibrational mode is, thus, to be treated as a whole and gives rise to definite absorption frequencies. If during the vibration a change in dipole moment occurs, an infra-red absorption corresponding to that frequency should result. It is not, however, simply a matter of looking at the infra-red spectrogram and reading off the fundamental vibrational frequencies from the absorption bands, since additional frequencies, which are usually weaker, may also be present. These extra frequencies result from:

(i) Integral multiples of the fundamental frequencies and are known as *overtones*. For example, if ν_a is the particular fundamental frequency, then the overtones may appear at frequencies of approximately $2\nu_a$, $3\nu_a$ and so on.

(ii) Combinations of the fundamental frequencies and their integral multiples as their sum and also of their difference. These bands are termed *combination bands*. For example, if ν_a and ν_b were two of the fundamental frequencies, then the possible combination frequencies would be $\nu_a+\nu_b$, $\nu_a+2\nu_b$, $\nu_a-\nu_b$, and so on.

Vibrational studies of diatomic molecules

Simple harmonic vibrations. Only the unsymmetrical type of diatomic molecule, X—Y, may have an infra-red spectrum under normal conditions. If the energy values of a vibrating diatomic molecule may be allowed to approximate to that of a harmonic oscillator, then

$$E_v = (v+\tfrac{1}{2})hc\omega \tag{4.29}$$

where v is a vibrational quantum number which can take the values 0, 1, 2, 3, . . ., and ω is the vibrational frequency of the oscillator in wave-numbers. Providing the vibrational and rotational energies do not interact, then the total rotation-vibration energy E_{vr} is given by

$$E_{vr} = E_v+E_r = (v+\tfrac{1}{2})hc\omega+J(J+1)\frac{h^2}{8\pi^2 I} \tag{4.30}$$

In the infra-red region simultaneous changes in both forms of energy are usually studied. Thus, the changes are of the form $v' \leftarrow v''$ and $J' \leftarrow J''$ where v'' and J'' are the values of the vibrational and rotational quantum numbers, respectively, in the lower energy levels from which absorption takes place. The selection rules, which limit the permissible values of the energy absorbed, that is ΔE where

$$\Delta E = (E_{v'} + E_{r'}) - (E_{v''} + E_{r''}) \tag{4.31}$$

are $\Delta v = (v' - v'') = \pm 1$, if the vibration is simple harmonic, and $\Delta J = (J' - J'') = 0, \pm 1$, or just ± 1. In the case when $J' - J'' = 0$ there is no change in the rotational energy accompanying the vibrational energy change, and

$$\Delta E = (v' - v'')hc\omega \tag{4.32}$$

and a single absorption line might be anticipated.

Anharmonic vibrations. Equation (4.29) applies only to strictly simple harmonic vibrations and leads to only one band, because the selection rule $v' - v'' = \pm 1$ would be rigidly obeyed. In fact, the vibrations of nuclei are never strictly simple harmonic ones. Since there is stretching of the oscillator, the vibrations are anharmonic, and the revised equation for the vibrational energy of such an oscillator is given by:

$$E_v = (v + \tfrac{1}{2})hc\omega_e - (v + \tfrac{1}{2})^2 hcx_e\omega_e + (v + \tfrac{1}{2})^3 hcy_e\omega_e + \ldots \tag{4.33}$$

where x_e and y_e are the so-called *anharmonicity constants*, and ω_e is the hypothetical vibration frequency of negligible amplitude about the equilibrium position of the nuclei.†

When the vibration is anharmonic, there is theoretically no restriction on the change of the vibrational quantum number. Thus, the change Δv may be greater than unity, that is the transitions $2 \leftarrow 0$, $3 \leftarrow 0$, may take place, although these higher frequency absorptions are of much lower intensity, and often the amount of absorbing gas has to be increased to observe them. For example, in the case of HCl, if the infra-red absorption spectrum is observed with a thin layer of absorbing gas, only the fundamental band is obtained corresponding to a $1 \leftarrow 0$ transition at a wave-number of about 2886 cm^{-1}. By studying the absorption with a thicker layer of HCl gas, in addition to the first band a second band appears corresponding to $2 \leftarrow 0$ at a wave-number of approximately 5668 cm^{-1}, that is at about twice the initial value. This is the *first overtone*. By increasing the thickness of HCl gas to several metres at atmospheric pressure, five bands may be obtained whose wave-numbers are approximately two, three, four, and five times that of the 2886 cm^{-1} band, and are, respectively, the first, second, third, and fourth overtones of this vibration. It is to be noted that when all five bands appear the intensities follow the order $1 \leftarrow 0 \gg 2 \leftarrow 0 > 3 \leftarrow 0 > 4 \leftarrow 0 > 5 \leftarrow 0$. If the third and higher terms on the right-hand side of equation (4.33) are neglected,

† When $v = 0$ then the zero point energy (E_0) is obtained by substituting this value into equation (4.33). This gives:

$$E_0 = \tfrac{1}{2}hc\omega_e - \tfrac{1}{4}hcx_e\omega_e + \tfrac{1}{8}hcy_e\omega_e + \ldots \tag{4.34}$$

then the energy change in a vibrational transition from the state v'' to the state v' is:

$$E_{v'} - E_{v''} = (v'-v'')hc\omega_e - \{v'(v'+1) - v''(v''+1)\}hcx_e\omega_e = \Delta E = hc\nu \quad (4.35)$$

where ν is the wave-number for the transition between these two vibrational levels.† The majority of the molecules are in the $v'' = 0$ state before absorption of energy, and if v'' is made equal to zero in equation (4.35) then:

$$v' \leftarrow 0 \quad \nu = \omega_e v' - v'(v'+1)x_e\omega_e \quad (4.36)$$

for

$$1 \leftarrow 0, \ \nu_1 = (1-2x_e)\omega_e \quad (4.37)$$

$$2 \leftarrow 0, \ \nu_2 = (1-3x_e)2\omega_e \quad (4.38)$$

$$3 \leftarrow 0, \ \nu_3 = (1-4x_e)3\omega_e \quad (4.39)$$

Since x_e is usually small, then from equations (4.37) to (4.39), $\nu_1 : \nu_2 : \nu_3$ are approximately as 1: 2: 3. In fact, it was observed for the near infra-red absorption spectrum of HCl gas, that $\nu_1 : \nu_2 : \nu_3 : \nu_4 : \nu_5 = 2886 : 5668 : 8347 : 10\,923 : 13\,397$, numbers which are very approximately in the ratio of 1: 2: 3: 4: 5. The population of the molecules in the $v = 0$ level is generally much greater than in the $v = 1$ level, and in the case of HCl, the ratio of the number of molecules in the first to that in the zero vibrational level at 300°K is 9.77×10^{-7}. Hence, it would be expected that the intensities of transitions from the $v = 1$ level would be very much weaker. The possibility of obtaining such bands is favoured by higher temperatures, where in the case of HCl the ratio at 1000°K is increased to 1.57×10^{-2}. In general, studies are usually made on transitions from $v'' = 0$ to v', where $v' = 1, 2, 3, 4 \ldots$

If the experimental frequencies are inserted in equations of the types (4.37) to (4.39), then mean values of x_e and ω_e may be calculated. This procedure is feasible for the infra-red transitions owing to the observable overtones. The values of ω_e and x_e may be applied as follows:

(i) For expression of the vibrational energy values in terms of v:

$$E_v = (v+\tfrac{1}{2})hc\omega_e - (v+\tfrac{1}{2})^2 hcx_e\omega_e \quad (4.40)$$

(ii) To obtain a very approximate value for the dissociation energy from $D_e \simeq \omega_e/4x_e$ (cf. p. 303). A much better value can be derived from a Birge-Sponer extrapolation (cf. p. 304).

(iii) To calculate the constant α in the Morse equation. The Morse equation is:

$$\text{potential energy} = D_e[1 - \exp\{-\alpha(r-r_e)\}]^2 \quad (4.41)$$

where $\alpha = (8\pi^2\mu x_e\omega_e c/h)^{\frac{1}{2}}$, D_e is the spectroscopic dissociation energy (see p. 298) which includes the zero point energy, μ the reduced mass, and r_e the value of r at the minimum of the potential energy curve.

† The value of ν inserted corresponds with the transition between two vibrational levels where both J' and J'' are zero. This line is normally absent from the observed structure of the rotation-vibration band (see p. 100).

The value of ω_e itself may be employed:

(i) To calculate force constants from the equation

$$\omega_e c = \frac{1}{2\pi}(k/\mu)^{\frac{1}{2}} \tag{4.42}$$

where μ is the reduced mass and k the force constant.

(ii) In conjunction with other data for the calculation of thermodynamic quantities such as entropy and heat capacity (cf. p. 329).

Vibrational studies of triatomic molecules

For a diatomic molecule executing single harmonic motion with a vibrational frequency of ω the vibrational energy is given by equation (4.29).

For a triatomic molecule, however, there are three fundamental frequencies ω_1, ω_2 and ω_3, and for a simple harmonic oscillator the vibrational energy of the molecule would be given by:

$$E_v = (v_1+\tfrac{1}{2})hc\omega_1+(v_2+\tfrac{1}{2})hc\omega_2+(v_3+\tfrac{1}{2})hc\omega_3 \tag{4.43}$$

where the change in vibrational energy, $E_{v'}-E_{v''}$, is governed by the (v_1', v_2', v_3') and the (v_1'', v_2'', v_3'') values in the upper and lower levels, respectively.

If the vibrational motion were strictly a simple harmonic one, then the changes in the vibrational quantum numbers for each vibration would be restricted to:

$$\left.\begin{aligned} v_1'-v_1'' &= 1 = \Delta v_1 \\ v_2'-v_2'' &= 1 = \Delta v_2 \\ v_3'-v_3'' &= 1 = \Delta v_3 \end{aligned}\right\} \tag{4.44}$$

In addition, each vibrational change would occur independently and combination frequencies such as:

$$\left.\begin{aligned} &\omega_1+\omega_2 \\ &\omega_1+\omega_3 \\ &\omega_2+\omega_3 \\ &\omega_1+\omega_2+\omega_3 \end{aligned}\right\} \tag{4.45}$$

would be forbidden. However, in practice the motion is not strictly a simple harmonic one, and combination frequencies may be obtained. Since the motion is not strictly a simple harmonic one, then Δv_1, Δv_2, and Δv_3 are not limited to unit changes, and, in fact, may be small integers. The frequencies of the bands composed of these combination or overtone frequencies are given approximately by the general formula:

$$\nu = \Delta v_1\omega_1+\Delta v_2\omega_2+\Delta v_3\omega_3 \tag{4.46}$$

where Δv_1, Δv_2 and Δv_3 are small integers (or zero). When two of the Δv values are zero (e.g. $\Delta v_2 = \Delta v_3 = 0$), and $\Delta v_1 > 1$ and $v_1'' = 0$, then overtones of the fundamental vibrational frequency $c\omega_1$ are obtained, and when $\Delta v_1 = 2$ this frequency is the *first overtone*, while when $\Delta v_1 = 3$ this is the *second overtone*.

Symmetry considerations may restrict the number of permissible overtone and combination bands. Detailed consideration is too involved to be treated here, although one important restriction will now be mentioned. For molecules with a centre of symmetry, one limitation is that for antisymmetrical vibrations such as:

$$\longleftarrow \text{O—C} \longrightarrow \longleftarrow \text{O}$$

the odd overtones are forbidden.

To represent the experimentally determined vibrational data most accurately, equations more complex than (4.43) have to be employed.

For non-linear triatomic molecules, such as water, where the fundamental frequencies are ω_1, ω_2 and ω_3 the experimental data may be fitted to equation (4.47):

$$\frac{E_{v'}}{hc} = x_0 + x_1 v_1 + x_2 v_2 + x_3 v_3 + x_{11} v_1^2 + x_{22} v_2^2 + x_{33} v_3^2 + x_{12} v_1 v_2 + \\ + x_{13} v_1 v_3 + x_{23} v_2 v_3 \quad (4.47)$$

The unknowns x_1, x_2, x_3, x_{11}, x_{22}, x_{33}, x_{12}, x_{13}, x_{23} may be determined from the data on nine band centres. The fundamental vibrational frequencies can be calculated from these constants by means of the equations:

$$\omega_1 = x_1 - x_{11} - \tfrac{1}{2} x_{12} - \tfrac{1}{2} x_{13} \quad (4.48)$$

$$\omega_2 = x_2 - x_{22} - \tfrac{1}{2} x_{12} - \tfrac{1}{2} x_{23}$$

$$\omega_3 = x_3 - x_{33} - \tfrac{1}{2} x_{13} - \tfrac{1}{2} x_{23} \quad (4.49)$$

Except in the case of diatomic molecules, it will be assumed in future that the vibrational motion is a simple harmonic one. In fact, this is never strictly true, but, as might be inferred from the example of water which has just been considered, unless this assumption is made the treatment becomes too complex, even for very simple molecules.

TABLE 4.6

Rotation-vibration bands of H_2O *in transitions from the ground state (i.e. the* $v_1'' = 0$, $v_2'' = 0$, $v_3'' = 0$ *state)*

	Values of v in excited state $v_1' v_2' v_3'$	Wave-number of band (cm^{-1})	Type of frequency
(*a*)	1, 0, 0	3652	fundamental
(*b*)	0, 1, 0	1595	fundamental
(*c*)	0, 2, 0	3151	first overtone of (*b*)
(*d*)	0, 0, 1	3756	fundamental
(*e*)	0, 0, 3	11 032	second overtone of (*d*)
(*f*)	1, 1, 1	8807	combination of (*a*), (*b*) and (*d*)
(*g*)	0, 1, 1	5332	combination of (*b*) and (*d*)
(*h*)	2, 1, 1	12 151	combination
(*i*)	3, 1, 1	15 348	combination

The number of rotation-vibration bands which may be observed for such a simple molecule like water is quite considerable, and in Table 4.6 some of the vibrational transitions from the ground state, that is the (0, 0, 0) level to the (v_1', v_2', v_3') levels, are given, and the corresponding band is identified as either a fundamental, overtone or a combination frequency. From this table the overtone and combination frequency values may be accounted for in terms of the given fundamentals.

Infra-red rotation-vibration spectra of diatomic molecules

The rotational structure of vibrational infra-red bands has not been observed for solutions. The case of those gases whose band structure it is possible to resolve will now be considered. In the section on the vibrational studies of diatomic molecules the determination of ω_e, x_e, and the useful information which may be calculated from a knowledge of their values have been studied. The examination of the structure of the rotation-vibration bands for both diatomic and simple polyatomic molecules using the infra-red and Raman methods will be considered in the following sections; the main object of such work is to determine internuclear distances, and in relevant cases, bond angles.

If the vibrational and rotational energies may be regarded as additive, then the total rotation-vibration energy (E_{vr}) of the molecule is given by equation (4.50):

$$E_{vr} = (v+\tfrac{1}{2})hc\omega_e-(v+\tfrac{1}{2})^2hcx_e\omega_e+\ldots hcB_vJ(J+1)-hcD_vJ^2(J+1)^2+\ldots \tag{4.50}$$

When a rotation-vibration change takes place between $v' \leftarrow v''$ and $J' \leftarrow J''$ the wave-number of the resultant energy change ΔE is given by the term differences (see p. 11):

$$\nu = G(v')-G(v'')+F_{v'}(J')-F_{v''}(J'') \tag{4.51}$$

and this leads to:

$$\nu = \nu_0+B_{v'}J'(J'+1)-D_{v'}J'^2(J'+1)^2-B_{v''}J''(J''+1)+D_{v''}J''^2(J''+1)^2 \tag{4.52}$$

Equation (4.52) is formed from the vibrational and rotational energy equations, where $\nu_0 = G(v')-G(v'')$ and is the wave-number of the pure vibrational transition and corresponds with a transition between two vibrational levels, where both J' and $J'' = 0$.

Because interaction takes place between the rotational and vibrational energies v is permitted to change by any integral amount. The selection rule for J depends on whether the molecule has electronic angular momentum ($\Lambda h/2\pi$, see p. 47) about the internuclear axis. If $\Lambda = 0$, then the selection rule for J is:

$$\Delta J = \pm 1 \tag{4.53}$$

For diatomic molecules Λ normally is zero and only two branches are observed. These branches are the *P*-branch when $\Delta J = -1$, and the *R-branch* when $\Delta J = +1$. An exceptional case is that of nitric oxide† which has $\Lambda = 1$, and the infra-red spectrum of this molecule is governed by the selection rule:

$$\Delta J = 0, \pm 1 \tag{4.54}$$

The branch where $\Delta J = 0$ is termed the *Q-branch*.

The absorption curve for the fundamental transition, that is the $1 \leftarrow 0$ transition of HCl, is given in Fig. 4.13. The lines in the *P*- and *R*-branches may be observed while a gap between these two branches occurs at 2886 cm^{-1},

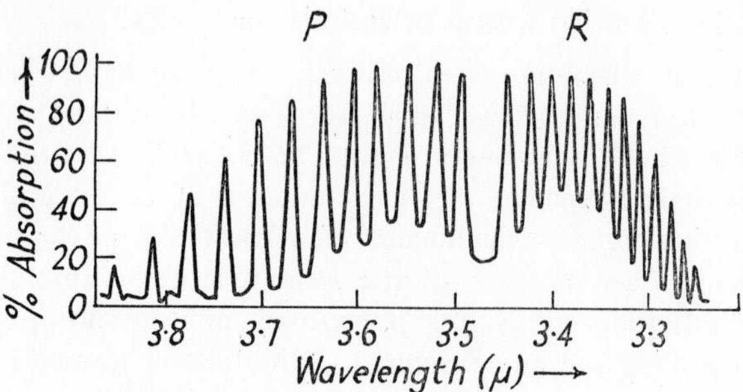

FIG. 4.13 Fine structure in the fundamental absorption band of HCl at 2886 cm^{-1} (*After Imes.*[18] *Courtesy of 'The Astrophysical Journal'*)

and this position is termed the null line or band origin. It will be noted that no *Q*-branch is observed. If such a branch had been theoretically possible and had actually appeared, the centre of its maximum would have been at the same frequency as that of the null line. In Fig. 4.14 the type of transition which led to the *R*- and *P*-branches for the fundamental transition of HCl is indicated. In addition, some of the transitions which lead to the lines of the *R*- and *P*-branches of the first overtone $(2 \leftarrow 0)$ are also given.

The wave-number of the lines in rotation-vibration changes may be obtained from equation (4.52). The wave-number of a *P*-line may be obtained in terms of J'' by substituting $J''-1$ for J' in this equation, while for an *R*-line the substitution would be $J''+1$. The resulting equations would reproduce the wave-numbers of the observed lines exactly when the appropriate value of J'' was inserted. However, other simpler cases may be considered, where approximations are involved.

Case 1. When both $D_{v'}$ and $D_{v''}$ can be neglected, the resulting equation is:

$$\nu = \nu_0 + B_{v'}J'(J'+1) - B_{v''}J''(J''+1) \tag{4.55}$$

The results for each branch are:

(*a*) For the *R*-branch on substitution of $J''+1$ for J' in equation (4.55):

$$\nu_R = \nu_0 + 2B_{v'} + (3B_{v'} - B_{v''})J + (B_{v'} - B_{v''})J^2 \tag{4.56}$$

where ν_R is the wave-number of the line whose rotational quantum has the value J. $J'' = J$ and may take the values 0, 1, 2, 3, . . .

† Nitric oxide has an unpaired electron.

(*b*) For the *P*-branch on substitution of $J''-1$ for J'

$$\nu_P = \nu_0-(B_{v'}+B_{v''})J+(B_{v'}-B_{v''})J^2 \qquad (4.57)$$

where ν_P is the wave-number of the line whose rotational quantum number has the value J. $J'' = J$ and J may take the values 1, 2, 3, . . .

(*c*) For the *Q*-branch on substitution of J'' for J'

$$\nu_Q = \nu_0+(B_{v'}-B_{v''})J+(B_{v'}-B_{v''})J^2 \qquad (4.58)$$

where ν_Q is the wave-number of the line whose rotational quantum number has the value J. $J'' = J$ and J may take the values: 1, 2, 3, . . .

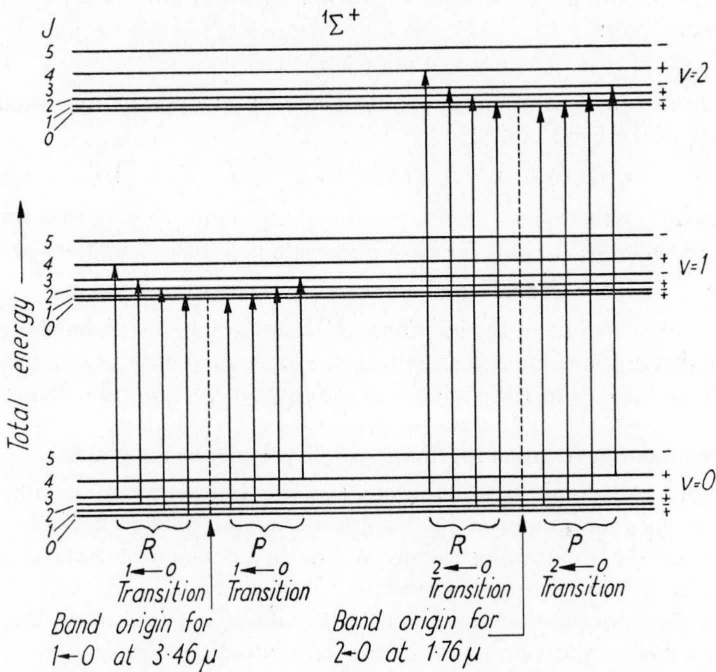

FIG. 4.14 Infra-red rotation-vibration transitions for the fundamental and first overtone bands of HCl with a $^1\Sigma^+$ ground electronic state.

It is possible to represent the *P*- and *R*-branch lines by means of the formula:

$$\nu = \nu_0+(B_{v'}+B_{v''})m+(B_{v'}-B_{v''})m^2 \qquad (4.59)$$

where m takes the values 1, 2, 3, . . . for the *R*-branch (i.e. $m = J''+1$), and for the *P*-branch the values -1, -2, -3 (i.e. $m = -J''$). Since m does not equal zero for either the *R*- or *P*-branches then a line is missing for this value of m. This missing line whose wave-number $\nu = \nu_0$ is the null line and corresponds with the forbidden transition between $J' = 0$ and $J'' = 0$.

Case II. Equation (4.59) usually gives a good fit to the experimentally observed wave-numbers although it often does not represent them exactly.

An exact fit may be obtained by replacing that equation by equation (4.60)

$$\nu = \nu_0+(B_{v'}+B_{v''})m+(B_{v'}-B_{v''}-D_{v'}+D_{v''})m^2- \\ 2(D_{v'}+D_{v''})m^3-(D_{v'}-D_{v''})m^4 \quad (4.60)$$

which takes into account the centrifugal stretching. However, $D_{v'}$ is almost equal to $D_{v''}$, and the $(D_{v'}-D_{v''})m^4$ term is normally very small, and even for exact analyses is often neglected. If $D_{v'}$ is approximately equal to $D_{v''}$ then equation (4.60) reduces to

$$\nu = \nu_0+(B_{v'}+B_{v''})m+(B_{v'}-B_{v''})m^2-4D_{v''}m^3 \quad (4.61)$$

and this equation is of the form of the empirical formula (4.62) employed in such analyses:

$$\nu = \nu_0+am+bm^2+cm^3 \quad (4.62)$$

The constants a, b, and c may be evaluated by analysis of the rotational structure of the band. Since:

$$a = (B_{v'}+B_{v''}), \quad b = (B_{v'}-B_{v''}) \quad \text{and} \quad c = -4D_{v''} \quad (4.63)$$

it follows that the values of the rotational constants may be determined. Once the values of $B_{v'}$ and $B_{v''}$ have been obtained, then from the equations

$$B = \mathbf{h}/8\pi^2cI \quad \text{and} \quad I = \mu r^2 = m_1m_2r^2/(m_1+m_2) \quad (4.64)$$

the appropriate value of the internuclear distance (r) follows immediately. If several absorption bands are examined, the value of B_e may be obtained (see p. 217), and from this the equilibrium internuclear separation r_e follows.

Infra-red rotation-vibration spectra of simple polyatomic molecules

Simple polyatomic molecules will now be considered whose infra-red spectrum may be examined in the gaseous phase, where either the band contour or the rotational structure of the bands can be observed. Small molecules with low moments of inertia will be studied.

The rotational changes associated with vibrational transitions lead to a fine structure of the vibrational bands (cf. diatomic molecules). Since with polyatomic molecules there are three mutually orthogonal moments of inertia, which generally have quite different values, the rotational fine structure tends to be rather complex. Even if grating spectrophotometers of high resolving power are employed only small molecules have had their rotational structure completely resolved. If the resolution is very poor, then each band appears as a peak with no additional characterising shape and yields no fundamental information on internuclear distances. However, as the resolution is increased the shape of the band begins to emerge; such a case may be seen in Fig. 4.15 for the perpendicular band of CO_2. However, to observe the detailed rotational structure of the band greater resolution is required.

The shape and intensity of the P-, Q- and R-branches depend on the following factors: (a) whether the electric dipole moment change is parallel or perpendicular to an axis of symmetry; (b) the magnitude of the electric dipole moment change during the vibration; (c) the relative values of the three principal moments of inertia. In Fig. 4.16 the *R*-, *P*- and *Q*-branches for the perpendicular vibration (see below) of DCN are shown. For absorption studies if the vibrational motion is treated as being a simple harmonic one, then the vibrational transitions are governed by $\Delta v = +1$. Changes in

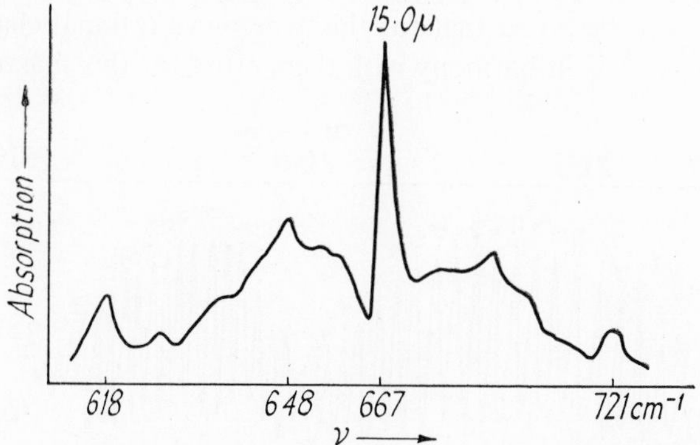

FIG. 4.15 Fundamental absorption band for the perpendicular vibration of CO_2 at 15.0 μ under low dispersion. (*After Martin and Barker.*[19c] *Courtesy of 'The Physical Review'*)

J, however, depend on the vibrational mode. If the change in electric dipole moment is in a direction parallel to the axis of symmetry, the vibration is said to be a *parallel vibration* and is given either the symbol $\|$ or π, while if the change in electric dipole occurs perpendicular to the symmetry axis, the

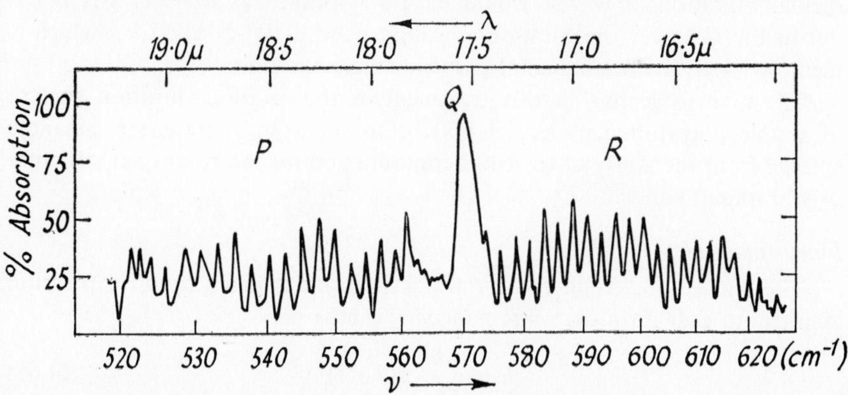

FIG. 4.16 The rotational fine structure of the 17.5 μ band of DCN corresponding to the fundamental perpendicular vibration. (*After Bartunek and Barker.*[19a] *Courtesy of 'The Physical Review'*).

vibration is described as a *perpendicular vibration* and is given either the shorthand symbol σ or $\perp$. Every band, either fundamental or overtone, may be classified as belonging to either the parallel or perpendicular type.

The best source of information for determining internuclear distances and bond angles in very simple molecules results when the rotational structure of a rotation-vibration band is completely resolvable. The rotation-vibration changes for CO_2 corresponding to the ←O—C→—←O vibration are an example of this. One of the rotation-vibration changes is given in Fig. 4.17, and the *m* values have been allotted to each peak value†. From the spacing between consecutive peaks the internuclear carbon–oxygen distance may be calculated. It will be noted that for this type of vibrational change there is no *Q*-branch. This is in harmony with theory and for this linear molecule it

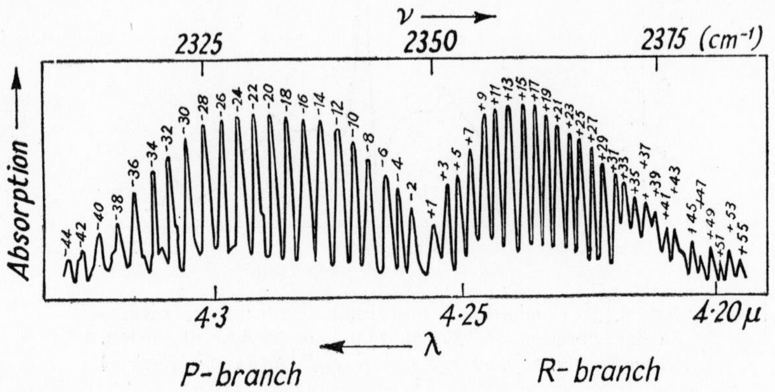

FIG. 4.17 Rotational fine structure of the fundamental absorption band for the antisymmetric vibration of CO_2 at 2349.3 cm^{-1}. (*After Cameron and Nielsen.*[19b] *Courtesy of 'The Physical Review'*)

would identify the vibrational change as being of the parallel type. A perpendicular vibration, however, would have a *Q*-branch as well. This is borne out in Fig. 4.16 for the rotation-vibration band of DCN at 17.5 μ which is identified with the fundamental perpendicular vibration.

The main objective in this treatment of the rotation-vibration spectra of simple polyatomic molecules will be to see how internuclear distances emerge from the study of (*a*) band contours and (*b*) the rotational structure of vibrational bands.

Linear molecules

The energy of a rigid rotator which is linear is given by an expression identical to that for a diatomic molecule, that is

$$E_r = \frac{h^2}{8\pi^2 I} J(J+1) \tag{4.65}$$

The vibrational energy (assuming simple harmonic motion) is given by an equation of the type

$$E_v = \Sigma(v+\tfrac{1}{2})hc\omega \tag{4.66}$$

† For this very strong parallel ν_3 band of CO_2 at 2349.3 cm^{-1} it will be noted that alternate lines having odd *J* values are absent. This arises because CO_2 is a linear symmetric molecule, and since the nuclear spin of both ^{12}C and ^{16}O is zero, the antisymmetric rotational levels are missing entirely. The ground vibrational state of CO_2 is a Σ_g^+ resulting in the odd rotational levels being absent.

which for a triatomic molecule would be that of equation (4.43). Assuming that the vibrational and rotational energies are additive, then for the total rotation-vibration energy:

$$E_{vr} = \Sigma(v+\tfrac{1}{2})hc\omega + \frac{h^2}{8\pi^2 I} \cdot J(J+1) \tag{4.67}$$

$$E_{vr} = \Sigma(v+\tfrac{1}{2})hc\omega + hcB_v J(J+1) \tag{4.68}$$

where B_v is the value of the rotational constant in the vth vibrational level.

The rotational quantum number selection rules for a linear molecule are $\Delta J = \pm 1$ for a parallel vibration and $\Delta J = 0, \pm 1$ for a perpendicular vibration. When $\Delta J = -1$ for a particular line, then this line is a member of the P-branch, while a line for $\Delta J = +1$ would be a member of the R-branch, and for $\Delta J = 0$ the Q-branch.

The rotational structure of typical parallel and perpendicular bands of a linear molecule is shown diagrammatically in Fig. 4.18, where it will be seen that apart from the Q-branch in the perpendicular band the two bands

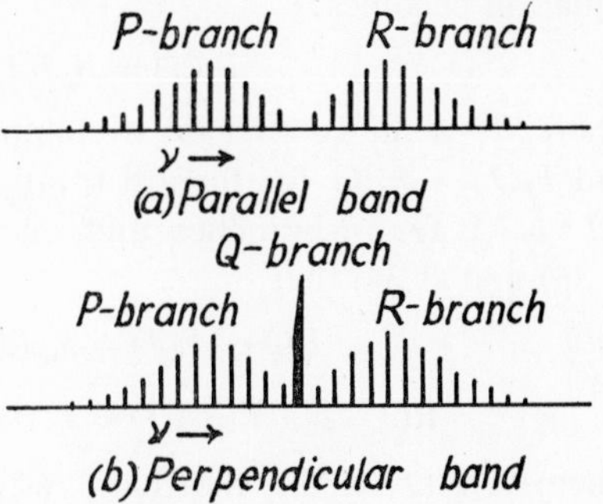

FIG. 4.18 Rotational structure of the vibration bands of a linear molecule, (*a*) a parallel band, (*b*) a perpendicular band. The height of the lines indicate the relative intensities. (*After Sutherland.*[68] *Courtesy of Messrs. Methuen and Co. Ltd.*)

have a similar appearance. In these two bands the intensities of the lines are represented by the heights, and the band contours would be obtained by drawing a line through the uppermost extremities of the lines.

Since the selection rule and the rotational energy part of the E_{vr} equation are the same for linear polyatomic molecules as for diatomic molecules, it follows that the equations for the P-, Q- and R-branches will have the same form as equations (4.57), (4.58), and (4.56) respectively if $D_{v'}$ and $D_{v''}$ may be neglected. In this case the equations for a linear polyatomic molecule are:

(i) for $\Delta J = +1$ $\quad R(J) = \nu_0 + 2B_{v'} + (3B_{v'} - B_{v''})J + (B_{v'} - B_{v''})J^2$ (4.69)

(ii) for $\Delta J = -1$ $\quad P(J) = \nu_0 - (B_{v'} + B_{v''})J + (B_{v'} - B_{v''})J^2$ (4.70)

(iii) for $\Delta J = 0$ $\quad Q(J) = \nu_0 + (B_{v'} - B_{v''})J + (B_{v'} - B_{v''})J^2$ (4.71)

where $\nu_R = R(J)$, $\nu_P = P(J)$ and $\nu_Q = Q(J)$. J is the rotational quantum number of the lower rotational state (i.e. J'') and ν_0 is the band origin. $B_{v'}$ is the rotational constant ($h/8\pi^2 cI'$) for the excited state and $B_{v''}$ ($h/8\pi^2 cI''$) that for the lower state. These formulae, therefore, take into account the alteration of the internuclear distance in the two vibrational levels. The lines in the R- and P-branches may be expressed in terms of the formula:

$$\nu = \nu_0 + (B_{v'} + B_{v''})m + (B_{v'} - B_{v''})m^2 \qquad (4.72)$$

where for the R-branch $m = (J+1)$, while for the P-branch $m = -J$. Since $J = 1$ is the lowest value m may have for a P-branch, then it follows from equation (4.72) that one missing line will separate the two branches. This is the case for parallel bands. For perpendicular bands a Q-branch occurs in the vicinity of this missing line. Since both the variable terms on the right-hand side of equation (4.71) involve $(B_{v'} - B_{v''})$, and this value is very small, then all the lines in the Q-branch fall very close to the band origin.

At one time the infra-red procedure for determining $B_{v'}$ and $B_{v''}$ values for linear molecules was to fit the observed P- and R-lines to equation (4.72). Unfortunately, this did not lead to very accurate B values. The accuracy was improved by as much as a factor of 10 by employing the method of combination differences (see p. 213). In addition, higher terms in J^3 and J^4 have to be added, that is the D_v term cannot be neglected and the rotational energy equation becomes:

$$F_v(J) = B_vJ(J+1) - D_vJ^2(J+1)^2 \qquad (4.73)$$

where D_v is the centrifugal stretching constant for the vth vibrational level and $F_v(J) = E_r/hc$ for the Jth rotational level. It follows from the fact that $\Delta J = +1$ for R-branches and $\Delta J = -1$ for P-branches and equations (1.36) and (1.34) that:

$$R(J) - P(J) = F_{v'}(J+1) - F_{v'}(J-1) = \Delta_2F'(J) \qquad (4.74)$$

$$R(J-1) - P(J+1) = F_{v''}(J+1) - F_{v''}(J-1) = \Delta_2F''(J) \qquad (4.75)$$

where $\Delta_2F'(J)$ is the shorthand way of expressing the difference between $F_{v'}(J+1)$ and $F_{v'}(J-1)$, and this is equal to the separation in cm^{-1} units of one of the upper state rotational levels from the next but one lower down in the upper vibrational level considered. Thus, the superscript dash on F indicates that it is a difference concerned with the upper vibrational state in the particular transition while the suffix 2 on Δ shows that the difference is of the form $F_v(J+1) - F_v(J-1)$. However, a suffix 1 on the Δ would indicate that the difference was of the type $F_v(J+1) - F_v(J)$, and this gives the separation of successive rotational levels and not the next but one. A double dash superscript on F means that the difference is for the lower vibrational state of the considered transition. The method of combination differences (see p. 213) then consists of forming these differences so that it becomes possible to separate the rotational constants for the upper and lower states. On employing equation (4.73), then on substitution in equation (4.74):

$$\Delta_2F'(J) = (4B_{v'} - 6D_{v'})(J+\tfrac{1}{2}) - 8D_{v'}(J+\tfrac{1}{2})^3 \qquad (4.76)$$

while on substitution from equation (4.73) into equation (4.75):

$$\Delta_2F''(J) = (4B_{v''} - 6D_{v''})(J+\tfrac{1}{2}) - 8D_{v''}(J+\tfrac{1}{2})^3 \qquad (4.77)$$

Equation (4.76) contains no $B_{v''}$ or $D_{v''}$ values and equation (4.77) no $B_{v'}$

or $D_{v'}$ values. The experimental data are fitted to equations (4.76) and (4.77) and the relationship:

$$R(J-1)+P(J) = 2\nu_0+2(B_{v'}-B_{v''})J^2-2(D_{v'}-D_{v''})J^2(J^2+1) \quad (4.78)$$

This rotational analysis leads to values of $B_{v'}$, $B_{v''}$, $D_{v'}$ and $D_{v''}$. $D_{v''}$ and $B_{v''}$ may be determined by plotting $\Delta_2F''(J)/(J+\frac{1}{2})$ against $(J+\frac{1}{2})^2$. It follows from equation (4.77) that the slope of the resulting straight line will be $-8D_{v''}$ while the intercept will be $(4B_{v''}-6D_{v''})$. Thus $B_{v''}$ and $D_{v''}$ values result. By a similar procedure with equation (4.76) the values of $D_{v'}$ and $B_{v'}$ may be obtained. To gain an impression of the factors involved in the analysis of the infra-red spectrum of a linear molecule some work on the nitrous oxide molecule will now be considered.

Thompson and Williams[20] measured seven rotation-vibration bands of N_2O with a high degree of resolution at which lines about 0.15 cm^{-1} apart could be separated. The fundamental vibrations of N_2O are:

(i) $\|$ vibration ←N—N—O→ at 1285 cm^{-1} and is designated ν_1

(ii) $\perp$ vibration N—N—O (↓ ↑ ↓) at 589 cm^{-1} and is designated ν_2

(iii) $\|$ vibration ←N—N→—←O at 2224 cm^{-1} and is designated ν_3

and the bands they studied are listed in Table 4.7.

TABLE 4.7

N_2O *bands observed in* 3.5 *to* 5 μ *region*

Observed wave-number of band (cm^{-1})	Type of band	Values of (v_1, v_2, v_3) in: Upper state $v'_1v'_2v'_3$	Lower state $v''_1v''_2v''_3$	Classification of band
2223.75	$\|$	0 0 1	0 0 0	ν_3
2209.53	$\perp$	0 1 1	0 1 0	$(\nu_3+\nu_2-\nu_2)$†
2461.97	$\|$	1 2 0	0 0 0	$(\nu_1+2\nu_2)$
2456.76	$\perp$	1 3 0	0 1 0	$(\nu_1+3\nu_2-\nu_2)$
2563.39	$\|$	2 0 0	0 0 0	$2\nu_1$
2577.13	$\perp$	2 1 0	0 1 0	$(2\nu_1+\nu_2-\nu_2)$
2798.30	$\perp$	0 1 1	0 0 0	$(\nu_2+\nu_3)$

† The meaning of this classification $(\nu_3+\nu_2-\nu_2)$ is that the transition takes place from the vibrational level where the ν_2 vibration is in the $v''_2 = 1$ level (this corresponds with the $-\nu_2$) to the vibrational levels, where the ν_3 vibration is in the $v'_1 = 1$ level and the ν_2 is again in the $v''_2 = 1$ level.

Three of the bands—the ν_3, $(\nu_1+2\nu_2)$, and the $2\nu_1$ bands—had a parallel type of structure and had, as would be expected, only *P*- and *R*-branches. The other four bands were of the perpendicular type and contained a *Q*-branch in addition to the *P*- and *R*-branches. Three of these four bands, the $(\nu_3+\nu_2-\nu_3)$, $(\nu_1+3\nu_2-\nu_2)$, and $(2\nu_1+\nu_2-\nu_2)$ arise from transitions from the first excited vibrational level of ν_2. The other perpendicular band $(\nu_2+\nu_3)$ has a more marked *Q*-branch.

Even with a linear molecule the analysis may be rather involved. This point may be illustrated by considering the rotational structure of the fundamental band, ν_3, which is given in Fig. 4.19. The integer above a peak indicates the value of the rotational quantum number J in the particular R- or P-branch, and the values of J are related to the wave-number involved in the transition in Table 4.8.

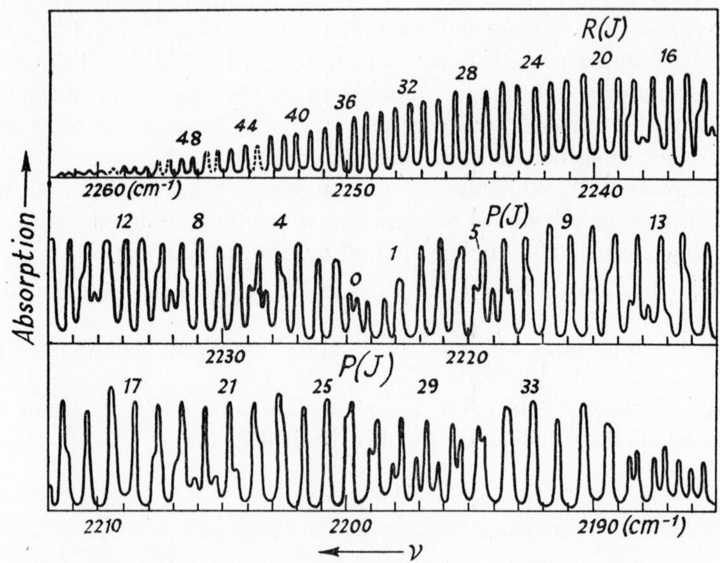

FIG. 4.19 Fine structure of the ν_3 fundamental absorption band of N_2O at 2223.5 cm^{-1}. (*After Williams and Thompson.*[20] *Courtesy of Dr. H. W. Thompson, F.R.S. and the Council of The Royal Society*)

However, the part of the spectrum in this region is not simply from this fundamental stretching vibration but involves a combination band $(\nu_3+\nu_2-\nu_2)$ as well. The frequencies of some of the lines in the combination band are given in Table 4.9. A further complication is that additional lines due to the $^{15}N^{14}N^{16}O$ 'impurity' of the isotopic species are to be found at:

(cm^{-1})	(cm^{-1})	(cm^{-1})
2168.30	2171.35	2174.41
2169.24	2172.40	2175.38
2170.36	2173.46	

The absorption band $(\nu_2+\nu_3)$, however, lacks these complications and is given in Fig. 4.20 where the resolved rotational structure of the R- and P-branches may be observed. The maximum of the unresolved Q-branch of this perpendicular band may be observed at 2798.15 cm^{-1}.

The analysis of the bands was based on equations (4.76)–(4.78) and the equation:

$$B_{v_1 v_2 v_3} = B_e - \alpha_1(v_1+\tfrac{1}{2}) - \alpha_2(v_2+1) - \alpha_3(v_3+\tfrac{1}{2}) \tag{4.79}$$

(see p. 217) and values of B for the various vibrational levels were obtained

TABLE 4.8

The rotational lines between 2224 and 2185 cm^{-1} in the ν_3 band of N_2O (after Williams and Thompson[20])

J	$R(J)$	$P(J)$	J	$R(J)$	$P(J)$
0	2224.59	—	21	2240.44	2204.73
1	5.48	2222.90	22	2241.12	2203.74
2	6.24	22.03	23	1.77	2.74
3	7.03	21.22	24	2.44	1.76
4	7.82	2220.38	25	3.10	2200.79
5	8.64	19.49	26	3.74	2199.78
6	9.46	18.61	27	4.39	8.75
7	2230.22	17.71	28	5.03	7.73
8	1.01	16.82	29	2245.64	2196.69
9	1.76	15.93	30	6.28	5.66
10	2.53	15.08	31	6.89	4.59
11	3.26	14.14	32	7.52	3.50
12	4.04	13.23	33	8.10	2.45
13	4.77	12.30	34	8.68	1.44
14	5.52	11.40	35	9.29	2190.38
15	6.23	10.44	36	9.84	2189.32
16	6.93	2209.51	37	2250.44	8.18
17	7.64	8.59	38	1.00	7.11
18	8.37	7.63	39	1.59	2186.01
19	9.06	6.66	40	2.10	
20	9.73	5.70	41	2.65	
			42	2253.20	

TABLE 4.9

The rotational lines between 2239 and 2185 cm^{-1} in the $(\nu_3+\nu_2-\nu_2)$ *band of* N_2O (after Williams and Thompson[20])

J	$R(J)$	$P(J)$	J	$R(J)$	$P(J)$
0	—	—	22	26.97	2189.45
1	2211.21		23	27.64	2188.51
2	11.98	2207.80	24	28.31	87.52
3	12.81	6.94	25	28.94	86.52
4	13.56	6.15	26	2229.57	2185.50
5	14.34	5.28	27	30.22	
6	15.16	4.43	28	30.92	
7	15.93	3.53	29	31.15	
8	16.77	2.62	30	32.15	
9	17.56	1.72	31	32.74	
10	18.32	2200.80	32	33.35	
11	19.03	2199.91	33	34.01	
12	19.77	99.02	34	34.62	
13	2220.50	98.11	35	35.18	
14	21.25	97.16	36	35.75	
15	22.00	96.25	37	36.28	
16	22.76	95.32	38	36.87	
17	23.46	94.38	39	37.48	
18	24.18	93.42	40	38.01	
19	24.90	92.43	41	2238.56	
20	25.54	91.44			
21	26.24	90.43			

together with ν_0, $D_{v'}$, $D_{v''}$ and the α-values. The combination plot of $\Delta_2F''(J)/(J+\frac{1}{2})$ against $(J+\frac{1}{2})^2$ for some of the vibration bands of N_2O is given in Fig. 4.21. From this plot $B_{v''}$ and $D_{v''}$ values may be derived. The wave-number of the band origin may be obtained from the wave-numbers of the lines

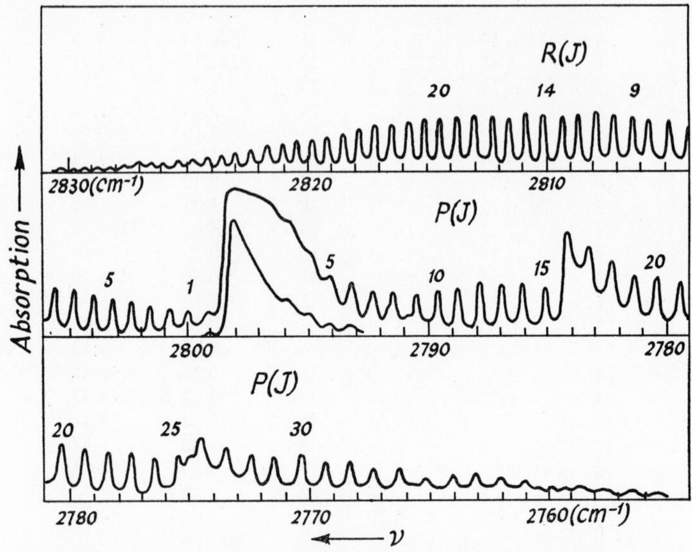

FIG. 4.20 Fine structure of the absorption band $\nu_2+\nu_3$ for N_2O at 2798.15 cm^{-1}. (*After Williams and Thompson.*[20] *Courtesy of Dr. H. W. Thompson, F.R.S. and the Council of The Royal Society*)

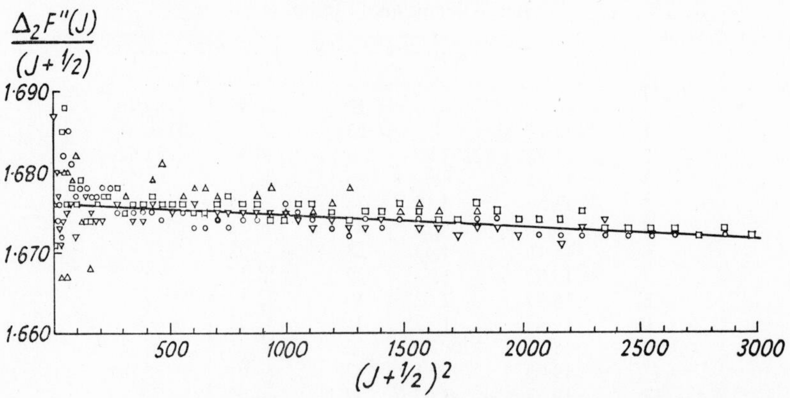

FIG. 4.21 Plot of $\Delta_2F\,(J'')/(J+\frac{1}{2})$ against $(J+\frac{1}{2})^2$ for different vibrational bands of nitrous oxide. ○, ν_3; □, $2\nu_1$; △, $\nu_2+\nu_3$; ▽, $\nu_1+2\nu_2$. (*After Williams and Thompson.*[20] *Courtesy of Dr. H. W. Thompson, F.R.S. and the Council of The Royal Society*)

and the $B_{v'}$, $B_{v''}$, $D_{v'}$, and $D_{v''}$ values by means of equation (4.78.) The method of least squares is employed in fitting the data to this equation. In order that the full extent of such an analysis may be appreciated the results of Williams and Thompson are listed in Table 4.10.

TABLE 4.10

Rotational constants (cm^{-1}) *of* N_2O (after Williams and Thompson[20])

Band	ν_3	$(\nu_3+\nu_2-\nu_2)$	$(\nu_1+2\nu_2)$	$(\nu_1+3\nu_2-\nu_2)$	$2\nu_1$	$(2\nu_1+\nu_2-\nu_2)$	$(\nu_2+\nu_3)$
B_{000}	0.4189_5 $\pm 0.0001_2$	—	0.4189_2 $\pm 0.0001_5$	—	0.4191_1 $\pm 0.0001_7$	—	0.4192 $\pm 0.0001_9$
B_{001}	0.4154_9 $\pm 0.0001_2$	—	—	—	—	—	—
B_{120}	—	—	0.4180_9 $\pm 0.0001_5$	—	—	—	—
B_{200}	—	—	—	—	0.4157_4 $\pm 0.0001_7$	—	—
B_{011}	—	0.4159 ± 0.0002	—	—	—	—	0.4160_2 $\pm 0.0001_9$
B_{010}	—	0.4194 ± 0.0002	—	0.4190 ± 0.0004	—	0.4203 ± 0.0005	—
B_{130}	—	—	—	0.4175 ± 0.0004	—	—	—
B_{210}	—	—	—	—	—	0.4173 0.0005	—
ν_0	2223.75	2209.53	2461.97	2457.50	2563.39	2577.13	2798.30
D_v''	$1.9_3 \pm 0.4 \times 10^{-7}$	—	$2.34 \pm 0.7 \times 10^{-7}$	—	$1.26 \pm 0.6 \times 10^{-7}$	—	$1.85 \pm 0.9 \times 10^{-7}$
D_v'	—	—	$2.94 \pm 0.7 \times 10^{-7}$	—	—	—	—
$\alpha = (B_v'' - B_v')$	0.00345 ± 0.000006	0.00341 $\pm 0.00001_6$	0.00083_1 $\pm 0.0000009_9$	0.00147 ± 0.000004	0.00335_8 $\pm 0.0000009_9$	0.00300 ± 0.00005	0.00319_2 $\pm 0.00001_2$

A weighted mean value for the B value of the lowest vibrational level (i.e. the B_{000} value) was determined to be 0.4190_1, and this agreed very closely with the value determined from the microwave spectrum of nitrous oxide.

Many linear molecules have had their rotation-vibration spectra studied, and recent investigations have been made of the rotational constants of DCN, COS and C_2H_2.

If the rotational fine structure cannot be resolved, an approximate estimate of the moment of inertia I may be made from the spacing of the intensity maxima of the P- or R-branches ($\Delta\nu$) in either the $||$ or $\perp$ bands by use of the equation:

$$\Delta\nu = \frac{1}{\pi c}\sqrt{\frac{kT}{I}}$$

where $\boldsymbol{k}$ is Boltzmann's constant, and T is the absolute temperature.

Symmetric-top molecules

This is the type of molecule where two of the moments of inertia are equal, and the third though finite is not the same as the other two. The two main types of molecules which have been examined have had either a pyramidal structure such as NF_3 and PCl_3 or a tetrahedral one such as $CHCl_3$ and CH_3Cl.

Two quantum numbers are necessary to define the rotational energy of a symmetric-top molecule. The customary J is employed to govern the total angular momentum of the molecule, but in addition another quantum number, K, is required to fix the angular momentum about the symmetry axis.† The possible values of J are 0, 1, 2 . . . whereas K may take the values

$$0,\ \pm 1,\ \pm 2,\ \ldots\ \pm J$$

for each value of J. Thus, the numerical value of K is either equal to or less than J, and there are $(2J+1)$ values of K for each value of J.

The vibrational and rotational energies are normally assumed to be additive, and the vibration a simple harmonic one. The rotation-vibration energy may be expressed by:

$$E_{vr} = \Sigma(v+\tfrac{1}{2})\boldsymbol{h}c\omega + \boldsymbol{h}c[B_vJ(J+1) - D_{vJ}J^2(J+1)^2 + (A_v - B_v)K^2 - D_{vJK}J(J+1)K^2 - D_{vK}K^4] \quad (4.80)$$

where

$$A_v = \boldsymbol{h}/8\pi^2 cI_A \quad \text{and} \quad B_v = \boldsymbol{h}/8\pi^2 cI_B$$

The constants D_{vJ}, D_{vJK}, and D_{vK} take into account the centrifugal stretching and normally result in very small contributions from the terms in which they are concerned.‡ More specifically the D_J term results from the stretching due to end-over-end rotation of the molecule whereas the D_K term results from the distortion caused by rotation about the symmetry axis. The D_{JK} term results from the interaction of these two types of motion.

† The total angular momentum of the molecule is $\sqrt{J(J+1)}\boldsymbol{h}/2\pi$, while the component of the angular momentum along the symmetry axis is $K\boldsymbol{h}/2\pi$.

‡ When it is not necessary to be specific the subscript "v" is frequently omitted.

For a rotation-vibration change the ΔJ and ΔK values depend on whether the vibration undergoing the change is parallel or perpendicular to the symmetry axis.

Symmetric-top molecules can be considered according to the way in which they may be analysed to gain information on moments of inertia and internuclear distance. These are:

(I) An analysis which neglects centrifugal stretching and ignores the difference between the rotational constants in the lower and excited vibrational states.

(II) An analysis which takes into account centrifugal stretching and determines both the $B_{v'}$ and $B_{v''}$ values. In fact, this type of analysis is based on equation (4.80).

(I) *Analysis of symmetric-top molecules neglecting centrifugal stretching and any alteration in the rotational constants*

When D_J, D_{JK} and D_K are each placed equal to zero equation (4.80) becomes:

$$E_{vr} = \Sigma(v+\tfrac{1}{2})hc\omega + hc[BJ(J+1)+(A-B)K^2] \tag{4.81}$$

The type of analysis about to be considered employs equation (4.81) and neglects any change in the rotational constants A and B in the rotation-vibration transition.

The analysis based on these assumptions may be divided into two types, depending on whether the change in dipole moment during the vibration is parallel or perpendicular to the symmetry axis.

Parallel bands. The selection rules are $\Delta J = 0, \pm 1$, and $\Delta K = 0$ where $\Delta J = 0$ is forbidden when $K = 0$. The equations for the P-, R- and Q-branches are obtained as follows.

P-branch. When the values of:

$$K' = K''$$

and

$$J' = J''-1$$

are substituted in equation (4.81) and the fact that:

$$E'_{vr} - E''_{vr} = \Delta E = hc\nu \tag{4.82}$$

is employed, where ν is the wave-number of the particular rotation-vibration transition then:

$$\nu_P = \nu_0 + B(J''-1)(J'') - BJ''(J''+1) + (A-B)(K''^2 - K''^2) \tag{4.83}$$

$$\nu_P = \nu_0 - 2BJ'' \tag{4.84}$$

where ν_0 is the band origin, and $J'' = 1, 2, 3 \ldots$

R-branch. In a similar manner on substituting $K' = K''$ and $J' = J''+1$, then:

$$\nu_R = \nu_0 + 2B(J''+1) \tag{4.85}$$

where $J'' = 0, 1, 2, 3 \ldots$

Q-branch. In this case $K' = K''$ and $J' = J''$
and

$$\nu_Q = \nu_0 \tag{4.86}$$

that is, a single line might be expected.

It should be noted that these *P*-, *Q*-, and *R*-branch equations have the same form as those for a linear molecule, where $B_{v'} = B_{v''}$ and $D = 0$. In practice owing to the rotation-vibration interaction the *Q*-branch is once again a band and not a single line. The separation of the rotational lines in the *P*- and *R*-branches is approximately equal to $\boldsymbol{h}/4\pi^2 cI_B$ where I_B is the moment of inertia about an axis perpendicular to the symmetry axis. There are, of course, two such directions, but for a prolate symmetric-top $I_B = I_C$. Thus, from parallel bands only one moment of inertia may be obtained; to determine I_A it is necessary to study the more complex perpendicular bands.

Perpendicular bands. The selection rules are $\Delta J = 0, \pm 1$ and $\Delta K = \pm 1$, and for each change in *K*, there will be a band with *P*-, *Q*-, and *R*-branches.

The equations for the *P*-, *R*- and *Q*-branches for the case where $\Delta K = +1$ are obtained as follows:

P-branch. When the values of

$$K' = K''+1 \quad \text{and} \quad J' = J''-1$$

are substituted in equation (4.81), using the fact that $E'_{vr} - E''_{vr} = \Delta E_{vr} = \boldsymbol{h}c\nu$ (where ν is the wave-number of the particular rotation-vibration transition) then:

$$\nu_P = \nu_0 + B(J''-1)J'' - BJ''(J''+1) + (A-B)(K''+1)^2 - (A-B)K''^2 \tag{4.87}$$

that is:

$$\nu_P = \nu_0 - 2BJ'' + (A-B)(2K''+1) \ldots \tag{4.88}$$

where ν_0 is the band origin and $J'' = K''+2, K''+3, K''+4. \ldots$

R-branch. In a similar manner on substitution of $K' = K''+1$ and $J' = J''+1$ the equation for lines in the *R*-branch is found to be

$$\nu_R = \nu_0 + 2B(J''+1) + (A-B)(2K''+1) \tag{4.89}$$

where $J'' = K'', K''+1, K''+2. \ldots$

Q-branch. In this case

$$J' = J'' \quad \text{and} \quad K' = K''+1$$

and the wave-numbers of the *Q*-lines are independent of the *J* values; they are given by:

$$\nu_Q = \nu_0 + (A-B)(2K''+1) \tag{4.90}$$

In each of these equations K'' has a fixed value, and the wave-numbers of the lines in a particular *P*- and *R*-branch are obtained from the formula by substituting the appropriate J'' values.

Each value of K'' gives rise to a *P*-, *Q*-, and *R*-branch of a band. The energy level diagram for a prolate symmetric-top molecule is illustrated in Fig. 4.22. A few typical transitions are given for the *R*-branch of the case where $K'' = 0$. The $K' \leftarrow K''$ value $1 \leftarrow 0$ is known as the *first positive subsidiary* and the $2 \leftarrow 1$ is the *second positive subsidiary band.* When $\Delta K = -1$ we have an additional series of *P*-, *Q*- and *R*-branches, called the *negative subsidiary bands.* Thus the $0 \leftarrow 1$ and $1 \leftarrow 2$ would be known as the *first* and *second negative subsidiary bands,* respectively. The equations relating the wave-numbers of the rotation-vibration lines to the quantum numbers J'' and K'' for the negative subsidiary bands may be obtained in the same way as for the positive subsidiary bands. In this case, however, $K' = K''-1$ would have to be substituted.

By inserting two consecutive J'' values in formula (4.88), it follows on subtraction of the resulting equations that the separation of consecutive rotational lines in a *P*-branch is $h/4\pi^2 cI_B$. The same result is obtained for consecutive *R*-branch lines. From equation (4.90) it may be readily shown that the wave-number separation between the *Q*-branches in consecutive subsidiary bands is

$$\Delta\nu = \frac{h}{4\pi^2 c}\left(\frac{1}{I_A} - \frac{1}{I_B}\right) \qquad (4.91)$$

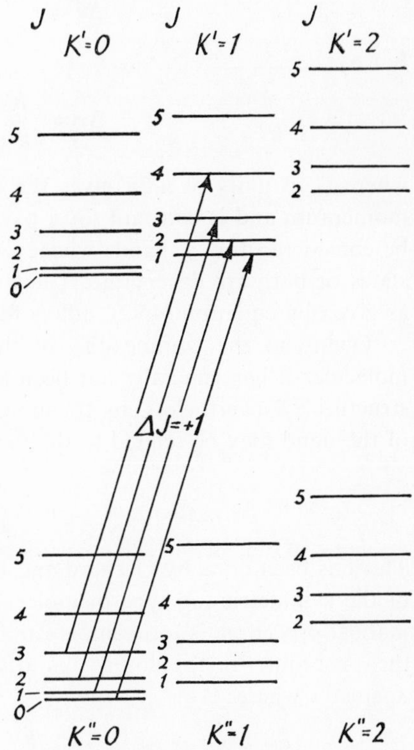

FIG. 4.22 Energy level diagram indicating a few transitions for the *R*-branch of the first positive band of a prolate symmetric-top molecule

Theoretically, then, I_B may be determined from the spacing of the rotational lines in the *P*- and *R*-branches in the parallel bands. From this knowledge of I_B and the measured separation of successive *Q*-branches I_A may be found.

In practice, however, it is not always possible to measure the separation between the *Q*-branches, since the background of the *P*- and *R*-branches may be strong enough to obscure the *Q*-branches unless $I_B \gg I_A$, e.g. in the methyl halides. A further complicating factor is that the spacing between consecutive *Q*-branches in different perpendicular bands is not constant but varies markedly. The effect is particularly noticeable in the perpendicular bands of the methyl halides, where the frequency difference between consecutive *Q*-branches in different bands is very variable. The reason for this variation in the separation of *Q*-branches in different bands is due to a coupling of the rotational and vibrational angular momenta giving rise to a force of interaction, called the *Coriolis force,* in the perpendicular vibration, which in effect is an additional internal vibrational angular momentum. Owing to the interaction of this force the spacing between consecutive Q-branches in perpendicular subsidiary bands is no longer given by:

$$\Delta\nu = \frac{h}{4\pi^2 c}\left(\frac{1}{I_A} - \frac{1}{I_B}\right)$$

but by:

$$\Delta\nu = \frac{h}{4\pi^2 c}\left(\frac{1-\zeta_i}{I_A} - \frac{1}{I_B}\right) \tag{4.92}$$

where ζ_i in units of $h/2\pi$ gives the correction due to the internal angular momentum and is constant for a particular band. This Coriolis force has to be considered for $\perp$ bands whenever either the upper or lower vibrational states or both are degenerate. The spacing between consecutive Q-branches, as given by equation (4.92), differs for each perpendicular band.

Owing to the complexities of the perpendicular bands of polyatomic molecules it has generally not been found possible to resolve the rotational structure.† Nevertheless, by theoretical processes the shape of the envelope of the band may be related to the factor β, where

$$\beta = \frac{I_B}{I_A} - 1, \tag{4.93}$$

This has been done by Gerhard and Dennison[22] for the perpendicular bands of the symmetric-top type of molecule for various values of β. The mathematical procedure is too complex and detailed to be considered here. Briefly, the procedure is to plot a quantity known as the *absorption coefficient* against x where:

$$x = \frac{\nu}{\alpha}\sigma^2, \quad \alpha = \frac{h}{4\pi^2 I_B}, \quad \text{and} \quad \sigma = \frac{h^2}{8\pi^2 I_B kT}$$

This has been done in Fig. 4.23, and the full curved lines represent the total absorption due to the whole of the perpendicular band. The dotted line, however, indicates the absorption due to all the Q-branches of the various subsidiary bands. The values of β are as indicated on the figure; for example in Fig. 4.23(a) $\beta = -\frac{1}{2}$, that is $I_A = 2I_B$, and the molecule is of a disk type, while in (e) $\beta = 4$, that is $I_B = 5I_A$, in which case the molecule approximates to a rod. By comparison of such theoretical contours with the experimentally observed ones it is possible to obtain a qualitative estimate of β and hence the general shape of the molecule. One complication in such deductions, however, can be the effect of any internal angular momentum ($\zeta_i h/2\pi$) since the unresolved contour of a band is dependent on the value of ζ_i.

The spacing between maxima in the contours of bands sometimes leads to an approximate value for one moment of inertia. In fact, Gerhard and

† The first successful resolution and analysis of a fundamental perpendicular band of a symmetric-top molecule was reported in 1954 by Pickworth and Thompson.[21]

Dennison have shown that the spacing $\Delta\nu$ between the successive maxima of the P- and R-branches in a || band is in certain cases given by:

$$\Delta\nu = \left\{\frac{S(\beta)}{\pi c}\sqrt{\frac{kT}{I_B}}\right\} \tag{4.94}$$

where k is the Boltzmann constant, while

$$\beta = (I_B/I_A)-1 \tag{4.95}$$

The empirical formula which Gerhard and Dennison employed relating $S(\beta)$ to β between $-\frac{1}{2}$ and 100 was:†

$$\log_{10} S(\beta) = \frac{0{\cdot}721}{(\beta+4)^{1{\cdot}13}} \tag{4.96}$$

Thus, if β can be estimated, $S(\beta)$ may be calculated: then if $\Delta\nu$ is determined from the separation of the maxima of the P- and R-branches, I_B may be

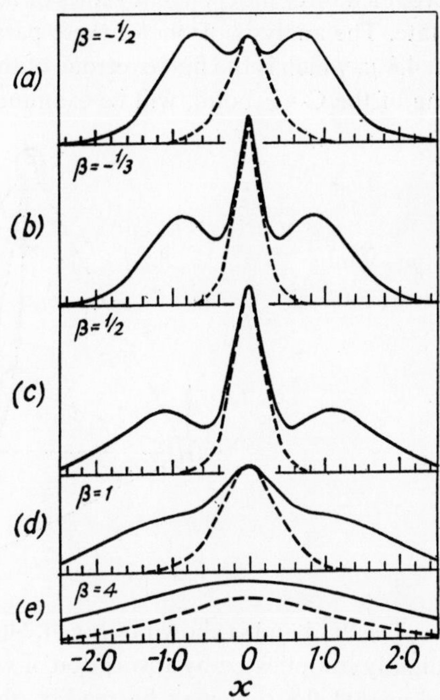

FIG. 4.23 The variation in the contour of the perpendicular band of a symmetric-top molecule in passing from a disk-type molecule where $\beta = -\frac{1}{2}$ to a rod-type molecule where β is large. The full line indicates the total absorption of the whole of the perpendicular band while the broken line indicates the contour of the Q-branches of all the various subsidiary bands. (*After Gerhard and Dennison.*[22] *Courtesy of 'The Physical Review'*)

obtained. If, however, I_B is known from work on parallel bands, then I_B and $\Delta\nu$ may be employed in equation (4.94) to calculate $S(\beta)$; hence, the value of β follows from equation (4.96) and the value of I_A from equation (4.95).

In any case, it is sometimes possible to decide whether the vibration is of the || or ⊥ type from the band contours; e.g. for a symmetric-top, if the band contour can be observed, and it has an intense narrow maximum in the middle of the band, a parallel vibration is involved. However, if a complex structure

† In the case of linear molecules $S(\beta)$ is approximately unity.

containing several maxima is observed, then most probably a perpendicular vibration is responsible. Such information may be most valuable in structural determinations.

(II) *Analysis of a symmetric-top molecule involving* $B_{v'}$, $A_{v'}$, $B_{v''}$ *and* $A_{v''}$ *values*

For simple symmetric-top molecules such as the methyl halides it is possible to resolve the rotational structure of the bands and to determine the values of the rotational constants A and B in both the ground state and excited vibrational states. The procedure is more involved than those already described based on formulae which do not take into account this variation of the rotational constants or the centrifugal stretching. As an example of the procedure employed in the analysis of a simple symmetric-top molecule, the work by Pickworth and Thompson[21] on the rotation-vibration bands of methyl fluoride will be considered. Three parallel bands were examined between 2.5 and 5 μ at a high degree of resolution; the analysis of these provided three independent values of $B_{v''}$, the rotational constant in the ground state. The analysis of one of these parallel bands, in particular, the $2\nu_3$ band at 4.8 μ, which is the first overtone of the vibration associated with the stretching of the C—F bond, will be examined. The vibrational mode of ν_3 is:

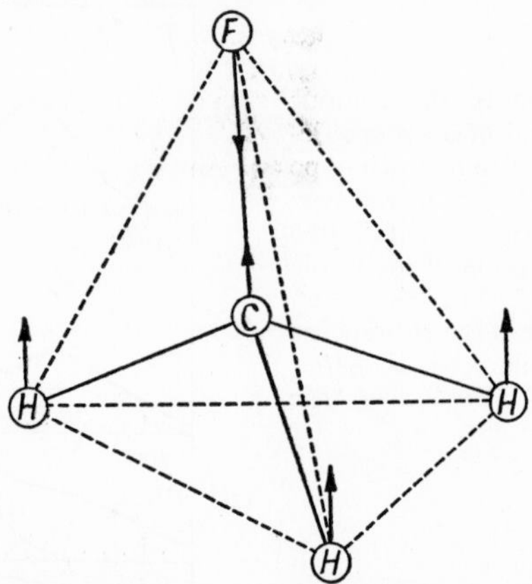

The $2\nu_3$ band is shown in Fig. 4.24(a). Although the rotational structure is slightly complicated by absorption of water vapour the P-, Q-, and R-branches of methyl fluoride may be readily observed, and it will be noted that the Q-branch shows a distinct head. The analysis was based on the rotational energy levels of the molecule, given by equation

$$F(J,K) = BJ(J+1)-D_J J^2(J+1)^2+(A-B)K^2-D_{JK}J(J+1)K^2-D_K K^4 \tag{4.97}$$

where the constants D_J, D_{JK}, and D_K take into account the centrifugal stretching (see p. 112) and $F(J, K) = Er/hc$ and A, B, J, and K are as already defined. The procedure is similar to that outlined on p. 106 for a linear molecule in that combination differences are taken for the P- and R-lines.

For example for the combination difference:

$$R(J)-P(J) = \Delta_2F'(J,K)$$

on substitution from equation (4.97) we get:

$$\Delta_2F'(J,K) = [(4B_{v'}-4D_{v'JK}K^2)-6D_{v'J}](J+\tfrac{1}{2})-8D_{v'J}(J+\tfrac{1}{2})^3 \quad (4.98)$$

while for the combination difference

$$R(J-1)-P(J+1) = \Delta_2F''(J,K)$$

we have

$$\Delta_2F''(J,K) = [(4B_{v''}-4D_{v''JK}K^2)-6D_{v''J}](J+\tfrac{1}{2})-8D_{v''J}(J+\tfrac{1}{2})^3 \quad (4.99)$$

It follows from equation (4.98) and (4.99) that, if the equation is satisfactory for the analysis of the rotational lines, a plot of $\Delta_2F(J,K)/(J+\frac{1}{2})$ against

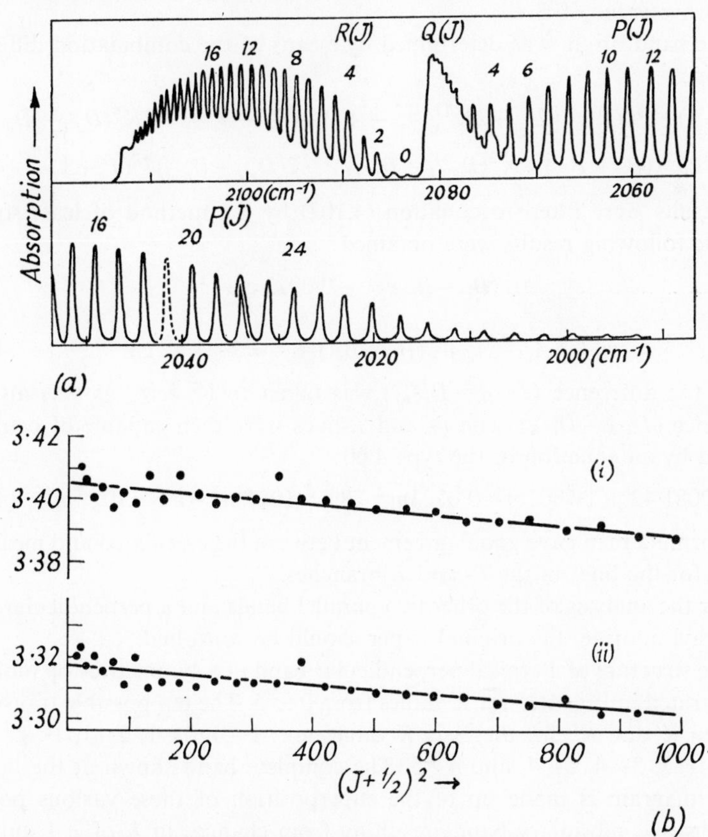

FIG. 4.24. (*a*) The $2\nu_3$ band at 2080 cm^{-1} of CH_3F. (*b*) Plots of $\Delta_2F(J,K)/(J+\frac{1}{2})$ against $(J+\frac{1}{2})^2$ giving constants for (i) the lower and (ii) the upper levels. (*After Pickworth and Thompson.*[21] *Courtesy of Dr. H. W. Thompson, F.R.S. and the Council of The Royal Society*)

$(J+\frac{1}{2})^2$ should give a straight line. This plot was carried out for both the lower and the upper states and is shown in Fig. 4.24(*b*). From these straight lines and equations (4.98) and (4.99) the rotational constants for both the lower and upper vibrational states may be obtained. In fact, the data were fitted to the combination relationships by the method of least squares and the following values resulted:

$$(B_{v''}-D_{v''JK}K^2) = 0{\cdot}8512 \pm 0{\cdot}0002 \text{ cm}^{-1} \quad (4.100)$$

$$(B_{v'}-D_{v'JK}K^2) = 0{\cdot}8289 \pm 0{\cdot}0002 \text{ cm}^{-1} \quad (4.101)$$

$$D_{v''J} = 2{\cdot}2_8 \times 10^{-6} \text{ cm}^{-1} \quad \text{and} \quad D_{v'J} = 2{\cdot}0_2 \times 10^{-6} \text{ cm}^{-1}$$

The constant D_{vJK} could only be obtained from the infra-red if the K splitting had been resolved. As it was not resolved the value of 1.5×10^{-5} cm^{-1} was taken for $D_{v''JK}$ from the microwave spectrum results on methyl fluoride, and equation (4.100) then gave a value of $B_{v''}$ which agreed closely with the microwave value of $B_{v''}$.

The band origin was determined by means of the combination difference relation:

$$\{R(J-1)+P(J)\} = [2\nu_0+2K^2\{(A_{v'}-A_{v''})-(B_{v'}-B_{v''})\}-2K^4(D_{v'K}-D_{v''K})]+ 2J^2\{(B_{v'}-B_{v''})-K^2(D_{v'JK}-D_{v''JK})\}-2(D_{v'J}-D_{v''J})J^2(J^2+1) \quad (4.102)$$

The results were fitted to equation (4.102) by the method of least squares and the following results were obtained:

$$(B_{v'}-B_{v''}) = -0{\cdot}0223 \text{ cm}^{-1}$$

and

$$\nu_0+\{(A_{v'}-A_{v''})-(B_{v'}-B_{v''})\}K^2 = 2081{\cdot}42 \text{ cm}^{-1} \quad (4.103)$$

where the difference $(D_{v'JK}-D_{v''JK})$ was taken to be zero, as was also the difference $(D_{v'K}-D_{v''K})$. The P- and R-lines were then capable of being expressed by an equation of the type 4.60:

$$\nu = 2081{\cdot}42 + 1{\cdot}6801m - 0{\cdot}0223m^2 - 8{\cdot}6 \times 10^{-6}m^3 + 2{\cdot}6 \times 10^{-7}m^4 \quad (4.104)$$

This formula then gave good agreement between the calculated and measured values for the lines in the P- and R-branches.

For the analysis of the other two parallel bands and a perpendicular band of methyl fluoride, the original paper should be consulted.

The structure of a typical perpendicular band of a symmetric-top molecule is illustrated in Fig. 4.25 for K values from 0 to 5. The ten possible transitions between K' and K'' for these six K values are: 1←0, 0←1, 2←1, 1←2, 3←2, 2←3, 4←3, 3←4, 5←4, and 4←5. The complete band shown at the bottom of the diagram is made up of the superposition of these various positive and negative subsidiary bands resulting from changes in K of ± 1 unit and changes in J of 0, ± 1 unit. Fig. 4.25 was constructed by Herzberg[17] and is based on the assumptions that $A_{v'} = 5.18$, $A_{v''} = 5.25$, $B_{v'} = 0.84$, and $B_{v''} = 0.85$ cm^{-1}. It serves to illustrate the complexity of a perpendicular band and the inadequacies of taking the rotational constants as being the same in the upper and lower vibrational states. The relative intensities of the rotation-vibration lines are indicated by the relative heights of the lines and were calculated for a temperature of 144°K.

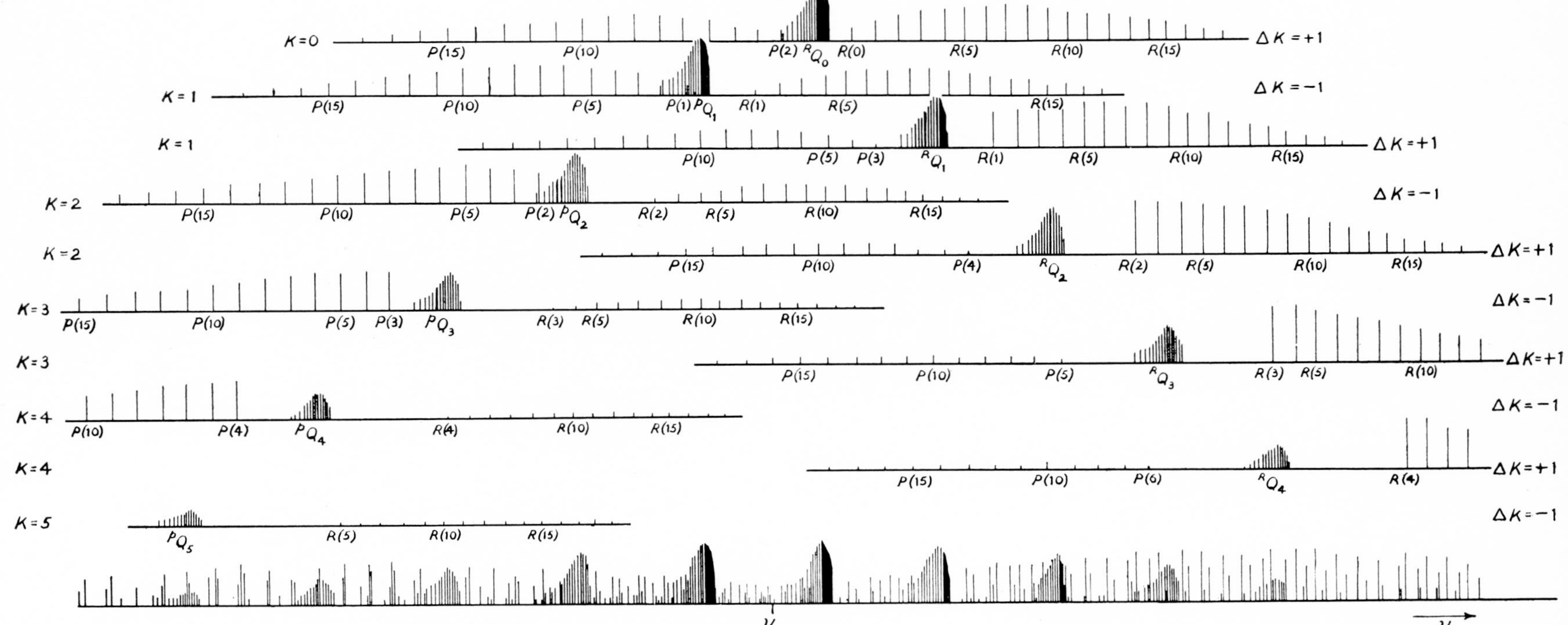

FIG. 4.25 Sub-bands of a perpendicular band, and complete perpendicular band of a symmetric-top molecule. (*From G. Herzberg*,[17] 'Infra-red and Raman Spectra of Polyatomic Molecules', *Vol.* 2, *2nd ed.*, 1945, *D. Van Nostrand Co., Princeton, N.J.*)

[*To face page* 120

The relevant J and K data for the first three subsidiary bands are given in Table 4.11 together with information about which lines are missing from each of these subsidiary bands.

TABLE 4.11

Data on the sub-bands of a symmetric-top molecule for a perpendicular band

Subsidiary bands	Changes in J	K values	J values	Lines missing
First positive	$P\ \Delta J-1$ $Q\ \Delta J\ 0$ $R\ \Delta J+1$	$\Delta K=1$ $K'=1$ $K''=0$	$J'\geqslant 1$ $J''\geqslant 0$	$P(1)$
First negative	$P\ \Delta J-1$ $Q\ \Delta J\ 0$ $R\ \Delta J+1$	$\Delta K=-1$ $K'=0$ $K''=1$	$J'\geqslant 0$ $J''\geqslant 1$	 $R(0)$
Second positive	$P\ \Delta J-1$ $Q\ \Delta J\ 0$ $R\ \Delta J+1$	$\Delta K=1$ $K'=2$ $K''=1$	$J'\geqslant 2$ $J''\geqslant 1$	$R(0)$ $P(1)\ P(2)$
Second negative	$P\ \Delta J-1$ $Q\ \Delta J\ 0$ $R\ \Delta J+1$	$\Delta K=-1$ $K'=1$ $K''=2$	$J'\geqslant 1$ $J''\geqslant 2$	$R(0)\ R(1)$ $P(1)$
Third positive	$P\ \Delta J-1$ $Q\ \Delta J\ 0$ $R\ \Delta J+1$	$\Delta K=1$ $K'=3$ $K''=2$	$J'\geqslant 3$ $J''\geqslant 2$	$R(0)\ R(1)$ $P(1)\ P(2)\ P(3)$
Third negative	$P\ \Delta J-1$ $Q\ \Delta J\ 0$ $R\ \Delta J+1$	$\Delta K=-1$ $K'=2$ $K''=3$	$J'\geqslant 2$ $J''\geqslant 3$	$R(0)\ R(1)\ R(2)$ $P(1)\ P(2)$

Types of symmetric-top molecules analysed

The moments of inertia of a number of symmetric-top molecules have been determined by the infra-red rotation-vibration technique and include NH_3, BF_3, C_2H_6, CD_3F, ClO_3F, $CH_3C\equiv CCH_3$, and CH_3X, where X = D, F, Cl, Br, and I. Only two different moments of inertia are obtained for these molecules, and it is not always possible to determine all the internuclear distances and bond angles without assuming data from other molecules or resorting to isotopes. For example:

(i) If BF_3 is assumed to be planar and symmetrical, the B—F internuclear distance is readily calculated.

(ii) In the methyl halides, if the C—H internuclear distance is assumed to be the same as in CH_4, then the C—X internuclear distance and the angles can be evaluated.

Spherical-top molecules

Where all the three principal moments of inertia are equal the molecule is described as spherical-top. Methane is a typical example of a tetrahedral spherical-top molecule, where the theoretical number of fundamental vibrational modes is $(3\times5-6)$, that is nine modes. However, only four different vibrational modes may be detected by both the infra-red and Raman methods together and these are illustrated in Fig. 4.26. The ν_2 mode is doubly degenerate, while the ν_3 and ν_4 modes are triply degenerate. Thus, the theoretical value of nine fundamental vibrational modes may be accounted for.

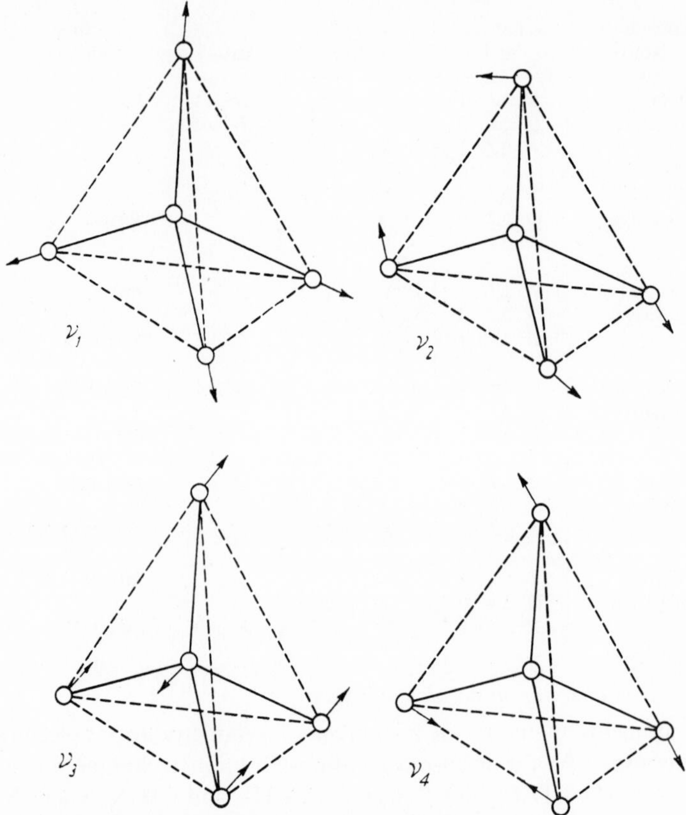

FIG. 4.26 Normal vibrations of a tetrahedral spherical-top molecule

Of the four detectable vibrational modes only the ν_3 and ν_4 are active in the infra-red region. In fact, only those vibrations which are anti-symmetric with respect to the centre of symmetry of the molecule will be active in the infra-red.

Disregarding any form of rotation-vibration interaction the equation governing the rotation-vibration energy is identical with the equation for a linear molecule (equation 4.68). The selection rule is:

$$\Delta J = 0, \ \pm 1 \qquad (4.105)$$

The equations for the wave-numbers of the lines constituting the *P*- and *R*-branches are, therefore, the same as for linear molecules, where the separations of the lines should be approximately given by $\boldsymbol{h}/4\pi^2cI$ in both the

P- and *R*-branches, but in practice this is not found to hold exactly owing to strong Coriolis interaction; this type of interaction is mentioned under symmetric-top molecules. The Coriolis coupling between rotation and vibration occurs in the upper degenerate (triplet) vibrational state but differs for each excited vibrational state. The derived formulae for the *P*- and *R*-branches take this coupling into account by means of the Coriolis coupling constant ζ_i. The *P* and *R* may be represented in the form of one series by the formula:

$$\nu = \nu_0 + (B_{v'} + B_{v''} - 2B_{v'}\zeta_i)m + (B_{v'} - B_{v''})m^2 \qquad (4.106)$$

where $m = -J$ for the *P*-branch and $m = J+1$ for the *R*-branch and the $m = 0$ line is absent. The value of ζ_i differs with each band. The fine structure of the fundamental ν_3 band of CH_4 at 3.31 μ is given in Fig. 4.27. The numbers

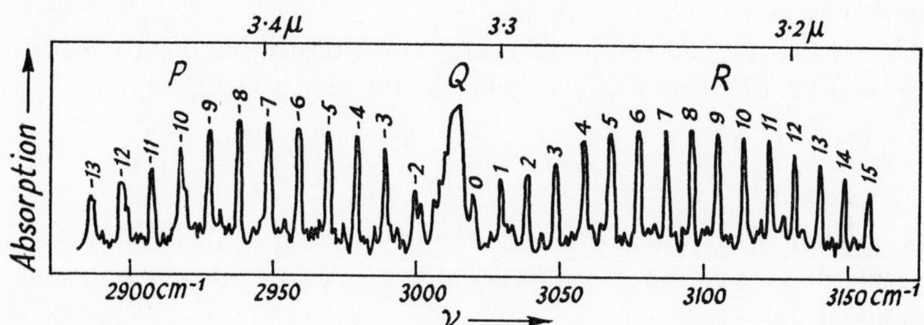

FIG. 4.27 Fine structure of the ν_3 fundamental band of CH_4 at 3.31 μ. (*After Nielsen and Nielsen.*[23] *Courtesy of* '*The Physical Review*')

written at the top of the lines are *m* values. For the ν_3 band of CH_4, $B_{v'}$ is approximately equal to $B_{v''}$. The separation of successive lines is almost constant, and it follows from formula (4.106) that this is $2B_{v''}(1-\zeta_i)$. Since the value of ζ_i is dependent on the band, the spacing of the rotational lines varies, even though $B_{v'}$ is approximately equal to $B_{v''}$. The moment of inertia cannot be derived from one band alone, since both the values of $B_{v''}$ and ζ_i are unknown. It is possible, though, to determine the moment of inertia if the spacing of the rotational lines in both the fundamental infra-red active bands is known. This becomes feasible owing to rules which may be derived to relate the two ζ_i values. For example, in the case of CH_4, where the two infra-red active fundamental frequencies are ν_3 and ν_4, ζ_3 is related to ζ_4 by the equation:

$$\zeta_3 = \tfrac{1}{2} - \zeta_4 \qquad (4.107)$$

Thus, the spacing of the ν_3 band is

$$2B(1-\zeta_3) \quad \text{that is} \quad 2B(1-\tfrac{1}{2}+\zeta_4)$$

while that of the ν_4 band is:

$$2B(1-\zeta_4)$$

Thus, the sum of the spacings is $3B$. Hence, B, I_B and, therefore, the internuclear carbon–hydrogen distance may be determined.

The major obstacle in the analysis of spherical-top molecules by the infra-red technique is the resolution of the rotational structure of the bands.

Internuclear distances have been obtained for the following molecules: CH_4, CD_4, SiH_4, and GeH_4. For the analytical procedure a paper by Boyd, Thompson and Williams[24] should be consulted. The authors describe the analysis of the rotation-vibration bands of CH_4 and $^{13}CH_4$ in the region of 3 μ. A very complex system of overlapping vibration bands was revealed, and the rotational fine structure of these bands was partially analysed. The procedure, however, is too complex to be considered here.

Asymmetric-top molecules

Water is an example of this class, in which all three moments of inertia are finite and unequal. For such molecules there is no simple overall relation for the rotational energy, although this does not impose any serious limitations on the possibility of analysis.

One of the simplest rotational energy equations is that due to Wang, and if no rotation-vibration interaction occurs for such a molecule, then:

$$E_{vr} = E_v + \frac{h^2}{16\pi^2}\left\{\frac{1}{I_B}+\frac{1}{I_C}\right\}J(J+1)+\left\{\frac{h^2}{8\pi^2 I_A}-\frac{h^2}{16\pi^2}\left(\frac{1}{I_B}+\frac{1}{I_C}\right)\right\}W_\tau \tag{4.108}$$

This equation applies to asymmetric-top molecules provided that it is a rigid molecule, and the considered vibrational state does not interact with a nearby vibrational state.

The energy levels of such molecules are dependent on the total angular momentum quantum number J, and asssociated with each J value are $(2J+1)$ different energy levels. These energy levels cannot be interpreted in terms of a quantum number which has physical significance, so an index τ is employed to enable the $(2J+1)$ values to be arranged in the order of their magnitudes.

The selection rule governing changes in J is simply $\Delta J = 0, \pm 1$, but the selection rule for the index τ, according to Dennison,[25a,25b] depends on whether the electric moment of the molecule changes along: (*a*) the greatest axis of inertia, (*b*) the least axis of inertia, (*c*) the other axis of inertia.

The number of allowed transitions is very large and, in fact, the number of rotational lines in a vibrational band of an asymmetric-top molecule is considerable. Even if the rotational lines can be experimentally resolved, the procedure seems very complex, and at the present time the moments of inertia of only a few asymmetric-top molecules have been determined by the infra-red rotation-vibration approach.†

The most complete analysis of a strongly asymmetric-top molecule has been performed on the water molecule; this has been fully analysed for its three moments of inertia in the lowest vibrational level and also in the equilibrium position, and the corresponding O—H internuclear distance and the ∠HOH angle have been calculated. Hydrogen sulphide has been analysed for the three moments of inertia in the lower vibrational state; the internuclear distance H—S and the angle ∠HSH in this state were found

† This is to be contrasted with the microwave technique, where already an appreciable number of asymmetric-top molecules has been analysed.

to be 1.334 Å and 92°16′, respectively. Other studies of the rotation-vibration spectra of asymmetric-top molecules include D_2O, HDO, and H_2Te.†

The most suitable molecules for examination are those in which two moments of inertia are nearly equal and the molecule approximates to a symmetric-top. The procedure used in the analysis of symmetric-top molecules has to be modified. The three moments of inertia of the following molecules have been determined: C_2H_4, C_2D_4, CH_2O, CHDO and HCO_2H. In the case of formaldehyde the three moments of inertia in the ground state are 2.977×10^{-40}, 21.65×10^{-40} and 24.62×10^{-40} g-cm^2, where the similarity of the latter two values considerably simplifies the analysis. If the carbon-hydrogen distance is assumed to be the same as that found in ethylene, then the ground state values of the C—O distance and the angle ∠HCH are 1.225 Å and 123°26′, respectively.

It is not possible to evaluate the internuclear distances and bond angles of the C_2H_4 molecule solely from its determined moments of inertia, and either C_2D_4 has also to be studied or a value for one angle or an internuclear distance has to be assumed. One determination employed a C—H internuclear distance literature value and measured two bands in the region of 1 μ, where one band is essentially of the parallel type, and the other a perpendicular type band. From the three moments of inertia, and an assumed C—H distance of 1.085 Å, the C=C distance was found to be 1.331 Å and the angle ∠HCH 118°. Usually the infra-red bands of asymmetric-top molecules remain unresolved. However, useful vibrational analysis information may be gained from studying the band contours providing, of course, the dispersion is sufficient to bring these out (cf. symmetric-top molecules). For example, in the case of a planar molecule, from a study of the band contours it is sometimes possible to distinguish between vibrations perpendicular to the plane and those taking place in the plane of the molecule.

This section on simple molecules examined by the infra-red technique is only a brief introduction to the study, and many complicating factors have been neglected or only briefly mentioned. For a full treatment Herzberg[17] should be consulted.

Applications of infra-red spectroscopy

Much of infra-red work depends on associating a particular frequency with a characteristic group or structural unit and noting also the maximum intensities of the corresponding absorption band. These points lead into the first topic of qualitative analysis and structural problems, and then quantitative analysis. In order that some insight may be gained into these basic features the matter has to be studied in fair detail, although the description should be considered only as an introduction to other works (e.g. Bellamy[26] and West[27]).

† These are all planar molecules and for such $I_A + I_B = I_C$ would be anticipated from moment of inertia considerations. In practice $(I_A + I_B) - I_C \neq 0$ but shows a linear dependence on the value of the vibrational quantum number.

Vibrational frequencies and qualitative analysis

For the infra-red region when solids, liquids, and large molecules are examined only the peaks of the bands at particular frequencies are recorded. In the reference tables the intensity at the point of maximum absorption is noted for a particular concentration, and the observed peak frequency is also recorded. The absorption intensity of the band is described in terms of the symbols s, strong, m, medium, w, weak and v, variable. The procedure is to ignore the rotational energy changes which accompany the vibrational energy change and to relate absorption peaks to vibrational frequencies. The values of the observed vibrational frequencies depend on the molecular environment whether it is (*a*) inside the molecule or (*b*) outside. Thus, in case (*b*) the vibrational frequency is partly dependent on whether the molecule is studied in the solid, liquid or gaseous phase. Case (*a*) will now be considered with respect to the keto group.

In the molecule X, Y >CO the C→—←O stretching frequency depends on the substituents X and Y. In simple saturated aliphatic ketones the carbonyl absorption frequency lies within the range 1720 to 1740 cm^{-1}. However, when an aliphatic C=C is conjugated with the C=O group, the frequency range for simple ketones is 1685 to 1665 cm^{-1}. Table 4.12 illustrates the effect of X and Y on the frequency. In Table 4.12 the effect of conjugation on the keto vibration frequency may be observed in *B*, *C*, and *D*, while the effect of chelation is illustrated in *F*.

TABLE 4.12

Characteristic frequencies of ketonic carbonyl vibrations in dilute solution

Ketone		Frequency (cm^{-1})
A. Saturated straight chain ketones	—CH_2—CO—CH_2—	1740–1720
B. α, β-unsaturated ketones	—CH=CH—CO—	1685–1665
C. Aryl ketones	C_6H_5—CO—	1700–1680
D. Diaryl ketones	C_6H_5—CO—C_6H_5	1670–1660
E. α-diketones	—CO—CO—	1730–1710
F. β-diketones	—CO—CH_2—CO—	1640–1540

As will be readily observed the carbonyl frequency varies with the nature of the substituent and therefore, to interpret any absorption frequencies in this range, it is desirable to have all the data for the different types of X, Y >C=O. Thus, all the empirical data for these compounds relating frequency to the particular type of structural unit absorbing must be available. In practice correlation charts summarising this information can be used. In Table 4.13 the frequency range of some characteristic groupings is listed.

SYM.

However, considerable experience is required in the application of such charts and in the case of the ketonic carbonyl vibration, if the frequency range of the carbonyl were quoted to cover all types of ketones, the range would be too great to be useful. For example, the frequencies 1740–1540 cm^{-1} of the quoted ketonic values would include frequencies of the allenes and amines. If, however, a particular frequency, say 1690 cm^{-1}, was obtained, then the presence of an aryl ketone would be indicated. Further confirmatory evidence might be sought; for instance, the intensity of this one band could be compared with that obtained from a similar strength solution of an aryl ketone, and the fact that aryl ketones have another absorption band at 1210 to 1325 cm^{-1} could be used. Where overlapping between the frequency ranges occurs, e.g. in saturated straight chain ketones and α-diketones, then the classification of its type may sometimes be made by intensity studies.

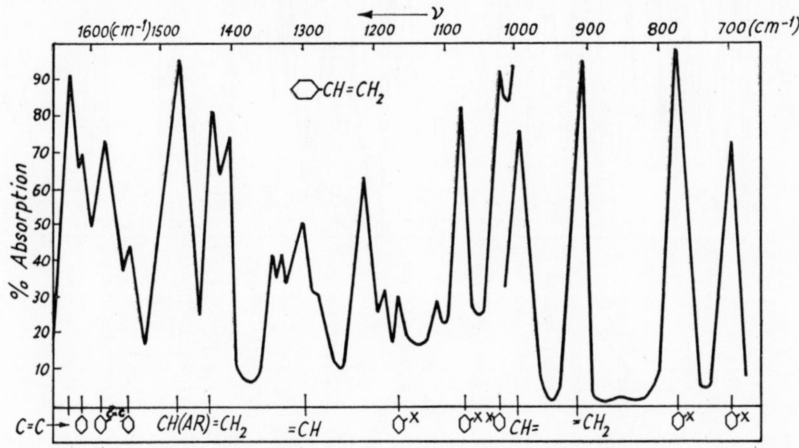

FIG. 4.28 Infra-red spectrogram of styrene. (*After Bellamy.*[26] *Courtesy of Messrs. Methuen and Co. Ltd.*)

To illustrate how the infra-red absorption spectrum may be used to identify the groups within the molecule styrene will be considered. Its spectrogram is reproduced in Fig. 4.28. The aromatic ring is recognised by the presence of ring carbon–carbon vibrational frequencies in the 1600–1500 cm^{-1} region, as these absorption bands are little affected by substitution. The fact that a mono-substituent is present is indicated by the strong absorption bands at approximately 770 to 700 cm^{-1}, while the band at approximately 1630 cm^{-1} suggests the C=C aliphatic linkage. From this type of approach the analysis may be made; the other frequencies identifiable in terms of molecular vibrations are indicated in Fig. 4.28. Absorption in the region 2000 to 1660 cm^{-1} is particularly characteristic for substituted benzene compounds and usually indicates the number of ring substituents. Emphasis is placed on the relative intensities and the number of bands in deciding the position of the substituent. For example, mono-substituted benzene materials usually give four bands of gradually diminishing intensity towards the longer wavelength region, and although the overall appearance of these bands alters with the type of mono-substituent varying both in position and relative intensities, the pattern differs so much from the other types obtained by di-, tri- and tetra-substitutions that it may be readily identified. The 2000–1650 cm^{-1} region patterns of di-, tri-, tetra- and hexa-substituted benzene compounds are given in Fig. 4.29. Confirmation of the position of the benzene substituents may be obtained by a similar type of study of the 1250 to 1000 cm^{-1} region or even the 1000 to 650 cm^{-1} region.

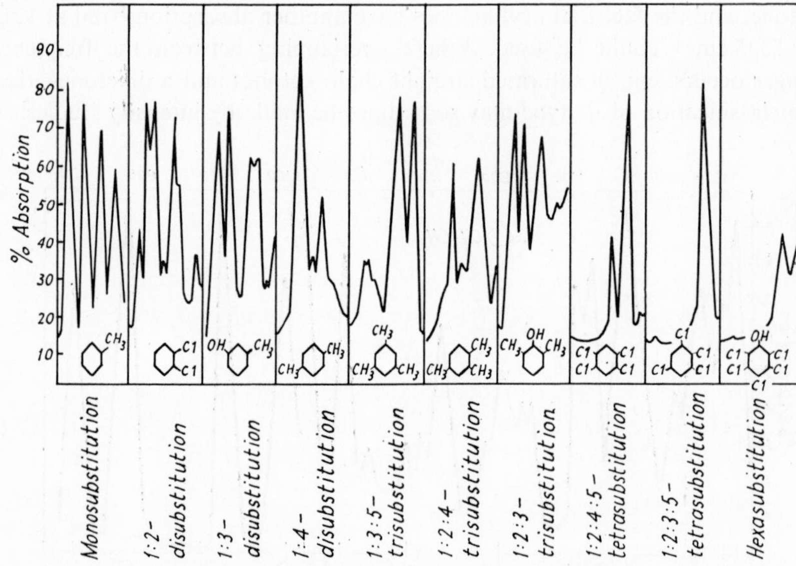

FIG. 4.29 Aromatic substitution patterns in the region 2000 to 1650 cm^{-1}. (*After Bellamy.*[26] *Courtesy of Messrs. Methuen and Co. Ltd.*)

Infra-red studies on the structure of a synthetic rubber

Thompson[29] made infra-red measurements on the synthetic rubber, Buna 85. It was shown that the strong absorption bands occurred between about 900 to 1000 cm^{-1} which could be identified from previous work on vinyl compounds. The vinyl compounds had the frequencies given in Table 4.14.

TABLE 4.14

C=C *vibrational frequencies (in cm^{-1} units) of vinyl compounds*

(1)	(2)	(3)
$(R_1)(R_2)C{=}CH_2$	$R_1HC{=}CH_2$	$R_1HC{=}CHR_2$
890 cm^{-1}	909 cm^{-1} 990 cm^{-1}	965 cm^{-1}

It will be appreciated from Fig. 4.30 that the spectrum for Buna 85, in conjunction with the frequencies in Table 4.14, shows the presence of the types (2) and (3), and the absence of (1). From this it may be concluded that polymerisation has proceeded by two routes:

(*a*) 1: 4-addition giving

$$—CH_2—CH{=}CH—CH_2—CH_2—CH{=}CH—CH_2—\cdot$$

(*b*) 1: 2 addition giving $—CH_2—CH—CH_2—CH—\cdot$

```
                              |           |
                              CH          CH
                              ||          ||
                              CH2         CH2
```

Identification of the degradation products of strychnine

The infra-red analysis of the degradation products of strychnine assisted in the formulation of the structure of the alkaloid and was accomplished with a minute amount of material. When the spectrogram of the products

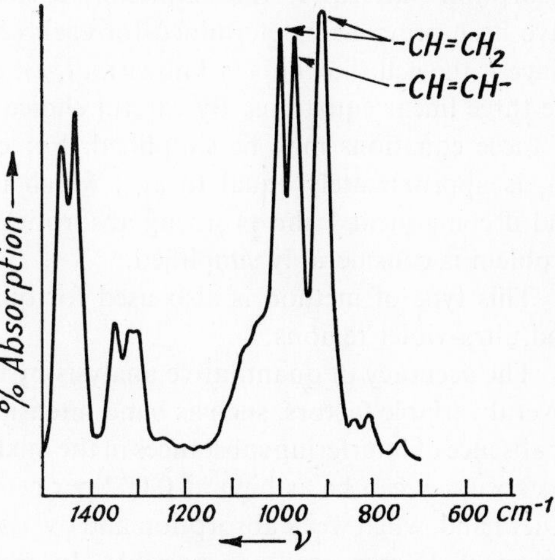

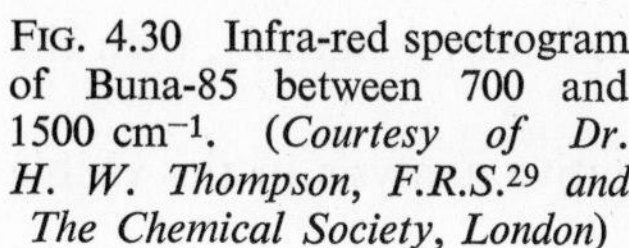

FIG. 4.30 Infra-red spectrogram of Buna-85 between 700 and 1500 cm^{-1}. (*Courtesy of Dr. H. W. Thompson, F.R.S.*[29] *and The Chemical Society, London*)

to be identified was compared with the spectrograms of the feasible carbazoles it seemed, from the various peaks and their intensities, that the mixture consisted mainly of carbazole plus a small amount of 3-methyl carbazole. This information was of great value in helping to elucidate the structure of the alkaloid. The probable absence of 1-, 2- and 4-methyl carbazoles was shown by the lack of bands at 790, 813 and 782 cm^{-1}, respectively. The infra-red approach is often most useful in indicating the probable absence of certain compounds.

Quantitative infra-red analysis

The quantitative studies in the infra-red region are based on the *Beer-Lambert law*: $\log_{10} I_0/I = \varepsilon cl = D$, where D is the optical density, I_0 is the intensity of incident light of wavelength λ, I is the intensity of the light after passing through the absorption cell, c is the concentration of the absorbing material (g-moles/l.), l is the thickness of the absorption cell (cm), and ε is the extinction coefficient. For a particular absorption band a calibration curve is constructed of $\log_{10} I_0/I$ against c for a number of solutions of known concentration; this curve is then used for estimating the concentration of an unknown solution.† A two- or three-component mixture could be analysed in favourable cases, and the procedure for a three-component mixture is outlined below. If the optical densities of the three components are D_1, D_2, and D_3, then at the wavelength λ_1, where for example $\varepsilon_{1\lambda_1}$ is the extinction coefficient of component 1 at wavelength λ_1:

$$D_{\lambda_1} = D_{1\lambda_1}+D_{2\lambda_1}+D_{3\lambda_1} = [\varepsilon_{1\lambda_1}c_1+\varepsilon_{2\lambda_1}c_2+\varepsilon_{3\lambda_1}c_3]l \qquad (4.109)$$

and similarly for absorption at wavelengths λ_2 and λ_3:

$$D_{\lambda_2} = D_{1\lambda_2}+D_{2\lambda_2}+D_{3\lambda_2} = [\varepsilon_{1\lambda_2}c_1+\varepsilon_{2\lambda_2}c_2+\varepsilon_{3\lambda_2}c_3]l \qquad (4.110)$$

$$D_{\lambda_3} = D_{1\lambda_3}+D_{2\lambda_3}+D_{3\lambda_3} = [\varepsilon_{1\lambda_3}c_1+\varepsilon_{2\lambda_3}c_2+\varepsilon_{3\lambda_3}c_3]l \qquad (4.111)$$

where D_{λ_1}, D_{λ_2}, and D_{λ_3} are determined directly from the experimental absorption pattern. If the extinction coefficients at the given wavelength have been previously determined for each of the components in the mixture (since l, the cell thickness is known), c_1, c_2, and c_3 may be determined from the three linear equations. By careful choice of the wavelengths the solution of these equations may be simplified. For example, if λ_1 is chosen so that $\varepsilon_{2\lambda_1}$ is approximately equal to $\varepsilon_{3\lambda_1}$, which is approximately equal to zero, and if component 1 shows strong absorption at this wavelength λ_1, then the problem is considerably simplified.

This type of method is also used for quantitative analysis in the visible and ultra-violet regions.

The accuracy of quantitative analysis by the infra-red method depends on several variable factors, such as band intensities (see p. 136), and the presence or absence of interfering substances in the mixture. In favourable circumstances the accuracy can be as high as 0.002 per cent of the amount present. On the other hand, when weak absorption and overlapping bands are being employed errors of 15 per cent are possible. In mixtures of absorbing substances detection by infra-red methods of 0.1 per cent of a particular component is usually quite difficult. The infra-red method may be an extremely powerful one for quantitative analysis especially when used for problems for which chemical analysis would prove very difficult or even impossible, e.g. in the estimation of one isomer in the presence of many others.

The following example illustrates the use of the infra-red method to solve a chemical problem. Confirmation of the products of mononitration of β-nitronaphthalene was needed and the relative abundance in which they occurred was unknown. Chemical methods had failed to confirm the dinitro-naphthalenes which had earlier been reported as products of this reaction.

† Direct proportionality exists between c and $\log I_0/I$, and this is known as *Beer's law*; deviations from this law sometimes occur. The law is only strictly accurate for monochromatic radiation, whereas the exit beam from a spectrophotometer always has a range of wavelengths. The range of wavelengths depends on: (i) the slit width; (ii) the dispersion of the spectrophotometer; (iii) its resolving power. In addition, the solution must not be too concentrated or exhibit strong molecular interaction; if association or dissociation occur then wide deviations from Beer's law may take place.

Comparison of the infra-red spectrum of the crude nitration mixture with those of pure dinitronaphthalenes revealed that the product consisted of a mixture of 1, 6- and 1, 7-dinitronaphthalene. After trials with various solvents and examination of the spectrum in the 2.5 to 15 μ range, a solution of each

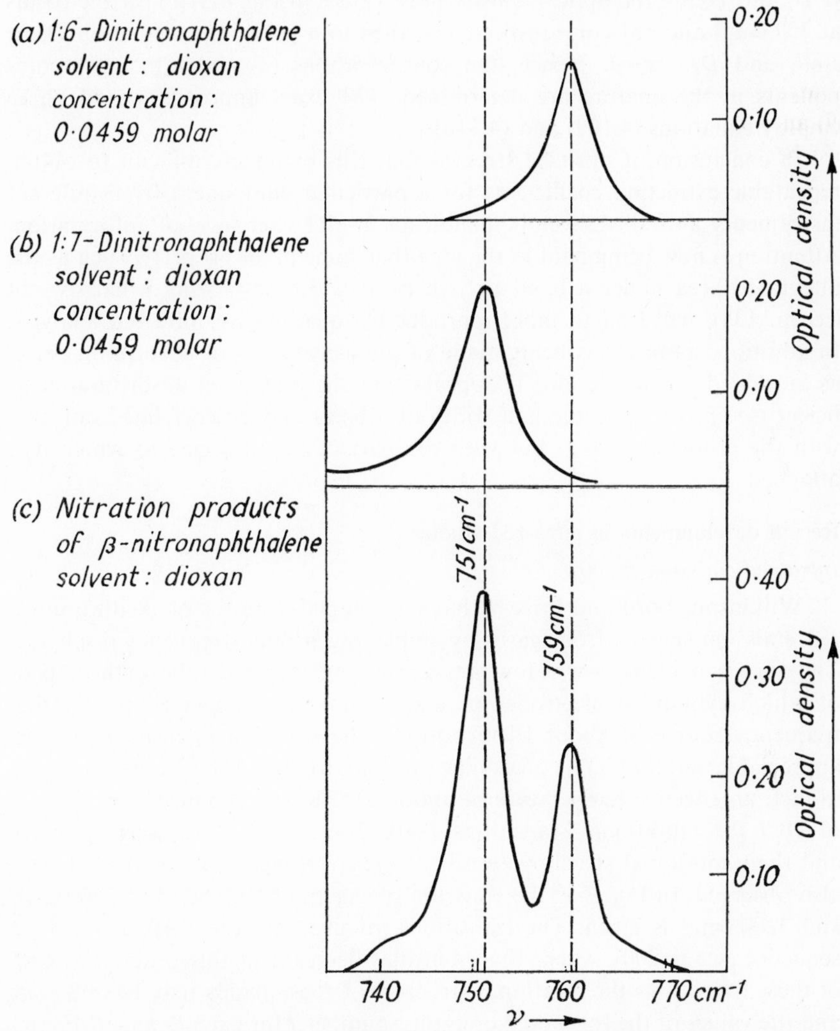

FIG. 4.31 Qualitative and quantitative estimation of the nitration products of β-nitronaphthalene from a study of the bands in the 740 to 770 cm^{-1} region. (*Courtesy of Dr. E. R. Ward and Mr. J. Hawkins*)

component, whose concentration was accurately known, and of the nitration mixture was measured in the 13.7 to 12.8 μ range, where characteristic bands of the 1, 6- and 1, 7-dinitronaphthalene compounds were to be found. The solvent employed was dioxan. The results of these measurements are shown in Fig. 4.31.

The height of the absorption peak in Fig. 4.31(*a*) is equal to $\varepsilon_1 c_1 l$, and thus knowing c_1 and l, ε_1 may be calculated. In a similar way ε_2 is obtained from Fig. 4.31(*b*). From the heights of the absorption peaks in Fig. 4.31(*c*) the concentration of the two components in the mixture may be analysed. If D_1' and D_2' are the optical density peak values in Fig. 4.31(*c*) for the bands at 759 cm^{-1} and 751 cm^{-1} respectively, then to a good approximation $D_1' = \varepsilon_1 c_1' l$, and $D_2' = \varepsilon_2 c_2' l$. Hence, the concentrations (c_1' and c_2') of the components in the mixture are determined. The exact approach would be to employ equations (4.109) and (4.110).

In conclusion, it must be stressed that it is extremely difficult to obtain repeatable extinction coefficients for a particular component from different instruments and this severely handicaps useful exchange of information. Attention is now being paid to the idea that some other property, such as the integrated area under a band or half-band width employing a narrow slit (see p. 138), will lead to more reproducible quantitative infra-red analysis. In addition, more use is being made of intensity values of absorption peaks as an added diagnostic aid; it appears that the integrated absorption coefficient (see p. 137) and the half-width of a band may be correlated not only with the absorbing group but with the part of the molecule to which it is attached.

Recent developments in infra-red studies

Infra-red emission spectra

Wilkinson, Ford and Price[30b] have developed a means of exciting infra-red emission spectra from gases by employing a radio-frequency discharge. The gas was made to flow at low pressure through a quartz tube on the outside of which cylindrical electrodes of aluminium were connected to a radio-frequency source of about 1 kW output. The emission intensity was quite appreciable and for CO_2 is of similar intensity to that of the Nernst filament; in fact, an effective temperature of about 2000°K was produced. In the case of HCl the vibrational transitions $1\rightarrow0$, $2\rightarrow1$, $3\rightarrow2$, $4\rightarrow3$ were observed and their rotational structure resolved; the overtones, $2\rightarrow0$, and $3\rightarrow1$ were also observed. In Fig. 4.32 the emission spectrum of HCl between 2400 cm^{-1} and 3200 cm^{-1} is given. The transitions involved are the $1\rightarrow0$, $2\rightarrow1$, $3\rightarrow2$, sequence (see p. 200), where the intensities decrease in this order. For each of these transitions the rotational structure of these bands may be observed, and the values of the rotational quantum number J for each P- and R-branch are indicated in the figure.

In Fig. 4.33 the emission spectrum of CO at poor resolution is given for the 4360 to 4060 cm^{-1} region. This sequence of bands occurs in the region of the first overtone ($2\rightarrow0$). Much less intense band heads have also been studied in the 6400 to 5700 cm^{-1} region and these are due to the $3\rightarrow0$, $4\rightarrow1$, $5\rightarrow2$, $6\rightarrow3$, $7\rightarrow4$, $8\rightarrow5$, $9\rightarrow6$, and $10\rightarrow7$ transitions. Finally, and more important, was the study of the rotational structure of the $1\rightarrow0$, and $2\rightarrow1$ bands in the 5 μ region.

The emission spectra of molecules and radicals in the infra-red region have the following attractive features:

(1) The probability of an emission transition depends on the factor ν^4 whereas in absorption the factor is ν. Thus, in emission there is a much more favourable intensity factor which could be most useful in the study of overtones of low intensity.

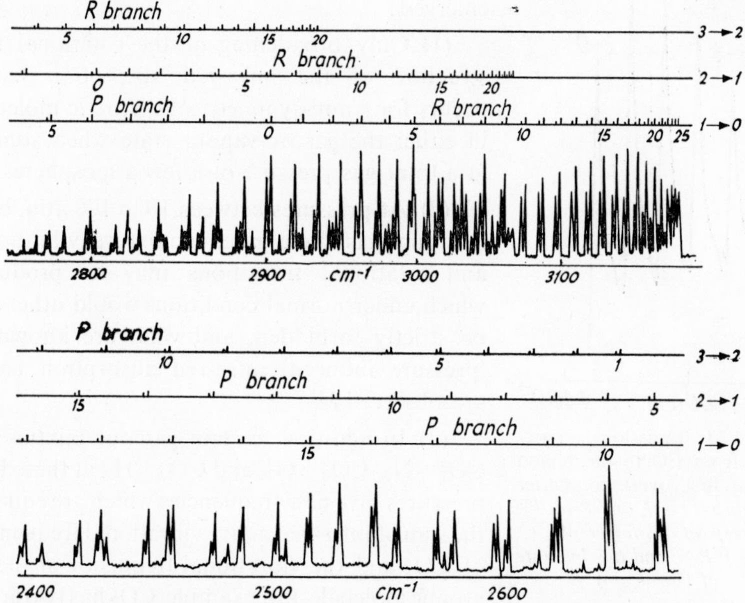

FIG. 4.32 Emission spectrum of HCl between 2400 and 3200 cm^{-1}. (*After Mould, Price and Wilkinson.*[30a] *Courtesy of Professor W. C. Price, F.R.S.*)

(2) A controllable high effective temperature (2000°K) may be obtained in the discharge tube which leads to observable high vibrational and rotational transitions. For example, in the transition of CO a peak near the 1→0 band head is due to the crowding together of lines in the *R*-branch whose *J* values lie between 80 and 100.

(3) Owing to the occurrence of high vibrational and rotational transitions more accurate values of the rotational constants ought to be obtained. The molecules studied so far by the infra-red emission method include HBr, LiH, the group II halides, CO_2, H_2O, and NH_3. In addition, the emission spectrum of the OH radical in the oxy-acetylene flame has been studied under high resolution; this flame emission work, though, is not a new technique for the infra-red emission from flames has been studied for many years.

Infra-red spectra of compressed gases and violation of selection rules

In 1949, Crawford, Welsh and Locke[31] reported that H_2, O_2, and N_2 under special conditions had an infra-red rotation-vibration absorption spectrum; these were molecules with no permanent electric dipole moment, and from their symmetry the dipole moment would not be expected to change during a normal vibration. The special conditions were a small partial pressure of H_2 in the presence of a high pressure of foreign gas such as He or N_2. Since then numerous studies have been made,[32a,32b] and the following are some of the points which have emerged:

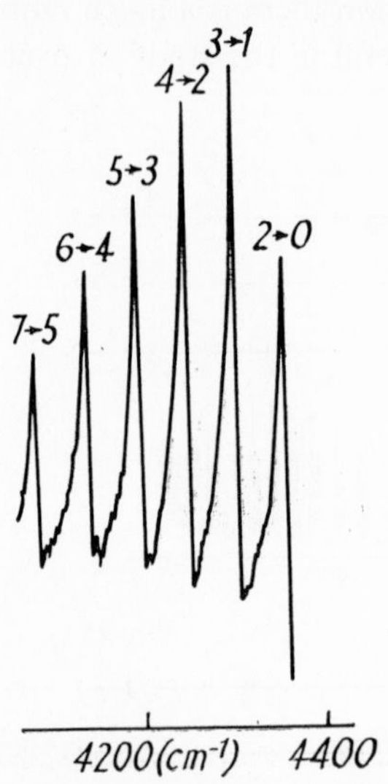

FIG. 4.33 Emission spectrum from CO in the region of the first overtone. (*After Wilkinson, Ford, and Price.*[30b] *Courtesy of Professor W. C. Price, F.R.S. and the Institute of Petroleum*)

(1) Only broadening of the rotational fine structure of the infra-red absorption bands occurs for a non-symmetrical diatomic molecule in either the gas or vapour state when studied at a total gas pressure of a few atmospheres.

(2) At pressures between 10 to 100 atm, both in a pure gas and a gaseous mixture, vibrational and rotational transitions may be produced which under normal conditions would otherwise be strictly forbidden, and what are known as 'pressure induced' infra-red absorption bands are observed.[33]

(3) In addition, certain gaseous mixtures of CO_2+N_2, CO_2+O_2, and CO_2+H_2 at these high pressures give new frequencies which are equal to the sum of infra-red active vibrational frequencies of CO_2 and the vibrational frequency of the diatomic molecule. For example, CO_2 has two active infra-red fundamental frequencies: one at 2349 cm^{-1} which corresponds to ←O—C→—←O and another at 667 cm^{-1} which is identified with O—C—O (C ↑, O's ↓). N_2 has its fundamental frequency at 2331 cm^{-1}, but the observed frequencies at high pressures were 2996 cm^{-1} and 4670 cm^{-1}; these may be explained as resulting from the combination of the frequencies from the individual molecules, i.e.

$$667+2331 = 2998 \text{ cm}^{-1}$$
$$2349+2331 = 4680 \text{ cm}^{-1}$$

The difference between these figures and the observed ones is permissible for combination frequencies. These new bands from mixtures of gases are attributed to 'simultaneous transitions' taking place for component molecules.

(4) The intensity of absorption of the 'pressure induced bands' was directly proportional to the square of the pressure, while for the 'simultaneous transitions' it was directly proportional to the product of the partial pressures of the two components in the mixture. This particular 'square' dependence on the pressure enables this type of transition to be distinguished from another type which arises when certain molecules have weak magnetic

dipole or electric quadrupole moments but undergo no change in electric dipole moment during the vibration. In fact, transitions involving molecules with weak magnetic dipoles or weak quadrupoles are not forbidden by the selection rule. Thus, the criterion of an infra-red spectrum contains a corollary that a change of the quadrupole moment or of the magnetic dipole moment may also result in emission or absorption of infra-red radiation. The 'pressure induced bands' and the 'simultaneous transitions', on the other hand, definitely break the selection rule for electric dipole radiation.

(5) The pure rotational absorption spectrum of H_2 has also been observed in the infra-red by high pressure studies. The $J' \leftarrow J''$ transitions observed were $3 \leftarrow 1$, $4 \leftarrow 2$, and $5 \leftarrow 3$ where the selection rule $\Delta J = \pm 1$ was disobeyed. Once again the intensity of absorption was proportional to the square of the pressure. In addition, the rotational transitions were also induced by the presence of A, N_2 or CO_2 at these high pressures. This violation of the rotational selection rule is not limited to pure rotational transitions; in fact, for the rotation-vibration transition of H_2 from the $v'' = 0$ to the $v' = 1$ level, $S(\Delta J = 2)$, $Q(\Delta J = 0)$ and $O(\Delta J = -2)$ branches are observed and not R and P branches.

It is thought that the bands which result at high pressures when the normally obeyed selection rules are defied are due to collision pair formation, where both the 'pressure induced' and the 'simultaneous transitions' result from the mutual deformation of the charge distribution of the molecules owing to the mutual interaction at such close proximity. At extremely high pressures the dependence of the intensity of absorption on the square of the pressure is no longer observed, and this is attributed to triple collisions and more involved molecular interactions. In conclusion, it must be stressed that the work on pressure induced infra-red studies offers an attractive way of gaining some insight into molecular interaction.[34]

Polarised infra-red radiation studies

When a parallel beam of plane-polarised infra-red radiation is directed at an oriented crystal and the absorption bands are studied, maximum absorption for one particular band will be observed when the polarisation vector for the corresponding vibration is in the same direction as the electric vector of the infra-red radiation. For the sake of simplicity instead of a crystal consider one particular group, the CHO group, where the vibrations are as illustrated in Fig. 4.34. If the plane of the CHO is at right angles to the incident radiation, and if the direction of the C—H vibration coincides with the electric vector of the plane-polarised infra-red radiation, then the corresponding CH band exhibits a more intense absorption maximum. However, when the —CHO group is rotated clockwise in the plane through the valence angle of the CHO group the intensity of the CH band considerably diminishes, while the intensity of the C═O group increases; it is a maximum when its direction coincides with that of the electric vector. Thus, on a simple model by noting the two positions of maximum absorption intensities of the two groups, the value of the angle θ may be determined. By careful measurement of intensities a great deal can be accomplished in the analysis of the structure of crystals. One early application was to find a crystal axis for use in the X-ray analysis of penicillin. This method has been used to study a wide variety of systems including rubber, polythene and proteins.

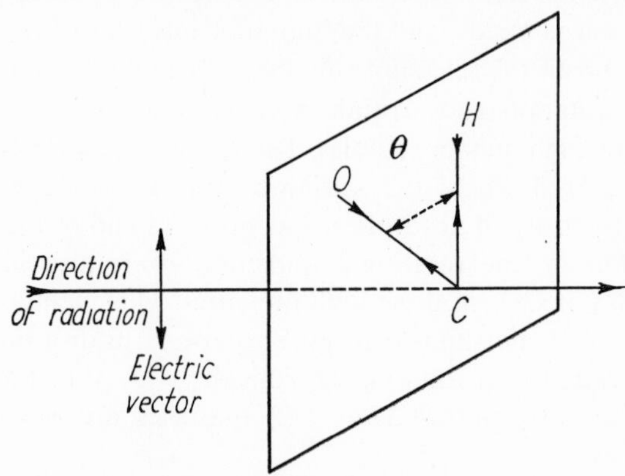

FIG. 4.34 Use of polarised infra-red radiation to investigate directional vibrations

In crystals, however, the position becomes more complex than in this simple CHO example, and the determination of the angle becomes much more involved and uncertain, owing to the electric forces at work within the lattice. A further complication is that the bond moment does not always act along the direction of the bond. In fact, during the bending vibration of H_2O (see p. 140) each O—H bond has not only a component electric dipole parallel to the bond but also one perpendicular to it; hence, the resultant dipole cannot act along the bond, and a misleading value of θ results. It should be noted that both these components contribute to the intensity of the band. Finally, another complication is that the polar group is usually set at a skew angle to the plane polarized infra-red radiation. This situation, however, may be treated mathematically.

Accurate band intensity considerations

Vibrational absorption band intensity determination. In the past few years much interest has centred around attempts at the measurement of the absolute intensity of vibrational absorption bands. Such measurements, however, are handicapped by the fact that intensity measurements made on one spectrophotometer are rarely repeatable on another. Before mentioning the causes of this discrepancy it will be necessary to introduce several terms. For monochromatic radiation of wave-number ν the absorption is governed by the equation:

$$I = I_0 \exp(-K_\nu cl) \qquad (4.112)$$

where I_0 is the intensity of the incident radiation and I that of the emergent radiation. The length of the absorbing path is l cm and the concentration c g-moles/l. From equation (4.112) K_ν the absorption coefficient is given by:

$$K_\nu = \frac{1}{cl} \log_e (I_0/I)_\nu \tag{4.113}$$

The absorption coefficient is related to the molecular extinction coefficient (ε_ν) by the equation:

$$K_\nu = 2.303\varepsilon_\nu \tag{4.114}$$

An infra-red band may be represented by a plot of ε_ν against the wave-number, and the value of ε_ν at the absorption maximum $\varepsilon_{\nu_{max}}$ is quoted to characterise the magnitude of the intensity of the vibrational band. Of more fundamental significance than $\varepsilon_{\nu_{max}}$ is the integrated absorption intensity A. This is given by:

$$A = \int K_\nu d\nu \tag{4.115}$$

$$A = 2.303 \int \varepsilon_\nu d\nu \tag{4.116}$$

where $\int \varepsilon_\nu d\nu$ is the area under the absorption curve. The integration extends over the whole of the band examined.

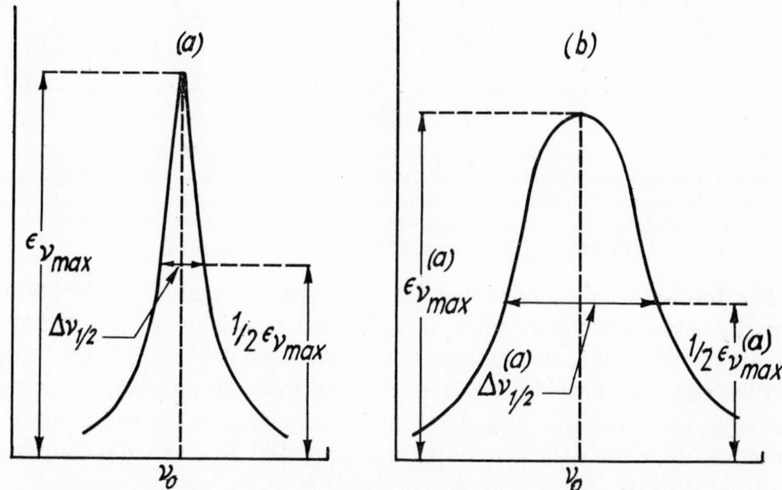

FIG. 4.35 Quantities characterising the shape and intensity of an infra-red absorption band: (*a*) the true absorption band, (*b*) the band as modified by the finite spectral slit width. (*After Jones and Sandorfy.*[35] *Courtesy of Interscience Publishers Inc., New York*)

The broadness of a band is defined in terms of the half-bandwidth $\Delta\nu_{\frac{1}{2}}$, that is the width of the band at 0.5 $\varepsilon_{\nu_{max}}$. These quantities are illustrated in Fig. 4.35(*a*).

In the equations (4.112) to (4.116) monochromatic radiation of wave-number ν has been assumed. In practice, however, the radiation in a spectro-photometer is never truly monochromatic but contains a range of wavelengths, the extent of which is partly determined by the effective slit width.

Instead of measuring K_ν, $\varepsilon_{\nu,\max}$ and $\Delta\nu_{\frac{1}{2}}$ what is actually obtained is K_ν^a, $\varepsilon_{\nu,\max}^a$ and $\Delta_{\nu\frac{1}{2}}^a$, where the superscript *a* signifies 'apparent' values. Some of these symbols are illustrated in Fig. 4.35(*b*). An example of the effect of finite slit width on infra-red absorption bands is illustrated in Fig. 4.36. As the slit width is increased the band becomes wider and flatter, and the area beneath the curve decreases.

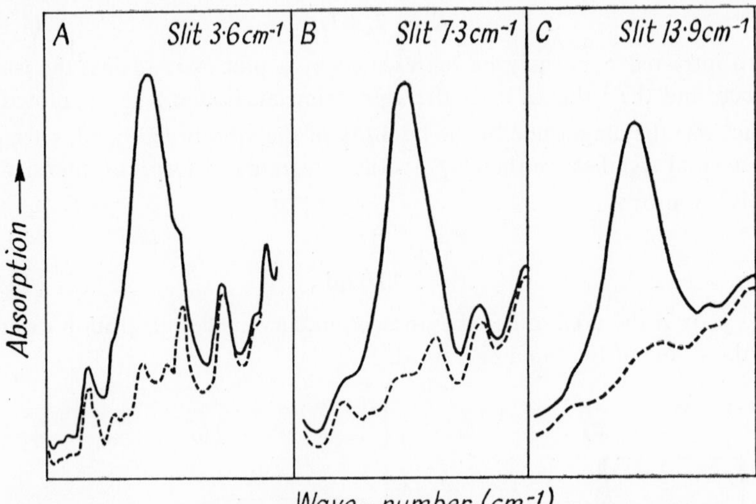

FIG. 4.36 The effect of finite slit width on the band intensity as determined by a single beam spectrophotometer. Curves *A*, *B*, and *C* were measured on the same CS_2 solution of camphor at increasing slit widths as indicated. Broken curve shows atmospheric water vapour absorption curve. (*After Jones and Sandorfy.*[35] *Courtesy of Interscience Publishers Inc., New York*)

The infra-red half-bandwidths for solutions of organic substances are normally between 5 and 20 cm^{-1}. In solids and especially in gases narrower lines are observed. It is now thought that a band does not reveal its true shape until the effective slit width has been reduced to about one-fifth of the true half-bandwidth, and this in general means very narrow slit widths indeed. Consequently, until such slit widths are employed *A*, ε, and $\Delta\nu_{\frac{1}{2}}$ cannot be measured directly. Since it is not practicable in the case of conventional prism spectrophotometers to reduce the slit width to these limits, the true band shape cannot be obtained. However, improvements in the band shape can be made by the use of greater resolving power as in suitable grating and double pass instruments.

Several methods are available for determining *A*, ε_ν, and $\Delta\nu_{\frac{1}{2}}$ from the observed values *B*, ε_ν^a, and $\Delta\nu_{\frac{1}{2}}^a$, respectively[36a,b], where these symbols are defined as follows:

$$\varepsilon_\nu^a = \frac{1}{cl}\log_{10}[T_0/T]_\nu \tag{4.117}$$

$$B = 2{\cdot}303\int \varepsilon_\nu^a \mathrm{d}\nu \tag{4.118}$$

$\Delta\nu^a_{\frac{1}{2}}$ is the apparent half-bandwidth at $0.5\varepsilon^a_\nu$, and T_0 and T are written for I_0 and I to indicate that truly monochromatic radiation is not being employed for the measurements.

Two methods of determining the true integrated band intensity from the apparent value will now be briefly considered.

Wilson and Wells studied the infra-red absorption bands of gases broadened by the introduction of a foreign gas at various pressures. They determined the value of $\int \log_e(T_0/T)_\nu d\nu$ for a particular band at different pressures and extrapolated these values to zero partial pressure of the absorbing gas; the integrated band intensity was then given by:

$$A = \lim_{p\to 0} \frac{1}{pl}\int \log_e(T_0/T)_\nu d\nu \tag{4.119}$$

In the case of a solution the true integrated absorption coefficient A can be obtained by measuring B at several concentrations and extrapolating to zero concentration; alternatively, the concentration can be maintained constant, and the extrapolation carried out to zero path length. These have been used by Ramsey *et al.*[37] and the extrapolation was based on the equations:

$$A = \lim_{c\to 0} \frac{1}{cl}\int \log_e\left(\frac{T_0}{T}\right)_\nu d\nu \tag{4.120}$$

$$A = \lim_{l\to 0} \frac{1}{cl}\int \log_e\left(\frac{T_0}{T}\right)_\nu d\nu \tag{4.121}$$

The extrapolation is linear and the line has a small negative slope.

Another procedure is to obtain by graphical integration the area A' beneath the fractional absorption $(I_0-I)/I_0$ versus wave-number curve, where:

$$A' = \int\left(\frac{I_0-I}{I_0}\right)_\nu d\nu \tag{4.122}$$

This area A' is independent of resolving power so that

$$A' = \int\left(\frac{T_0-T}{T_0}\right)_\nu d\nu \tag{4.123}$$

and A may be obtained by plotting A'/cl against cl and extrapolating to $cl = 0$. Since, however, the plot of A'/cl against cl is curved Ramsey[38] has employed the reciprocal cl/A' against cl; the plot is nearly linear, and the intercept gives the value $1/A$.

It is most desirable to obtain accurate band intensity measurements for the following reasons:

(1) To apply to the quantitative analysis of mixtures so that the data obtained on one spectrophotometer could be accurately used on another. This has not yet been achieved.

(2) In ultra-violet absorption spectra of solutions the structural diagnostic procedure is to measure not only the wavelength at which the peak absorption

occurs but also its intensity; the latter is often most useful in assisting identification of the particular group absorbing. Such a procedure would be most valuable in the infra-red.

(3) The absolute intensity of a vibrational band is related to the change of electric moment during the vibration, and in the case of small molecules it is sometimes possible to derive from the determined absolute intensity the individual bond moment and, thus, gain some intimate knowledge of molecular electronic structure.

Determination of bond moment from the absolute intensity of an infra-red absorption band

The intensity of an infra-red absorption band depends on the magnitude of the change in electric dipole moment during the vibrational displacement.[39] For a stretching vibration of, for example, a diatomic vibrating group the integrated intensity of a particular absorption band may be related to $(\partial\mu/\partial r)^2$, where $\partial\mu/\partial r$ is the rate of change of the bond moment with internuclear distance. For a molecule it is necessary to determine first the integrated absorption intensity, A, of the fundamental absorption band and from this the rate of change of dipole moment with each normal co-ordinate (see p. 90). That is $\partial\mu/\partial Q$ is calculated where Q is a normal co-ordinate. To a first approximation the integrated intensity, A, of a band is given by:

$$A = \frac{N\pi}{3c}\left(\frac{\partial\mu}{\partial Q}\right)^2 = \frac{N\pi}{3c}\left\{\left|\frac{\partial\mu_x}{\partial Q}\right|^2 + \left|\frac{\partial\mu_y}{\partial Q}\right|^2 + \left|\frac{\partial\mu_z}{\partial Q}\right|^2\right\} \qquad (4.124)$$

where x, y, and z represent fixed axes within the molecule, the $\partial\mu/\partial Q$ terms are vector quantities, N is the number of molecules per cubic centimetre of sample and c is the velocity of light. Q is expressed as some linear combination of the more elementary co-ordinates, such as bond length and bond angle. To convert $\partial\mu/\partial Q$ into $\partial\mu/\partial r$ it is essential to know the potential energy function which governs the molecular vibrational frequencies (see chapter on Force Constants). From this it is possible to relate the normal co-ordinates to the internal co-ordinates by a set of coefficients which govern the motions of atoms. After this mathematical treatment (normal co-ordinate treatment) the value of $\partial\mu/\partial r$ is obtained for each of the bonds concerned. In addition to the value of $\partial\mu/\partial r$ the method is capable of yielding individual bond moments in a molecule. One limitation of the method is that since a square root is involved in the derivation of μ, the sign of the bond moment has to be assumed.

Other complications which make the calculations involved are:

(1) It is necessary to take into account the movement of hybridised lone pairs during the vibration.

(2) The hybridisation may change during the vibration.

(3) Dipoles do not always act along the bond, contrary to what has been assumed in most dipole moment work. This was pointed out by Coulson.[40]

At present, only very simple molecules may be dealt with at all adequately to yield satisfactory bond moment values. A very interesting study was to determine the value of the C—H bond moment in different hydrocarbons; the bond moment varied with the amount of *sp* character in the orbital of the carbon atom. The value of the bond moment derived from a parallel vibration often disagrees with that derived from a perpendicular vibration. Sometimes the values determined from parallel vibrations are most improbable. A few values of the C—H bond moments from perpendicular vibrations are listed in Table 4.15, where the change in dipole moment with hybridisation will be noted. The two values quoted for ethylene in Table 4.15 were estimated from different bending vibrations.

In conclusion, it should be appreciated that certain points cannot yet be fully understood, but it would seem that much fundamental information should emerge from this kind of work in the future—especially on the theoretical side.

TABLE 4.15

Values of the C—H *bond moments in Debye units* (D), *and probable polarity*

Molecule	Bond moment irrespective of sign (D)	Polarity	C valency directed at H
CH_4	0.3	(δ^+)C—H(δ^-)	sp^3
$CH_3C{\equiv}C.CH_3$	0.4	(δ^+)C—H(δ^-)	sp^3
C_2H_4	0.3 or 0.7	(δ^-)C—H(δ^+)	sp^2
C_2H_2	1.05	(δ^-)C—H(δ^+)	sp

Only a very brief introduction to the procedure has been given here, and the original papers [41-44] should be consulted together with a critical survey by Hornig and McKean[45] who reviewed the position at the end of 1955.

Systematic solvent studies

In recent years work has been carried out in an attempt to relate the influences of solvents upon individual stretching vibrations to some characteristic property of the solvent, such as its dielectric constant. Recently, Bellamy, Hallam, and Williams[46] reported a study of the solvent-solute interaction which involved plotting the relative frequency shifts for one X—H solute in a wide range of different solvents directly against the relative shifts of some other solute in the same range of solvents; for example each of the relative frequency shifts of the X—H stretching frequency of H_2O, HBr, and $B_{10}H_{14}$ in a wide range of solvents was plotted against the corresponding values for pyrrole in the same solvents. Each of these three solutes gave straight lines of substantially different slopes. Since nine different solvents were used in the case of $B_{10}H_{14}$, sixteen for water and thirteen for HBr, and most points fell on the straight lines, it was concluded that the type of association between an X—H link and any one solvent was essentially the same in all cases regardless of whether it was the polar O—H link or virtually a non-polar B—H link. In addition, since the lines had greatly differing slopes it implied that some property of the solute—probably the polarity of the X—H bond—was also involved.

Two other conclusions which emerge from their work are:

(1) The dielectric constant of the medium often appears to play little or no part in determining the frequency shifts.

(2) In the cases studied, the solvent shifts arise from local dipolar associations and not from bulk dielectric constant effects.

This type of infra-red work seems to be of the utmost importance as it will have repercussions in other fields involving solvents, e.g. reaction kinetics and the measurements of electric dipole moments in solutions. A considerable amount of interest is, thus, centred on the solvent effect from different physico-chemical sides. In addition solvent studies are important generally for infra-red work since the solvent employed affects frequency, band intensity, and the shape of the vibration bands. In some cases large changes in band intensity result on merely changing the solvent, and this may occur even where no particular type of solvent-solute physical interaction would be anticipated. Thus, solely from an analytical point of view, it is most important that work should be directed to a deeper understanding of the solvent effects.

(B) RAMAN SPECTROSCOPY

Introduction

When monochromatic light of frequency $\bar{\nu}_0$ is directed at a cell containing molecules in the solid, liquid or gaseous phases, and the emergent light is studied at right angles to the incident radiation as in Fig. 4.37, in addition

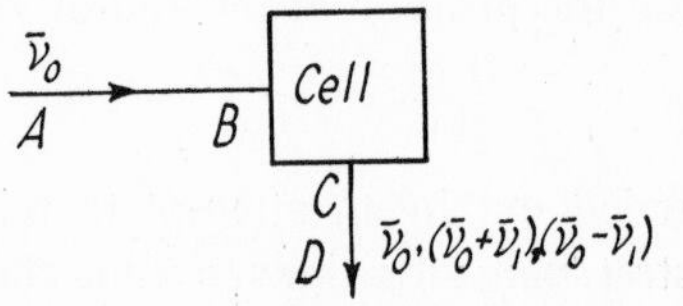

FIG. 4.37 Appearance of Raman frequencies

to the original frequency $\bar{\nu}_0$ the emergent light sometimes contains other frequencies such as $(\bar{\nu}_0 - \bar{\nu}_1)$ and $(\bar{\nu}_0 + \bar{\nu}_1)$. This was discovered by Raman in 1928, but it had been predicted by Smekal in 1923. The lines of lower frequency than the incident light $(\bar{\nu}_0)$ are known as *Stokes lines*, while the higher frequency lines are termed *anti-Stokes lines*.

Normally, an intense monochromatic source of light in the visible or near ultra-violet region is employed (e.g. the 4358 Å line or the 2537 Å line from a mercury lamp) as the incident radiation. When a spectrograph capable of high resolution is placed along the line CD in Fig. 4.37, the spectrogram may consist of an extremely strong line corresponding to the frequency of the incident light (Rayleigh scattering) and lines very close to the initial line

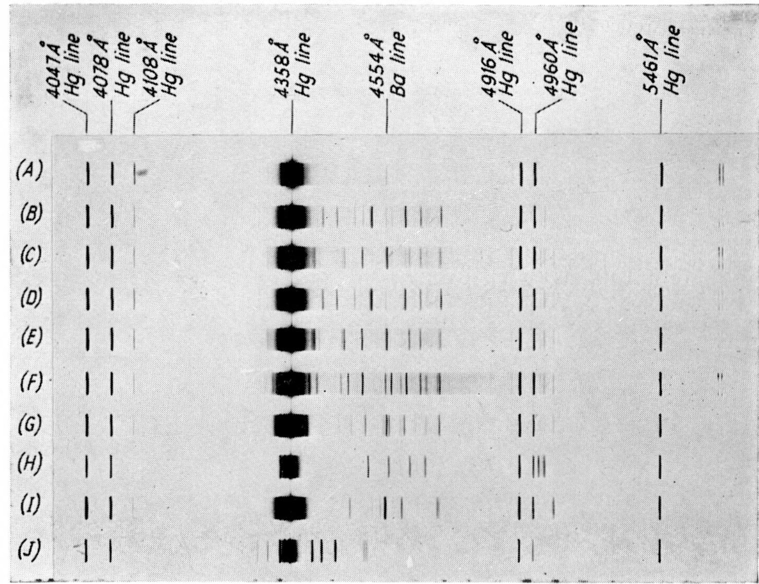

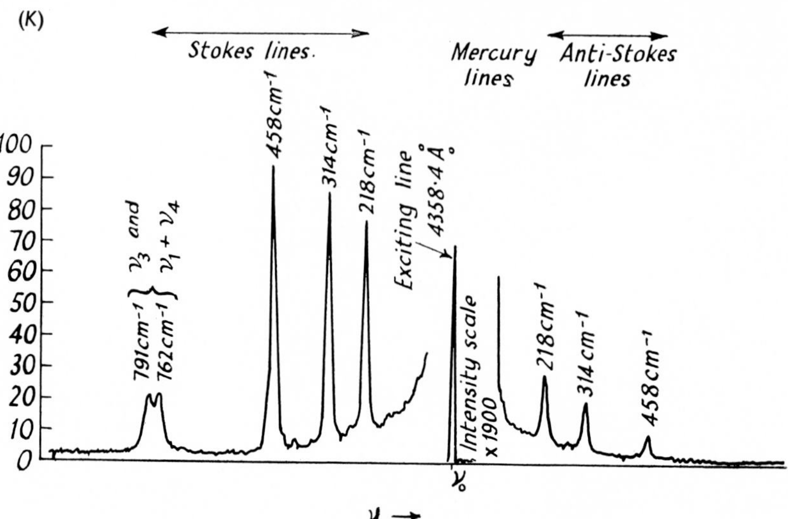

FIG. 4.38 Raman vibrational spectrograms of the following compounds compared to the mercury spectrum in *A*. *B*, 20 per cent o-xylene+80 per cent p-xylene; *C*, 15 per cent o-xylene+56 per cent m-xylene+8 per cent p-xylene+18 per cent ethyl benzene+1 per cent toluene+2 per cent styrene; *D*, p-xylene; *E*, m-xylene; *F*, o-xylene; *G*, ethyl benzene; *H*, cyclohexane; *I*, benzene; *J*, carbon tetrachloride; *K*, the Raman spectrum of carbon tetrachloride taken with a Hilger pen recording Raman spectrophotometer. (*A to J, Courtesy of Hilger and Watts Ltd., and K, Courtesy of Shell Research Ltd.*)

[*To face page* 143

with some much further removed. The lines are much more intense on the lower frequency side of the exciting frequency ($\bar{\nu}_0$).

The difference in frequency between the Hg exciting line and the lines most distant from the initial line corresponds with vibrational (and rotation-vibration) frequency changes; those very close to it correspond with pure rotational changes. However, unless the resolution is extremely good, the pure rotational lines are not observed, nor is any line structure detected for the rotation-vibration frequency change. Thus, even if the change is a rotation-vibration one at poor resolution, it has the definite appearance of a line. Some Raman spectrograms of polyatomic molecules examined in the liquid phase are given in Fig. 4.38.† Even though the measurements are made on liquids and not on gases, the resolution would be insufficient either for any rotational structure of the vibrational band to be observed or to separate any frequencies due to pure rotational energy changes from the exciting 4358 Å mercury line. In Fig. 4.38 spectrogram *A* gives only the lines of the mercury source; the additional lines in all the other spectrograms are interpreted as vibrational Raman lines. These vibrational Raman lines in the spectrograms *B* to *I* result from the following liquids:

B. *ortho*- and *para*-xylene; exposure *B* was made with a mixture of approximately 20 per cent *ortho*-xylene and 80 per cent *para*-xylene;

C. Exposure *C* was made with a mixture of approximately 15 per cent *ortho*-xylene, 56 per cent *meta*-xylene, 8 per cent *para*-xylene, 18 per cent ethyl benzene, 1 per cent toluene, 2 per cent styrene;

D. *para*-xylene;

E. *meta*-xylene;

F. *ortho*-xylene;

G. ethyl benzene;

H. cyclohexane;

I. benzene;

J. carbon tetrachloride;

K. the Raman spectrum of carbon tetrachloride taken with a Hilger pen recording Raman spectrophotometer.

It may be observed from Fig. 4.38 that the most intense of the mercury lines is the 4358 Å one. All the vibrational lines in the spectrograms result from excitation by this mercury line. Nearly all the observed vibrational Raman lines fall on the lower frequency side of the exciting 4358 Å mercury line and lie between this and the 4916 Å mercury line. Thus, in most cases the Stokes lines are readily observed. The anti-Stokes lines, however, are normally too weak to be detected under the conditions of the experiment; in fact, of all the spectrograms in Fig. 4.38 only the carbon tetrachloride one shows readily detectable anti-Stokes lines.

† These vibrational Raman spectra (*B* to *J*), where the dispersion is insufficient for any rotational structure to be observed, were taken with the Hilger E612 two-prism large-aperture glass spectrograph (see p. 32).

For carbon tetrachloride the wave-numbers of the first three Stokes lines and the two anti-Stokes lines are listed in Table 4.16. The difference between the wave-number values in rows (I) and (II) is given in row (III) and corresponds with three of the vibrational frequencies of the CCl_4 molecule.

TABLE 4.16

Relation of the first three Stokes and the two anti-Stokes lines to vibrational frequencies of the CCl_4 *molecule*

	Stokes lines			Anti-Stokes lines	
	Line *A*	Line *B*	Line *C*	Line *D*	Line *E*
(I) Wave-number of observed line	22 728	22 632	22 488	23 164	23 260
(II) Wave-number of the exciting Hg 4358 Å line	22 946	22 946	22 946	22 946	22 946
(III) Vibrational frequencies of the CCl_4 molecule (cm^{-1})	218	314	458	218	314

The frequency of 218 cm^{-1} is interpreted in terms of the fundamental vibrational frequency of type ν_2 (see Fig. 4.26) while those of 314 cm^{-1} and 458 cm^{-1} are the fundamental vibrational frequencies ν_4 and ν_1, respectively. Altogether eight Raman displacements (frequencies) have been obtained from the Raman spectrum of liquid CCl_4, and these have been interpreted in terms of fundamentals, overtones and combination frequencies (see p. 176).†

It should be appreciated that the values of the observed Raman vibrational frequencies are independent of which mercury line is chosen to excite them. For example, if an intense 4047 Å mercury line had been chosen as the exciting light for the CCl_4 spectrum, the same vibrational frequency values of 218, 314 and 458 cm^{-1} would have resulted.

Apart from practical considerations, the choice of the monochromatic light frequency is governed by the requirement that it should be sufficiently intense and that the molecule itself should not show its normal electronic absorption or fluorescence spectrum in the region of the chosen line. The 2537 Å mercury line is unsuitable for the investigation of the Raman frequencies of many aromatic compounds, since most of them absorb somewhere in this region.

Experimental Raman spectroscopy

Raman spectra may be obtained from the solid, liquid, and gaseous states, although mostly liquid samples are examined; the spectra are usually very weak and exposure times of several hours are often needed. The special requirements of Raman spectroscopy are:

† The vibrational frequencies 762 and 791 cm^{-1} in Fig. 4.38(*K*) for the carbon tetrachloride molecule are interpreted on p. 177.

(1) An intense source of radiation, such as a battery of mercury arcs, the number of which may vary from two to about twelve grouped around the outside of the sample.

(2) The radiation has to be monochromatic. This is achieved by surrounding the sample tube with concentric cylindrical filter solutions which eliminate the undesirable mercury lines.

(3) To cut out stray radiation.

(4) In order to study the polarisation of the Raman lines (see p. 158) a 90° split-field polaroid disk must be placed against the exit window of the source unit.

(5) A spectrograph capable of high-speed and suitable resolving power.

Both prism and grating spectrographs are employed in the study of Raman spectra. An example of the use of a grating spectrograph to study pure rotational Raman spectra is given on p. 154, while the prism instrument employed to obtain the spectrograms shown in Fig. 4.38(*A*) to (*K*) will be described here.

The Hilger Raman source unit is shown in detail in Fig. 4.39(*a*) and its location relative to the spectrograph in Fig. 4.39(*b*). The tube containing 7 ml of liquid sample slides vertically into the innermost of three coaxial glass tubes. These tubes provide a water jacket to protect the sample from the heat of the mercury lamps and also a liquid sheath acting as a colour filter. Grouped symmetrically around these tubes are four low-pressure mercury discharge lamps completely enclosed in a hollow cylindrical metal jacket, whitened internally to act as a diffuse reflector for all four lamps. These specially designed lamps emit an intense 4358 Å line, the mercury line in most frequent use, with only a comparatively weak background in the region between 4358 and 4916 Å. The mercury 4047 Å line and shorter wavelength radiation is prevented from reaching the sample by means of a concentrated sodium nitrite solution placed in the concentric cylindrical filter cell. The monochromatic mercury radiation is scattered in all directions but only the light at right angles to the incident radiation is picked up by the spectrograph. This minimises the amount of mercury light reaching the photographic plate. The manner in which this is achieved in the Hilger source is to take the scattered radiation from the specimen liquid out of the bottom of the sample cell through an adhesed window. The light is then concentrated on the slit of the spectrograph by means of a prism and lens which can be adjusted to eliminate scattered light from the sides of the tube. For quantitative photographic work the source unit is employed in conjunction with a constant voltage transformer.

The spectrograph shown in Fig. 4.39(*b*) is the Hilger large-aperture, two-prism, glass spectrograph (see p. 32) with one of the two camera positions occupied by a scanning attachment which enables the instrument to be converted into a direct recording one by means of a photomultiplier unit. This conversion enables the Raman spectra of liquid samples to be examined either photographically or by a direct photoelectric method. In the latter method the traces are presented on a pen recorder, and an accurate measurement of both line intensity and line position is obtained. The change-over from direct to photographic recording is made by swinging the appropriate

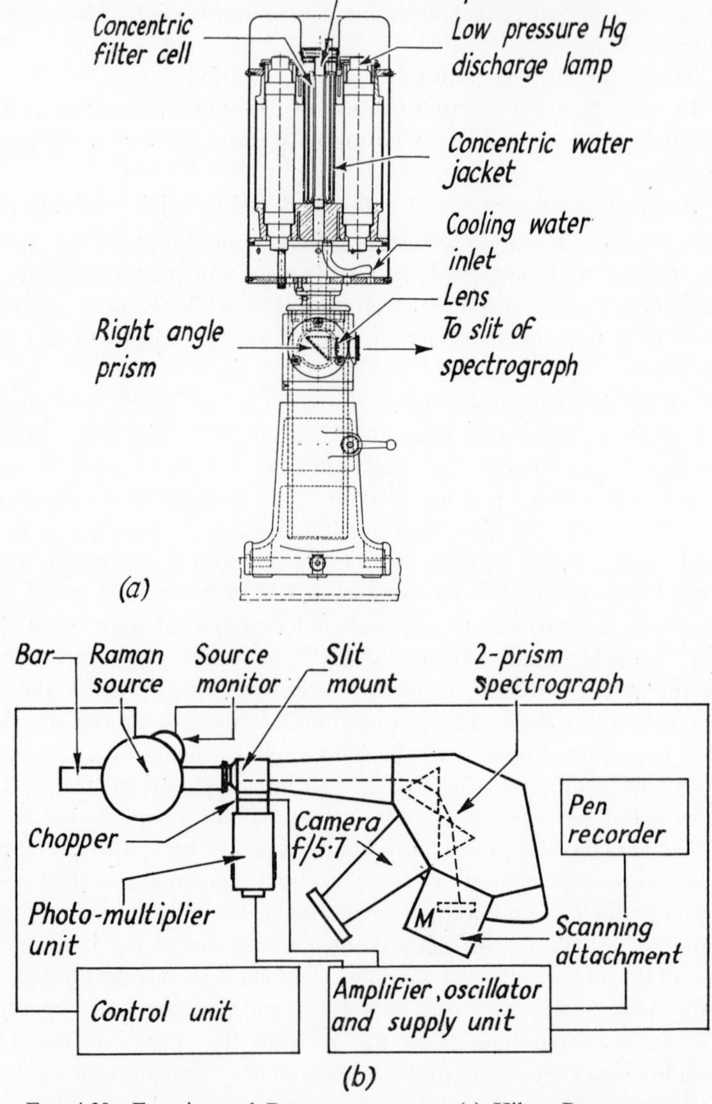

FIG. 4.39 Experimental Raman apparatus: (*a*) Hilger Raman source, (*b*) Hilger large aperture 2-prism glass spectrograph adapted for direct recording Raman spectroscopy. (*Courtesy of Hilger and Watts Ltd.*)

arm into position, a spring-loaded catch ensuring that the position actually in use is correctly aligned with the remainder of the optical system.

When used photographically the instrument has a camera of relative aperture equal to *f*/5.7 under which conditions the spectrograph has a reciprocal linear dispersion of 16 Å/mm at a wavelength of 4358 Å. The spectrograms shown in Fig. 4.38(*A*) to (*J*) were obtained using the Hilger large-aperture, two-prism, glass spectrograph with the *f*/5.7 camera.

For use as a direct-reading instrument the scanning attachment is swung into position and the paths of the light rays are then those indicated in Fig. 4.39(*b*). Radiation from the Raman source is concentrated on to the entrance slit of the spectrograph by the lens and prism built into the source unit. The spectrum is scanned by a plane mirror, *M*, rotated automatically about a vertical axis at one of four possible speeds. The scanning mirror *M* returns the radiation through the prisms where the light again suffers dispersion (resulting in a total reciprocal linear dispersion of 6.8 Å/mm at 4358 Å) to a further reflector (not shown in the figure) located in the slit mount which causes the light to pass out of the exit slit of the monochromator. The light from this slit is interrupted by a chopper and then brought to a focus on the cathode of a photomultiplier. The signal from this photomultiplier is then amplified and used to operate a pen recorder.

To compensate for variations in source intensity, a monitor is used on the light exciting the sample, and the record is made of the ratio of the main signal from the monochromator to the signal from the monitor. The spectrogram shown in Fig. 4.39(*K*) was obtained using the Hilger large-aperture, two-prism, glass spectrograph as a direct-recording instrument.

Raman frequencies and criterion for their appearance

When a molecule is introduced into an electric field of strength F(V/cm) an electric dipole moment, P, is induced in the molecule. If α is the polarisability of the molecule, then the magnitude of the induced dipole moment is given by:

$$|P| = \alpha |F| \tag{4.125}$$

When electromagnetic radiation of frequency $\bar{\nu}_o$ falls on the molecule this introduces a varying electric field, F, whose dependence on the time t is given by:

$$F = F^\circ \cos 2\pi\bar{\nu}_o t \tag{4.126}$$

where F° is the equilibrium value of the electric field strength. Hence, from equations (4.125) and (4.126):

$$P = \alpha F^\circ \cos 2\pi\bar{\nu}_o t \tag{4.127}$$

Thus, the electromagnetic radiation induces a varying electric dipole moment which then permits emission of light identical in frequency with that of the incident radiation. This is Rayleigh scattering.

In the equation $|P| = \alpha |F|$, both P and F are vectors, and in the case of an isotropic molecule both their directions are identical. This makes α scalar. However, for non-isotropic molecules the application of an electric field in a fixed direction induces a moment in a different direction, and α becomes a tensor. In general, molecules are non-isotropic, and the three equations which take account of the unequal polarisability along the different principal axes of the molecule are:

$$P_x = \alpha_{xx}F_x + \alpha_{xy}F_y + \alpha_{xz}F_z \tag{4.128}$$

$$P_y = \alpha_{yx}F_x + \alpha_{yy}F_y + \alpha_{yz}F_z \tag{4.129}$$

$$P_z = \alpha_{zx}F_x + \alpha_{zy}F_y + \alpha_{zz}F_z \tag{4.130}$$

where for example P_z is the induced electric dipole moment in the direction of the z-axis. The meaning of a coefficient such as α_{xy} is that it is the electric moment induced in the x-direction by a unit field F_y polarised along the y-axis. The tensor α is defined by these nine coefficients α_{xx}, α_{xy} . . . α_{zz}. However, since $\alpha_{xy} = \alpha_{yx}$, $\alpha_{yz} = \alpha_{zy}$, and $\alpha_{zx} = \alpha_{xz}$ the tensor α is really defined by six coefficients.

These six coefficients together with the coordinates x, y and z may be expressed in the equation

$$\alpha_{xx}x^2 + \alpha_{yy}y^2 + \alpha_{zz}z^2 + 2\alpha_{xy}xy + 2\alpha_{yz}yz + 2\alpha_{zx}zx = 1 \tag{4.131}$$

This is the equation of an ellipsoid. Thus, the polarisability of the molecule is divided into three components at right angles along the x, y and z axes, and the values of these components fix the dimensions of what is termed the polarisation ellipsoid. If any of the six polarisability tensors change during a rotation or a vibration, then the theoretical criterion for a Raman spectrum is satisfied. For very small vibrational amplitudes the polarisability of the molecule is related to the normal vibrational co-ordinate, q_v, by the equation:

$$\alpha = \alpha^o + \left(\frac{\partial \alpha}{\partial q_v}\right)_0 q_v \tag{4.132}$$

where the attached zero refers to the co-ordinate values at the equilibrium configuration. Such an equation as (4.132) holds for each of the six coefficients which define α.

The dependence of the normal vibrational frequency $\bar{\nu}_v$ on the normal co-ordinate q_v is given by:

$$q_v = q_0 \cos(2\pi\bar{\nu}_v t) \tag{4.133}$$

where q_0 is the normal co-ordinate of the initial position.

By substitution of equations of the type (4.126) into equation (4.128):

$$P_x = \{\alpha_{xx}F_x^\circ + \alpha_{xy}F_y^\circ + \alpha_{xz}F_z^\circ\} \cos 2\pi\bar{\nu}_0 t \tag{4.134}$$

On substitution of α from equation (4.132) and q_v from equation (4.133) the following expression is obtained:

$$P_x = (\alpha_{xx}^\circ F_x^\circ + \alpha_{xy}^\circ F_y^\circ + \alpha_{xz}^\circ F_z^\circ) \cos 2\pi\bar{\nu}_0 t +$$
$$\left\{\left(\frac{\partial \alpha_{xx}}{\partial q_v}\right)_0 F_x^\circ + \left(\frac{\partial \alpha_{xy}}{\partial q_v}\right)_0 F_y^\circ + \left(\frac{\partial \alpha_{xz}}{\partial q_v}\right)_0 F_z^\circ\right\} q_0 \cos 2\pi\bar{\nu}_v t \cos 2\pi\bar{\nu}_0 t \tag{4.135}$$

Equation (4.135) may be readily transformed into:

$$P_x = (\alpha^\circ_{xx}F^\circ_x + \alpha^\circ_{xy}F^\circ_y + \alpha^\circ_{xz}F^\circ_z)\cos 2\pi\bar{\nu}_0 t + \frac{q_0}{2}\left\{\left(\frac{\partial\alpha_{xx}}{\partial q_v}\right)_0 F^\circ_x + \left(\frac{\partial\alpha_{xy}}{\partial q_v}\right)_0 F^\circ_y + \left(\frac{\partial\alpha_{xz}}{\partial q_v}\right)_0 F^\circ_z\right\}\{\cos 2\pi(\bar{\nu}_0 - \bar{\nu}_v)t + \cos 2\pi(\bar{\nu}_0 + \bar{\nu}_v)t\} \quad (4.136)$$

The first term on the right-hand side of equation (4.136) contains only one frequency factor $\bar{\nu}_0$ which is that of the incident radiation. This term is interpreted in terms of Rayleigh scattering. The second term on the right side contains, in addition to the incident frequency $\bar{\nu}_0$, the frequencies $\bar{\nu}_0 \pm \bar{\nu}_v$. Thus, the induced dipole moment can also oscillate with the two frequencies:

$$\bar{\nu}_0 + \bar{\nu}_v \quad \text{and} \quad \bar{\nu}_0 - \bar{\nu}_v$$

These two frequencies are interpreted as the vibrational Raman frequencies. The $\bar{\nu}_0 - \bar{\nu}_v$ and $\bar{\nu}_0 + \bar{\nu}_v$ frequencies are known, respectively, as the *Stokes* and *anti-Stokes lines*. The intensity of the Raman lines for a light source of fixed intensity is determined by the value of $(\partial\alpha/\partial q_v)_0$. In fact, the properties of Raman radiation (e.g. state of polarisation, see later) are determined by the tensor $(\partial\alpha/\partial q_v)_0$. Equation (4.132) is important since the α_0 in the first term on the right-hand side determines the properties of Rayleigh radiation, while in the second term $(\partial\alpha/\partial q_v)_0$ determines the properties of Raman radiation.

For a pure rotational change of a diatomic molecule it may be shown that the three frequencies are $\bar{\nu}_0$, $(\bar{\nu}_0 - 2\bar{\nu}_r)$, and $(\bar{\nu}_0 + 2\bar{\nu}_r)$, where $2\bar{\nu}_r$ is the frequency corresponding to the increase of rotational energy. Thus, very simple classical considerations can explain the appearance of both vibrational and rotational changes and of Stokes and anti-Stokes lines. However, once the intensity of Stokes and anti-Stokes lines is considered this classical theory is most unsatisfactory, for it predicts that the Stokes and anti-Stokes lines should be of equal intensity, whereas in practice the latter are very much less intense than the former. A quantum mechanical approach, however, predicts that the anti-Stokes lines will be much weaker than the Stokes lines.

As has been already indicated the criterion for a vibrational Raman spectrum is that one or more of the dimensions of the polarisability ellipsoid must change during the vibration, in order that the vibration may interact with suitable electromagnetic radiation to produce a Raman effect. In the case of a diatomic molecule such as X_2 the polarisability components give an ellipsoid, and during the vibration X↔X the polarisability ellipsoid must change its dimensions. Thus, the condition for a Raman spectrum† is satisfied; it is also satisfied for X→—←Y. In order to decide which vibrational frequencies will appear as Raman frequencies each bond should be considered as associated with a polarisability ellipsoid, and the criterion for such a change is that the total polarisation should change during the vibration. In the case of the parallel vibrations of carbon dioxide (see p. 93) for the ν_1 vibrational

† This should be contrasted with the infra-red method where X→—←X frequency is not obtained under ordinary conditions.

mode there is reinforcement and a strong Raman spectrum, but for the ν_3 vibrational mode, the change in one polarisability ellipsoid tends to be cancelled out by the opposite change in the other, and there is no Raman spectrum.

For a molecule which possesses a centre of symmetry such as CO_2 there is a useful rule known as the *mutual exclusion rule.* This states that: 'For molecules with a centre of symmetry fundamental transitions which are permitted in the infra-red are forbidden in the Raman and vice-versa.'† For example, in the acetylene molecule (see p. 174) the frequencies ν_3 and ν_5 occur in the infra-red but not in the Raman, while ν_1, ν_2 and ν_4 appear in the Raman but not in the infra-red. For linear molecules this mutual exclusion rule is readily applied. In a tetrahedral molecule XY_4 the fundamental frequencies ν_3 and ν_4 are infra-red active (see p. 122) as would be anticipated. However, in the Raman spectrum of XY_4 all the possible fundamental frequencies ν_1, ν_2, ν_3, and ν_4 are observed. Complex symmetry considerations are involved in the explanation of the appearance of the ν_3 and ν_4 frequencies in the Raman spectrogram, and for this point Herzberg[17] should be consulted.

On many occasions both the infra-red and Raman methods have to be employed to obtain a complete pattern of the different vibrational frequencies in a molecule; the two methods are often complementary, since when a certain group lacks strong features in the infra-red spectrum, they often appear in the Raman and vice-versa.

Pure rotational Raman spectra of diatomic and polyatomic molecules

In general, in order to observe a pure rotational Raman spectrum it is necessary to have a spectrograph of very high resolving power. In addition since the lines lie very close to the most intense exciting mercury line, experimental observation becomes difficult owing to the breadth of the corresponding Rayleigh radiation. However, this difficulty may be overcome if the molecule has no electronic absorption spectrum in the 2537 Å region, since if this line is employed from a low-pressure mercury arc the Rayleigh scattering may be diminished considerably by the presence of mercury vapour in the path of the emergent ray. This mercury vapour absorbs the 2537 Å line. If the interference of the rotational spectrum with the Rayleigh line is overcome, then two problems may remain:

(1) Insufficient dispersion of the rotational lines.

(2) Insufficient intensity of these dispersed lines.

The criterion for the occurrence of a pure rotational Raman spectrum is that during the rotation the polarisability in a fixed direction should change; in other words, the molecule should have a non-spherical polarisation ellipsoid. This is borne out by:

(1) The absence of such spectra for spherically-symmetrical molecules, e.g. CH_4 and CCl_4, which have spherical polarisability.

† It is not to be inferred that the transitions which are forbidden in the infra-red appear in the Raman and vice-versa. Some transitions may be forbidden to both methods.

(2) The fact that linear molecules always have a pure rotational Raman spectrum. This is because the 'polarisability ellipsoid' of a linear molecule is not a sphere, and hence the polarisability in a fixed direction changes during the rotation of the molecule about an axis perpendicular to the internuclear axis.

The attractive feature about pure rotational Raman spectra of diatomic molecules was that the method could be used to obtain internuclear distances for certain symmetrical diatomic molecules, which were until recently inaccessible in the infra-red. However, by the use of an extreme high-pressure technique, which is outlined on p. 133, it has now been found possible to study H_2 in the rotation-vibration infra-red. The hydrogen molecule, however, had been studied in the pure rotational Raman spectra as early as 1930. In general, the selection rule for pure rotational Raman changes is $\Delta J = 0, \pm 1, \pm 2$. For linear molecules the selection rule is modified to $\Delta J = 0, \pm 2$; the values of the rotational Raman shifts of the linear rigid rotator for the Stokes lines, if centrifugal stretching is neglected, are given by:

$$\Delta\nu = BJ'(J'+1) - BJ''(J''+1) \tag{4.137}$$

$$\Delta\nu = B\{(J''+2)(J''+3) - J''(J''+1)\}$$

$$\Delta\nu = 2B(2J+3) \tag{4.138}$$

where $J'' = J$. This is on the low-frequency side of the exciting line; for the anti-Stokes line which is on the high-frequency side:

$$\Delta\nu = -2B(2J+3) \tag{4.139}$$

where $\Delta\nu$ is the wave-number separation of the observed rotational line from the exciting line (e.g. 2537 Å mercury line), and the values of J are 0, 1, 2, 3. . . . Since the convention employed is $\Delta J = J' - J''$, that is ΔJ is the difference between the upper and lower values of J, it follows for pure rotational Raman transitions that only ΔJ equals a positive integer will apply. In the case of a linear molecule, therefore, only an S-branch (see p. 135) would be observed. The frequency of the $\Delta J = 0$ transitions would correspond with that of the exciting line.

However, since both Stokes and anti-Stokes lines are feasible there will be two series of rotational Raman lines for this S-branch: one will be on the high-frequency side and the other on the low-frequency side of the exciting Hg line. An energy level diagram is given in Fig. 4.40 to illustrate some of the rotational energy changes in the pure rotational Raman spectrum of a linear molecule.

The representation of the pure rotational transitions by the paths such as ABC and DEF is only a diagrammatic method of showing that the incident light interacts with the molecule and either loses or gains the amount of rotational energy indicated. The points such as B and E should not be taken as representing energy levels of the molecule.

In Table 4.17 the $\Delta\nu$ values are listed for the S-branch for both the Stokes and anti-Stokes lines.

TABLE 4.17

Raman values Δν for ΔJ = 2 of both Stokes and anti-Stokes lines

	$J = 0$	$J = 1$	$J = 2$	$J = 3$
Δν	$6B$	$10B$	$14B$	$18B$
	$-6B$	$-10B$	$-14B$	$-18B$

The difference between consecutive J columns gives the spacing of the rotational lines for both the Stokes and anti-Stokes lines to be $4B$. This value should be compared with that of $2B$ for the infra-red. Fig. 4.41 (*a*) is a diagrammatic representation of the rotational Raman spectrum based on equations (4.138) and (4.139) while Fig. 4.41 (*b*) is the rotational Raman spectra of CO_2 and N_2O.

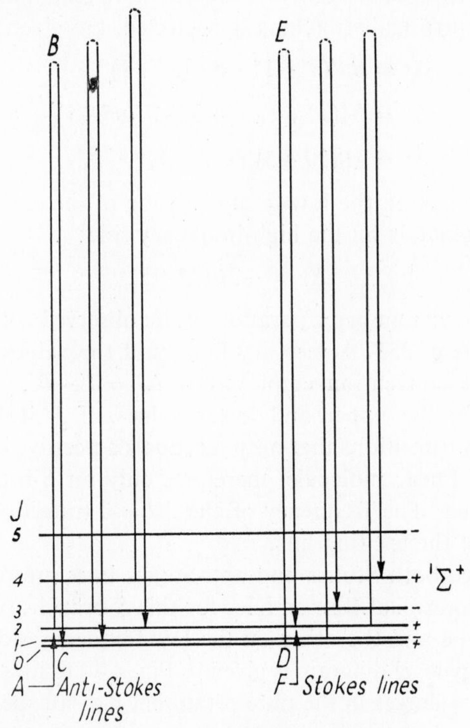

FIG. 4.40 Energy level diagram illustrating some of the rotational energy changes of a linear molecule

The Raman spectrum of fluorine (F_2) was studied by Andrychuk[47] who obtained and resolved the rotational fine structure. Gaseous fluorine at 1 atm pressure contained in a quartz tube was irradiated by two water-cooled mercury arc lamps. A prism spectrograph was employed with a linear dispersion of 58 cm^{-1}/mm at 4047 Å. The time of exposure was up to 48 h.

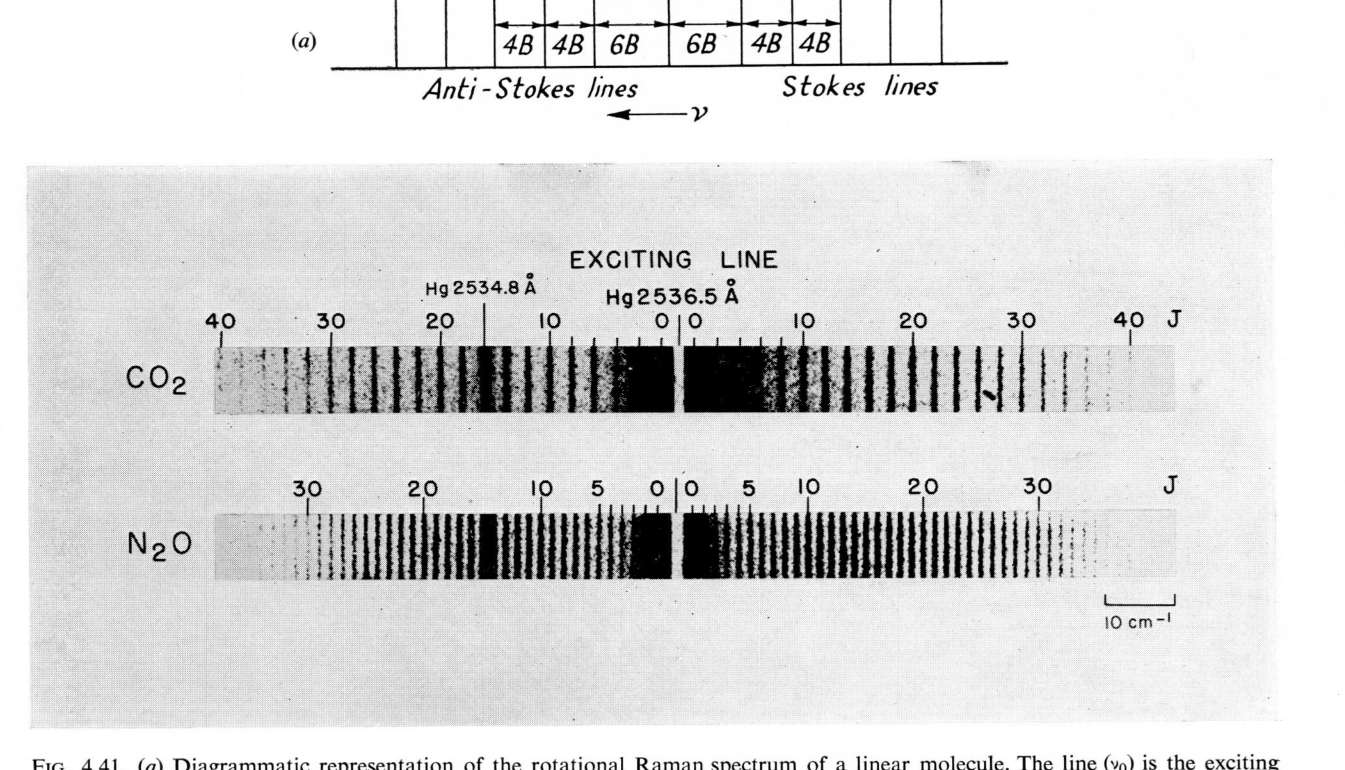

FIG. 4.41. (*a*) Diagrammatic representation of the rotational Raman spectrum of a linear molecule. The line (ν_0) is the exciting mercury line. (*b*) Rotational Raman spectra of CO_2 and N_2O excited by the 2537 Å line of the isotope ^{198}Hg. The exciting line has been absorbed by mercury vapour placed between the Raman tube and the spectrograph slit. In the case of the spectrum of the linear symmetrical CO_2 molecule, lines of odd J are missing, the line spacing being $8B$, while in that of the linear unsymmetrical N_2O molecule all the rotational lines are present with a spacing between them of $4B$. (*Spectra by courtesy of Dr. B. P. Stoicheff*[48b])

[*To face page* 152

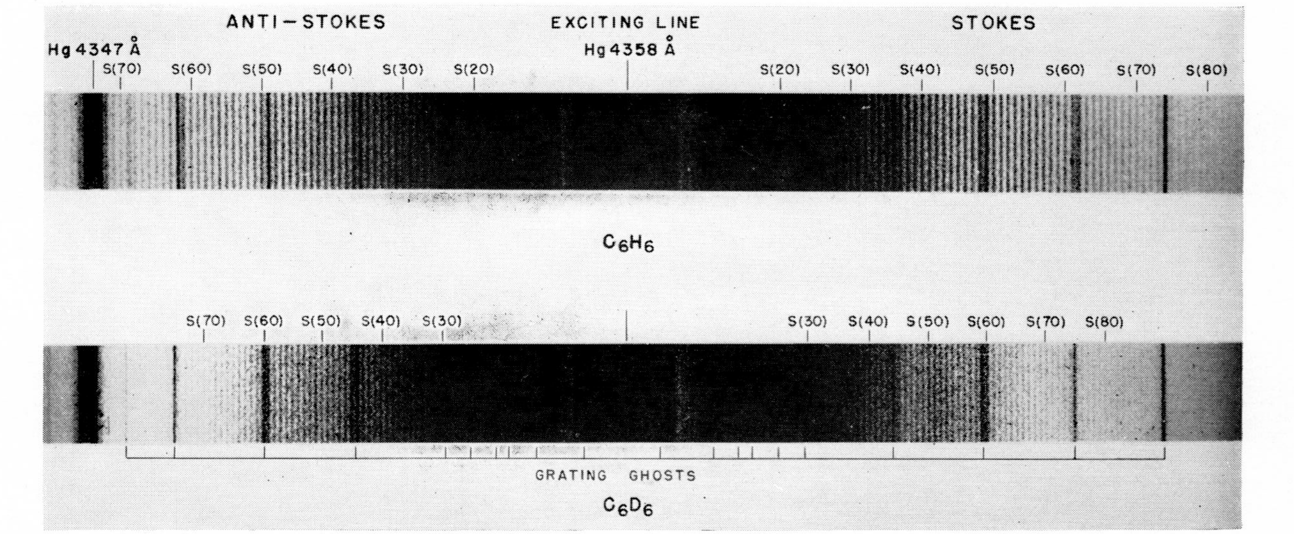

FIG. 4.44 Rotational Raman spectra of C_6H_6 and C_6D_6 photographed in the second order of a 21-ft grating. The vapour pressure of C_6H_6 was about $\frac{1}{2}$ atm. (*Courtesy of Dr. B. P. Stoicheff*[48a] *and 'The Canadian Journal of Physics'*)

[*To face page* 153

A microphotometer trace of the rotational Raman spectrogram is shown in Fig. 4.42. The mercury 4047 Å line was employed as the source.

From the analysis of the Raman lines the value of B_0 was found to be 0.8828 ± 0.0010 cm^{-1} and $r_{F-F} = 1.417_7 \pm 0.001_5$ Å.

Other pure rotational Raman studies of linear molecules have been made on, for example, H_2, O_2, N_2, HCl, CO_2, CS_2, C_2H_2, C_3O_2, and C_2N_2. A striking feature of the study on H_2 was that liquid hydrogen yielded basically the same rotational lines as gaseous hydrogen.

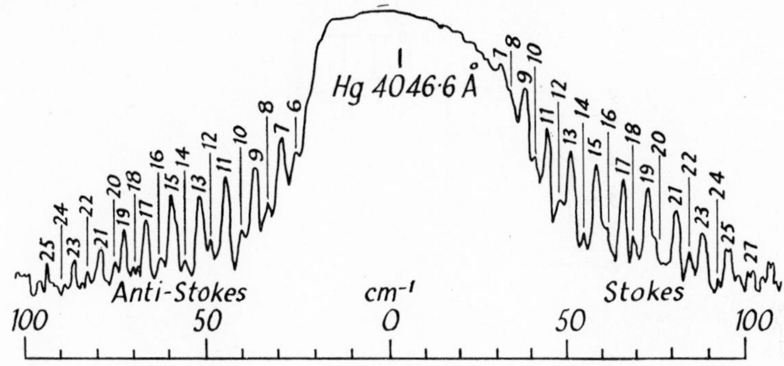

FIG. 4.42 Microphotometer trace of the rotational Raman spectrum of fluorine gas. The numbers on the maxima are J values. (*Courtesy of Dr. D. Andrychuk*,[47] *and 'The Canadian Journal of Physics'*)

In symmetric-top molecules rotations about the symmetry axis yield no change in polarisability during the rotation and hence do not satisfy the criterion for such a spectrum. The rotations analysed in terms of the axes perpendicular to the symmetry axis do lead to a pure rotational Raman spectrum. The rotational energy of a symmetric-top molecule is given by:

$$E_r = J(J+1)\frac{h^2}{8\pi^2 I_B} + \left(\frac{1}{I_A} - \frac{1}{I_B}\right)\frac{h^2 K^2}{8\pi^2} \qquad (4.140)$$

where $Kh/2\pi$ is the component of the total angular momentum $\sqrt{J(J+1)}h/2\pi$ in the direction of the symmetry axis.† The selection rules are $\Delta J = 0, \pm 1, \pm 2$ and $\Delta K = 0$. In fact, only the positive values of ΔJ apply (cf. the rotational Raman spectrum of linear molecules). Thus, there should be a set of Stokes and anti-Stokes lines for $\Delta J = +2$ and another for $\Delta J = +1$ (see Fig. 4.43 (*a*) and (*b*)). The $\Delta J = 0$ transitions would not be detected since they would correspond with the frequency of the exciting mercury line. Hence, altogether four sets of lines might be anticipated. Such a spectrum is illustrated diagrammatically in Fig. 4.43, where the points to be noted are:

(1) The Stokes lines of both the *R*- and *S*-branches lie on the low-frequency side of the exciting line, whereas the anti-Stokes lines of the *R*- and *S*-branches are on the high-frequency side.

† Further terms are added to this equation when centrifugal stretching is taken into account.

(2) The $\Delta J = +1$ transitions of even J values are superposed on the lines of the $\Delta J = +2$ transitions.

(3) The wave-number separation between adjacent lines is approximately $h/4\pi^2 cI_B$, and the first R branch line is $h/2\pi^2 cI_B$ from the exciting line.

Little work has been done on the pure rotational Raman spectrum of symmetric-top molecules. Ammonia was the only molecule to be studied in detail this way until quite recently. However, Stoicheff[48a,48b] has now developed

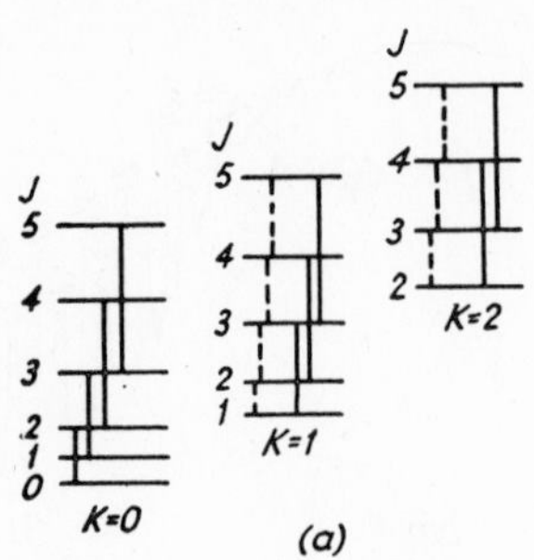

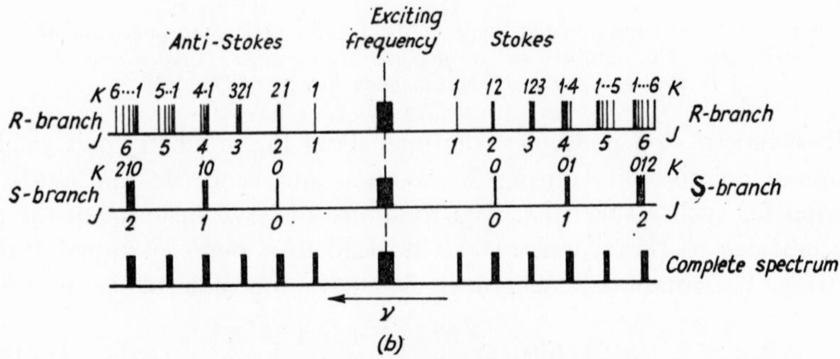

FIG. 4.43 (*a*) Energy level diagram for a prolate symmetric-top molecule. Full lines indicate the transitions $\Delta J = +2$ (S-branch), broken lines $\Delta J = +1$ (R-branch). (*b*) Diagrammatic representation of the rotational Raman spectrum of a symmetric-top molecule indicating the fine structure in the R- and S-branches and the appearance of the complete spectrum under low resolution. The $J = 0$ line in the R-branch is absent since $\Delta J = +1$ does not occur for $K = 0$. The different intensities in the Stokes and anti-Stokes branches has been neglected. (*Courtesy of Dr. B. P. Stoicheff*[48b])

an accurate method for the study of gases at ordinary pressures, and he employs a 21-ft grating spectrograph with an Eagle mounting. The concave grating has an area of 7 in. × 3 in. ruled with 15 000 lines/in. and is blazed to give maximum intensity in the second order at 5000 Å. The reciprocal linear dispersion is 6.75 cm^{-1}/mm. Two high-intensity mercury lamps are used giving a very sharp 4358 Å line, and the time of exposure used ranged from 6 to 24 hr. Stoicheff has obtained accurate rotational constants for C_6H_6, C_6D_6 and allene and deuterated allenes (C_3D_4, $C_3H_2D_2$).

The Raman selection rules for pure rotational transitions in benzene are those expected for a symmetric-top molecule. In Fig. 4.44(*a*) the pure rotational Raman spectrum of benzene vapour may be observed, and this consists of an *R*-branch ($\Delta J = +1$) and an *S*-branch ($\Delta J = +2$) on either side of the undisplaced line ($\Delta J = 0$). In addition, in Fig. 4.44(*b*) the Raman spectrum of C_6D_6 is also given.

The sharp rotational lines in Fig. 4.44(*a*) are each separated by about 0.75 cm^{-1}/mm and extend from 20 to about 50 cm^{-1} on both sides of the exciting 4358 Å Hg line. The rotational lines in the *S*-branch are numbered at intervals of ten from 30 to 80. The lines in the *R*-branches would extend only half as far as those of the *S*-branches, that is to approximately 25 cm^{-1} from the exciting line. This region, however, is masked by many grating ghosts (see p. 39 and a continuum. Only in the C_6H_6 spectrum was it possible to observe some lines which might belong to the *R*-branches, but these were not measurable. The main series of lines constitutes the *S*-branch, and the Raman displacements for the *S*-branches taking centrifugal stretching into account are:

$$|\Delta\nu| = 4B_0(J+\tfrac{3}{2}) - 6D_J(J+\tfrac{3}{2}) - 4D_{JK}K^2(J+\tfrac{3}{2}) - 8D_J(J+\tfrac{3}{2})^3 \quad (4.141)$$

where B_0 is the value of the rotational constant in the lowest vibrational level about an axis perpendicular to the symmetry axis. The last three terms on the right-hand side of the equation (4.141) are corrections for centrifugal distortion. If the third term on the right-hand side of the equation (4.141) were important, then a splitting of each line would be expected. However, since no splitting was detected and the lines were sharp, this third term was neglected in the analysis. Thirty-five lines in each of the Stokes and anti-Stokes *S*-branches were measured with an accuracy of ± 0.03 cm^{-1}. A graph of $|\Delta\nu|/(J+\frac{3}{2})$ was plotted against $(J+\frac{3}{2})^2$, which from equation (4.141) would be expected to be linear. From the resulting straight line shown in Fig. 4.45 the values of B_0 and D_J were obtained. Since the intercept of the line with the ordinate axis is equal to $(4B_0 - 6D_J)$ and the slope is $-8D_J$, this gave a value of the effective moment of inertia about the *B*-axis of the molecule.

In addition, gaseous C_6D_6 has also been studied by Stoicheff, and the results for both this molecule and C_6D_6 are listed in Table 4.18.

TABLE 4.18

Data from pure rotational Raman spectrum of C_6H_6 *and* C_6D_6

	B_0 (cm^{-1})	$I_B \times 10^{-40}$ (g–cm^2)
C_6H_6	0.18960 ± 0.00005	147.59 ± 0.40
C_6D_6	0.15681 ± 0.00008	178.45 ± 0.09

From these values of the moments of inertia, the internuclear distances of carbon–carbon (r_{CC}) and carbon–hydrogen (r_{CH}) were calculated from equations (4.142) and (4.143). The r_{CH} internuclear distance was assumed to be the same as that of the r_{CD}†. The formulae employed were:

$$\text{for } C_6H_6, \quad I_B = 3\{m_C r_{CC}^2 + m_H(r_{CH}+r_{CC})^2\} \tag{4.142}$$

$$\text{for } C_6D_6, \quad I_B = 3\{m_C r_{CC}^2 + m_D(r_{CD}+r_{CC})^2\} \tag{4.143}$$

where m_H, m_D, and m_C are the masses of the hydrogen, deuterium and carbon atoms, respectively. These combined data led to a carbon–carbon distance of 1.397 ± 0.001 Å and a carbon-hydrogen distance of 1.084 ± 0.005 Å.

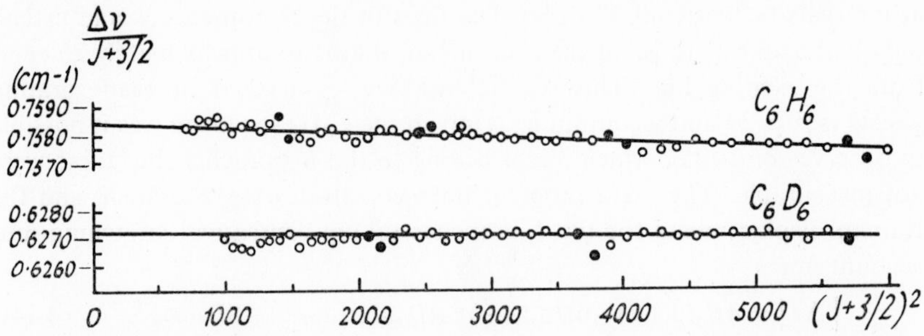

FIG. 4.45 Plot of $\Delta\nu/(J+\frac{3}{2})$ against $(J+\frac{3}{2})^2$ for the ground state of C_6H_6 and C_6D_6. (*Courtesy of Dr. B. P. Stoicheff*[48a] *and 'The Canadian Journal of Physics'*)

These internuclear distance values are in good agreement with those obtained by other methods. A similar study has also been made on the asymmetric-top molecule, ethylene, and recently Herzberg and Stoicheff[49] have considered the C—C and C—H distances in various molecules, including those recently obtained by Raman spectroscopy. In general, though, unless the asymmetric-top molecule approximates to a symmetric-top as in the case of ethylene, the difficulties facing the analysis of the Raman spectra of asymmetric-top molecules seem to be formidable, at present.

Raman vibrational studies of diatomic molecules

All diatomic molecules are in theory capable of a vibrational Raman spectrum, since the polarisability must alter during the vibration along the bond. If the diatomic molecule may be treated as a simple harmonic vibrator then:

$$E_v = (v+\tfrac{1}{2})hc\omega \tag{4.144}$$

where v is the vibrational quantum number which can take the values 0, 1, 2. . . . The selection rule for a transition is $\Delta v = \pm 1$, but in practice only the value $\Delta v = +1$ transitions are observed. When $v'' = 0$ is the initial level then a Stokes line is obtained whereas when $v' = +1$ is the initial

† This assumption holds rigorously only for equilibrium distances (r_e). It is thought that for these r_0 values the assumption holds to within 0.005 Å. In order to determine r_e values it would be necessary to determine data for other vibrational levels and use a formula of the type:

$$B_v = B_e - \Sigma\alpha_i(v+\tfrac{1}{2})$$

level an anti-Stokes line results. This is illustrated in Fig. 4.46 where any accompanying rotational energy change is neglected. The representation of the Stokes transitions by the route *ABC* and the anti-Stokes by *DEF* is only a diagrammatic way of indicating that the molecule interacts with an incident quantum of light and either diminishes or increases its energy value by the amount ΔE_v, where:

$$\Delta E_v = E_{v'} - E_{v''} = (v' + \tfrac{1}{2})hc\omega - (v'' + \tfrac{1}{2})hc\omega \tag{4.145}$$

On application of the selection rule $\Delta v = +1$:

$$\Delta E_v = hc\omega = hc\Delta\nu \tag{4.146}$$

where $\Delta\nu$ is the difference in wave-number of the observed Raman line from that of the exciting line.

Since the majority of molecules are in the $v = 0$ level, then the Stokes line is obviously the more intense. In fact, the anti-Stokes lines are often so weak that they are difficult to observe; in addition, overtones are too weak to be observed. Thus, it is generally not possible to obtain data on the higher vibrational levels, and consequently it is also impossible to determine ω_e or x_e values. This is to be contrasted with the infra-red method (see p. 96). The vibrational Raman approach is normally limited to determining ω, where ω is the vibrational frequency (in cm^{-1}) of the diatomic oscillator based on the assumption of simple harmonic motion. This is, of course, an approximation since the motion is never strictly a simple harmonic one.

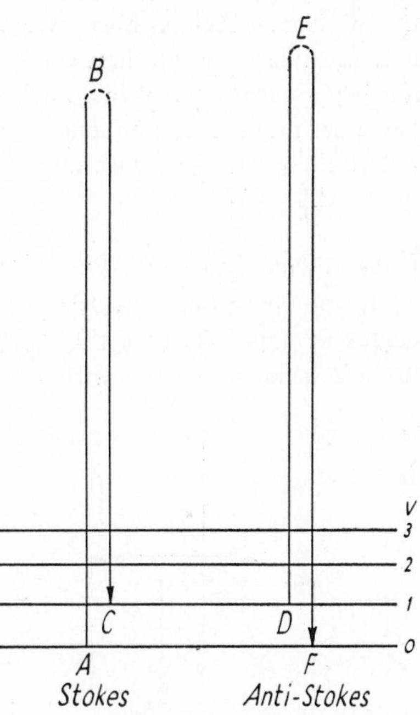

FIG. 4.46. Schematic representation of a vibrational Raman change

Vibrational Raman spectra involving the theory of light scattering

Introduction

Some of the vibrational Raman studies with the emphasis on structural determination may now be considered. In the past, the infra-red technique has been more widely used than the Raman for structural determination; this bias has been mainly due to experimental considerations.† Both methods yield highly desirable information in structural work, and for molecules with any degree of symmetry the two methods work hand in hand. Since the

† It seems highly probable, though, that the gap between the amount of work done by the two methods will considerably diminish in the future.

intensity of an infra-red band depends on the magnitude of the electric dipole moment change during the vibration, and the Raman band on the magnitude of the change in polarisability, it is not surprising that the appearance of a photoelectrically recorded Raman band normally differs from the corresponding infra-red band. The frequency at the point of maximum absorption, though, is usually in good agreement.

A large number of vibrational frequencies of simple and even relatively complex molecules has been obtained from the vibrational Raman approach. The Raman method is particularly useful for determining low vibrational frequencies which are not readily determined in the infra-red. An integral part of the Raman approach to structural problems is the study of whether the lines corresponding to the fundamental frequencies are polarised. From the number of Raman lines observed and how many of these are polarised it is possible to decide between certain structural configurations. Although it is beyond the scope of this work to consider why a certain molecular model has a set number of frequencies (lines) and which of these lines should be polarised, we can at least attempt to attach some meaning to the terms involved.

Polarisation and depolarisation of Raman lines

In the vibrational analysis of simple molecules, the measurement of the degree of polarisation of the Raman line gives most valuable information, for it associates that line with a particular vibrational mode besides helping to decide the geometrical arrangement of the atoms themselves. The degree of polarisation depends on the anisotropic character of the molecules. From an experimental viewpoint polarised lines are normally sharp and intense, whereas depolarised lines are diffuse and have a lower intensity. The meaning of the term *depolarisation factor* ρ, which measures the degree of depolarisation of the line, will now be illustrated. In Fig. 4.47 the three axes x, y and z are at right angles. If the axis Ox' is the direction of the incident monochromatic radiation, the Raman frequencies are examined in the plane $zy'z'$. If interaction of the unpolarised monochromatic incident light occurs with the molecules in the cell and Raman lines are produced, then these lines may become polarised to different extents. If i is the intensity of the polarised light perpendicular to the plane $x'yxy'$, and I the intensity of the polarised light parallel to this plane, then the ratio of i to I is known as the *depolarisation factor* (ρ).

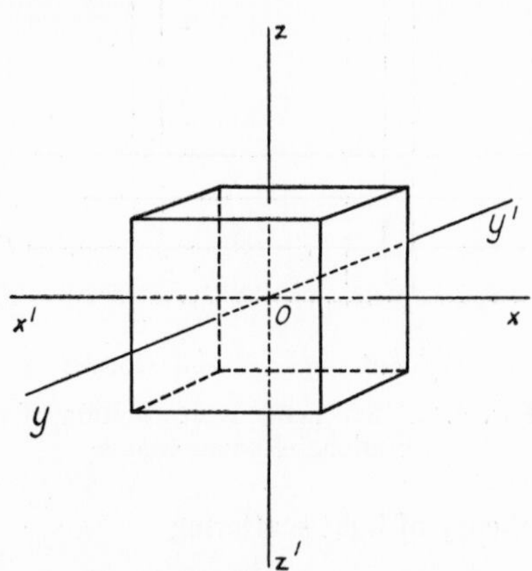

FIG. 4.47 Schematic representation of depolarisation of scattered radiation

It may be shown from considering the polarisability ellipsoid for the molecule that in the case where all orientations of the scattering molecules are equally probable (e.g. in a fluid) then for Rayleigh scattering of unpolarised light

$$\rho = 6v^2/(45a^2+7v^2) \tag{4.147}$$

v measures the anisotropy and may be looked upon as indicating the departure of the ellipsoid from its spherical shape; and a is some measure of the overall size of the polarisability ellipsoid. If the ellipsoid reduces to a sphere, then by definition v is zero, and, therefore, from equation (4.147) ρ is also zero, and the Rayleigh line is termed completely polarised. Since a by definition may never be zero it follows from equation (4.147) that ρ must always be less than $\frac{6}{7}$. In the case of Raman lines equation (4.147) must be modified and for a detailed treatment more advanced works should be consulted.[27] Broadly, what emerges is:

(1) Equation (4.147) becomes modified to:

$$\rho = 6(v')^2/\{45(a')^2+7(v')^2\} \tag{4.148}$$

where a' in this case can be zero.

(2) If both v' and a' are zero, then the Raman line is forbidden.

(3) If v' is zero and a' is positive then ρ is zero and the line is completely polarised.

(4) If a' is zero and v' is positive then ρ is $\frac{6}{7}$, i.e. 0.86, and the line is said to be depolarised.

(5) If $0<\rho<\frac{6}{7}$ then the line is said to be polarised.

These cases are most important in deciding the actual geometrical arrangement of atoms in simple molecules (see later). Obviously, then, a major part of structural Raman work is the experimental determination of the value of ρ. The formula $\rho = i/I$ may be used and i and I can be found by separating the perpendicular component from the parallel component. A 90° split-field polaroid disk is placed against the exit window of the Raman tube. The disk consists of two semi-circular pieces of polaroid the upper half of which permits the passage of the i component, while the lower half allows the I component to pass. Thus, the intensity of each Raman line is divided into two halves, a less intense upper half corresponding to i and a more intense lower half corresponding to I. Thus, from the ratio of i to I, ρ is determined.†

By consideration of the polarisation ellipsoid for simple molecules and how a' and v' are affected during the vibration, it is often possible to predict whether the Raman line will be polarised or depolarised. A few conclusions are listed below, which apply only to permitted Raman lines.

(1) Completely symmetrical vibrations result in highly polarised lines, that is, they have a small value of ρ. For example: O→—C—←O where in

† In practice various corrections have to be made, and the density of the line has to be related to intensity (see Volume 1, p. 96).

this type of vibration the full symmetry of the molecule is involved, and the value of ρ is <0.2. In a similar way the two linear Raman active vibrational modes of acetylene (ν_1 and ν_2, see p. 174) are polarised. For symmetrical vibrations of linear molecules the value of ρ often falls in the 0.1 to 0.3 region.

(2) Antisymmetrical vibrational modes are depolarised, e.g.

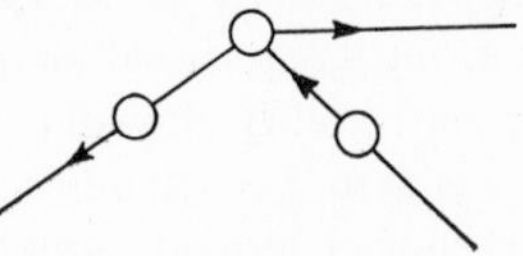

This applies to symmetrical, non-linear, triatomic molecules, and ions such as SO_2 and NO_2^-.

In general, totally symmetrical and unsymmetrical vibrations may be distinguished by their ρ values, the totally symmetrical having a value of $\rho < \frac{6}{7}$, whereas if ρ is equal to $\frac{6}{7}$, the vibration is most probably unsymmetrical and is certainly so if the line is very broad. A value of about $\frac{6}{7}$ itself for ρ does not definitely mean that the vibrations are unsymmetrical, since totally symmetrical vibrations may have a value close to $\frac{6}{7}$. It must be emphasised, however, that in simple molecules a value of ρ less than $\frac{6}{7}$ is definite proof of a symmetrical vibration.

(3) Totally symmetric breathing modes of regular tetrahedral molecules, e.g. P_4, or $SnCl_4$, and octahedral molecules, e.g. SF_6, are completely polarised (i.e. $\rho = 0$).

(4) Raman lines of degenerate vibrational modes are depolarised.

(5) In large unsymmetrical molecules most vibrations are polarised to some degree, although vibrations of symmetrical groups within such molecules may be detected by virtue of their large degree of polarisation of the Raman lines.

Structural determinations

A few of the different types of molecules whose frequencies (or some of them) have been determined by their vibrational Raman spectra are listed below.

(1) Diatomic molecules F_2, ClF, and NO^+.

(2) Triatomic molecules. For linear symmetric molecules of the type X_3 and XY_2, the selection rules allow the appearance of only one single polarised line where the frequency corresponds with the vibration:

$$X\!\rightarrow\!\!-\!X\!-\!\!\leftarrow\!X \quad \text{or} \quad Y\!\rightarrow\!\!-\!X\!-\!\!\leftarrow\!Y$$

In the non-linear symmetrical triatomic molecules such as SO_2 all three fundamental frequencies are permitted to Raman spectra where two of the three lines are polarised. Thus, the linear and non-linear symmetrical triatomic molecules ought to be readily distinguished.

(3) Tetra-atomic molecules. The linear C_2N_2 molecule has been examined,

where three fundamental Raman frequencies are permitted and two of these lines are polarised. The three frequencies are:

```
(a) ←N——C→—←C——N→
(b)   N→—C→—←C—←N

            ↑            ↑
(c)   N——C————C——N
        ↓            ↓
```

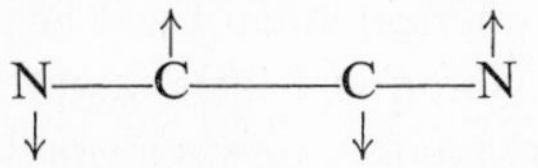

where the frequencies (*a*) and (*b*) lead to polarised lines.

For the planar symmetrical XY_3 type and the pyramidal XY_3 it may be possible to distinguish between them when attempting to decide a particular XY_3 structure, since for the planar type three lines are permitted (one polarised) whereas for the pyramidal four lines are observed (two polarised).

(4) Some other important structural determinations are of:

(*a*) Ions, e.g. BF_4^-, AlH_4^-, and $AuCl_4^-$ which have been shown to be planar, for instance, three lines were obtained for $AuCl_4^-$, one of which was polarised; this is what would be anticipated for a plane square shape.

(*b*) Liquid PCl_5 where the Raman spectrum is consistent with a molecule of the trigonal bipyramidal shape, since six Raman lines are obtained, two of which are polarised; solid PCl_5, however, gives more lines, and these are interpreted in terms of the ionic structure (PCl_4^+) (PCl_6^-).

(*c*) S_8 whose Raman spectrum consists of seven lines, two of which are polarised. This behaviour is consistent with the molecular shape being a puckered octagonal ring.

(*d*) The boron hydrides were examined, and the Raman spectrum ruled out an ethane-like model and favoured a bridge structure:

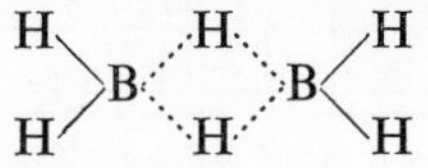

```
H       .H.       H
  \   .     .   /
   B          B
  /   .     .   \
H       'H'       H
```

The bridge structure consists of the

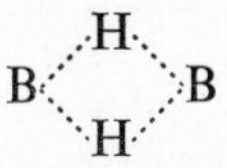

```
   .H.
B       B
   'H'
```

structure in one plane, while the four outer B—H bonds are also in a plane which is perpendicular to the first one. Again, the employment of the Raman method to distinguish between these two types of structure was based on how many lines would be anticipated from each structure. For the bridge type of structure three polarised and three depolarised lines would be expected. This was what was experimentally obtained.

Sufficient examples have now been given to indicate that it is possible to distinguish between certain molecular models of different symmetry from the number of fundamental frequencies observed and the number of these which are polarised. Other applications (not involving the theory of light scattering) are discussed later. For a review of the types of problem studied an article by Woodward[50] should be consulted.

Rotation-vibration Raman studies

So far only Raman lines have been discussed, and not Raman bands. Further, the difference in frequency between the exciting line and the Raman line has been associated with a vibrational frequency. However, if the change of polarisability during a vibration is not spherical, then it will be influenced by the rotation of the molecule, and the vibrational lines ought to have a rotational fine structure. The reason *lines* are referred to when *bands* are being observed is that the rotation-vibration changes are seen with a spectrograph of poor resolving power, where each single line is really composed of a number of lines so close together that they cannot be distinguished; thus, because of their line-like appearance the term *band* is not normally used.† Consider now the case of gases where with good resolution and long exposures the rotational structure of the bands may sometimes be observed. The low intensity of these spectra is one of the major difficulties, but the position has recently been improved by the use of a more intense mercury source.

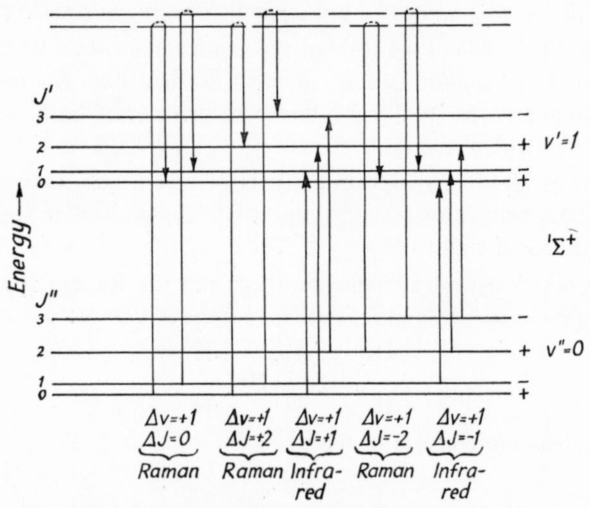

FIG. 4.48 Comparison of some infra-red and Raman rotation-vibration transitions

Rotation-vibration Raman spectra of diatomic and polyatomic molecules

In general, the selection rules governing such simultaneous changes in rotational and vibrational energy are $\Delta J = -2, -1, 0, +1, +2$, resulting in O, P, Q, R, S branches, respectively; the changes in v are given by $\Delta v = \pm 1$. In the case of linear molecules Δv is still ± 1, but $\Delta J = 0, \pm 2$, although sometimes $\Delta J = \pm 1$, is also involved. In Fig. 4.48 a comparison is made of the Raman and infra-red rotation-vibration transitions of a linear molecule.‡

† This does not rule out the pure vibrational energy change which would result in a single spectral line.

‡ The higher " energy levels " represented by dotted lines in Fig. 4.48 do not correspond with any energy states of the system, but are merely a diagrammatical way of indicating the energy of the light quantum above the initial state.

It may be observed from Fig. 4.48 that although the mechanism of accomplishing the energy change for the infra-red differs from that of the Raman, the effect is similar.

So far the *Q*-branch has been resolved only for a very limited number of cases, e.g. for H_2 and HCl, which have very small moments of inertia and consequently a larger separation of their rotational energy levels.

Assuming that the vibrational and rotational energies are additive, and that the centrifugal constant D_J may be neglected and letting $\Delta\nu_0$ be the vibrational frequency shift in cm^{-1} units, then $\Delta\nu$ the Raman displacement for the associated rotation-vibration transition of a linear molecule will be given by:

$$\Delta\nu = \Delta\nu_0 + (E_r' - E_r'')/hc = \Delta\nu_0 + B_{v'}J'(J'+1) - B_{v''}J''(J''+1)\dagger \quad (4.149)$$

where $\Delta\nu = \nu_{Hg} - \nu$ or $\Delta\nu = \nu - \nu_{Hg}$ and ν is the wave-number of the Raman line. Since nearly all molecules will be in their ground state, i.e. $v'' = 0$, and the usual change in the vibrational quantum number is $\Delta v = \pm 1$, it follows that, in general, $v' = +1$. The equations for the *S*-, *O*- and *Q*-branches may be obtained from equation (4.149) by substitution into it of:

$$J' = J''+2, \quad J' = J''-2 \quad \text{and} \quad J' = J'',$$

respectively. Thus:

S-branch:

$$J' = J''+2$$

$$\Delta\nu = \Delta\nu_0 + 6B_{v'} + (5B_{v'} - B_{v''})J'' + (B_{v'} - B_{v''})J''^2 \quad (4.150)$$

where

$$J'' = 0, 1, 2, 3, \text{etc.}$$

O-branch:

$$J' = J''-2$$

$$\Delta\nu = \Delta\nu_0 + 2B_{v'} - (3B_{v'} + B_{v''})J'' + (B_{v'} - B_{v''})J''^2 \quad (4.151)$$

where

$$J'' = 2, 3, 4, \text{etc.}$$

Q-branch:

$$J'' = J'$$

$$\Delta\nu = \Delta\nu_0 + (B_{v'} - B_{v''})J'' + (B_{v'} - B_{v''})J''^2 \quad (4.152)$$

where

$$J'' = 0, 1, 2, 3, \text{etc.}\ddagger$$

So far only H_2, CO_2, CS_2, and C_2H_2 have been examined.

The relative intensities of the *O*-, *S*-, and *Q*-branches for linear molecules depends on whether the vibrational angular momenta differ for the two vibrational states concerned, thus:

† For convenience the symbol ν_r or even ν is sometimes used instead of $\Delta\nu$.

‡ In equations (4.150), (4.151) and (4.152) it is customary to replace J'' by J.

(1) If it is the same, then the *Q*-branch is much the more intense, and the *O*- and *S*-branches do not appear to be even detectable.

(2) If it differs, then the intensity of the *Q*-branch will be low and the *O*- and *S*-branches more intense; in addition, *R*- and *P*-branches may appear.

Anti-Stokes, *Q*-, *S*-, and *O*-branches are possible, but since the majority of the molecules at ordinary temperatures are in the ground vibrational state, then in the $v = 1$ to $v = 0$ transition, the intensity of the lines would normally be very weak.

In the case of spherical-top molecules, e.g. CH_4, SF_6, CCl_4, for a totally symmetrical vibration, for example:

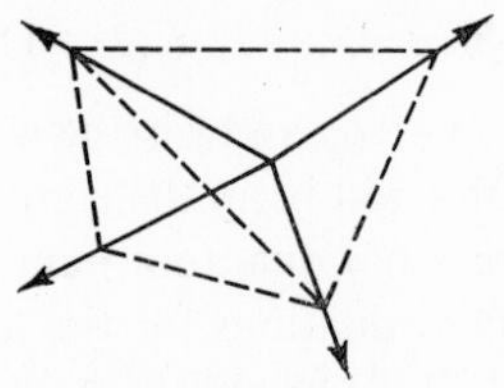

the selection rule is $\Delta J = 0$, and this results in a very sharp Raman line. The B_0's have been obtained for CH_4 and CD_4 from the $\frac{1}{2}$ and $\frac{1}{3}$ vibrational bands (see p. 122). For unsymmetrical vibrations, since the symmetry is altered, rotational changes accompany the vibrational change.

For symmetric-top molecules, when the top axis is not an axis of symmetry, the second quantum number *K* is involved, and the selection rules are:

$$\Delta K = 0, \pm 1, \pm 2, \quad \text{and} \quad \Delta J = 0, \pm 1, \pm 2$$

although if the molecule possesses some symmetry, certain values of ΔK do not appear, depending on the type of vibrational transition. The treatment is quite complex and the standard work by Herzberg[17] should be consulted. The spectrum of gaseous ammonia is one of the few examples of a rotation-vibration Raman study.

The difficulties of resolving a rotation-vibration Raman band for an asymmetric-top molecule are formidable,† and ethylene is the only such molecule to have had the rotational structure of some of its bands resolved.

So far not much Raman work has been done on the determination of rotational constants, from the rotational structure of vibrational Raman bands; the difficulties of such high resolution work have been discussed in a recent paper.[51]

† However, information may be gathered about the symmetry of the vibrations concerned:

(1) By studying the Raman line width; if a particular Raman line is much broader than the other Raman lines in the spectrogram, then it may be attributed to a non-totally symmetric vibration.

(2) If the degree of depolarisation of the Raman line is less than $\frac{6}{7}$, then it may be related to a totally symmetric vibration (see p. 160).

Applications of Raman spectroscopy

Qualitative and quantitative analysis

The vibrational frequencies determined from the Raman spectrum of a substance may be used in its identification. The normal spectroscopic procedure of comparing the spectrum of the unknown with that of known compounds is used.

To illustrate the application of the method, benzene and some of its substitution products will be considered. Liquid benzene has two intense absorption bands, one at 3047 cm^{-1} and the other at 3062 cm^{-1} which are due to the fundamental vibrational modes (*a*) and (*b*), respectively:

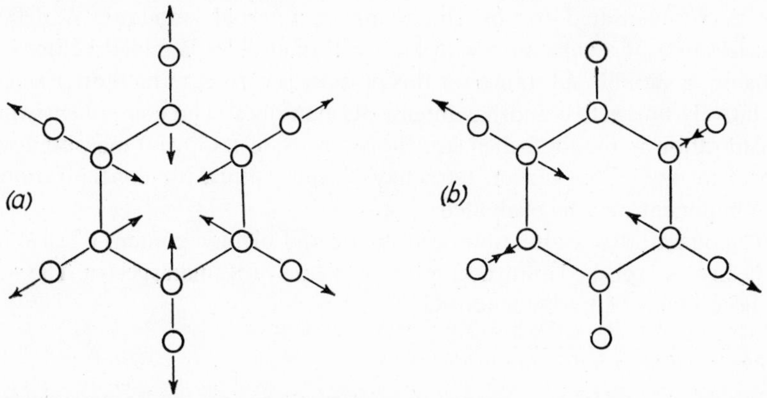

(a)

(b)

together with weak bands at 2925, 2948, 3164, 3187 cm^{-1}. These bands serve to identify benzene, but in addition there are a number of other bands at different magnitudes of frequency. The mono-, di- and tri-substituted benzenes have strong absorption bands between 3045 and 3070 cm^{-1}. All these frequencies are Raman active. In the case of the di-substituents, it is possible to distinguish the ortho-, meta- and para-isomers. Only the meta-substituent has an intense strongly polarised line at 995 cm^{-1}, while the para-substituent has one at about 625 cm^{-1} which is generally absent in ortho-derivatives. In addition, the ortho-compound usually has a more detailed spectrum than the para-compound.

The Raman spectra of a mixture consists simply of the superposed spectra of the components in the mixture. One extensive application of its usefulness has been in the qualitative analysis of mixtures of hydrocarbons. Such analysis have been particularly valuable to oil companies where a standard procedure can be employed. The instruments used for this work are automatically scanning and produce a record on a chart. Before this development the time required to photograph the Raman effect was longer than the time required for a recording infra-red spectrophotometer, and this caused the infra-red technique to be much more widely used for the study of qualitative analysis problems. This led to the Raman technique being applied to more special problems, for instance as a guide in preparative work; one example of this was to follow the reaction:

$$SeF_4+SeO_2 \rightarrow 2SeOF_2$$

The appearance of the $SeOF_2$ spectrum was noted, while the completion of the reaction was detected by the disappearance of the lines due to SeF_4.

The Raman effect is also used in quantitative analysis. Unlike the infra-red method, the intensity of a Raman line is, in general, directly proportional to the volume concentration of the species. Several experimental difficulties may be encountered in its application to quantitative problems. Two of the most important are the presence of fluorescent materials in the sample to be analysed and the fluctuation in the intensity of the light source. The latter may be compensated for by employing an internal standard. A definite concentration of a substance with known Raman lines is added before each exposure; a suitable substance for this purpose is carbon tetrachloride since it is relatively unreactive and has intense Raman lines. The component whose concentration is required then has the intensity of its line(s) measured with respect to one of the carbon tetrachloride lines; thus, the concentration of the component may be evaluated.

The quantitative estimation of aromatic and olefinic content of gasolines has been accomplished quite accurately by means of Raman spectra. The work has been reviewed by Dudenbostel.[52]

Raman studies on inorganic acids

Ingold *et al.*[53a,53b] have carried out investigations on the Raman spectrum of nitric acid. There is a line† at 1050 cm^{-1} in the Raman spectrum of aqueous nitric acid which is also found in the spectrum of the alkali nitrates, and thus this must be a frequency of the nitrate ion itself. The 1050 cm^{-1} line is less intense in concentrated nitric acid solution than in solutions of alkali nitrates of the same concentrations. This is taken as evidence of un-dissociated molecules. By using the above fact and the relation of the intensity of the 1050 cm^{-1} line to the nitrate ion concentration, it has been possible to calculate dissociation constants for nitric acid at various concentrations.

The Raman spectrum of pure nitric acid consists of the following bands:

610 cm^{-1} due to bending of the O—N—OH angle;
680 cm^{-1} due to bending of the O—N—O group;
925 cm^{-1} due to stretching of the N—OH bond;
1300 cm^{-1} due to symmetric stretching of the NO_2 group;
1675 cm^{-1} due to antisymmetric stretching of the NO_2 group;
3400 cm^{-1} due to O—H stretching, diffuse owing to intermolecular hydrogen bonding;
1535 cm^{-1} due to first overtone of the out-of-plane vibration of the NO_3 group;

† As a microphotometric plot will be considered the word 'band' is perhaps more appropriate.

1050 cm^{-1} due to nitrate ion NO_3^-;

1400 cm^{-1} due to nitronium ion NO_2^+.

The 1050 and 1400 cm^{-1} lines are weak and have been attributed to the self-dissociation of the nitric acid molecule; thus:

$$2HNO_3 = H_2O + NO_2^+ + NO_3^-$$

Support for the identification of the 1400 cm^{-1} line with the NO_2^+ ion is forthcoming from the Raman spectra of several nitronium salts which have been studied, e.g. ($NO_2^+ClO_4^-$). Furthermore, it has been shown that the addition of either perchloric acid or selenic acid reduces the 1050 cm^{-1} line while the 1400 cm^{-1} line is enhanced. This could be explained by the following reactions:

$$HNO_3 + 2HClO_4 = H_3O^+ + NO_2^+ + 2ClO_4^-$$

$$HNO_3 + 2H_2SeO_4 = H_3O^+ + NO_2^+ + 2HSeO_4^-$$

where the consumption of HNO_3 diminishes the amount available for ionisation to NO_3^-. If sulphuric acid is used

$$HNO_3 + 2H_2SO_4 = H_3O^+ + NO_2^+ + 2HSO_4^-$$

i.e. the same behaviour is observed. It seemed at first that both the NO_3^- and NO_2^+ lines at 1050 and 1400 cm^{-1}, respectively, were enhanced, but it was later shown that HSO_4^- itself has a Raman line at 1050 cm^{-1}, owing to the stretching of the S—OH bond. These points are illustrated in the microphotometric spectrograms for these mixtures in Fig. 4.49. Considerable work has also been done on the ionisation of aqueous H_2SO_4 using a line at 910 cm^{-1} to identify the undissociated sulphuric acid molecule, the 1050 cm^{-1} line for the HSO_4^-, and a line at 980 cm^{-1} for the SO_4^{2-}. Thus, by comparing the intensity of the 980 cm^{-1} line in a solution of $(NH_4)_2SO_4$, of known concentration where the salt is totally ionised, and in H_2SO_4 solution, the SO_4^{2-} concentration can be calculated. The HSO_4^- concentration is obtained from the 1050 cm^{-1} line, and the concentration of H_2SO_4 molecules is obtained by difference. The latter should probably be proportional to the intensity of the 910 cm^{-1} line. The data satisfied this test.

It was shown that the HSO_4^- ion is the major constituent of moderately concentrated sulphuric acid; only above 14 molal does the H_2SO_4 molecule contribute significantly. The SO_4^{2-} concentration is small except in extremely dilute solutions.

Raman studies on inorganic ions and molecules

A very simple but striking Raman study was made by Woodward[54] who verified that the mercurous ion in aqueous solution was $(Hg—Hg)^{2+}$, since it gave a vibrational Raman effect. If it had been Hg^+, then obviously it could not have done this.

Many studies have been made on inorganic ions and molecules. Of particular interest is the result when certain metallic halides, e.g. $SnCl_4$ and $SnBr_4$, are mixed together; in addition to the Raman lines attributable to the individual halides themselves, new lines, i.e. vibrational frequencies, are

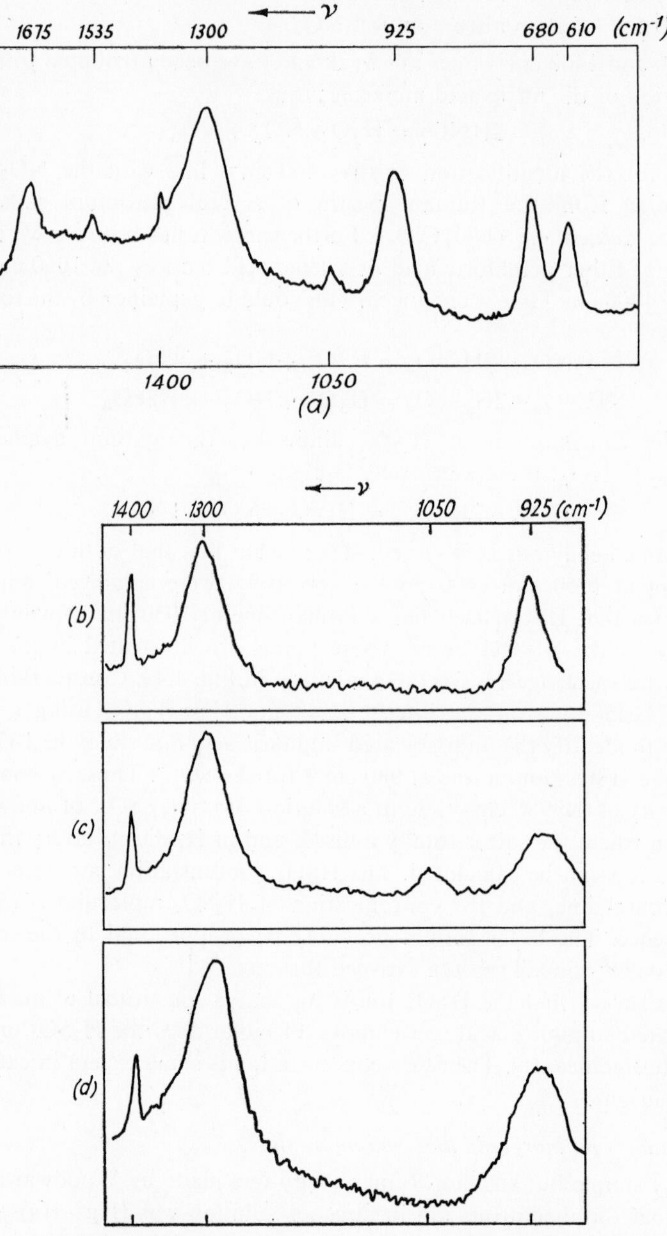

FIG. 4.49 Microphotometric record of part of the Raman spectra of: (*a*) pure HNO_3, (*b*) HNO_3+HClO_4, (*c*) $HNO_3+H_2SO_4$, (*d*) $HNO_3+H_2SeO_4$. The 4358 Å line of mercury was employed as the exciting line. (*a*) *After Ingold and Millen.*[53a] *and* (*b*), (*c*) *and* (*d*) *after Ingold, Millen and Poole.*[53b] *Courtesy of Professor C. K. Ingold, F.R.S. and The Chemical Society, London*)

observed. These lines have been related to the formation of mixed halides in labile equilibrium with one another and with the original molecules themselves.

(C) CORRELATION OF INFRA-RED AND RAMAN SPECTRA

The infra-red and Raman methods of investigating molecules have been treated separately earlier in this chapter. It is the object of this section to show that, in fact, the two methods are often complementary; the studies in one field frequently supplement or confirm the information derived from the other.

For linear molecules which have a centre of symmetry the fundamental vibrations symmetrical about the centre are not active in the infra-red but are active in the Raman and vice versa. Studies on molecules possessing a centre of symmetry would then be incomplete if both methods were not used.

For both the infra-red and Raman methods the frequency corresponding to a particular vibrational energy change (changes in rotational energy are neglected in these considerations) may be related to definite types of atomic displacement within the molecule. The methods by which the observed frequencies are related to the vibrational frequencies include the following:

(*a*) Intensity and symmetry considerations.

(*b*) Polarisation of Raman lines.

(*c*) Band contours.

Each of these will now briefly be mentioned in turn.

The intensity of an observed frequency corresponding to a particular vibrational energy change is not usually the same in infra-red and Raman spectra. Generally, in fact, if the infra-red absorption band is strong, the Raman line will be weak and vice versa. The reason for the differing intensities of the two types of spectra is related to the factors which determine the intensities. The intensity of an infra-red band depends on the magnitude of the electric dipole moment change associated with the molecular vibration whose vibrational energy is being altered; that of a Raman band depends on the magnitude of the change in polarisability associated with the vibration Hence frequencies related to the motion of strong polar linkages lead to intense infra-red spectra, while the presence of highly-polarisable linkages gives rise to intense Raman spectra. For a group such as C—Cl, which has an appreciable electric dipole moment and is readily polarisable, both the infra-red and Raman methods lead to intense vibrational bands.

The symmetry of a molecule also plays a part in determining the intensity of absorption. For example, with small molecules the more symmetric vibrations will often lead to a strong Raman band, while less symmetric vibrations will often give an intense infra-red band.

The application of the degree of polarisation of a Raman line to indicate whether symmetrical or anti-symmetrical vibrations are being considered was dealt with on p. 160.

A highly polarised Raman line may be associated with a symmetric vibration, while a depolarised line implies an asymmetric vibrational mode.

The appearance of the band contour may be employed to distinguish between a parallel and a perpendicular vibration (see p. 104). For example in the case of a linear molecule the perpendicular vibration has a *Q*-branch while a parallel vibration does not. This may be observed by comparing Figs. 4.16 and 4.17.

Infra-red and Raman vibrational studies of the alkanes

Infra-red and Raman spectra have been widely used to characterise molecules or groups within molecules. Consider now the different types of vibrations encountered in the alkanes. For more details on the infra-red and Raman spectra of hydrocarbons a review by Sheppard and Simpson[55] should be consulted; a wider background of spectral procedure may be obtained from this.

C—H *group*

In alkane systems one type of absorption may be related to the stretching vibration of the carbon-hydrogen bonds, i.e.

$$\leftarrow\!\!-\text{H}\text{——C}$$

and this usually appears in the 3000 to 2700 cm^{-1} range. This frequency may be determined by both the infra-red and Raman methods. The precise value of the frequency depends on the other three groups attached to this carbon atom.

Fox and Martin[56] have distinguished between the methyl, methylene, and tertiary CH groups by infra-red spectra using the following values for the symmetric stretching vibration for the carbon–hydrogen bond:

H
H—C 2872cm^{-1}
H

H
C 2853cm^{-1}
H

H—C 2890cm^{-1}

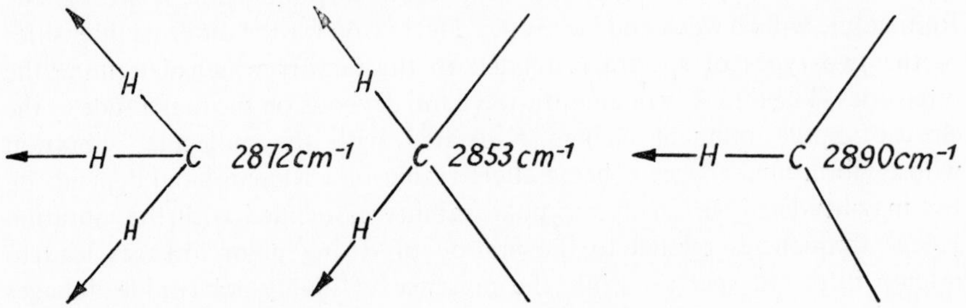

and for the asymmetrical modes:

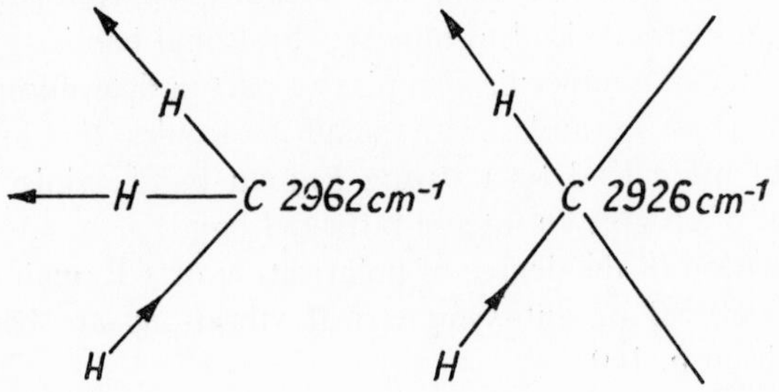

H
H—C 2962cm^{-1}
H

H
C 2926cm^{-1}
H

CH_2 *group*

The CH_2 group is capable of the four deformation modes—*bending*, *rocking*, *twisting*, and *wagging vibrations* shown in Fig. 4.50. The CH_2 group itself when attached to a heavy framework has all four of these vibrational modes. These deformation modes involving changes in the valence angles and the frequencies occur in the range 1500 to 600 cm^{-1}.

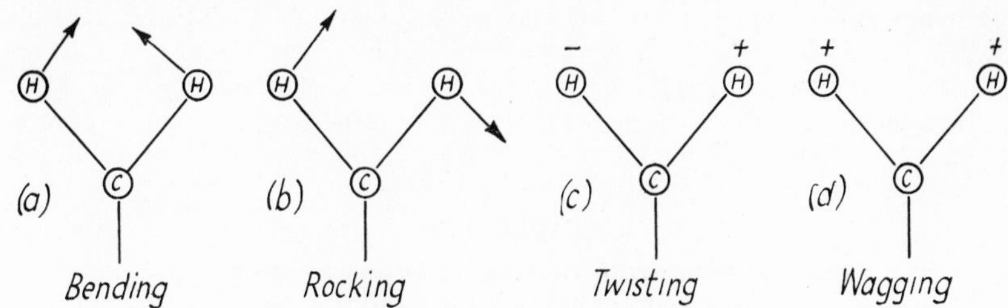

FIG. 4.50 Deformation vibrations of the CH_2 group

The bending and rocking modes take place in the plane of the paper, and the wagging involves simultaneous movement of the hydrogens out of the plane of the paper both in the same direction; this is indicated by means of the positive signs, while for the twisting motion the positive and negative signs indicate displacements in opposite directions perpendicular to the plane of the paper.

The bending vibration is both infra-red and Raman active and occurs in the 1470 to 1440 cm^{-1} range. The CH_2 wagging and twisting frequencies, however, are not found in such a narrow frequency region, and, in fact, their range is approximately 1350 to 1150 cm^{-1} and may be both infra-red and Raman active. The CH_2 rocking mode, however, is only active in the infra-red and for long chain n-paraffins in the liquid phase occurs in the 720 cm^{-1} region.

CH_3 *group*

Methyl groups have the following characteristic C—H bending vibrations:

(1) Where all the three C—H bonds bend in and out in phase. This is termed the *symmetrical breathing vibration.*

(2) An asymmetrical mode where two C—H bonds bend in while the third bends out.

The asymmetrical mode appears in the range 1470 to 1440 cm^{-1} and leads to intense infra-red and Raman spectra. The symmetrical bending mode occurs as an intense band in the infra-red region at about 1380 cm^{-1}. The effect on the 1380 cm^{-1} band for the symmetrical C—H bending vibrations of the CH_3 group brought about by replacing successive hydrogen atoms by methyl groups is indicated in Table 4.19.

Thus, the infra-red 1380 cm^{-1} band splits on replacement of the hydrogen atoms by methyl groups.

TABLE 4.19

Symmetrical C—H *bending frequencies* (cm^{-1}) *of the methyl group*

Group	Frequency (cm^{-1})		Relative intensity
Methyl CH_3—C<	1378		—
*iso*propyl $(CH_3)_2C<$	1385	1368	1 : 1
tert.-butyl $(CH_3)_3C$—	1397	1370	1 : 2

TABLE 4.20

Principal characteristic vibrations of saturated hydrocarbons
(after Jones and Sandorfy[35])

Frequency	Group	Type of vibration †
3040	methylene	C—H stretching vibration in cyclopropane ring.
2962	methyl	Asymmetrical stretching vibration of C—H bond.
2926	methylene	Asymmetrical stretching vibration of C—H bond.
2890‡	*tert.*-CH group	Stretching vibration of C—H bond.
2872	methyl	Symmetrical stretching vibration of C—H bond.
2853	methylene	Symmetrical stretching vibration of C—H bond.
1467	methylene	C—H bending vibration in linear methylene chain.
1460	methyl	Asymmetrical C—H bending vibration.
1455	methylene	C—H bending vibration in cyclopentane ring.
1452	methylene	C—H bending vibration in cyclohexane ring.
1397§ 1370§	*tert.*-butyl group	Symmetrical C—H bending vibrations of methyl groups.
1385§ 1368§	*iso*propyl and *gem.*-dimethyl groups	Symmetrical C—H bending vibrations of methyl groups.
1378§	methyl	Symmetrical C—H bending vibrations.
1350–1150	methylene	C—H wagging and twisting vibrations.
1345‖	*iso*propyl	?
1305¶	methylene	C—H wagging.
1250 1210	*tert.*-butyl	CH_3—C rocking vibration (?).
1170	*iso*propyl	CH_3—C rocking vibration (?).
1141–1132	methyl in *n*-paraffins	CH_3—C rocking vibration (?).
955	*iso*propyl	C—C vibration.
930	*tert.*-butyl	C—C vibration.
920	*iso*propyl	C—C vibration.
835–739¶	*tert.*-butyl	C—C vibration.
720§	—$(CH_2)_3$—	C—H rocking vibration.

† These refer to *n*-paraffins unless otherwise indicated.
‡ Inferred from indirect evidence only. § Not observed in the Raman spectrum.
‖ Not observed in the infra-red spectrum.
¶ Strong in Raman but weak in infra-red spectrum.

In addition, the CH_3 group also has two rocking modes. The rocking modes give rise to strong Raman lines and intense infra-red bands and appear in the range 1250 to 800 cm^{-1}. Table 4.20 summarises the principal characteristic vibrations of the saturated hydrocarbons.

Skeletal vibrations are also present in the alkanes. To illustrate what is meant by this type of vibration consider the $C(CH_3)_4$ molecule. Some of the vibrations in this seventeen-atom molecule are due essentially to the five unit system of CX_4, where X is CH_3. X is regarded as a single unit. Vibrations which can be attributed to the movements of the X groups as a whole against the central carbon atom are known as *skeletal vibrations.*

Three of the skeletal vibrational modes of neo-pentane $C(CH_3)_4$ have been identified with certainty, and these are listed in Table 4.21; note that only one of these three modes is obtained by the infra-red method.

TABLE 4.21

Three of the skeletal modes of neo-pentane

Type of vibration	Degeneracy	Wave-number (cm^{-1})	Raman line	Infra-red line
Symmetrical skeletal stretching	1	733	Polarised	Inactive
Doubly degenerate skeletal deformation vibration	2	335	Depolarised	Inactive
Triply degenerate skeletal deformation vibration	3	415	Depolarised	Active

Vibrational analysis of acetylene molecule

Many absorption bands are known for the acetylene molecule in the infra-red region. Two of these bands are reproduced in Figs. 4.51 and 4.52

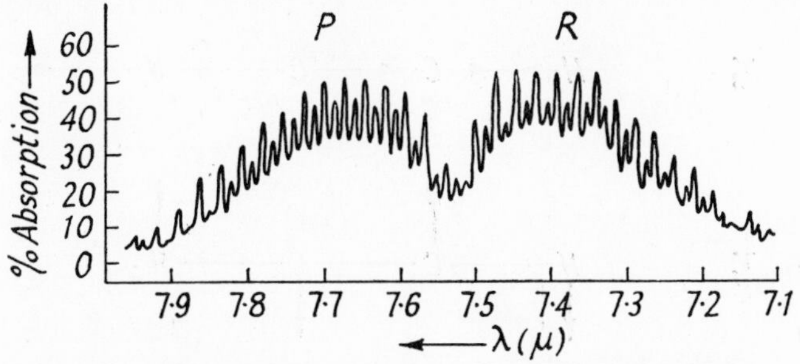

FIG. 4.51 Rotational fine structure of the combination band $\nu_4+\nu_5$ for the acetylene molecule in the 7.5 μ region. (*After Levin and Meyer.*[57] *Courtesy of 'The Journal of the Optical Society of America'*)

where it is immediately apparent that the 7.5 μ band has quite a simple structure. It consists of two branches—the *P*- and *R*- branches separated by a gap. In addition, the alternating intensities of the individual rotational lines in both the 7.5 μ and the 13.7 μ bands may be readily observed.

Since spherical-top, symmetric-top, and asymmetric-top molecules can never give infra-red bands consisting of a single *P*- and *R*-branch separated by a gap, it follows, without any detailed study, that the acetylene molecule is linear. Moreover, the presence of the intensity alternation in these two

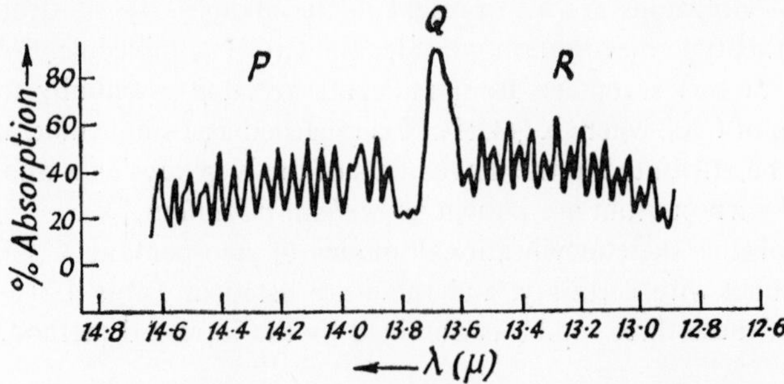

FIG. 4.52 Rotational fine structure of the fundamental vibration band ν_5 of the acetylene molecule in the 13.7 μ region. (*After Levin and Meyer.*[57] *Courtesy of 'The Journal of the Optical Society of America'*)

bands proves that the linear acetylene molecule is also symmetrical. Bearing these two facts in mind together with the valency of carbon and hydrogen there can be no doubt that the acetylene molecule has the atoms arranged as follows:

H—C—C—H

A linear molecule which contains four atoms should have seven ($3n-5$) fundamental modes of vibration. Of these only the following five are known:

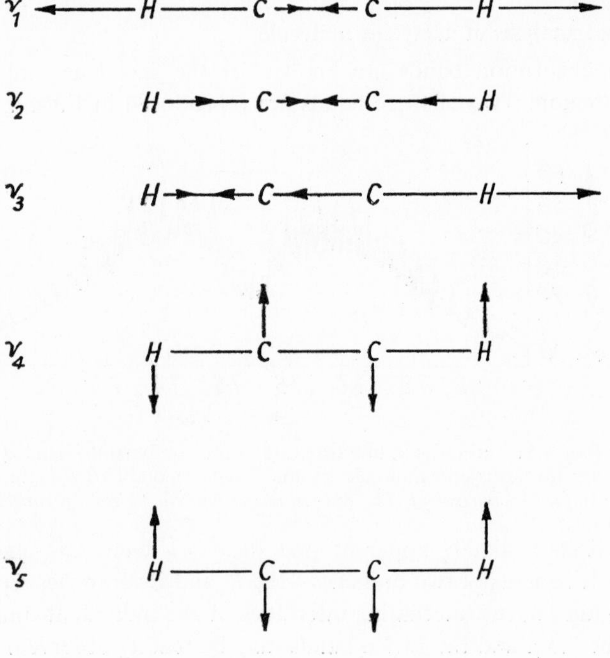

These vibrations may be accounted for as follows. The acetylene molecule can be regarded as consisting of three units, two CH and one C≡C group, each of which may vibrate with a frequency related to the force constant of the particular diatomic unit, while the other units are considered fixed. Each C—H group will then vibrate with a frequency related to the ≡C—H stretching or bending force constant. These vibrations may only be symmetric or antisymmetrical with respect to each other giving two ≡C—H vibrations in the axis of the molecule, ν_1 and ν_3, and two perpendicular to it, ν_4 and ν_5. Finally there is the ν_2 vibration which is largely governed by the force constant of the C≡C stretching mode where the CH groups are regarded as moving as rigid units. Thus, the five vibrational modes listed may be explained. In addition ν_4 and ν_5 are both doubly degenerate since they can take place in a plane perpendicular to the plane in which they are represented. This gives two additional modes, and therefore the seven theoretical modes may be accounted for.

Since the ν_1, ν_2 and ν_4 vibrations are completely symmetric with respect to the centre of the molecule no change in electric dipole moment will result. ν_1, ν_2, and ν_4 are, therefore, inactive in the infra-red. Since, however, the polarisability of the molecule will change during these vibrations they should be Raman active. For the ν_3 and ν_5 vibrations, however, there is a change of dipole moment during the vibration. There are thus two infra-red active vibrations ν_3 and ν_5 and three Raman active vibrations ν_1, ν_2, and ν_4.

Below 3500 cm^{-1} acetylene has three intense infra-red absorption bands at 3287 cm^{-1}, 1327 cm^{-1}, and 729 cm^{-1}. The 729 cm^{-1} band exhibits a strong *Q*-branch (see Fig. 4.52). Since this 729 cm^{-1} band is the only intense perpendicular band it is identified with the only perpendicular infra-red active vibration ν_5. Furthermore, a deformation vibration would be expected to be at a lower frequency than a valence vibration. The remaining infra-red active vibration can be identified with the 3287 cm^{-1} parallel band since it is known from diatomic spectra that the CH vibration of which ν_3 is composed has a characteristic value in the 3000 cm^{-1} region. The remaining intense infra-red 1327 cm^{-1} absorption band is, therefore, likely to be an overtone or a combination frequency. One possibility for this 1327 cm^{-1} band would be that it was the combination band $\nu_4+\nu_5$. This would make $\nu_4 \simeq 597$ cm^{-1}, and, in fact, the value of 612 cm^{-1} is obtained as the experimental Raman value.

As regards the Raman spectrum of acetylene there are three strong Raman frequencies observed at 612 cm^{-1}, 1974 cm^{-1}, and 3374 cm^{-1}. For the same reason as for the 3287 cm^{-1} band the 3374 cm^{-1} frequency is identified with the CH valence vibration ν_1, while the 1974 cm^{-1} frequency being too large for a deformation vibration is identified with the ν_2 mode. Since the 612 cm^{-1} is the only observed Raman frequency of the order of a bending vibration, then its most probable identification is with the ν_4 mode. This value of 612 cm^{-1} for ν_4 is consistent with the assignment of the 1327 cm^{-1} band in the infra-red to the combination band $\nu_4+\nu_5$.

Although the C_2H_2 and the C_2D_2 molecules have a centre of symmetry it should be noted that the C_2HD molecule is not symmetrical, and, therefore, all fundamentals are infra-red and Raman active. In fact, all the C_2HD fundamentals have been observed by the infra-red method and are given in column 3 of Table 4.22. The ν_1, ν_2, and ν_4 frequencies in columns 2 and 4 were determined by the Raman method, and the ν_3 and ν_5 frequencies by the infra-red.

TABLE 4.22

The fundamental frequencies (cm^{-1}) of C_2H_2, C_2HD, and C_2D_2

Fundamental	C_2H_2	C_2HD	C_2D_2
ν_1	3374	3335	2700
ν_2	1974	1851	1762
ν_3	3287	2584	2427
ν_4	612	519	505
ν_5	729	683	539

Vibrational analysis of carbon tetrachloride molecule

From a spectral point of view various investigators have doubted the symmetric tetrahedral nature of CCl_4. However, when the spectral data on this molecule was finally collated and assessed, it definitely supported a symmetric tetrahedral model. The eight Raman frequencies observed for liquid CCl_4 are listed in column (1) of Table 4.23 while some infra-red frequencies are listed in column (2). Five of the Raman shifts may be seen in the spectrogram in Fig. 4.38(J).

TABLE 4.23

Some vibrational frequencies of liquid CCl_4

Vibrational frequencies obtained by the Raman method (cm^{-1})	Bands observed in the infra-red† (cm^{-1})	Assignment of observed frequencies
145		$\nu_1-\nu_4$
218 strongly depolarised		ν_2
314 strongly depolarised	305	ν_4
434		$2\nu_2$
~460 very strongly polarised		ν_1
762 medium depolarised	768	} ν_3, $\nu_1+\nu_4$
791 medium depolarised	797	} ν_3, $\nu_1+\nu_4$
1539 very weakly polarised	1546	$2\nu_1+2\nu_4$

† For simplicity some of the infra-red bands have been omitted.

Three of the Raman shifts, the 145, 434, and 1539 cm^{-1} were too faint to be observed under the exposure time in that experiment. These very faint lines are, therefore, probably overtone or combination bands. In addition, since the vibrational frequency of diatomic CCl is 844 cm^{-1}, this rules out the 1539 cm^{-1} frequency from being a fundamental as the CCl breathing frequency would have the largest value of the fundamental frequencies. For a tetrahedral model four Raman active fundamental frequencies ν_1, ν_2, ν_3, and ν_4 (see p. 122) and two infra-red active fundamental, ν_3 and ν_4, would be anticipated. In addition, with a tetrahedral model as regards the four fundamentals and their Raman spectrum, one of the Raman lines, the ν_1, should be almost completely polarised, while the other three should be depolarised. Since the 460 cm^{-1} line is strongly polarised and none of the others is, then this line may be identified with ν_1. The 762 and the 791 cm^{-1} lines are considered to be a doublet and are not treated as two distinct vibrational frequencies. They are termed the 775 cm^{-1} doublet band.† The infra-red spectrum shows two very strong bands—one at 305 cm^{-1}, and the other is the 775 cm^{-1} doublet band; these bands are identified with ν_4 and ν_3 respectively. Since the Raman 145, 434, and 1539 cm^{-1} bands are probably either overtone or combination ones, then since ν_1, ν_3, and ν_4 have been identified, it follows that the 218 cm^{-1} band is probably the ν_2 one. These facts together and the absence of the 218 cm^{-1} and 460 cm^{-1} bands in the infra-red lead to the interpretation of Raman and infra-red spectra in terms of a tetrahedral model. Some of the other frequencies observed by the infra-red and Raman methods are interpreted in column 3 in Table 4.23 as overtone and combination frequencies.

Hydrogen bond studies‡

The hydroxyl absorption band due to the O—H stretching frequency in Z—O—H compounds is dependent on the nature of Z and on the phase in which the measurements are made. As an example of the latter, methyl alcohol may be considered. In the gaseous phase at reasonably high temperatures or in very dilute solution this compound has an OH band at about 3640 cm^{-1}, whereas in the pure liquid both infra-red and Raman spectra indicate that it has an additional absorption band at about 3400 cm^{-1}. The 3640 cm^{-1} band is attributed to a monomeric form of CH_3OH, whereas the 3400 cm^{-1} is attributed to some form of methyl alcohol polymer.

The dependence of the OH stretching frequency on the nature of Z is given in Table 4.24.

The O—H (stretching frequency) band of CH_3OH in very dilute solution occurs at 3640 cm^{-1}, whereas that of water is at 3750 cm^{-1}. This lowering of

† The 775 cm^{-1} doublet structure may be explained in terms of what is known as *Fermi resonance* between ν_3 and $(\nu_1+\nu_4)$. This may occur when the two excited levels arising from the different vibrations have almost the same energy. In addition, these vibrational levels must have the same symmetry. What is known as a *perturbation* of the energy levels takes place, and this results in the two vibrational levels modifying each other, so that one has a lower vibrational energy than would be anticipated, while the other has a higher one.

‡ The *hydrogen bridge* would seem a more satisfactory term since the similarity with a conventional chemical bond is small.

frequency from H_2O to CH_3OH has been ascribed to such resonance contributions as:

$$H^-CH_2 = \overset{+}{O}—H$$

which weaken the O—H bond. In general, the O—H stretching frequency is lowered with increasing positive charge on the oxygen atom, and in a dilute solution of phenol the lowering of the value to 3610 cm^{-1} is to be associated with a resonance form such as:

$$^{-}:\!C_6H_4\!=\!\overset{+}{O}—H$$

Furthermore, if electron-attracting substituents are substituted into the phenol ring, then an increased positive charge is to be found in the oxygen atom, and the O—H stretching frequency is lowered.

TABLE 4.24

The dependence of the OH *stretching frequency in some alcohols on the nature of* Z (after Flett[58])

Compound	Molality of compound in CCl_4	Wave-number of peak (cm^{-1})
methyl alcohol	0.00324	3640
ethyl alcohol	0.00322	3632
*iso*propyl alcohol	0.00300	3620
allyl alcohol	0.00309	3620
cyclohexanol	0.00327	3615

In monomeric formic acid the fundamental —O→—←H stretching frequency is found at 3570 cm^{-1}. The monomer exists only at higher temperatures, and at the lower temperature the dimer is formed, and a band is observed at 3080 cm^{-1} which has to be ascribed to the O—H stretching vibration frequency in the dimer. Thus, a substantial shift in frequency has occurred, and this is attributed to what is known as *intermolecular hydrogen bonding*. This type of bonding is sufficient to hold the two formic acid molecules together so that they behave as one unit. However, the strength of such intermolecular hydrogen bonds is usually of the order of 2 to 10 kcal/mole, and this value is much less than of a normal chemical bond. Such intermolecular hydrogen bonds exist in solutions of alcohols and phenols except the very dilute ones.

The hydrogen bond is found to occur when a hydrogen atom lies in between two highly electronegative atoms such as O and F or O and N and would be represented as follows:

$$—O—H\ .\ .\ .\ F \qquad —O—H\ .\ .\ .\ N\!\lessdot$$

When the hydrogen bonding takes place within the molecule itself, this is known as intra-molecular hydrogen bonding, and an example of this is to be found in salicyclic acid:

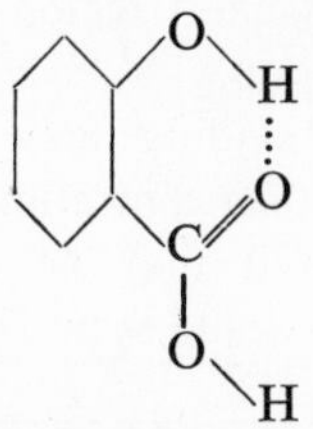

$$\text{(salicylic acid: benzene ring bearing } -O-H \cdots O{=}C(-O-H)\text{)}$$

Sutherland[59] has listed the frequency displacements which take place on intermolecular hydrogen bonding and has given the following regions for the fundamental band of the O—H stretching frequency for the different types of hydrogen bonding:

—O—H · · · O—	3500–3200 cm^{-1}
—O—H · · · O=C—	3300–2830 cm^{-1}
—N—H · · · O=C—	3320–3240 cm^{-1}
—N—H · · · N$\lessdot$	3300–3156 cm^{-1}

Hydrogen bonding may be recognised by such shifts in the fundamental frequency[60] and by the splitting or broadening of such bands with an enhanced intensity of the vibrational transitions.

In dilute solution the free N—H fundamental bands are to be found at 3500 and 3380 cm^{-1}; these free N—H bands are usually narrow and sharp and correspond to the N—H stretching vibrations;

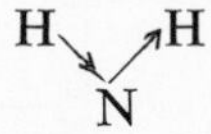

H↘ ↗H N	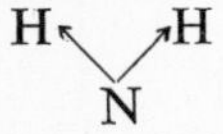 H↖ ↗H N
3500 cm^{-1}	3380 cm^{-1}

that is the asymmetrical and symmetrical vibrations, respectively. The N—H stretching bands have been studied by both the infra-red and Raman techniques for a number of primary and secondary aliphatic amines in carbon tetrachloride solution. This approach may be employed to follow the effect of concentration on intermolecular hydrogen bonding. As the concentration is increased both the symmetrical and asymmetrical stretching frequencies shift to lower frequencies. This has been attributed to the following type of hydrogen bond formation:

—N—H · · · N$\lessdot$

Both the infra-red and Raman methods may be employed to study the effect of hydrogen bonding on the O—H stretching frequency. In the case of alcohols the non-hydrogen bonding O—H in solution results in a sharp infra-red band between about 3640 and 3610 cm^{-1}. For pure alcohols and those in sufficiently-concentrated solution to be intermolecularly hydrogen-bonded a fairly broad infra-red band occurs in the 3380 to 3300 cm^{-1}

region. This behaviour of the infra-red spectra of the alcohols is very similar to that of their Raman bands which are to be found between about 3630 cm^{-1} and 3380 cm^{-1}, where the 3630 cm^{-1} region is to be attributed to the non-hydrogen bonding hydroxyl group.

Intermolecular hydrogen bonding may be detected by examining a number of solutions of different concentrations. When the spectrum becomes independent of dilution, then it may be concluded that intermolecular hydrogen bonding is absent. It would seem from the majority of compounds

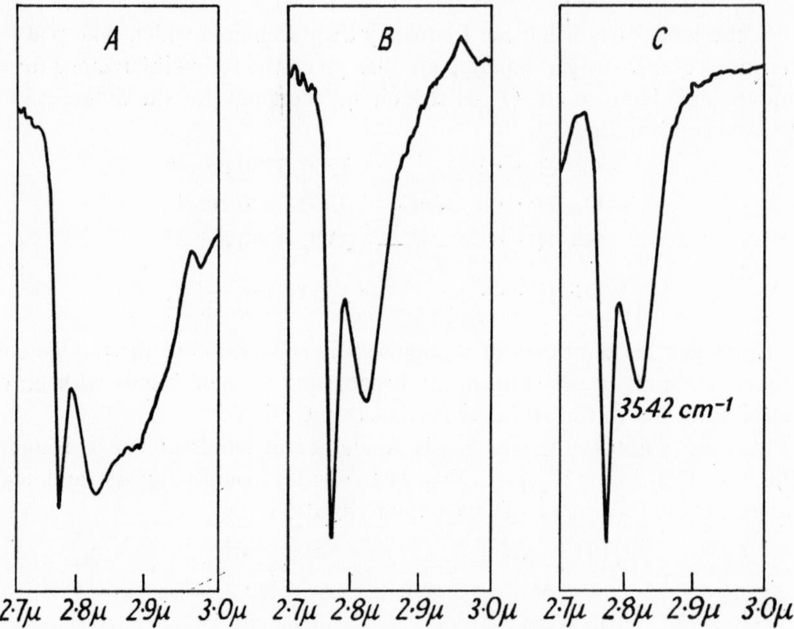

FIG. 4.53 The infra-red spectrum between 2.7 and 3.0 μ of 2-allylphenol in carbon tetrachloride solution, where the curves *A*, *B*, and *C* are those for 0.7, 0.07, and 0.007 M solutions, respectively. The ordinates are proportional to percentage transmission. (*After Baker and Shulgin.*[61] *Courtesy of 'The Journal of the American Chemical Society'*)

containing OH that the intermolecular hydrogen bonding is no longer present (or detectable) at concentrations less than about 0.0005 M. Broadening, strengthening, and splitting of the fundamental OH band are good indications of the presence of hydrogen bonding. Generally, as the strength of a linear hydrogen bond increases the stretching frequency is lowered, the band is broadened in contour and has an enhanced integrated intensity. In addition, non-linear bonded systems are also affected in these ways, although their behaviour is less pronounced.

The intermolecular bonding may be distinguished from the intramolecular hydrogen bonding in that the intra type is independent of dilution. Some of the strongest intramolecular hydrogen bonds occur in aromatic systems when an OH substituent is adjacent to a nitrogen atom.

The majority of hydrogen-bond studies has been made in dilute solution, and in such cases—especially when the bands are broad, as, for example, with alcohols—then the infra-red method is to be preferred. In general, the Raman approach is more suited to hydrogen-bond studies in concentrated solution, the pure liquid, and the solid state.

To illustrate how the infra-red method may be employed to study both inter- and intra-molecular hydrogen bonding some work by Baker and Shulgin[61] will now be considered. Their results for 2-allylphenol in carbon tetrachloride solutions are given in Fig. 4.53.

In the 0.7 M solution of 2-allylphenol there is a band at 3605 cm^{-1}. This band is given by each of the three solutions and is almost identical with that of the stretching frequency of the OH group in phenol. Hence, this frequency is attributed to a non-hydrogen bonded hydroxyl group. As the concentration is diminished from 0.7 to 0.07 M the very broad band at 2.9 μ is markedly decreased, and in the 0.007 M solution has disappeared. This band is, therefore, attributed to intermolecular hydrogen bonding, since this would diminish with decreasing concentration. The band at 3542 cm^{-1} which is given by all three solutions and not by phenol itself is, therefore, attributed to the following intramolecular hydrogen bonding:

CH₂
O—H · · · ‖
CH
|
CH₂ (attached to the benzene ring ortho to O)

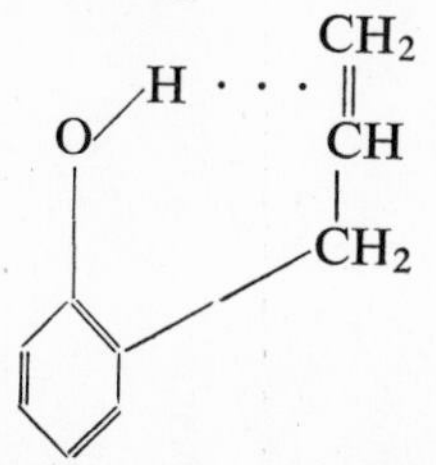

where the hydrogen in the OH group is bonded to the π electrons of the ethylenic double bond. This results in an average shift ($\Delta\nu_{O-H}$) of the OH frequency of 3605–3542, that is of 63 cm^{-1}.

Richards and Walker in a series of papers[62] have shown how it can be advantageous in certain cases to couple the dipole moment and infra-red approaches for the study of certain intramolecular hydrogen bonding problems. This is particularly so when (i) the intramolecular hydrogen bonding is weak, (ii) two orientations of the O—H are feasible as in o-halophenols, (iii) dipole attachment occurs between the intramolecularly hydrogen bonded and the solvent molecule.

So far only the X—H stretching frequency of the type:

$$R{-}X{-}\vec{H}\cdots Y{-}R'$$

has been considered here for intermolecular hydrogen bonding. This type of vibration and its first overtone have been the ones most used in both inter- and intra-molecular hydrogen-bond studies. However, hydrogen bonding may also be detected by other types of stretching and bending vibrations. These are listed and classified in Table 4.25. In addition, the

TABLE 4.25

The effect of hydrogen bonding on the vibrational frequency

(after Sheppard[63])

Type of vibration	Description	Notation	Vibrational frequency (cm^{-1})	
			Absence H bonding	Presence H bonding
$R\diagup X—\vec{H} \cdots Y—R'$	XH stretching	νXH	3700–3500 (narrow)	3400–1700 (very broad)
$R\diagup X—H\downarrow \cdots Y—R'$	XH in-plane bending	δXH	1300–1200	~1400
$R\diagup X—\underset{\pm}{H} \cdots Y—R'$	XH out-of-plane bending	γXH	600–250 (very broad)	1000–500 (broad)
$(R\vec{X}H) \cdots \vec{Y}—R'$	Hydrogen bond stretching	ν(XH · · · Y)	—	250–100
$\downarrow(R—XH)\uparrow \cdots \uparrow(Y—R')\downarrow$	Hydrogen bond bending	δ(RXH · · · YR′)	—	~100

effect on the vibrational frequency when hydrogen bonding occurs may also be observed.

In Fig. 4.54 the infra-red spectrum of the acetic acid dimer in the 3500–800 cm^{-1} region is given and the positions of the νOH, δOH, and γOH frequencies are indicated. These frequencies are in the range to be expected for a hydrogen-bonded species.

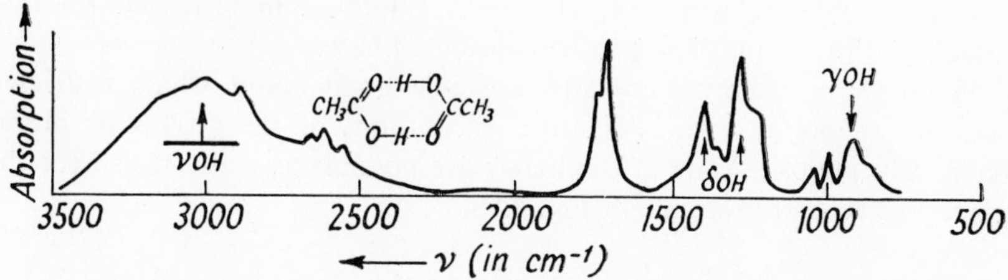

FIG. 4.54 Infra-red spectrum of the acetic acid dimer between 3500 to 800 cm^{-1}. (*Courtesy Dr. N. Sheppard*[63] *and The Pergamon Press Ltd.*)

In conclusion, it must be stressed that the main bulk of the inter- and intramolecular spectral studies has been carried out by the infra-red approach. However, for the low vibrational frequencies such as those due to the hydrogen bond stretching, the Raman approach is more suited. Gross and his colleagues[64] have made such Raman studies on the ν (XH · · · YR′) frequencies in the 250–100 cm^{-1} range.

For an excellent straightforward account of the present position and of the factors involved in hydrogen bonding there is a review by Coulson,[65] and in addition, the papers presented at a symposium on hydrogen bonding.[63] The total energy of a hydrogen bond consists principally of electrostatic energy, delocalisation energy, repulsive energy, and probably also dispersion energy. One piece of evidence which indicates that the electrostatic contribution alone is insufficient to account for the energy involved in hydrogen bond formation comes from the OH infra-red absorption band around 3 μ associated with the XH stretching frequency. On hydrogen bond formation a substantial increase in band intensity occurs. However, from theory it is only possible to account for about a 30 per cent increase in intensity due to electrostatic interaction, but in practice much larger increases are sometimes found. The explanation of this is that during the OH vibration, movement of charge occurs on to and away from the atom to which the H is hydrogen-bonding. Thus, if the hydrogen bond is represented by —O—H · · · O′, then delocalisation of electrons occurs away from and on to the OH region from the O′ region during, respectively, the ←O—H→ · · · O′ and the —O→—←H · · · O′ motion of the vibration. Such an effect would account for the enhanced band intensity.

Low-temperature studies[66,67]

In the study of low-temperature vibrations in solids both infra-red and Raman spectra have become increasingly important in recent years. Crystals have been examined at low temperatures, and the type of problem studied includes:

(*a*) Interaction forces between molecules in close proximity.

(*b*) The structure of crystals particularly those containing hydrogen atoms which are not amenable to complete X-ray analysis.

(*c*) The study of complex molecular species which exist only in crystals.

Low-temperature work has also been employed in restricted rotation studies, and this is the aspect to be considered here.

Whenever a molecule contains a single bond about which restricted rotation can occur, various relative orientations of the groups or atoms attached to opposite ends of the bonds are possible as is illustrated for the ethane-like type of molecule in Fig. 4.55.

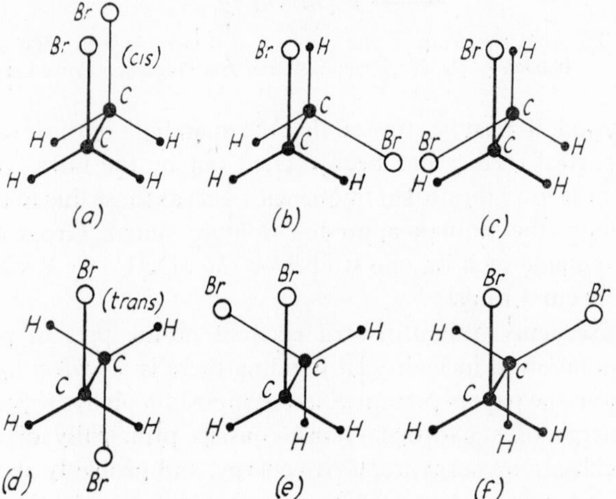

FIG. 4.55 *Cis*, *trans*, and *gauche* rotational isomers of di-bromoethane. (*From G. Herzberg,*[17] 'Infra-red and Raman Spectra of Polyatomic Molecules', Vol. 2, 2*nd ed.* 1945. *D. Van Nostrand Co., Princeton, N.J.*)

The number and relative concentrations of the different stable rotational isomers represented by the orientations will depend, respectively, on the number of minima in the potential energy curve associated with rotation about the C—C bond, and on the potential energy barriers between these different configurations. If, as in ethane, the molecule is sufficiently symmetrical about the C—C linkage, the different potential energy minima configurations allowed will be indistinguishable, and the spectra will show approximately the expected number of fundamental vibration frequencies for a single molecular species. If, on the other hand, the configurations have different symmetries as in 1:2-di-bromoethane, spectroscopically distinguishable rotational isomers will be present, each one of which contributes its own set of fundamental vibrational frequencies. In the case of di-bromoethane the stable configurations are the *trans* and the *gauche* isomers. Although the various stable configurations will normally be present in both the liquid and gaseous states, it often happens that at low temperatures in the crystalline solid state only the very lowest potential energy configuration is present. Consequently a simplification in the spectrum should result on sufficiently cooling the material. An example is given in Fig. 4.56 which is the infra-red spectrum of di-bromoethane in the liquid form and as a crystalline solid at a low temperature.

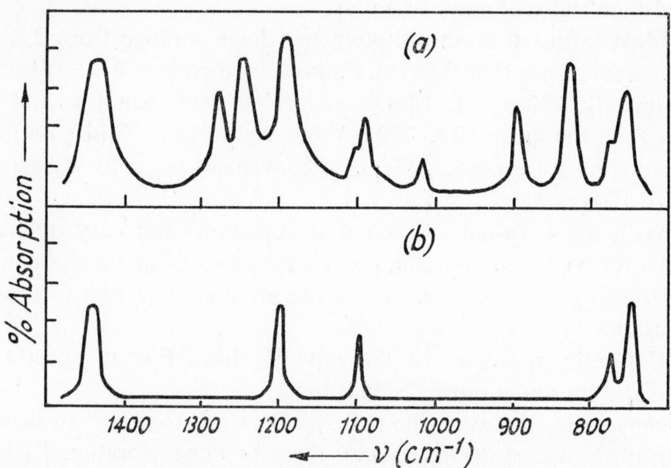

FIG. 4.56 Infra-red spectrum of 1:2-dibromoethane (*a*) in the liquid state, (*b*) in the solid state. (*After Brown and Sheppard.*[66] *Courtesy of Dr. N. Sheppard and the Council of The Faraday Society*)

The energy differences between the configuration of the isomers can be obtained from measurements of the temperature dependence of the intensity of the Raman or infra-red bands associated with the several configurations. In addition, if only two isomers are to be expected in reasonable concentration, then an assignment of the fundamental frequencies of one, the solid state form, may enable a corresponding assignment of the other to be made by a comparison of the liquid and solid state spectra, since the new peaks which appear when the liquid is examined may be attributed to the other isomer. From a study of the liquid and solid states of di-chloro- and di-bromoethane a fairly complete analysis has been made of both the *gauche* and the *trans* forms.

Choice of infra-red or Raman technique

(1) For gases the infra-red technique is the obvious choice, as the intensity of the Raman spectrum is usually very weak. However, it is possible to make successful studies of gases by the Raman method by using high-intensity sources.

(2) For liquids either method is feasible. Most Raman observations require at least 1 ml of liquid, and a modern automatic recording spectrometer may require up to 10 ml. Generally the infra-red method requires less liquid, but the amount required depends on the group absorbing.

(3) In dilute solutions the intensity of the Raman spectrum is weak, but this is not so with infra-red. However, if water is used as a solvent the infra-red 'blacks-out' in most regions; with the Raman water has only a weak spectrum which in most cases does not overlap with the spectrum of the solute.

(4) In observations on solids both techniques have made some useful contributions, although generally the spectra of liquids are more readily obtained than those of gases or solids.

(5) Most infra-red spectrophotometers have a range from 2.5 to 15 μ. The lowest frequency that they can examine is, therefore, $1/\lambda = (1/15)\times 10^{-4}$ (approximately 700 cm^{-1}). Many molecules have bending and skeletal frequencies in the range 50 to 700 cm^{-1} or 200 to 15 μ. This is no limitation to Raman spectra: in general the most convenient range for Raman spectra is 5000 to 100 cm^{-1}.

(6) With the infra-red method it is sometimes not easy to distinguish between overtones and fundamental frequencies. With the Raman spectra the overtones are usually so weak as to be unobservable, and there is no risk of confusion.

(7) Diatomic molecules of the type X_2 have Raman spectra but no infra-red spectra under normal conditions.

In many cases, however, the two spectra work together: in linear molecules with a centre of symmetry and three or more vibrational frequencies (for example C_2H_2, CO_2, and C_2N_2) the fundamental frequencies which appear in the infra-red are absent in the Raman spectra, and vice-versa.

(8) Finally, it must be concluded that in the number of problems so far studied and in the amount of work done the infra-red method has far outpaced the Raman, especially in the three most important uses of spectra: the determination of accurate internuclear distances, structural determinations, and in qualitative analysis.

For an elementary account of infra-red and Raman spectroscopy there is a book by Sutherland,[68] but for an advanced account Herzberg[17] or one by West[27] should be consulted. In addition, there is a book by Hibben[69] on Raman spectroscopy. For practical details of both the Raman and infra-red techniques Harrison *et al.*[70] should be referred to, and also a book edited by Strouts *et al.*[71] for the infra-red. Recently accounts have appeared by Brugel,[72] Cross,[73] Crawford,[74] and Beaven *et* al.[75] on infra-red spectroscopy.

References

1. WALSH, A. *J. Opt. Soc. Amer.* **42** (1952), 94.
2. WALSH, A. *Nature, Lond.* **167** (1951), 810.
3. SAYCE, L. A. and JACKSON, A. *Molecular Spectroscopy. Institute of Petroleum Conference*, 1955, p. 54.
4. SUTHERLAND, G. B. B. M. and WILLIS, H. A. *Disc. Faraday Soc.* **41** (1945), 181.
5. WILLIAMS, V. Z. *Molecular Spectroscopy. Institute of Petroleum Conference*, 1955, p. 42.
6. RICHARDS, R. E. and THOMPSON, H. W. *Disc. Faraday Soc.* **41** (1945), 183.
7. FORD, M. A., WILKINSON, G. R. and PRICE, W. C. *Molecular Spectroscopy. Institute of Petroleum Conference*, 1955, p. 82.

8. CZERNY, M. *Z. Phys.* **34** (1925), 227.
9. MCCUBBIN, T. K. and SINTON, W. M. *J. Opt. Soc. Amer.* **40** (1950), 537.
10. HAUSLER, R. L. and OETJEN, R. A. *J. Chem. Phys.* **21** (1953), 1340.
11. PALIK, E. D. *J. Chem. Phys.* **23** (1955), 217.
12. SLAWSKY, Z. I. and DENNISON, D. M. *J. Chem. Phys.* **7** (1939), 509.
13. WRIGHT, N. and RANDALL, H. M. *Phys. Rev.* **44** (1933), 391.
14. BARNES, R. B. *Phys. Rev.* **47** (1935), 658.
15. FOLEY, H. M. and RANDALL, H. M. *Phys. Rev.* **59** (1941), 171.
16*a*. RANDALL, H. M., DENNISON, D. M., GINSBURG, N. and WEBER, L. R. *Phys. Rev.* **52** (1937), 160.
16*b*. FUSON, N., RANDALL, H. M. and DENNISON, D. M. *Phys. Rev.* **56** (1939), 982.
17. HERZBERG, G. *Infra-red and Raman Spectra of Polyatomic Molecules.* D. Van Nostrand (Princeton, New York, 1945).
18. IMES, E. S. *Astrophys. J.* **50** (1919), 251.
19*a*. BARTUNEK, P. F. and BARKER, E. F. *Phys. Rev.* **48** (1935), 516.
19*b*. CAMERON, D. M. and NIELSEN, H. H. *Phys. Rev.* **53** (1938), 246.
19*c*. MARTIN, P. E., BARKER, E. F., *Phys. Rev.* **41** (1932), 291.
20. THOMPSON, H. W. and WILLIAMS, R. L. *Proc. Roy. Soc., Lond.* **220A** (1953), 435.
21. PICKWORTH, J. and THOMPSON, H. W. *Proc. Roy. Soc., Lond.* **222A** (1954), 443.
22. GERHARD, S. L. and DENNISON, D. M. *Phys. Rev.* **43** (1933), 197.
23. NIELSEN, A. H. and NIELSEN, H. H. *Phys. Rev.* **48** (1935), 864.
24. BOYD, D. R. J., THOMPSON, H. W. and WILLIAMS, R. L. *Proc. Roy. Soc., Lond.* **213A** (1952), 42.
25*a*. DENNISON, D. M. *Rev. Mod. Phys.* **3** (1931), 280.
25*b*. DENNISON, D. M. *Rev. Mod. Phys.* **12** (1940), 175.
26. BELLAMY, L. J. *Infra-red Spectra of Complex Molecules.* Methuen (London,1954); John Wiley (New York, 1954).
27. WEST, W. (Editor). *Chemical Applications of Spectroscopy.* Interscience Publishers (New York, 1956).
28. COLTHUP, N. B. *J. Opt. Soc. Amer.* **40** (1950), 397.
29. THOMPSON, H. W. *J. Chem. Soc.* **148** (1944), 183.
30*a*. MOULD, H. M., PRICE, W. C. and WILKINSON, G. R. *Spectrochimica Acta,* **16** (1960), 479.
30*b*. WILKINSON, G. R., FORD, M. A. and PRICE, W. C. *Molecular Spectroscopy. Institute of Petroleum Conference*, 1955, p. 192.
31. CRAWFORD, M. F., WELSH, H. L. and LOCKE, J. L. *Phys. Rev.* **75** (1949), 1607.
32*a*. CRAWFORD, M. F. and DAGG, I. R. *Phys. Rev.* **91** (1953), 1569.
32*b*. CHISHOLM, D. A., MACDONALD, J. C. F., CRAWFORD, M. F. and WELSH, H. L. *Phys. Rev.* **88** (1952), 957.
33. KETELAAR, J. A. A. *Molecular Spectroscopy. Institute of Petroleum Conference*, 1958.
34. KETELAAR, J. A. A. *Rev. Trav. Chim.* **75** (1956), 857.
35. JONES, R. N. and SANDORFY, C. *Chemical Applications of Spectroscopy.* Interscience Publishers (New York, 1956), p. 247.
36*a*. WILSON, E. B. and WELLS, A. J. *J. Chem. Phys.* **14** (1946), 578.
36*b*. BOURGIN, D. G. *Phys. Rev.* **29** (1927), 794.
37. JONES, R. N., RAMSAY, D. A., KEIR, D. S. and DOBRINER, K. *J. Amer. Chem. Soc.* **74** (1952), 80.
38. RAMSEY, D. A. *J. Amer. Chem. Soc.* **74** (1952), 72.
39. THOMPSON, H. W. *Molecular Spectroscopy. Institute of Petroleum Conference*, 1955, p. 94; 1958.
40. COULSON, C. A. *Molecular Spectroscopy. Institute of Petroleum Conference*, 1958.
41. WILSON, E. B. and WELLS, A. J. *J. Chem. Phys.* **14** (1946), 578.
42. THORNDIKE, A. M., WELLS, A. J. and WILSON, E. B. *J. Chem. Phys.* **15** (1947), 157.
43. CALLOMON, H. J., MCKEAN, D. C. and THOMPSON, H. W. *Proc. Roy. Soc., Lond.* **208A** (1951), 332.
44. WEBER, D. and PENNER, S. S. *J. Chem. Phys.* **19** (1951), 974.
45. HORNIG, D. F. and MCKEAN, D. C. *J. Phys. Chem.* **59** (1955), 1133.
46. BELLAMY, L. J., HALLAM, H. E. and WILLIAMS, R. L. *Molecular Spectroscopy. Institute of Petroleum Conference*, 1958.
47. ANDRYCHUK, D. *Canad. J. Phys.* **29** (1951), 151.

48a. STOICHEFF, B. P. *Canad. J. Phys.* **32** (1954), 339.

48b. STOICHEFF, B. P. *Advances in Spectroscopy*, Vol. 1. Interscience Publishers (New York, 1959), p. 91.

49. HERZBERG, G. and STOICHEFF, B. P. *Nature, Lond.* **175** (1955), 79.

50. WOODWARD, L. A. *Quart. Rev.* **10** (1956), 185.

51. WELSH, H. L., STANSBURY, E. J., ROMANKO, J. and FELDMAN, T. *J. Opt. Soc. Amer.* **45** (1955), 338.

52. DUDENBOSTEL, B. F. *Molecular Spectroscopy. Institute of Petroleum Conference*, 1955, p. 20.

53a. INGOLD, C. K. and MILLEN, D. J. *J. Chem. Soc.* (1950), 2612.

53b. INGOLD, C. K., MILLEN, D. J. and POOLE, H. G. *J. Chem. Soc.* (1950), 2576.

54. WOODWARD, L. A. *Phil. Mag.* **18** (1934), 823.

55. SHEPPARD, N. and SIMPSON, D. M. *Quart. Rev.* **6** (1952), 1.

56. FOX, J. J. and MARTIN, A. E. *Proc. Roy. Soc. Lond. A*, **167** (1938), 257.

57. MEYER, C. F. and LEVIN, A. *J. Opt. Soc. Amer.* **16** (1928), 146.

58. FLETT, M. ST. C. *Spectrochim. Acta*, **10** (1957), 21.

59. SUTHERLAND, G. B. B. M. *Trans. Faraday Soc.* **36** (1940), 889.

60. PAULING, L. *The Nature of the Chemical Bond.* Cornell University Press (1945).

61. BAKER, A. W. and SHULGIN, A. T. *J. Amer. Chem. Soc.* **80** (1958), 5358.

62. RICHARDS, J. H. and WALKER, S. *Trans. Faraday Soc.* **57** (1961), pp. 399, 406, 412, 418.

63. HADZI, D. and THOMPSON, H. W. (Editors). *Hydrogen Bonding.* Pergamon Press (London, 1959), p. 85.

64a. GROSS, E. F. and VALKOV, V. I. *Dokl. Akad. Nauk. S.S.S.R.* **68** (1948), 473, 1013.

64b. GROSS, E. F. and VALKOV, V. I. *Izvest Akad. Nauk. S.S.S.R.* **14** (1950), 426.

65. COULSON, C. A. *Research* **10** (1957), 149.

66. BROWN, J. K. and SHEPPARD, N. *Disc. Faraday Soc.* **9** (1950), 144.

67a. HORNIG, D. F. *Disc. Faraday Soc.* **9** (1950), 115.

67b. SHEPPARD, N. *Advances in Spectroscopy*, Vol. 1. Interscience Publishers (New York, 1959), p. 288.

68. SUTHERLAND, G. B. B. M. *Infra-red and Raman Spectra.* Methuen (London, 1935).

69. HIBBEN, J. H. *The Raman Effect and its Chemical Applications.* Reinhold (New York, 1939).

70. HARRISON, G. R., LORD, R. C. and LOOFBOUROW, J. R. *Practical Spectroscopy.* Prentice-Hall (New York, 1948).

71. STROUTS, C. R. N., GILFILLAN, J. H. and WILSON, H. N. (Editors). *Analytical Chemistry*, Vol. 2. Oxford University Press (London, 1955).

72. BRÜGEL, W., *Introduction to Infra-red Spectroscopy.* (Translated by A. R. and A. J. D. Katritzky.) Methuen, 1961.

73. CROSS, A. D. *Introduction to Practical Infra-red Spectroscopy.* Butterworths (London, 1960).

74. CRAWFORD, V. A. *Quart. Rev.* **14** (1960), 378.

75. BEAVEN, G. H., JOHNSON, E. A., WILLIS, H. A., and MILLER, R. G. J. *Molecular Spectroscopy.* Heywood (London, 1961).

5

Molecular electronic spectra

Introduction

THE absorption and emission of energy in the range 10 Å to about 10 000 Å is almost entirely restricted to changes in electronic energy with accompanying vibrational and rotational energy changes. Unlike the microwave (see Vol. I), infra-red, and Raman changes there is no simple criterion as to whether a molecule may exhibit an electronic spectrum. The criterion is very difficult to evaluate and involves a number of approximations.

If the electronic energy alone changed during a transition, then only one line would result, but since changes in electronic energy are normally accompanied by vibrational and rotational energy changes a whole set of very closely spaced lines is obtained. The group of lines resulting from transitions between the different rotational levels in two vibrational levels in each of two electronic states is termed a *band*. The sum of all the bands for the transitions between two electronic states is termed a *band system*.

If any change in rotational energy is neglected, representation of a transition between two vibrational levels in different electronic states may be made as in Fig. 5.1 using potential energy diagrams. For a diatomic species each electronic state may be associated with a particular potential energy curve, and in Figs. 5.1(*a*), (*b*), and (*c*) two electronic states are shown in each case, corresponding to the ground and excited states, respectively.† In curves (*a*) the positions of the minima in the upper and lower states lie very nearly one above the other, that is they have almost equal internuclear distance in the two states, while in (*b*) and (*c*) the minima of the curves representing the upper electronic levels are displaced to different extents. Transitions between the two electronic states are represented by vertical lines drawn in accordance with the Franck–Condon principle (see p. 18).

† In this chapter if it is not definitely stated otherwise, we shall be concerned with the spectra of diatomic species, that is either diatomic molecules, charged molecules, or radicals.

This requires that the internuclear distance does not alter during the small period of time (about 10^{-16} sec) required for the transition. In Fig. 5.1(*a*), (*b*), and (*c*) absorption transitions are indicated from the lowest vibrational level in the ground electronic state of the molecule. Neglecting any interaction between different forms of energy, the total energy E of a molecule apart

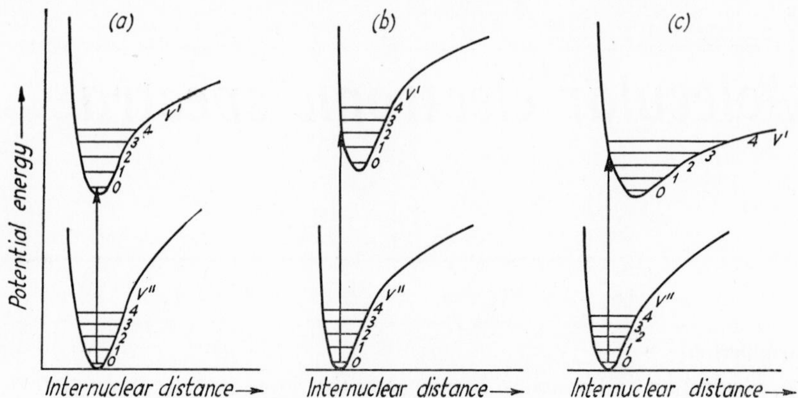

FIG. 5.1 Absorption transitions from the lowest vibrational level in the ground electronic state of the molecule

from translational energy may be regarded as the sum of the individual contributions of the rotational (E_r), vibrational (E_v), and electronic (E_e) energies where the total energy E is given by:

$$E_e+E_v+E_r = E \tag{5.1}$$

Expressed in wave-number units this becomes:

$$T_e+G(v)+F(J) = T \tag{5.2}$$

where T_e, $G(v)$, and $F(J)$ are the term values for the electronic, vibrational and rotational energies, respectively (see p. 11); for example, the vibrational term value is given by:

$$G(v) = E_v/hc = (v+\tfrac{1}{2})\omega_e-(v+\tfrac{1}{2})^2x_e\omega_e+(v+\tfrac{1}{2})^3y_e\omega_e+\ \ldots \tag{5.3}$$

In a transition the wave-numbers of the spectral lines are given by the difference of the two term values in the upper (T') and lower (T'') electronic states, that is:

$$\nu = T'-T'' = (T_e'-T_e'')+\{G'(v')-G''(v'')\}+\{F_{v'}(J')-F_{v''}(J'')\} \tag{5.4}$$

The representation of the wave-number (ν) of one of the spectral lines in an electronic transition by means of term value differences is given in Fig. 5.2. Equation (5.4) has the form:

$$\nu = \nu_e+\nu_v+\nu_r \tag{5.5}$$

where the emitted or absorbed wave-number may be regarded as the sum of an electronic, vibrational, and a rotational part. ν_v and ν_r are the wave-numbers corresponding to the vibrational and rotational energy changes, respectively, and $\nu_e = (E'_e - E''_e)/hc$, that is ν_e is the energy difference in cm^{-1} units between the minima of the upper and lower electronic states.

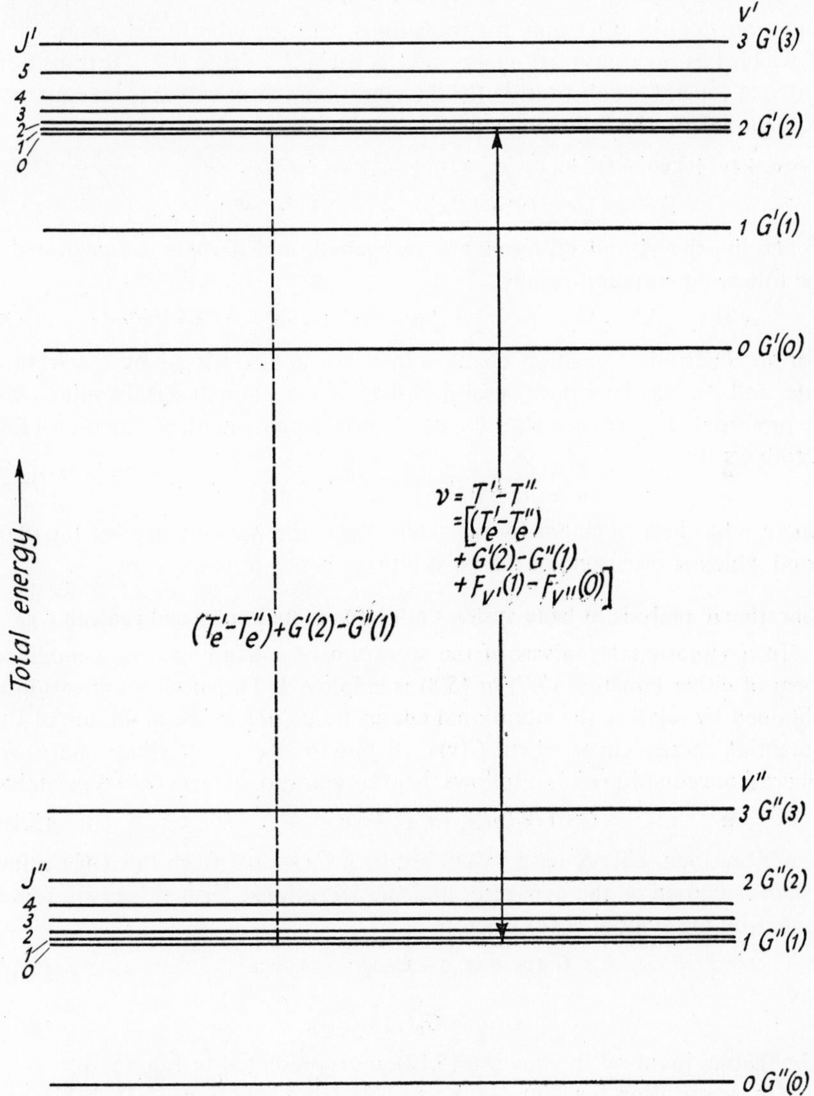

FIG. 5.2 The representation of one wave-number (ν) in an electronic transition by means of term value differences. The line chosen is for the $v' \leftrightarrow v''$ change of $2 \leftrightarrow 1$ and the $J' \leftrightarrow J''$ of $1 \leftrightarrow 0$. The term difference $\{(T'_e - T''_e) + G'(2) - G''(1)\}$ is also indicated

For the transitions between the different rotational and vibrational levels in two different electronic states ν_e is constant. In addition, since ν_r is small compared with ν_v, this may in general be neglected in a vibrational analysis, and the wave-numbers of the electronic changes between the different vibrational levels are given approximately by:

$$\nu = \nu_e + \{G'(v') - G''(v'')\} \tag{5.6}$$

Equation (5.6) is exact only for transitions between vibrational states, each of which has no rotational energy that is for a $J' = 0$ to $J'' = 0$ transition and vice versa. On substitution for the vibrational term values from equation (5.3) into (5.6), the following equation is obtained:

$$\nu = \nu_e + (v'+\tfrac{1}{2})\omega_e' - (v'+\tfrac{1}{2})^2 x_e'\omega_e' + (v'+\tfrac{1}{2})^3 y_e'\omega_e' + \ldots - [(v''+\tfrac{1}{2})\omega_e'' - (v''+\tfrac{1}{2})^2 x_e''\omega_e'' + (v''+\tfrac{1}{2})^3 y_e''\omega_e'' + \ldots] \tag{5.7}$$

Generally, the y_e' and y_e'' terms are very small, and if these are neglected,† the following equation results:

$$\nu = \nu_e + (v'+\tfrac{1}{2})\omega_e' - (v'+\tfrac{1}{2})^2 x_e'\omega_e' - [(v''+\tfrac{1}{2})\omega_e'' - (v''+\tfrac{1}{2})^2 x_e''\omega_e''] \tag{5.8}$$

For an electronic transition changes in v are not restricted by a selection rule, and Δv may be a positive or negative integer, though certain values will be preferred. In the case $v' = 0 \leftarrow v'' = 0$ on employment of equation (5.8) it follows that:

$$\nu_{00} = \nu_e + \tfrac{1}{2}\omega_e' - \tfrac{1}{4}x_e'\omega_e' - \tfrac{1}{2}\omega_e'' + \tfrac{1}{4}x_e''\omega_e'' \tag{5.9}$$

where ν has been replaced by ν_{00}. Thus, ν_{00} is the wave-number of the (0,0) band which is often one of the most intense bands in the system.

Vibrational analysis of band systems of diatomic molecules and radicals

In a vibrational analysis of the spectrum of a band system, a modified form of either equation (5.7) or (5.8) is employed. The modified equation is obtained by relating the vibrational energy terms not to the minimum of the potential energy curve where $G(v) = 0$ but to the $v = 0$ vibrational level where from equation (5.3) it follows that this vibrational term $G(0)$ is given by:

$$G(0) = \tfrac{1}{2}\omega_e - \tfrac{1}{4}x_e\omega_e + \tfrac{1}{8}y_e\omega_e + \ldots \tag{5.10}$$

The vibrational energy term values are then measured from this $G(0)$ value, which is chosen as the new zero, and the vibrational term values are represented by the symbol $G_0(v)$ where:

$$G_0(v) = \omega_0 v - x_0\omega_0 v^2 + y_0\omega_0 v^3 \tag{5.11}$$

and

$$G(v) = G_0(v) + G(0). \tag{5.12}$$

The factors involved in equation (5.12) are represented in Fig. (5.3).

On substitution for $G(v)$, $G_0(v)$, and $G(0)$ from equations (5.3), (5.11), and (5.10), respectively into equation (5.12) and on rearrangement of the resulting equation we obtain:

$$(\omega_e - x_e\omega_e + \tfrac{3}{4}y_e\omega_e + \ldots)v - (x_e\omega_e - \tfrac{3}{2}y_e\omega_e + \ldots)v^2 + y_e\omega_e v^3 + \ldots = \omega_0 v - x_0\omega_0 v^2 + y_0\omega_0 v^3 + \ldots \tag{5.13}$$

† In actual analyses the $(v+\frac{1}{2})^3 y_e\omega_e$ term has sometimes to be included. It should be noted that ω_e is the infinitesimal vibrational frequency and is, of course, a theoretical quantity.

If the coefficients of like powers of v on the left- and right-hand sides of equation (5.13) are equated, it follows that:

$$\omega_0 = \omega_e - x_e\omega_e + \tfrac{3}{4}y_e\omega_e + \ldots \tag{5.14}$$

$$x_0\omega_0 = x_e\omega_e - \tfrac{3}{2}y_e\omega_e + \ldots \tag{5.15}$$

$$y_0\omega_0 = y_e\omega_e + \ldots \tag{5.16}$$

From the vibrational analysis the values of x_0, y_0 and ω_0 are obtained and from equations (5.14), (5.15), and (5.16) the values of x_e, y_e, and ω_e follow.

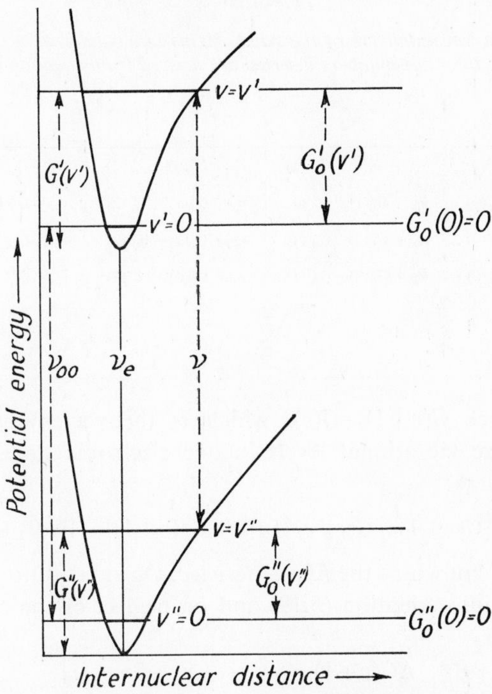

FIG. 5.3 Representation of the symbols used in the vibrational analysis of a band system

One of the main objects of the analysis is to obtain the value of ω_e since from its value the force constant of the bond may be readily calculated (see p. 97).

The equation to which the experimental data is fitted may be deduced from Fig. 5.3 from which it may be observed that:

$$\nu = \nu_{00} + G_0'(v') - G_0''(v'') \tag{5.17}$$

On substitution into equation (5.17) for the values of $G_0(v)$ from equation (5.11), we obtain the equation to which the experimental data are fitted, that is

$$\nu = \nu_{00} + \{\omega_0'v' - x_0'\omega_0'v'^2 + y_0'\omega_0'v'^3 + \ldots\} - \{\omega_0''v'' - x_0''\omega_0''v''^2 + y_0''\omega_0''v''^3 \ldots\} \tag{5.18}$$

Déslandres table

The spectroscopic procedure is to allot the values of (v',v'') to each of the bands in the band system; this is dealt with on p. 206. The wave-numbers of each of the (v',v'') bands are then arranged in what is known as a *Déslandres table*. This is illustrated in Table 5.1 where the wave-number of each band origin is given for the purpose of representation in terms of equation (5.17). In practice the wave-number of each band origin experimentally observed is entered into this form of table.

TABLE 5.1

The arrangement of the wave-numbers of the band origins in a band system in terms of their (v',v'') values; the wave-numbers inserted are derived from equation (5.17)

v' \ v''	0	1	2	3	
0	$\nu_{00}+G_0'(0)-G_0''(0)$	$\nu_{00}+G_0'(0)-G_0''(1)$	$\nu_{00}+G_0'(0)-G_0''(2)$	$\nu_{00}+G_0'(0)-G_0''(3)$	
					$\Delta G'(\frac{1}{2})$
1	$\nu_{00}+G_0'(1)-G_0''(0)$	$\nu_{00}+G_0'(1)-G_0''(1)$	$\nu_{00}+G_0'(1)-G_0''(2)$	$\nu_{00}+G_0'(1)-G_0''(3)$	
					$\Delta G'(1\frac{1}{2})$
2	$\nu_{00}+G_0'(2)-G_0''(0)$	$\nu_{00}+G_0'(2)-G_0''(1)$	$\nu_{00}+G_0'(2)-G_0''(2)$	$\nu_{00}+G_0'(2)-G_0''(3)$	
					$\Delta G'(2\frac{1}{2})$
3	$\nu_{00}+G_0'(3)-G_0''(0)$	$\nu_{00}+G_0'(3)-G_0''(1)$	$\nu_{00}+G_0'(3)-G_0''(2)$	$\nu_{00}+G_0'(3)-G_0''(3)$	
	$\Delta G''(\frac{1}{2})$	$\Delta G''(1\frac{1}{2})$	$\Delta G''(2\frac{1}{2})$		First ↑ ←difference

The difference $G(v+1)-G(v)$, which is the wave-number separation of two successive vibrational levels in one electronic state, is represented by $\Delta G(v+\frac{1}{2})$ where:

$$\Delta G(v+\tfrac{1}{2}) = G(v+1)-G(v) = \{G(0)+G_0(v+1)\}-\{G(0)+G_0(v)\} \quad (5.19)$$

and $\Delta G(v+\frac{1}{2})$ is known as the *first difference*. On substitution for $G_0(v)$ from equation (5.11) into equation (5.19) and on neglect of the cubic terms it is seen that:

$$\Delta G(v+\tfrac{1}{2}) = \omega_0-\omega_0 x_0-2x_0\omega_0 v \quad (5.20)$$

These values of $\Delta G(v+\frac{1}{2})$ may be obtained from the Déslandres table. For example, a $\Delta G'(\frac{1}{2})$ value is obtained by subtracting a $v' = 0$ value from a $v' = 1$ value vertically below it in the table. On application of this to Table 5.1 four values of $\Delta G'(\frac{1}{2})$ would result.† These four values would then be added together and divided by four, and the resulting value would be regarded as $\Delta G'(\frac{1}{2})$. By a similar procedure the values of $\Delta G'(1\frac{1}{2})$ and $\Delta G'(2\frac{1}{2})$ would follow. The values of $\Delta G''(\frac{1}{2})$ would be obtained by subtracting adjacent horizontal numbers in the $v'' = 1$ column from the ones in the $v'' = 0$ column. An arithmetic mean of the four resulting $\Delta G''(\frac{1}{2})$ values would then be regarded as the $\Delta G''(\frac{1}{2})$ value. By a similar treatment the $\Delta G''(1\frac{1}{2})$ and $\Delta G''(2\frac{1}{2})$ values would result.

† The value of four is an arbitrary one for the chosen Déslandres table, and in practice this would be the number of $\Delta G'(\frac{1}{2})$ values which could be taken for the number of experimentally observed bands.

If either the $\Delta G'(v+\frac{1}{2})$ or $\Delta G''(v+\frac{1}{2})$ values are plotted against v, then if the analysis was correct and it was permissible to neglect the cubic terms, it follows from equation (5.20) that a straight line should be obtained, the slope of which should give the value of $-2x_0'\omega_0'$ or $-2x_0''\omega_0''$, respectively. The plot of $\Delta G''(v+\frac{1}{2})$ against v for the lower electronic energy state of the Swan emission system of C_2 is given in Fig. 5.4.

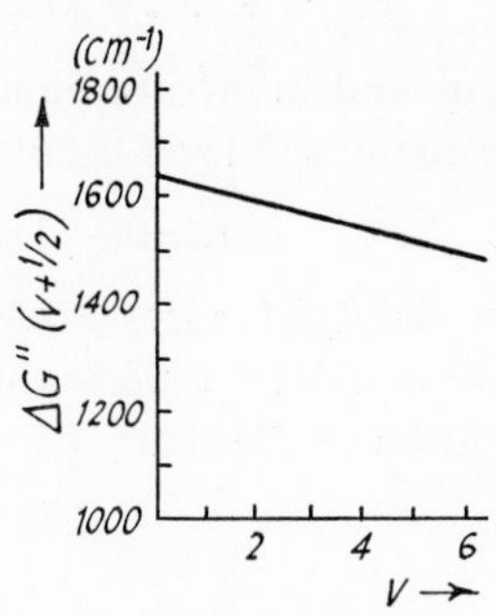

FIG. 5.4 The plot of $\Delta G''(v+\frac{1}{2})$ against v for the $X^3\Pi_u$ state of the C_2 Swan band system. The symbol X indicates this electronic state is the ground one. (*After Phillips.*[1] *Courtesy of 'The Astrophysical Journal'*)

The most satisfactory check on the vibrational analysis is then to employ the determined mean first difference values and to obtain what is known as the *second difference* $\Delta^2G(v+1)$ where this is defined by:

$$\Delta^2G(v+1) = \Delta G(v+\tfrac{3}{2}) - \Delta G(v+\tfrac{1}{2}) \tag{5.21}$$

It follows from equations (5.20) and (5.21) that this second difference is given by:

$$\begin{aligned}\Delta^2G(v+1) &= \{\omega_0-\omega_0x_0-2x_0\omega_0(v+1)\}-\{\omega_0-\omega_0x_0-2x_0\omega_0v\}\\ &= -2x_0\omega_0\end{aligned} \tag{5.22}$$

Thus, if the analysis is correct, the second difference values for both the upper and lower electronic states have to give constant values of $-2x_0'\omega_0'$ and $-2x_0''\omega_0''$ respectively. If the values are not roughly constant, then the analysis is unsatisfactory. The arithmetical mean of the $\Delta^2G'(v+1)$ values gives the value of $-2x_0'\omega_0'$, and similarly that of the $\Delta^2G''(v+1)$ values gives the $-2x_0''\omega_0''$ values. If these $x_0\omega_0$ values are employed in conjunction with the plot of $\Delta G(v+\frac{1}{2})$ against v, then satisfactory values of x_0', x_0'', ω_0', and ω_0'' may be obtained. In addition, if these values are substituted in equations (5.14) and (5.15), where the y_e terms are neglected, then values of x_e', x_e'', ω_e', and ω_e'' result.

This method of vibrational analysis will now be applied to the C_2 molecule. This molecule is readily produced in a vigorous form of discharge through aromatic hydrocarbons. Part of the spectrogram for the C_2 molecule is given in Fig. 5.6 for the Swan band system which is the transition $A^3\Pi_g \rightarrow X^3\Pi_u$, that is an emission spectrum from the excited electronic state $A^3\Pi_g$ to the ground state $X^3\Pi_u$. The potential curves for these two electronic states are given in Fig. 5.9(*a*). The band origin data for the Swan band system is arranged in Table 5.2 in the form of a Déslandres table. The $\Delta'G(v+\frac{1}{2})$ and $\Delta''G(v+\frac{1}{2})$ values have been inserted together with the mean of the first differences and the values of the second differences. From these second difference values the values of ω_0' and ω_0'' may be evaluated as follows. The mean of the second difference $\Delta^2 G'(v+1)$ is:

$$(38{\cdot}2+38{\cdot}9+38{\cdot}7)/3 = 38{\cdot}6 = 2x_0'\omega_0'$$

and for $\Delta^2 G''(v+1)$:

$$(23{\cdot}1+23{\cdot}7+23{\cdot}2+23{\cdot}3+23{\cdot}4)/5 = 23{\cdot}34 = 2x_0''\omega_0''$$

Thus, $x_0'\omega_0'$ and $x_0''\omega_0''$ are equal to 19.3 and 11.67, respectively. Equation (5.20) for the $v = 0$ level becomes:

$$\Delta G(0+\tfrac{1}{2}) = \omega_0 - \omega_0 x_0 - 2x_0\omega_0 \times 0 \qquad (5.23)$$

and from the Déslandres table it may be noted that the mean values of $\Delta G'(\tfrac{1}{2})$ are equal to 1753.8 and that of $\Delta G''(\tfrac{1}{2}) = 1618.2$. It follows thus from equation (5.23) that:

$$1753{\cdot}8 = \omega_0' - 19{\cdot}3$$

$$\omega_0' = 1773{\cdot}5$$

and that:

$$1618{\cdot}2 = \omega_0'' - 11{\cdot}67$$

$$\omega_0'' = 1629{\cdot}87$$

Since the ν_{00} value is 19 373.9 cm^{-1} it follows by substitution of this value and the values for x_0', ω_0', x_0'', and ω_0'' into equation (5.18) that the equation which represents the wave-numbers of the band origin of each of the bands is:

$$\nu = 19\,373{\cdot}9 + (1773{\cdot}5v' - 19{\cdot}3v'^2) - (1629{\cdot}87v'' - 11{\cdot}67v''^2) \qquad (5.24)$$

where the $y_0\omega_0$ terms are neglected.

The vibrational analysis just considered for the Swan bands of C_2 is based on band origin data. If, however, the dispersion of the spectrum is not sufficient for the band origins to be determined and only band head data are available, the procedure is slightly more empirical.† The band head data for the Swan bands of C_2 are listed in Table 5.3.

In this case the equation which expresses the wave-numbers of the heads of the bands with reasonable accuracy is:

$$\nu = 19\,355 + (1770v' - 20v'^2) - (1625v'' - 11{\cdot}5v''^2) \qquad (5.25)$$

It will be noted that the constants in this equation differ slightly from those in equation (5.24).

To express the band head data adequately equation (5.8), which is a band origin formula, is modified slightly by including a small term $k(v'+\tfrac{1}{2})\times(v''+\tfrac{1}{2})$ and becomes:

$$\nu = \nu_e + \{(v'+\tfrac{1}{2})\omega_e' - (v'+\tfrac{1}{2})^2 x_e'\omega_e'\} - \{(v''+\tfrac{1}{2})\omega_e'' - (v''+\tfrac{1}{2})^2 x_e''\omega_e''\} - k(v'+\tfrac{1}{2})(v''+\tfrac{1}{2}) \qquad (5.26)$$

† Since the head of the *Q*-branch lies closer to the band origin position than that of the *P*- or *R*-branches, it is desirable that the wave-number of the *Q*-head should be employed in the Déslandres table in preference to that of the *P* or *R*.

TABLE 5.2

The Déslandres table for the Swan band system of C_2 *where the electronic transition is* $A^3\Pi_g \rightarrow X^3\Pi_u$

v' \ v''	0	$\Delta G''(\frac{1}{2})$	1	$\Delta G''(1\frac{1}{2})$	2	$\Delta G''(2\frac{1}{2})$	3	$\Delta G''(3\frac{1}{2})$	4	$\Delta G''(4\frac{1}{2})$	5	$\Delta G''(5\frac{1}{2})$	6	$\Delta G'(v+\frac{1}{2})$	$\Delta^2 G'(v+1)$
0	19 373.9	1618.2	17 755.7	1594.9	16 160.8	1571.5	14 589.3								
$\Delta G'(\frac{1}{2})$	(1754.0)		(1754.0)		(1753.2)		(1754.0)							1753.8	
1	21 127.9	1618.2	19 509.7	1595.7	17 914.0	1570.7	16 343.3	1548.2	14 795.1						38.2
$\Delta G'(1\frac{1}{2})$	(1715.4)		(1715.4)		(1716.2)		(1715.4)		(1715.4)					1715.6	
2	22 843.3	1618.2	21 225.1	1594.9	19 630.2	1571.5	18 058.7	1548.2	16 510.5	1524.8	14 985.7				38.9
$\Delta G'(2\frac{1}{2})$			(1676.7)		(1676.7)		(1676.7)		(1676.7)		(1676.5)			1676.7	
3			22 901.8	1594.9	21 306.9	1571.5	19 735.4	1548.2	18 187.2	1525.0	16 662.2	1501.4	15 160.8		38.7
$\Delta G'(3\frac{1}{2})$					(1638.0)		(1637.9)		(1637.9)		(1638.1)		(1638.0)	(1638.0)	
4					22 944.9	1571.6	21 373.3	1548.2	19 825.1	1524.8	18 300.3	1501.5	(16 798.8)	↑	
$\Delta G''(v+\frac{1}{2})$		1618.2		1595.1		1571.4		1548.2		1524.9		1501.5		←Mean of first differences	
$\Delta^2 G''(v+1)$			23.1		23.7		23.2		23.3		23.4			←Mean of second differences	↑

TABLE 5.3

Déslandres table for the Swan bands of C_2 *based on band heads*

v' \ v''	0		1		2		3		4		5		6		7	
0	19 355	1615	17 740	1593	16 147											
	1749		1750		1752											$\Delta G'(\frac{1}{2})$
1	21 104	1614	19 490	1591	17 899	1569	16 330									
	1708		1712		1712		1713									$\Delta G'(1\frac{1}{2})$
2	22 812	1610	21 202	1591	19 611	1568	18 043	1545	16 498	1526	14 972					
			1668		1671				1673		1677					$\Delta G'(2\frac{1}{2})$
3			22 870	1588	21 282				18 171	1522	16 649	1500	15 149			
					1620						1627		1629			$\Delta G'(3\frac{1}{2})$
4					22 902	1562	21 340				18 276	1498	16 778	1477	15 301	
		$\Delta G''(\frac{1}{2})$		$\Delta G''(1\frac{1}{2})$		$\Delta G''(2\frac{1}{2})$		$\Delta G''(3\frac{1}{2})$								↑ First ←difference

The difference in wave-numbers between two consecutive members $(v'+1)$ and v' in a column of the Déslandres table based on band head data would then be given by inserting these values into equation (5.26) and is:

$$\omega_e'-2(v'+1)x_e'\omega_e'-k(v''+\tfrac{1}{2}) \tag{5.27}$$

and similarly the difference between two consecutive members $(v''+1)$ and v'' in a row would be:

$$\omega_e''-2(v''+1)x_e''\omega_e''-k(v'+\tfrac{1}{2}) \tag{5.28}$$

and by equating these to the mean values of actual differences between consecutive members of a column and row, respectively, a suitable value of k may be chosen.

The determination of the band origin wave-number is dealt with on p. 218 where its value may be obtained from consideration of the fine structure data.

Application of vibrational analysis data

A large number of diatomic species have had their ω_e, $x_e\omega_e$, and $y_e\omega_e$ values determined by vibrational analysis. Herzberg[2] lists over 350 values and, in addition, a large number of their dissociation energies which have also been determined by these studies (see p. 303). The additional information which results from a knowledge of ω_e and x_e is:

(i) Calculation of the force constant for both the upper and lower electronic states from the equation:

$$\omega_e c = \frac{1}{2\pi}\sqrt{\frac{k}{\mu}} \tag{5.29}$$

where μ is the reduced mass of the molecule.

(ii) To assist in the statistical calculation of thermodynamic functions such as entropy and free energy (see p. 329).

(iii) Calculation of the value of α in the Morse equation:

$$\alpha = \sqrt{\frac{8\pi^2\mu x_e\omega_e c}{h}} \tag{5.30}$$

(iv) The value of the constants in the vibrational energy equation are, thus, known and the following equation:

$$E_v = (v+\tfrac{1}{2})hc\omega_e-(v+\tfrac{1}{2})^2hcx_e\omega_e+(v+\tfrac{1}{2})^3hcy_e\omega_e+\ \dots \tag{5.31}$$

may be then employed to calculate the vibrational energy for any value of v. In addition, this equation may be used to obtain a very approximate value for the dissociation energy (see p. 303).

Progressions and sequences

So far it has been assumed that the (v',v'') values for a band can be allotted. The allocation of these values is, of course, an essential step in the analysis, and at least a provisional allotment of (v',v'') values has to be made before the Déslandres table can be formed. This allotment of (v',v'') values is greatly assisted by picking out what are known as *progressions* and *sequences*.

It has been seen that the wave-number differences between the adjacent (v',v'') values in any row or column are nearly constant for that particular row or column. The bands in a particular column where v'' is constant and v' varies are called v' *progressions*; similarly, those in a row where v' is constant and v'' progressively varies are termed v'' *progressions*. Progressions with constant v' appear as bands whose wave-number separations decrease towards longer wavelengths, while those with constant v'' have decreasing separations towards shorter wavelengths. These points may be deduced from Fig. 5.5 bearing in mind that as v increases the spacing of the vibrational energy levels decreases. These progressions may be illustrated by the energy level diagrams shown in Fig. 5.5.

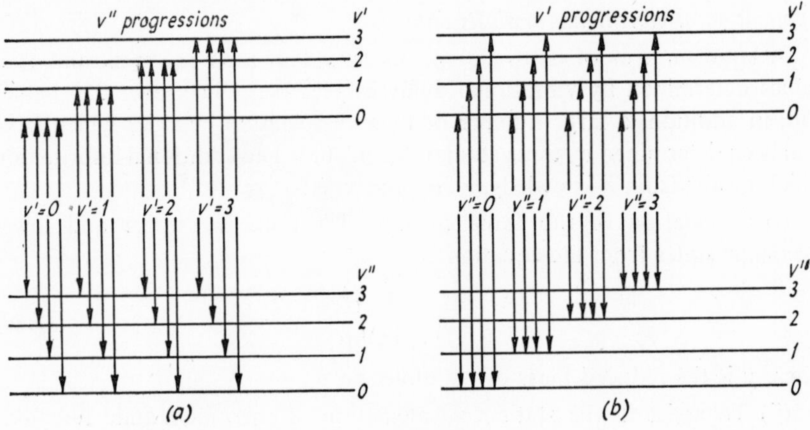

FIG. 5.5 (*a*) Transitions in some v'' progressions, (*b*) transitions in some v' progressions

Bands which fall in diagonal rows of the Déslandres array have a constant value of $v'-v''$. These groups of bands are characteristic in the spectrum and called *sequences*, e.g. the (0,0), (1,1), (2,2), and (0,1), (1,2), (2,3) bands in Table 5.4 given for C_2 form two types of sequences. The wave-numbers of the

TABLE 5.4

Six sequences in the Swan bands of C_2

4383 Å	4737 Å	5165 Å	5636 Å	6191 Å	6677 Å
2–0	1–0	0–0	0–1	0–2	0–3
3–1	2–1	1–1	1–2	1–3	1–4
4–2	3–2	2–2	2–3	2–4	2–5
	4–3	3–3	3–4	3–5	3–6
	5–4		4–5	4–6	
			5–6	5–7	
			6–7	6–8	

bands in a sequence do not differ considerably; thus, a group of bands close together, of gradually changing intensity, would suggest a sequence. Some of the C_2 Swan bands may be observed in Fig. 5.6 where it will be noted that there

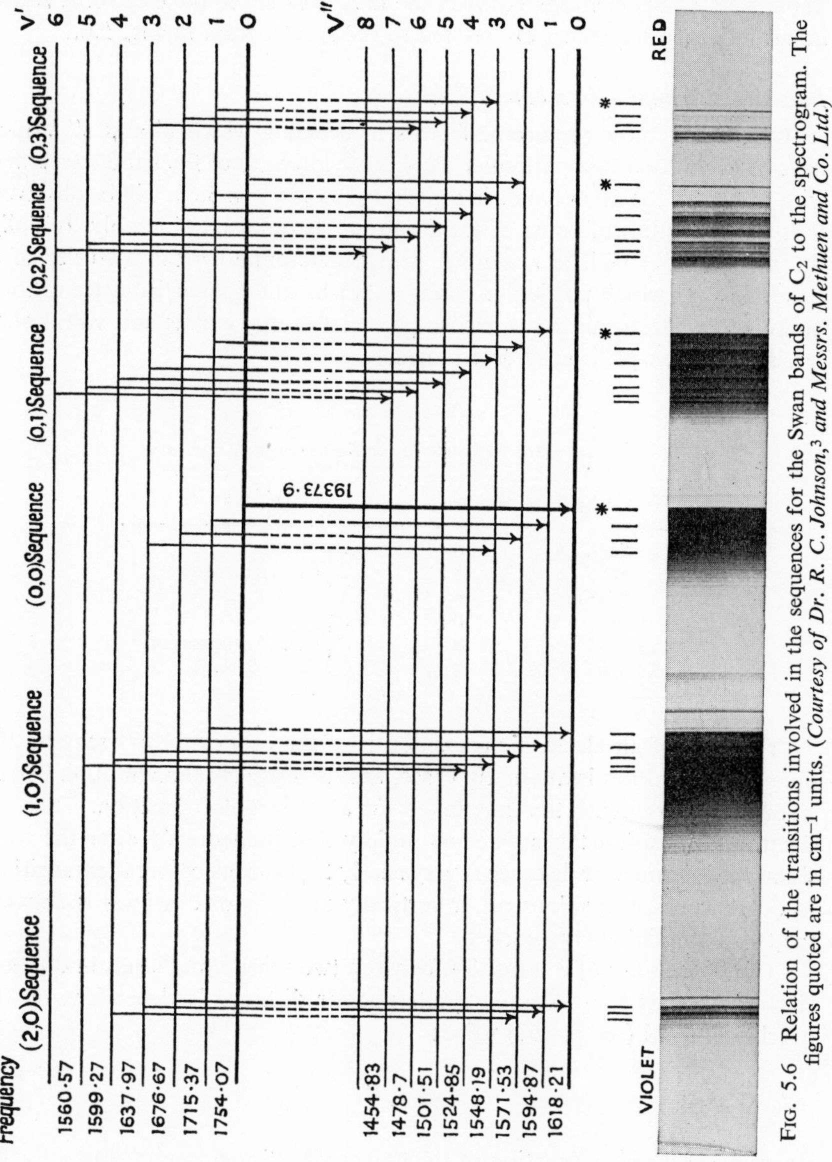

FIG. 5.6 Relation of the transitions involved in the sequences for the Swan bands of C_2 to the spectrogram. The figures quoted are in cm^{-1} units. (*Courtesy of Dr. R. C. Johnson*,[3] *and Messrs. Methuen and Co. Ltd.*)

are six separate groups of bands. Each of these groups is a sequence. In Table 5.4 the wavelength of the first band in each sequence is listed, and the bands in that particular sequence are identified in terms of their (v',v'') values. Thus, each of the vertical groups in Table 5.4 is a sequence. Progressions may be picked out of the horizontal groups; for example, two progressions are the 2–0, 1–0, 0–0, and the 3–3, 3–4, 3–5, 3–6 bands. In the C_2 Swan band spectrogram the bands in a progression, unlike those in sequences, are widely separated and may be readily distinguished from one another (e.g. see Table 5.5). The transitions between the (v',v'') values in the electronic states involved in the sequences are related to the spectrogram in Fig. 5.6.

Intensity distribution in a band system

One of the most important factors in deciding which v' and v'' values have to be allotted to a particular band is the intensity of the band concerned with respect to the other bands in a given system. In Fig. 5.6 it will be observed that the intensities of some of the Swan bands differ considerably. Initially the main factors will be examined, which determine (*a*) the intensity of a band, and (*b*) which particular bands might be anticipated from transitions between two electronic states whose potential energy curves and vibrational levels have been previously determined.

TABLE 5.5

Intensities of some of the Swan bands of C_2

Wavelength	Intensity	(v', v'')	
5636	8	0,1	One sequence
5585	8	1,2	
5541	6	2,3	
5165	10	0,0	One v' progression
4737	9	1,0	
4383	2	2,0	

The time of an electronic transition is of the order of 10^{-16} sec and the time for a vibration is about 10^{-14} sec, that is relatively the vibration period is long compared with the time taken for an electronic transition. Thus, an electronic transition takes place so rapidly that immediately after the transition the internuclear distance is very nearly the same as before the transition. In other words, transitions occur vertically upwards or downwards between the two potential energy curves.

The probability of a transition between two vibrational levels in different electronic states for a common internuclear distance is dependent on the overlap integral (see p. 367) value:

$$\int \psi_{v'}\psi_{v''}\mathrm{d}r$$

where $\psi_{v'}$ is the eigenfunction of the higher vibrational level, $\psi_{v''}$ that for the lower one. The value of ψ_v for a particular vibrational level is dependent on the internuclear distance (r). The greater the value of the overlap integral the more probable it is that the transition will take place.

In Fig. 5.7 both the potential energy curves have their minima at equal internuclear distances. The variation of the eigenfunction ψ_v with internuclear distance for the $v' = 0$ and $v'' = 0$ levels is given by the dotted lines in Fig. 5.7. The ordinates of the wave-function are, of course, independent of the energy scale for the potential energy curves. When an electronic transition takes place from the $v'' = 0$ level, the product $\psi_{v'}\psi_{v''}$ has a maximum value when the maxima of the two wave-functions lie one immediately above the other. Thus, the transition between the $v' = 0$ and $v'' = 0$ levels may best be represented by the line AB in Fig. 5.7.

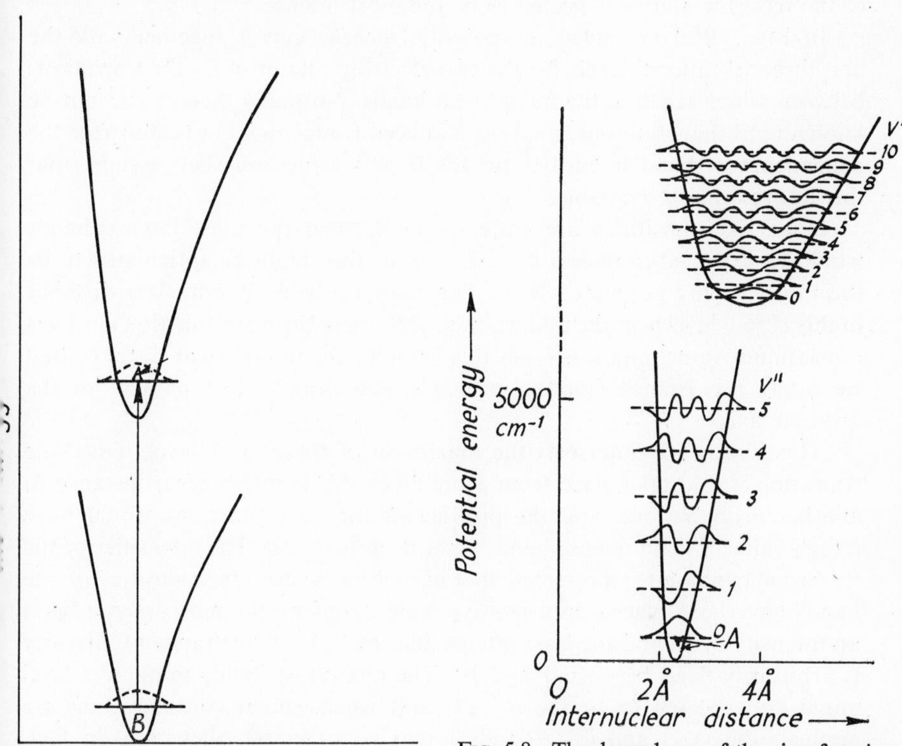

FIG. 5.7 Electronic absorption transition from the $v'' = 0$ to the $v' = 0$ vibrational level

FIG. 5.8 The dependence of the eigenfunction on the vibrational levels for the upper and lower electronic states of rubidium hydride. (*After Gaydon*)

The dependence of the eigenfunction (ψ_v) on the vibrational level concerned may be seen for rubidium hydride in Fig. 5.8. In order to decide which of the absorption bands might be obtained in a transition from the $v'' = 0$ level for rubidium hydride, a line should be drawn from the point A parallel to the ordinate axis—really applying the Franck–Condon principle (see p. 18)—and where this line intersects the terminal maximum or minimum† of any of the

† In the higher vibrational levels the two end maxima (or minima) are the largest, and in between these the contributions of the smaller and narrower maxima and minima very approximately cancel one another out when the overlap integral is evaluated. Hence, for these higher vibrational levels to a rough approximation at least only the terminal loops need be considered.

wave-functions a band might be anticipated. In this case the absorption bands expected would be the (7,0), (8,0), (9,0). However, the electronic transitions for rubidium hydride are too complex for a detailed consideration here. Instead, we shall now examine the relevant potential energy curves for the emission transition in the Swan bands of C_2 and apply (i) the Franck–Condon principle, and (ii) the fact that the greater the product of $\psi_{v'}\psi_{v''}$ then the more probable is the transition, to gain some indication as to which of the bands would be expected to be the most intense.

In Fig. 5.9(*a*) are given the potential energy curves together with the first three vibrational levels for the two electronic states of C_2 the transitions between which result in the main Swan bands. Normally these would not be known until the vibrational analysis had been completed, but to illustrate the dependence of band intensities on the (v',v'') values we shall assume that this information is available.

Since the transitions are emission ones, then the most intense bands would be expected to have a $v' = 0$ value as this might be anticipated to be the most heavily populated level. The most probable internuclear distance in this $v' = 0$ level is at the mid-point of AB where the wave-function ($\psi_{v'}$) has a maximum value, and it is from this value of the internuclear distance that we apply the Franck–Condon principle and draw a line parallel to the ordinate axis.

This line nearly intersects the maximum of the $v'' = 1$ level. Thus, the transition would take place from a highly probable internuclear distance to another probable one, and the product of the wave-functions would have a high value, and an intense band might be anticipated. The intensities of the C_2 Swan bands are represented in Fig. 5.9(*b*), where the intensities of the bands have been placed on a relative scale by giving the most intense band an intensity of 10 and the least intense that of 1. Thus, the range of intensity is arbitrarily fixed between 1 and 10. The next most highly populated level might be expected to be the $v' = 1$, and when similar considerations are applied, the (1,1) and (1,2) bands might be expected; these are, in fact, obtained. From the $v' = 2$ level the most intense bands should be the (2,1) which again proves to be the case. However, the fact that the (0,0) band is the most intense is not readily accounted for. In general, it is not always certain as to which $v'-v''$ transitions will appear and what the approximate order of their intensities will be. We have entirely neglected the effects of the intermediate maxima and minima of the eigenfunctions and have only indirectly considered the fact that many molecules have internuclear distances other than the most probable value. This range of r values in the $v' = 0$ level may lead to v'' progressions in emission transitions, while in absorption transitions from the $v'' = 0$ level a number of bands of a v' progression may result. The number of bands obtained in these progressions depends on the relative positions of the potential energy curves and the steepness of the curve to which the transition is taking place. In fact, the object has been to gain some qualitative insight into the basic factors involved. For more quantitative

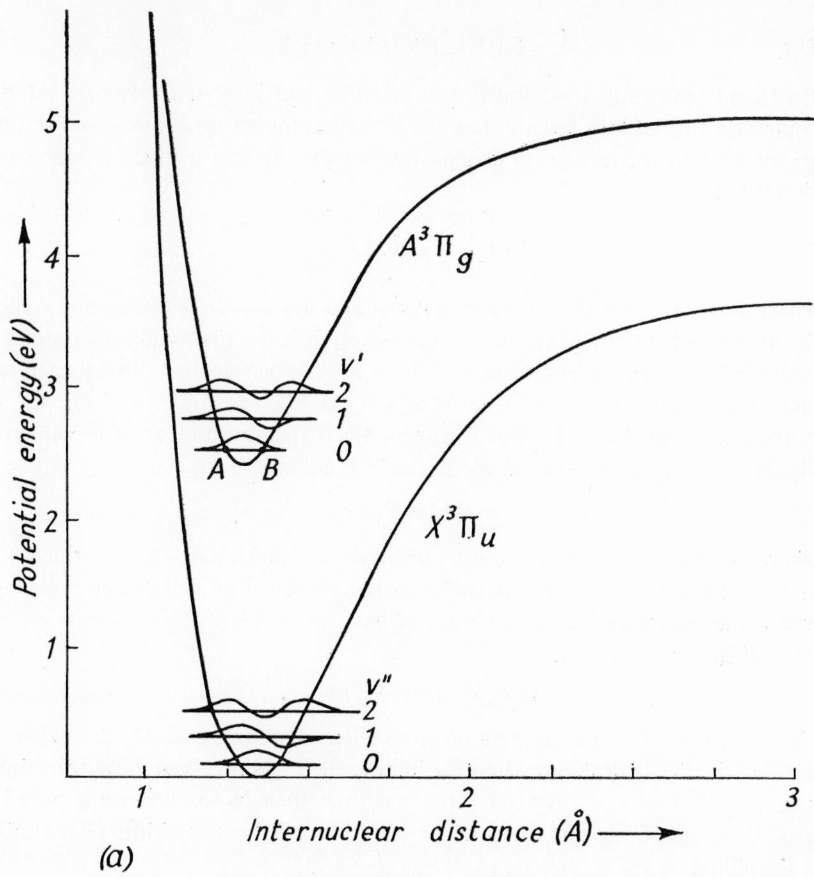

v' \ v''	0	1	2	3	4	5	
0	10	8	3	3			
1	9	6	8	4			
2	2	8	1	6	3		
3		4	7		4	3	
4				4		2	

(b)

FIG. 5.9 (*a*) Potential energy curves † and eigenfunction plot, (*b*) intensity distribution in the Swan bands of C_2 and the Condon parabola

† The ground state is a $^3\Pi_u$ state while the excited one is a $^3\Pi_g$. In addition, there are other $^3\Pi_g$-states, and this one is characterised by placing the letter *A* in front. Thus, the excited state in the Swan band system is an $A^3\Pi_g$-state while the ground state is $X^3\Pi_u$. The letter *X* is commonly employed to signify that the electronic state concerned is the ground state. For molecules several excited electronic states may exist, and in the case of CuH the following are known:

$$^1\Sigma^+,\ ^1\Sigma^+,\ ^1\Pi,\ ^1\Pi$$

The ground state is $X^1\Sigma^+$. The excited electronic states are characterised by placing a letter in front of the symbol. For example, the excited electronic states of CuH are represented by $A^1\Sigma^+$, $B^1\Sigma^+$, $C^1\Pi$, and $D^1\Pi$, where the ν_{00} values for the

$$A^1\Sigma^+ \leftrightarrow X^1\Sigma^+,\quad B^1\Sigma^+ \leftrightarrow X^1\Sigma^+,\quad C^1\Pi \leftrightarrow X^1\Sigma^+,\quad D^1\Pi \leftrightarrow X^1\Sigma^+$$

transitions are, respectively, 23 311.1, 26 281.7, 27 107, and 44 651.2 cm^{-1}.

treatment transition probabilities have to be considered. Evaluation of the transition probability for any band is a most complex procedure, and it may be shown that the transition probability for an emission transition is proportional to:

$$\nu^4\left[\int_0^\infty \psi_{v'} M \psi_{v''} \mathrm{d}r\right]^2$$

where ν is the emitted wave-number, $\psi_{v'}$ and $\psi_{v''}$ are the wave-functions for the upper and lower vibrational energy states, M is the electric dipole moment, and r is the internuclear distance. M is a variable electric dipole moment and may be subdivided into the components M_x, M_y, and M_z along the x, y, and z axes, respectively. For instance, M_x is the component of the electric dipole moment of the system along the x axis, and

$$M_x = \Sigma_j e_j x_j$$

where e_j is the charge and x_j the co-ordinate of the jth particle and the summation is taken over all the particles of the system. For a diatomic molecule where the nuclei and several electrons have to be considered M can be expressed in a $r-r_e$ series:

$$M = M_o + \varepsilon(r-r_e) + \ . \ . \ .$$

ε is a constant, r_e the equilibrium internuclear distance, and M_o the value of the electric dipole moment when the internuclear distance has the equilibrium value. If M does not vary too rapidly with r, then in some cases it may be treated as constant, and then the evaluation of the transition probability is simplified.

If the most intense bands as represented in Fig. 5.9(*b*) are joined together by a dotted line, a parabolic curve whose axis is the principal diagonal is obtained. This is called the *Condon parabola.* The width of the Condon parabola depends on the internuclear separations in the upper and lower electronic states. When the separations of the nuclei are very different in the upper and lower states an open parabola is obtained; should they be appreciably different, the parabola is very open, and the (0,0) and neighbouring bands are not observed. This Condon parabola is a most important feature in verifying the correct assignment of the v' and v'' values to a particular band, as the most intense of them should lie on the Condon parabola. In fact, if in the above analysis a band of intensity 8 for a (3,0) transition had been observed and this was correct, then some of the other allotted (v',v'') values would be incorrect.

Assignment of v' and v'' values

In the treatment so far when v' and v'' have been correlated it has been assumed that the two potential energy curves have been known. This is rarely the case. In practice the v' and v'' values have first to be allotted by observing various points about the spectrum itself. Such a procedure is not for the student but for the practising spectroscopist, whose previous experience and intuition greatly assist in achieving this end. However, a few of the factors which help in the allotment of values will now be considered.

The most intense sequences are noted. In the case of the C_2 molecule for the Swan bands the most intense sequences are the (1,0) and (0,0) ones (see p. 201). One complication is that sequences sometimes overlap. The C_2 molecule is not a case in point. Other factors which assist in the allotment of v' and v'' values are:

(i) An attempt is made to pick out the progressions. This may be assisted by long exposures when the appearance of weak additional bands may help in the identification of a progression. In emission the $v' = 0$ progression might be anticipated. For C_2 the (0,0), (0,1), and (0,2) bands of such a progression are observed. For a band system in absorption at ordinary temperatures, however, then a $v'' = 0$ progression might be anticipated since the molecules are mainly in the $v'' = 0$ level.

(ii) The wave-numbers of the bands heads have to be arranged in a Déslandres table so that:

(*a*) The first difference between adjacent rows is very approximately constant and similarly so for adjacent columns.

(*b*) The second difference should be almost constant. It was shown on p. 195 that this is $-2x_0\omega_0$, and depending on which difference is being considered this would either be $-2x_e'\omega_e'$ or $-2x_e''\omega_e''$. If this value is not nearly constant, then a third difference should be taken, and this would be $6y_0\omega_0$.†

(*c*) The v',v'' values of the most intense bands should lie on the Condon parabola in the Déslandres table itself; otherwise, the analysis is incorrect.

(iii) In general, for the diatomic molecules and radicals so far reported in the literature at least three or four band systems have been obtained. Hence, in the analysis of new band systems of such species it is likely that one of the previously analysed electronic states whose vibrational data will be available (i.e. ω_e, x_e and y_e values) is one of the electronic states in the new transition. The analysis for the assignment of v' and v'' values may then be considerably assisted, since some of the frequency differences may be directly related to the known vibrational levels. This may thus assist the picking out of a progression involving such levels.

Rotational structure of electronic bands of diatomic molecules and radicals

As yet we have been mainly concerned with bands at poor dispersion where the vibrational analysis could be carried out after measurement of the position of the band heads. In Fig. 5.31(*b*) the 4315 Å band of CH is given at such a moderate dispersion that it would not be possible to measure the positions of all the lines in the band. However, in Fig. 5.31(*a*), which gives

† By taking these second and third differences, values of $x_e\omega_e$ and $y_e\omega_e$ values are obtained.

this CH band at greater dispersion, the rotational structure may be readily observed. From the measurement of the position of the lines in this fine structure of the band and by allotting the correct J' and J'' values to each of these lines, the $B_{v'}$ and $B_{v''}$ values may be determined. This type of study will be the next objective, and the approach will be made by consideration of the equations which may be employed to express the wave-numbers of the spectral lines in terms of J values.

It was indicated on p. 190 that the emitted or absorbed wave-number in an electronic transition is given by:

$$\nu = \nu_e + \nu_v + \nu_r \tag{5.32}$$

For one particular band in an electronic transition both ν_e and ν_v are constant and may be replaced by ν_0 where ν_0 is termed the *band origin* or *zero line*. The wave-numbers of the spectral lines are then given by:

$$\nu = \nu_0 + \nu_r \tag{5.33}$$

where ν_r is the wave-number for the difference in the two rotational term values for the particular spectral line. Thus, the equation may be modified to:

$$\nu = \nu_0 + \{F_{v'}(J') - F_{v''}(J'')\} \tag{5.34}$$

where the rotational term values are given by the formula:

$$F_v(J) = \frac{E_r}{hc} = B_v J(J+1) - D_v J^2(J+1)^2 + \ldots \tag{5.35}$$

The wave-numbers of the lines in a particular band are then represented by:

$$\nu = \nu_0 + \{B_{v'}J'(J'+1) - D_{v'}J'^2(J'+1)^2 + \ldots\} - \{B_{v''}J''(J''+1) - D_{v''}J''^2(J''+1)^2 + \ldots\} \tag{5.36}$$

For an electronic transition, the upper and lower energy states may have different orbital angular momenta about the internuclear axis where this momentum is $\Lambda h/2\pi$. When $\Lambda = 0$, that is for a Σ-state (see p. 47), the selection rule for J is:

$$\Delta J = \pm 1 \tag{5.37}$$

but when $\Lambda \neq 0$ for either or both the electronic states between which the transition takes place the selection rule becomes:

$$\Delta J = 0, \pm 1 \tag{5.38}$$

Thus, in the case of a $^1\Sigma - ^1\Sigma$ transition only P- and R-branches would be anticipated corresponding to $J' - J'' = -1$ and $+1$, respectively. However, in a $^1\Pi - ^1\Sigma$ transition, since $\Lambda = 1$ for a Π-state, then P-, Q-, and R-branches would be expected. The wave-numbers of the R-, Q-, and P-branches are:

$$\nu = \nu_0 + F_{v'}(J+1) - F_{v''}(J) = R(J) \tag{5.39}$$

$$\nu = \nu_0 + F_{v'}(J) - F_{v''}(J) = Q(J) \tag{5.40}$$

$$\nu = \nu_0 + F_{v'}(J-1) - F_{v''}(J) = P(J) \tag{5.41}$$

where $R(J)$, $Q(J)$ and $P(J)$ are employed to represent the wave-numbers of the lines in the R-, Q- and P-branches, respectively, for a particular value of J.

The centrifugal constants $D_{v'}$ and $D_{v''}$ are normally very small. In fact:

$$D_v = \frac{4B_v^3}{\omega^2}\dagger \tag{5.42}$$

where $\omega \gg B_v$, and D_v is generally something of the order of $10^{-5}B_v$. The case will now be considered where this D_v term is neglected. On substitution of equation (5.35) into equations (5.39), (5.40), and (5.41), and assuming $D_v = 0$, then by expression of the J' values in terms of J'' by means of $J' = J''-1$ for a P-branch, $J' = J''$ for a Q-branch and $J' = J''+1$ for an R-branch, the following equations result for the P-, Q- and R-branches:

$$\nu = \nu_0 - (B_{v'}+B_{v''})J + (B_{v'}-B_{v''})J^2 = P(J) \tag{5.43}$$

$$\nu = \nu_0 + (B_{v'}-B_{v''})J + (B_{v'}-B_{v''})J^2 = Q(J) \tag{5.44}$$

$$\nu = \nu_0 + 2B_{v'} + (3B_{v'}-B_{v''})J + (B_{v'}-B_{v''})J^2 = R(J) \tag{5.45}$$

These equations which give the wave-numbers of the lines of the P-, Q- and R-branches have exactly the same form as those derived for rotation-vibration transitions on p. 105. In addition, as was the case for rotation-vibration transitions, the P- and R-branches may be represented by the equation:

$$\nu = \nu_0 + (B_{v'}+B_{v''})m + (B_{v'}-B_{v''})m^2 \tag{5.46}$$

where $m = -J = -J''$ for the P-branch and $m = J+1 = J''+1$ for the R-branch.

As regards an electronic spectrum $B_{v'}$ and $B_{v''}$ refer not only to different vibrational energy levels but also to different electronic states and depend on how one potential energy curve lies with respect to the other. In fact, sometimes these B-values may be very different from one another.‡

If there is no Q-branch (as for a $^1\Sigma-{}^1\Sigma$ transition), no line appears in the position of ν_0 which is the band origin. A $^1\Sigma-{}^1\Sigma$ transition is illustrated diagrammatically in Fig. 5.10 between the vibrational levels $v' = 0$ and $v'' = 0$. For a $^1\Pi-{}^1\Sigma$ transition, however, a Q-branch is permitted in addition to the P- and R-branches, and in addition the $P(1)$ line is absent.

Band head and Fortrat parabola

$B_{v'} > B_{v''}$. If the internuclear distance in the upper electronic state is smaller than that in the lower, then, since B_v varies inversely as r^2, the term $(B_{v'}-B_{v''})$ will be positive. By reference to the following formula:

$$\nu = \nu_0 + (B_{v'}+B_{v''})m + (B_{v'}-B_{v''})m^2 \tag{5.47}$$

it may be noted that in the case of a P-branch, where $m = -J$, the term in m^2, as m increases, will eventually outweigh the term in m, and consequently ν

† This equation is derived in Herzberg.[2]

‡ For a rotation-vibration infra-red or Raman change the alteration in the moment of inertia is small in passing from one vibrational level to the next in the same electronic state. However, in an electronic transition there may be an appreciable change in the moment of inertia; hence, the spacing of the lines may differ markedly between the two types of spectra.

at first decreases and then increases. If sufficient J values are available, the P-branch consists of lines which grow closer together then gradually turn back on themselves; and their spacing then begins to increase. The frequency at which the lines begin to turn back is known as the band head. A band where ν decreases and then increases is termed *degraded towards the violet*, that is to shorter wavelengths. The P-branch represented in Fig. 5.11 is such a case. In general, the wave-number at which the band head occurs depends

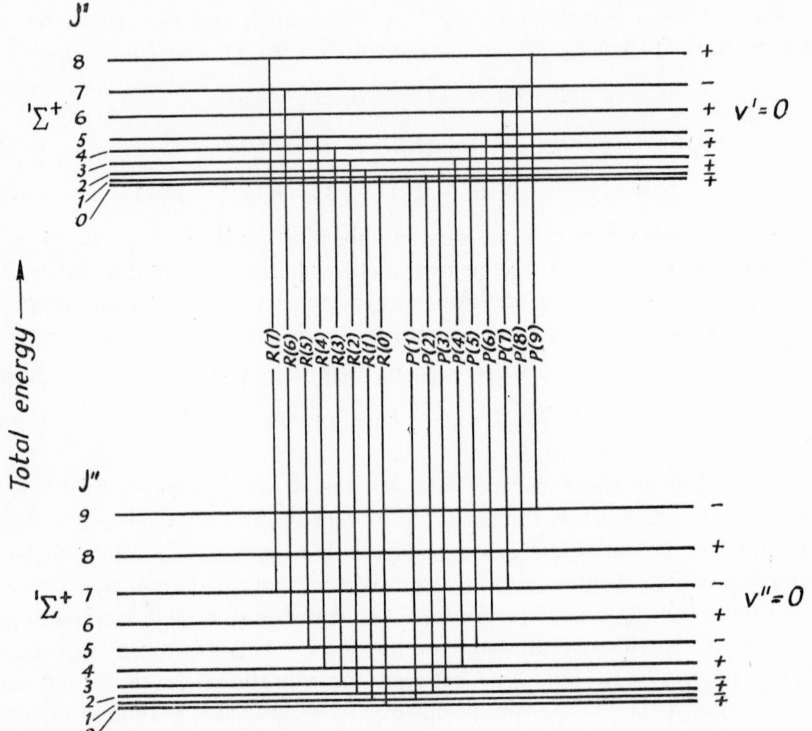

FIG. 5.10 Energy level diagram illustrating the rotational transitions of the (0,0) band of a $^1\Sigma^+ - {}^1\Sigma^+$ transition

on the difference between the $B_{v'}$ and $B_{v''}$ values, and normally the band head may easily be recognized and measured directly. This is to be contrasted with the band origin, that is the $J' \leftrightarrow J''$ transition, where both the J values are zero. The band origin has, in fact, to be determined from the analysis of the rotational branches. As regards the R-branch for this case of $B_{v'} > B_{v''}$ it follows from equation (5.47) and the fact that $m = J+1$ that as m increases the wave-numbers of the lines will steadily diverge; this may also be noted in Fig. 5.11. Fortrat was the first to employ the type of representation given in Fig. 5.11 for the P- and R-branches, and this $\nu - m$ plot is known as the *Fortrat parabola*.

The case shown in Fig. 5.11 is one which does not exhibit a Q-branch. The negative values of m, which are those of the P-branch, are drawn above the zero line, and the positive values of m, that is those of the R-branch, are shown below this line. The diagram illustrates most clearly the formation of a band head in the P-branch. The parabola cuts the axis at $m = 0$ at a point N and has its vertex $\Delta\nu/\Delta m = 0$ at a point H which is the band head.

$B_{v'} < B_{v''}$. The condition which has to be satisfied for the formation of a head in the R-branch is that the internuclear distance in the lower electronic state has to be smaller than that in the upper, that is $(B_{v'} - B_{v''})$ must be

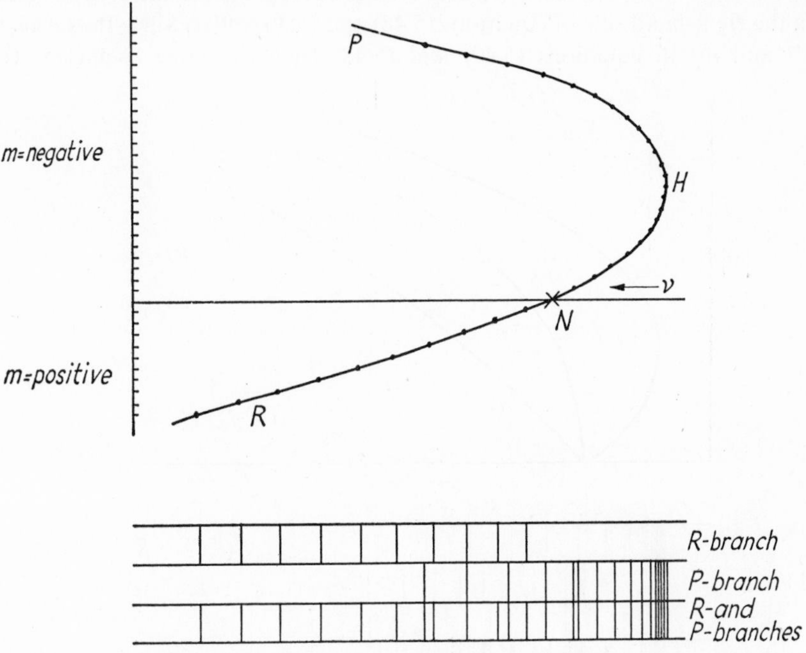

FIG. 5.11 Fortrat parabola for a $^1\Sigma - {}^1\Sigma$ transition where the band head is degraded to the violet

negative. It then follows from equation (5.47) and the fact that $m = J+1$ for an R-branch that initially the $(B_{v'}+B_{v''})m$ term may outweigh the $(B_{v'}-B_{v''})m^2$ term and the wave-numbers will increase. However, as J increases the squared term will eventually outweigh the single power term and the wave-numbers will decrease. In this case the band is termed *degraded towards the red*, that is to longer wavelengths. Such an example is that of the R-branch in the (0,0) band of the $A^1\Sigma^+ - X^1\Sigma^+$ transition of CuH in Fig. 5.12(a). In addition, an intensity distribution representation of the lines in the P- and R-branches of this band is given in Fig. 5.12(c), and in Fig. 5.12(b) each of the rotational lines in the P- and R-branches may be related to an appropriate point on the Fortrat parabola.

For transitions between two electronic states where in one or both of the electronic states the orbital angular momentum is not zero, that is for transitions other than $\Sigma - \Sigma$, a Q-branch is to be anticipated in addition to the *P*- and *R*-branches. In general, the lines in the *P*- and *R*-branches may be represented by the formula:

$$\nu = \nu_0 + (B_{v'} + B_{v''})m + (B_{v'} - B_{v''})m^2 \tag{5.48}$$

but those in a *Q*-branch by:

$$\nu = \nu_0 + (B_{v'} - B_{v''})J'' + (B_{v'} - B_{v''})J''^2 \tag{5.49}$$

The lines in the *Q*-branch will be represented by a different parabola from those of the *P*- and *R*-branches because the coefficients for the second terms on the right-hand side of equations (5.48) and (5.49) differ. Since the terms in J''^2 and m^2 in equations (5.49) and (5.48) have the same coefficient the

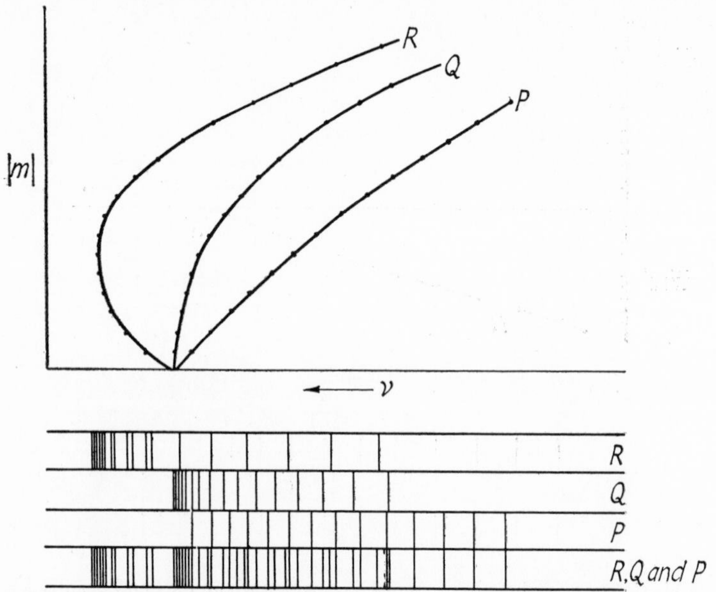

FIG. 5.13 Fortrat parabola for a $^1\Pi - {}^1\Sigma$ transition where the lines in *R*- and *Q*-branches are degraded to the red. $|m|$ values have been plotted on the ordinate axis. The *m* values for the *P*-branch have a negative sign. If respect were paid to the sign of *m*, then the *P*-branch parabola would be a continuation of the *R*-branch parabola. It should be noted that *m* does not take the values 0 or -1 for a $^1\Pi - {}^1\Sigma$ transition

vertices of the two parabolae lie in the same direction. If the $B_{v'}$ and $B_{v''}$ values are of the same magnitude, then the *Q* parabola will intersect the wave-number axis nearly vertically owing to the smallness of the $(B_{v'} - B_{v''})$ value. When a *Q*-branch is present, then two band heads are generally observed; (i) a head in *P* and *Q* when $B_{v'} > B_{v''}$ and these are degraded towards shorter wavelength or (ii) when $B_{v''} > B_{v'}$ a head in *R* and *Q* which are degraded to longer wavelength. A representation of the fine structure for a $^1\Pi - {}^1\Sigma$ transition together with the Fortrat parabolae is given in Fig. 5.13 for the case where $B_{v''} > B_{v'}$. In general, all the bands in a band system are degraded in the same direction, since the sign of the difference $B_{v'} - B_{v''}$ does not

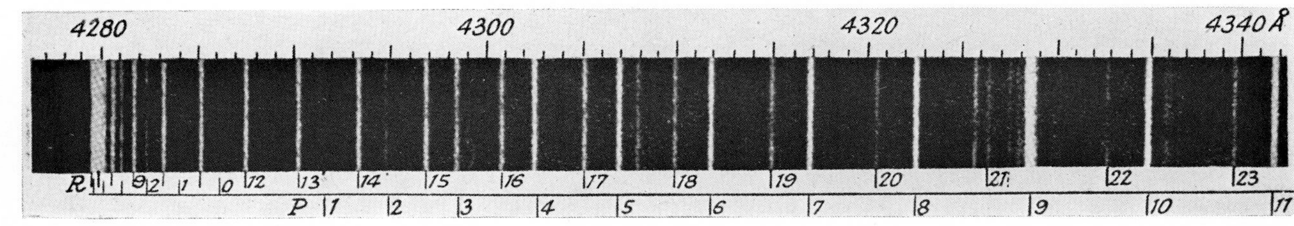

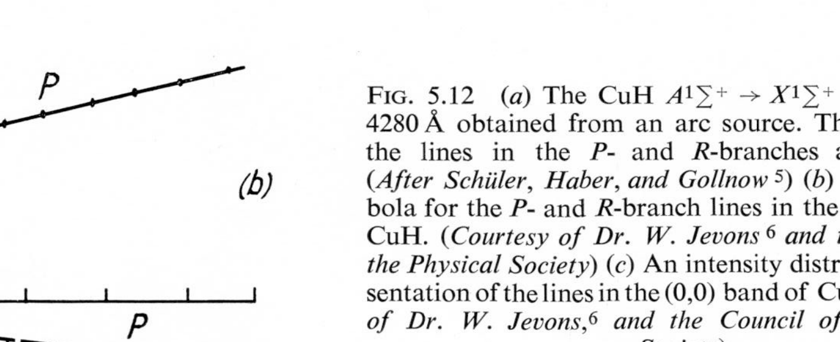

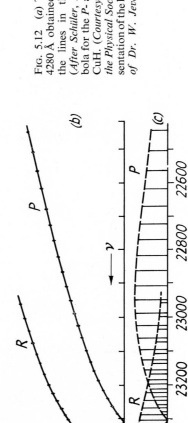

FIG. 5.12 (*a*) The CuH $A^1\Sigma^+ \rightarrow X^1\Sigma^+$ (0,0) band at 4280 Å obtained from an arc source. The position of the lines in the *P*- and *R*-branches are indicated. (*After Schüler, Haber, and Gollnow* [5]) (*b*) Fortrat parabola for the *P*- and *R*-branch lines in the (0,0) band of CuH. (*Courtesy of Dr. W. Jevons* [6] *and the Council of the Physical Society*) (*c*) An intensity distribution representation of the lines in the (0,0) band of CuH. (*Courtesy of Dr. W. Jevons,*[6] *and the Council of the Physical Society*)

[*To face page* 212

normally change. However, if $B_{v'}$ and $B_{v''}$ are almost equal, and since the B values for the upper and lower electronic levels are dependent on the value of v' and v'', respectively, the possibility exists that $B_{v'}$ may be greater than $B_{v''}$ for one band but less than $B_{v''}$ for another band in the same band system. In fact, this is so for the electronic transition $B^2\Sigma^+ - X^2\Sigma^+$ in the band system of CN where some of the bands are degraded to the violet and others to the red.

In order to determine the m value corresponding to the vertex of the Fortrat parabola for a P- or R-branch, the following equation is differentiated:

$$\nu = \nu_0 + (B_{v'} + B_{v''})m + (B_{v'} - B_{v''})m^2 \tag{5.50}$$

and we obtain:

$$\frac{\Delta\nu}{\Delta m} = (B_{v'} + B_{v''}) + 2m(B_{v'} - B_{v''}) \tag{5.51}$$

where $\Delta\nu/\Delta m = 0$ is the band head and the corresponding m value is termed m_{head}:

$$m_{\text{head}} = -\frac{(B_{v'} + B_{v''})}{2(B_{v'} - B_{v''})} \tag{5.52}$$

On substitution of this m_{head} value into equation (5.50) we obtain:

$$\nu_{\text{head}} - \nu_0 = -\frac{(B_{v'} + B_{v''})^2}{4(B_{v'} - B_{v''})} \tag{5.53}$$

When $B_{v'} < B_{v''}$, then it follows from equation (5.53) that $\nu_{\text{head}} - \nu_0$ is positive, that is the head of the band is at a higher frequency than the band origin. Hence, the band must be degraded to the red. However, if $B_{v'} > B_{v''}$ then the value is negative and the shading must be towards the violet. It can be seen from equation (5.53) that if $B_{v'} \sim B_{v''}$, then the wave-number separation of ν_{head} and ν_0 will be very great; thus, the band head may be so far separated from the band origin that for these high m values the intensity of the lines will be so weak that the head is not observable.

Intensity distribution within a band

It has just been considered how the appearance of a band depends on the positions of its constituent lines and on the relative values of $B_{v'}$ and $B_{v''}$. An additional factor which affects its appearance is the relative variation of intensities in these constituent lines and their distribution. The intensity distribution of the lines in the $^1\Sigma^+ - {}^1\Sigma^+$ (0,0) band of CuH under certain experimental conditions is given in Fig. 5.12(*c*). The intensity of a line in the simplest case of a $^1\Sigma - {}^1\Sigma$ transition in absorption and emission is given by equations of the type (1.39) and 1.40) respectively.

Combination relationships

For P- and R-branches. In order to determine the values of $B_{v'}$ and $B_{v''}$ most accurately and to allot the J' and J'' values unambiguously it is necessary to make use of what are known as *combination relations.* To illustrate the combination principle Fig. 5.10 will be employed, and this involves one band of a $^1\Sigma-{}^1\Sigma$ transition. In this figure the spectral lines, whose wave-numbers are $R(2)$ and $P(4)$, have a common upper rotational level of $J = 3$. The wave-number difference of these lines is:

$$R(2)-P(4)$$

and this may be interpreted from the figure as the difference in wave-number between the rotational levels $J'' = 4$ and $J'' = 2$. Hence, it follows:

$$R(2)-P(4) = F_{v''}(4)-F_{v''}(2) \tag{5.54}$$

where $F_{v''}(4)$ is the term value (see p. 11) for the $J'' = 4$ level. In general, for two such lines involving a common upper rotational level J, the difference of wave-numbers of the two lines would be:

$$R(J-1)-P(J+1) = F_{v''}(J+1)-F_{v''}(J-1) = \Delta_2F''(J) \tag{5.55}$$

where $\Delta_2F''(J)$ is the wave-number difference of one of the lower $^1\Sigma$-state rotational energy levels from the second lower down. This equation could also be deduced from equations (5.39) and (5.41) as follows.

Since

$$R(J) = \nu_0+F_{v'}(J+1)-F_{v''}(J) \tag{5.56}$$

then

$$R(J-1) = \nu_0+F_{v'}(J)-F_{v''}(J-1) \tag{5.57}$$

and similarly:

$$P(J+1) = \nu_0+F_{v'}(J)-F_{v''}(J+1) \tag{5.58}$$

On subtraction of equation (5.58) from equation (5.57) we obtain:

$$R(J-1)-P(J+1) = F_{v''}(J+1)-F_{v''}(J-1) \tag{5.59}$$

It may be readily shown that the difference between the wave-numbers of two lines in electronic transitions with a common lower rotational level (J) equals the separation of one of the upper electronic state rotational levels from the one next but one above it. This may be shown by means of the figure or by means of equations (5.39) and (5.41) as follows:

$$\begin{aligned} R(J)-P(J) &= \{\nu_0+F_{v'}(J+1)-F_{v''}(J)\}-\{\nu_0+F_{v'}(J-1)-F_{v''}(J)\} \\ &= F_{v'}(J+1)-F_{v'}(J-1) = \Delta_2F'(J) \end{aligned} \tag{5.60}$$

where $\Delta_2F'(J)$ is the separation in wave-numbers between these two rotational terms of the same vibrational level of the upper electronic state.

On substitution for the appropriate rotational term values from the equation:

$$F_v(J) = B_vJ(J+1)-D_vJ^2(J+1)^2 \tag{5.61}$$

into equations (5.60) and (5.59) we obtain:

$$R(J)-P(J) = (4B_{v'}-6D_{v'})(J+\tfrac{1}{2})-8D_{v'}(J+\tfrac{1}{2})^3 \tag{5.62}$$

$$R(J-1)-P(J+1) = (4B_{v''}-6D_{v''})(J+\tfrac{1}{2})-8D_{v''}(J+\tfrac{1}{2})^3 \tag{5.63}$$

Equations (5.62) and (5.63) may be employed to determine the $B_{v'}$, $B_{v''}$, and $D_{v'}$ and $D_{v''}$ values. One of the graphical methods by which this is achieved is to plot $\{R(J)-P(J)\}/(J+\frac{1}{2})$ against $(J+\frac{1}{2})^2$ when a straight line should be obtained which has a slope of $-8D_{v'}$ and an intercept of $4B_{v'}-6D_{v'}$. In a similar way the plot of $\{R(J-1)-P(J+1)\}/(J+\frac{1}{2})$ against $(J+\frac{1}{2})^2$ gives a straight line of slope $-8D_{v''}$ and an intercept value of $(4B_{v''}-6D_{v''})$. Thus, in this way the B and D values may be obtained. In Table 5.6 the $R(J)-P(J)/(J+\frac{1}{2})$ and $\{R(J-1)-P(J+1)\}/(J+\frac{1}{2})$ data are given for the (0,0) and (0,1) bands of CuH at the wavelengths of 4280 Å and 4650 Å, respectively, in the

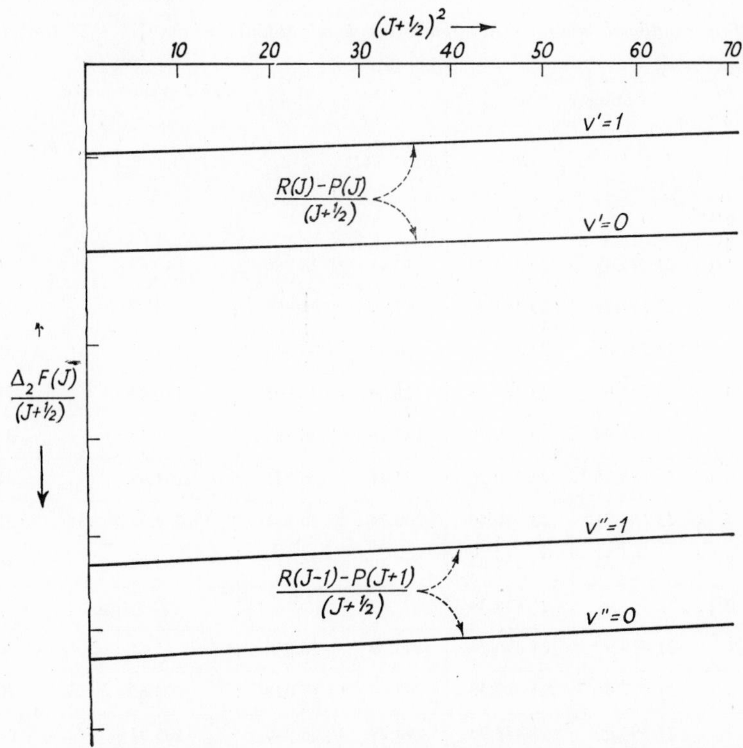

FIG. 5.14 Plot of $\{R(J-1)-P(J+1)\}/(J+\frac{1}{2})$ against $(J+\frac{1}{2})^2$ for the $v''=0$, $v''=1$ vibrational levels and the plot of $\{R(J)-P(J)\}/(J+\frac{1}{2})$ against $(J+\frac{1}{2})^2$ for the $v'=0$ and $v'=1$ levels. The data were obtained from the (0,0) and (0,1) bands of CuH for the $A^1\Sigma^+ \rightarrow X^1\Sigma^+$ transition. (*Courtesy of Dr. W. Jevons*[6] *and the Council of The Physical Society*)

$A^1\Sigma^+ \rightarrow X^1\Sigma^+$ transition. The plot of $\{R(J)-P(J)\}/(J+\frac{1}{2})$ and $\{R(J-1)-P(J+1)\}/(J+\frac{1}{2})$ against $(J+\frac{1}{2})^2$ is given in Fig. 5.14. The rotational structure of the 4280 Å (0,0) band is given in Fig. 5.12(*a*) for this $A^1\Sigma^+ \rightarrow X^1\Sigma^+$ transition.

From the procedure outlined the values of $B_{v'}$, $B_{v''}$, $D_{v'}$, and $D_{v''}$ are obtained. The correctness of the analysis may be checked by calculating the values of ω_e' and ω_e'' from the formula:

$$\omega_e = \sqrt{\frac{4B_e^3}{D_e}} \tag{5.64}$$

and comparing the values of ω_e with the ones obtained from the vibrational analysis (see p. 195).

For P-, Q- and R-branches. The combination relations considered so far have been for *P*- and *R*-branches. When a *Q*-branch is observed further combination relationships exist in addition to those already given involving the *P*- and *R*-branches, since a common upper or lower state rotational level

TABLE 5.6

Part of the rotational data for the (0,0) *and* (0,1) *bands of* CuH *for the* $^1\Sigma^+ \rightarrow {}^1\Sigma^+$ *transition*

Band	J	Wave-number of observed lines		$\Delta_2F(J)$ values			
		$P(J)$	$R(J)$	$R(J)-P(J)$	$\frac{R(J)-P(J)}{(J+\frac{1}{2})}$	$R(J-1)-P(J+1)$	$\frac{R(J-1)-P(J+1)}{(J+\frac{1}{2})}$
	0		23 324.68				
	1	23 295.47	23 335.95	40.48	26.986	46.89	31.260
	2	23 277.79	23 345.06	67.27	26.908	78.09	31.236
(0,0)	3	23 257.86	23 352.18	94.32	26.948	109.11	31.176
head	4	23 235.95	23 357.04	121.09	26.908	140.24	31.164
at	5	23 211.94	23 359.70	147.76	26.865	171.19	31.124
4280 Å	6	23 185.85	23 360.26	174.41	26.832	201.99	31.075
	7	23 157.71	23 358.45	200.74	26.764	232.72	31.028
	8	23 127.54	23 354.64	227.10	26.717	263.06	30.94
	0		21 458.39				
	1	21 429.97	21 470.26	40.29	26.860	45.41	30.273
	2	21 412.98	21 480.55	67.57	27.028	75.60	30.240
(0,1)	3	21 394.66	21 488.95	94.29	26.940	105.94	30.268
head	4	21 374.61	21 496.01	121.40	26.976	135.72	30.160
at	5	21 353.23	21 501.31	148.08	26.924	166.26	30.228
4650 Å	6	21 329.75	21 504.57	174.82	26.895	195.96	30.147
	7	21 305.35	21 506.52	201.17	26.824	225.38	30.057
	8	21 279.19	21 506.52	227.33	26.744	254.80	29.976

may be common to three spectral lines. In an exactly similar way to which the combination relations for *P*- and *R*-branches were developed, it may be deduced from equations (5.39), (5.40) and (5.41) that:

$$R(J)-Q(J) = F_{v'}(J+1)-F_{v'}(J) = \Delta_1 F'(J) \tag{5.65}$$

$$R(J)-Q(J+1) = F_{v''}(J+1)-F_{v''}(J) = \Delta_1 F''(J) \tag{5.66}$$

$$Q(J)-P(J+1) = F_{v''}(J+1)-F_{v''}(J) = \Delta_1 F''(J) \tag{5.67}$$

$$Q(J+1)-P(J+1) = F_{v'}(J+1)-F_{v'}(J) = \Delta_1 F'(J) \tag{5.68}$$

Since the right-hand sides of equations (5.65) and (5.68) are equal it follows that:

$$R(J)-Q(J) = Q(J+1)-P(J+1) \tag{5.69}$$

and, in addition, from equations (5.66) and (5.67) that:

$$R(J)-Q(J+1) = Q(J)-P(J+1) \tag{5.70}$$

If two bands have the same upper vibrational state, the combination differences (5.65) and (5.68) must be satisfied for each J value, while for the same lower vibrational level the combination relationships (5.66) and (5.67) must be satisfied. A thorough test of the successful analysis of a band then follows, if the combination relationships (5.69) and (5.70) hold.

In a similar way as for $^1\Sigma - {}^1\Sigma$ transitions the equation:

$$F_v(J) = B_vJ(J+1)-D_vJ^2(J+1)^2 \tag{5.71}$$

may be employed to substitute for the $F(J+1)$ and $F(J)$ terms in equations (5.65) to (5.68), and the resulting equations may be used as before to determine $B_{v'}$, $B_{v''}$, $D_{v'}$, and $D_{v''}$ values.

Determination of B_e, D_e, and r_e

If the rotational analysis has been carried out on a number of bands in a band system, then the dependence of $B_{v'}$, $B_{v''}$, $D_{v'}$, and $D_{v''}$ on the value of the vibrational quantum number in the upper and lower electronic states may be followed. In general, their dependence on v is adequately represented by equations of the type:

$$B_v = B_e - \alpha_e(v+\tfrac{1}{2}) \tag{5.72}$$

$$D_v = D_e + \beta_e(v+\tfrac{1}{2}) \tag{5.73}$$

where B_e and D_e are the extrapolated values of B_v and D_v and correspond with the hypothetical vibrationless state. From the plot of B_v against v the constant α_e may be determined, and from equation (5.72) it then follows that the value of B_e is given by:

$$B_e = B_0 + \tfrac{1}{2}\alpha_e \tag{5.74}$$

where B_0 is the value of the rotational constant for the $v = 0$ vibrational level. Since

$$B_e = \frac{h}{8\pi^2 cI_e} \tag{5.75}$$

$$I_e = \frac{m_1m_2}{(m_1+m_2)}r_e^2 \tag{5.76}$$

then the internuclear distance (r_e) at the minimum of the potential energy curve may be determined from the analysis. The electronic spectrum method is unique in that it yields r and r_e values not only for the ground state but for excited electronic states as well. The values of r_e are usually quoted to within 0.01 to 0.001 Å. Such r_e values have been obtained for a very large number of diatomic molecules and radicals. In fact, some of the species recorded may be quite unfamiliar, e.g. AgO, AlH, AsN, BF, CaBr, CS, HS, SiH, VO, ZnH, and $(ZnH)^+$.

It is most important to note that the detailed analysis of the rotational structure of the electronic bands not only yields r_e values but if, in addition, it gives what appears to be a reasonable value of r_e, then this is proof that the correct molecular species was postulated.

Determination of band origin

In order to obtain accurate vibrational constants for a molecule it is necessary to determine the value of ν_0, the wave-number of the band origin. In fact, as was indicated when the vibrational analysis was considered, for the best analysis of the vibrational frequencies by means of the Déslandres table, it is desirable to employ band origin data and not band head.

The determination of ν_0 may be accomplished by a combination relationship. For a band with only a *P*- and *R*-branch present, on employment of equations (5.43) and (5.45) we obtain:

$$R(J-1)+P(J) = 2\nu_0+2(B_{v'}-B_{v''})J^2 \tag{5.77}$$

By plotting $R(J-1)+P(J)$, which is obtained from the fine structure analysis against J^2, a straight line is obtained whose intercept on the ordinate axis gives the value $2\nu_0$.

Allotment of J values to spectral lines

So far it has been assumed that the branches of a band may be picked out and that the J values have been allotted. If the fine structure of the band is completely resolved, and the zero line position (band origin) is apparent, then the allotment of J values to a particular band is readily carried out. An example of this type of band may be observed in Fig. 1.6 for the (0,0) band of CN at 3883 Å of the $B^2\Sigma^+-X^2\Sigma^+$ violet band system at low temperatures. Only *P*- and *R*-branches are present. The first line on the short wavelength side of the zero gap is the $J'' = 0$ line of the *R*-branch, and the first line on the longer wavelength side of the zero gap is the $J'' = 1$ line of the *P*-branch. Thus, the numbering of the *P*- and *R*-branches is readily achieved for a Σ type transition where the zero line position is apparent as a gap between the two branches.

The assignment of the m values and consequently J values of a particular series of lines in a branch may be checked as follows. The lines of a *P*- and *R*-branch of a band may be, at least approximately, represented by the formula:

$$\nu = c+dm+em^2 \tag{5.78}$$

where $m = J+1$ for an *R*-branch and $m = -J$ for a *P*-branch. It follows that

$$\frac{\Delta\nu}{\Delta m} = d+2em \tag{5.79}$$

and

$$\frac{\Delta^2\nu}{\Delta m^2} = 2e \tag{5.80}$$

where e is a constant. Hence, the second difference between the wave-numbers of consecutive m values should have a constant value for all the members of the branch. This point is illustrated in Table 5.7 where the first and second

TABLE 5.7

The first and second differences between consecutive lines in part of the P- and R-branches in the ${}^1\Sigma^+ - {}^1\Sigma^+$ (0,0) *band of* CuH *at* 4280 Å

m	Observed wave-number (cm^{-1})	First difference	Second difference
P-branch			
−10	23 061.27		
		34.12	
−9	23 095.39		1.97
		32.15	
−8	23 127.54		1.98
		30.17	
−7	23 157.71		2.03
		28.14	
−6	23 185.85		2.05
		26.09	
−5	23 211.94		2.08
		24.01	
−4	23 235.95		1.90
		21.91	
−3	23 257.86		1.98
		19.93	
−2	23 277.79		2.25
		17.68	
−1	23 295.47		
R-branch			
1	23 324.68		
		11.27	
2	23 335.95		2.16
		9.11	
3	23 345.06		1.99
		7.12	
4	23 352.18		2.26
		4.86	
5	23 357.04		2.20
		2.66	
6	23 359.70		2.10
		0.56	
7	23 360.26		2.37
		−1.81	
8	23 358.45		2.00
		−3.81	
9	23 354.64		2.26
		−6.07	
10	23 348.57		2.24
		−8.31	
11	23 340.26		

difference between the wave-numbers of consecutive lines in each of the *P*- and *R*-branches for the (0,0) band of the $^1\Sigma^+ - {}^1\Sigma^+$ transition of CuH are given in columns (3) and (4), respectively. The second difference values are sufficiently constant for the assignment of the *m* values to be regarded as correct.

When, however, the fine structure of adjacent bands overlaps, then it may become difficult to pick out the lines in the branches of a particular band. One of the procedures is then to attempt to allot the *m* values of a few of the lines which, from their wave-number separation, look as though they are members of the same branch. The first and second differences for these lines are formed, and from these differences it becomes possible to calculate the anticipated wave-numbers of additional lines on each side of these lines. In this manner a number of lines may be allotted *m* values and designated to a particular branch. To check this *m* allocation in a particular branch the first difference in wave-number values for consecutive *m* values is taken and plotted against *m*. From formula (5.79) it follows that these wave-number differences for a particular *P*- or *R*-branch should lie on a straight line.† This type of plot may be employed to determine whether the lines allocated to particular *P*- and *R*-branches belong solely to these two branches.‡ If this is the case, then the points should group themselves along two lines of different slope. If any further branches are present, these should group themselves along other lines. In addition, if scattered points occur which cannot be identified with these *P*- and *R*-lines, then these may be attributed to spectral lines in other bands. If a $^1\Pi - {}^1\Sigma$ transition is considered, the lowest rotational level in a Π-state is $J = 1$ and two rotational lines are missing, one at ν_0 and another corresponding to the first line of the *P*-branch. In addition, for this type of transition a *Q*-branch is to be anticipated.

The numbering of the lines in the *P*-, *Q*- and *R*-branches of the 2430 Å $C^2\Pi \rightarrow X^2\Sigma^+$ band of MgH is indicated in Fig. 5.15 where the *Q*-branch overlaps the *R*-branch and the *P*-branch is separated from these branches by a zero gap. When the *Q*-branch overlaps either the *P*- or *R*-branches, the lines of the *Q*-branch may be fairly readily distinguished by the spectroscopist from those of the other branch, since the spacing of the lines in the two branches is normally quite different.

A case where overlap of the *P*- and *R*-branches occurs is in the 4280 Å $A^1\Sigma^+ \rightarrow X^1\Sigma$ band of CuH which is given in Fig. 5.12(*a*) and in which no *Q*-branch is observed. From the appearance of the lines near the head of the band at 4280 Å and the gradually increased line spacing between 4283 and 4290 Å the branch responsible for the band head may be readily identified. Furthermore, the faint lines at about 4291 Å and 4295 Å, which interrupt the spacing pattern of the 4285, 4287, 4290, 4293, 4297 Å lines, suggest the

† Since formula (5.78) does not normally now hold exactly for higher *m* values, slightly curved lines usually result.

‡ The same procedure may be employed if there are *P*-, *Q*- and *R*-branches present in the band. In this case three straight lines would be obtained.

commencement of a new branch. In this manner the lines in the two branches may be separated, and the spectroscopist is then in a position to attempt a trial numbering of the lines in each of the branches. The correctness of the allocated J values may be checked by considering another band of the same electronic band system. If, for example, the same upper vibrational state is involved for both of these bands, and then if the J numbering is correct in both of these bands, the combination differences :

$$R(J)-P(J) = \Delta_2 F'(J)$$

must be in good agreement for every J value. If the two bands have the same lower vibrational energy state, then the $\Delta_2 F''(J)$ values must be in good agreement for every J value. This approach provides a most sensitive means of detecting whether the correct J values have been allotted. In general, the J values first allotted will be incorrect, and in that case the numbering has to be continually adjusted until the $\Delta_2 F'(J)$ and $\Delta_2 F''(J)$ criteria are satisfied.†

Determination of the nuclear spin quantum number from band spectra

For a diatomic molecule whose nuclei possess a nuclear spin quantum number I_1 and I_2, respectively, the total nuclear spin quantum number T of the molecule is given by:

$$T = I_1+I_2, \quad I_1+I_2-1, \; . \; . \; . \; |I_1-I_2|.$$

When $I_1 = I_2 = \frac{1}{2}$, T has the values 1 and 0. The value of 1 corresponds with parallel nuclear spins and antisymmetric rotational levels, while that of 0 corresponds with antiparallel spins and symmetric levels. In the presence of a magnetic field each state with a given T value is split into $(2T+1)$ levels of slightly different energy which are characterised by the quantum number (M_T) of the component of $\sqrt{T(T+1)}(h/2\pi)$ in the direction of the applied field. In the absence of a magnetic field a $(2T+1)$ degeneracy in T exists, and the total statistical weight for a given J value is $(2T+1)(2J+1)$.‡ When $T = 1$ the statistical weight for a particular J value is $3(2J+1)$ while for $T = 0$ the statistical weight is $1(2J+1)$. It follows, therefore, that the antisymmetric levels are three times more frequent than the symmetric.

Since according to the selection rule transitions are only possible between two symmetric or two antisymmetric states § (see p. 61) and the latter has a statistical weight three times that of the former, it follows that the intensities of alternate rotational lines in a band of the electronic spectrum will be in

† These $\Delta_2 F'(J')$ and $\Delta_2 F''(J'')$ criteria apply not only to bands with the same lower or upper vibrational level of one electronic band system but also to bands with a common lower or upper vibrational level in two different band systems. In fact, these criteria may be employed to check whether or not a particular electronic state is common to each of the band systems.

‡ The $(2J+1)$ factor arises since each rotational level is $(2J+1)$-fold degenerate in the absence of a magnetic field.

§ Owing to a small interaction between the magnetic moment of a spinning nucleus and the remainder of the molecule a small probability of a transition between symmetric and antisymmetric rotational levels does exist.

the ratio of 3 : 1. The rotational lines in the band spectrum of $^{1}H_2$ have been observed to have just this 3:1 intensity alternation, the lines with odd J values being more intense than those with even J values. It may be concluded, therefore, that the spin of the proton is $\frac{1}{2}$.

In the general case the intensity ratio of adjacent strong to weak lines of a homonuclear molecule, where each nucleus has a nuclear spin quantum number I, is given by the ratio:

$$\frac{(I+1)}{I}$$

When $I = 0$, as for $^{16}O_2$, $(I+1)/I = \infty$ and alternate rotational lines are absent, and when I is large, $(I+1)/I$ tends to unity.

By photometric measurements of the relative intensities of a rotational line in a band of an electronic transition with respect to an adjacent rotational line in the same branch the alternation intensity may be obtained† and the nuclear spin quantum number determined. For example, in Fig. 5.16 in the P-branch of the (0,0) band in the electronic transition $B^2\Sigma_u^+ \rightarrow X^2\Sigma_g^+$ of the N_2^+ negative system the intensity ratio is 2:1. Hence, it follows that the nuclear spin quantum number of ^{14}N is 1. In Table 5.8 the observed intensity alternation was used to calculate the nuclear spin quantum numbers of homonuclear molecules.

TABLE 5.8

Values of nuclear spin quantum numbers derived from observed intensity alternations

Molecule	Observed intensity alternation	I
$^{1}H_2$	3 : 1	$\frac{1}{2}$
$^{7}Li_2$	5 : 3	$\frac{3}{2}$
$^{12}C_2$	∞	0
$^{14}N_2$	2 : 1	1
$^{16}O_2$	∞	0
CH≡CH	3 : 1	$\frac{1}{2}$
$^{19}F_2$	3 : 1	$\frac{1}{2}$

The acetylene molecule has been examined and a rotational intensity alternation of 3 : 1 has been obtained in the near infra-red rotation-vibration bands. This ratio of 3 : 1 gives a value of $I = \frac{1}{2}$ which must be due to the proton, since ^{12}C has no nuclear spin. For a homonuclear molecule such as $^{16}O_2$, where every alternate rotational line is missing, it is certain proof that the nuclear spin quantum number is zero.

Visible and ultra-violet spectra of gaseous polyatomic molecules

The analysis of the visible and ultra-violet spectra of polyatomic molecules which normally correspond to electronic transitions and simultaneous

† Allowance must be made for the variation in the Boltzmann factor with increasing J.

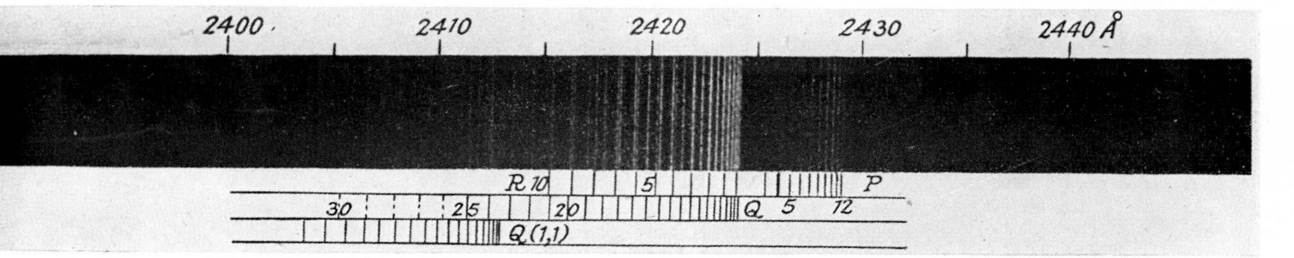

FIG. 5.15 The 2430Å $C^2\Pi - X^2\Sigma^+(0, 0)$ band of MgH taken by a large quartz spectrograph. This emission band was obtained from a magnesium arc in hydrogen. (*After Gaydon* [4])

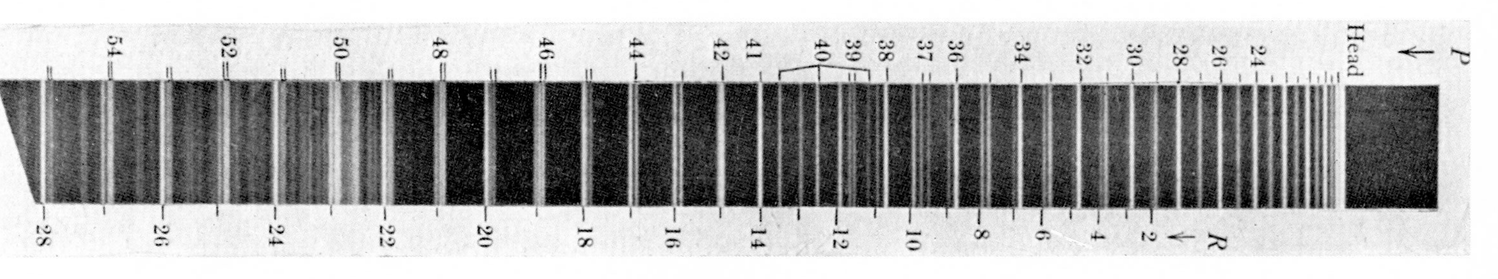

FIG. 5.16 Part of the P and R branches in the 3914Å (0, 0) band in the $B^2\Sigma_u^+ \rightarrow X^2\Sigma_g^+$ transition of the N_2^+ negative system where alternating intensities may be observed in consecutive rotational lines in each branch. (*After Jevons*[6] *by courtesy of W. H. J. Childs*)

[*To face page* 222

The gross features of the vibrational structure are dependent on the Franck–Condon principle. During an electronic transition the positions of the nuclei relative to one another do not have time to change, and only those vibrations which preserve the same symmetry of the molecule in both the upper and lower levels (i.e. totally symmetric vibrations) will exhibit intense absorption.

Generally, except for a few simple linear molecules which have a small moment of inertia the rotational fine structure of electronic bands cannot be studied since their resolution is almost impossible at the present time. Nevertheless, even in such cases information of a qualitative nature can sometimes be obtained concerning the very approximate magnitudes of the moments of inertia. Different geometrical arrangements in the two electronic states may also sometimes occur; for example, CS_2 appears to be linear in the ground state and non-linear in the excited state. On p. 246 the case of the CHO polyatomic radical is considered; this, however, is linear in the excited state and non-linear in the ground state. This information was derived from an analysis of the rotational structure of the bands.

Some fundamental work has also been performed on polyatomic electronic spectra as regards the assignment of various fundamental vibrational frequencies of both the lower and upper excited states of the molecules. Garforth, Ingold, and Poole[7] have used the vibrational frequencies obtained from the analysis of benzene and deuterobenzene to calculate among other things the dimensions of the excited molecules. They arrived at the values for the C—C and C—H bond lengths in these excited molecules as being close to 1.43 and 1.07 Å, respectively. In the ground state the values are C—C 1.39 Å and C—H 1.08 Å, that is the ring expands in the excited electronic state.

Ingold and King[8] have made a detailed study of a band system of acetylene and deuteroacetylene, reaching the conclusion that in this particular excited electronic state the molecule is not linear but has a centrally symmetric *trans*-configuration with the dimensions C—C 1.383 Å, and C—H 1.08 Å, the CCH angle being 120.2°. These dimensions as they point out are very similar to those in the ground state of benzene.

For an account of the work on polyatomic molecules up to 1941 a paper by Sponer and Teller[9] should be consulted. In addition, a Faraday Society Discussion[10] should be viewed, this dealing in the main with electronic spectra of some aromatic compounds.

In Chapter 3 it was shown that the electronic states of diatomic molecules could be classified by means of molecular quantum numbers. A corresponding treatment for even simple polyatomic molecules is far too complex to be dealt with here. However, it is possible to classify certain electronic transitions into different types, and this procedure will now be considered.

Types of electronic transitions in polyatomic molecules

$V \leftarrow N$ transitions†

When the valence electrons of the atoms are combined, and a molecule is formed, some of the valence electrons may be in bonding orbitals and others in anti-bonding orbitals. For example, as regards the C=C bonds in ethylene, if the wave-function ψ is plotted in a direction parallel to the CC axis, then the following possibilities exist:

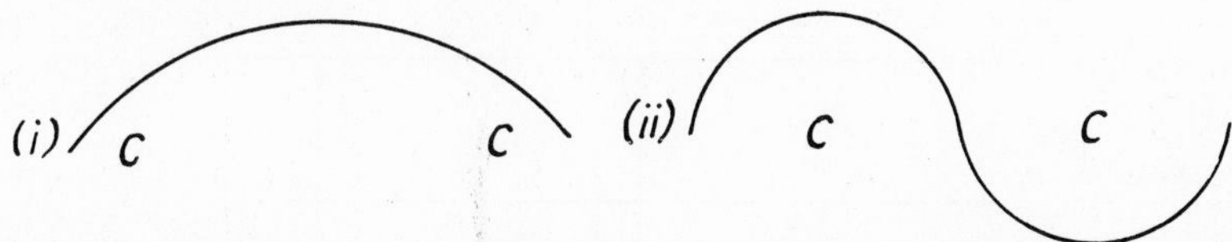

where (i) is regarded as a bonding orbital and (ii) an anti-bonding orbital. The probability of finding the electron is dependent on ψ^2, and in case (ii) the probability of finding the electron in the centre of the bond is negligible. In this case the electron is considered not to be concentrated in the bond. When the orbital is such that the electron tends to avoid the bond centre, the orbital is termed an *anti-bonding orbital.* To illustrate these terms further, buta-1 : 3-diene will now be considered. Since the σ electrons are to be regarded as occupying orbitals localised in a particular CC or CH bond, these bonding electrons will not be dealt with ; instead the π-type electrons will be considered, and these may be regarded as occupying orbitals which extend over the whole carbon chain. If ψ is plotted in a direction parallel to the CC axis, then the possible orbital types for the π electrons are:

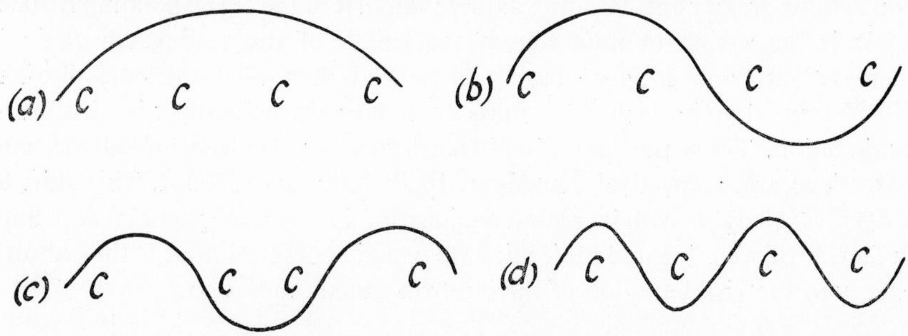

Of these four orbitals (*a*) is bonding in all bonds, (*b*) is anti-bonding in the central CC bond, (*c*) is anti-bonding in both the end CC bonds, and (*d*) is anti-bonding in all CC bonds. There is one π-electron from each carbon atom in the molecule, and in the ground state of the molecule the occupied orbitals are of the (*a*) and (*b*) types. For each of the four possible orbitals there is a corresponding electronic energy state for the molecule. These four energy states may be represented as in Fig. 5.18. The *n* values in the energy

† It is customary in the literature to write this absorption as an $N \rightarrow V$ transition, but since the convention adopted in our treatment of molecular spectra is to give the higher energy state first, this absorption transition will be given as $V \leftarrow N$.

level diagram indicate the number of nodes in the wave-form of a particular orbital, and, thus, the $n = 1, 2, 3$, and 4 values are to be related to the orbitals (*a*), (*b*), (*c*), and (*d*).

In the ground state of the molecule the π-energy levels occupied are the $n = 1$ and $n = 2$ levels, and the possible electronic transitions from these levels are *AB*, *CD*, *EF*, and *GH*. Each of these four transitions is termed a $V \leftarrow N$ transition, and since all the terms have been introduced, we are now in a position to define what is meant by such a transition. A $V \leftarrow N$ transition

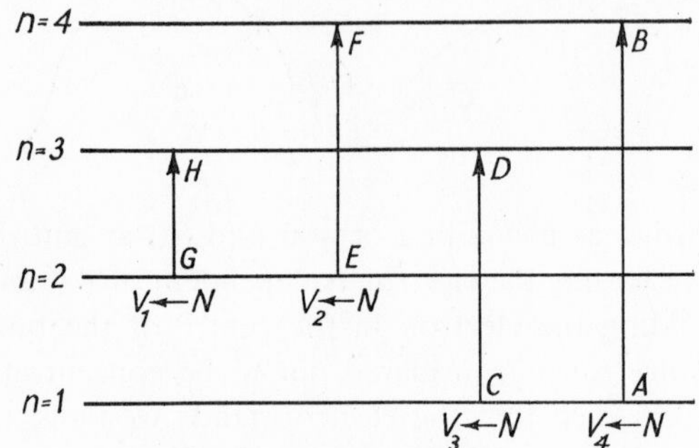

FIG. 5.18 Transitions between the Π energy levels in buta-1 : 3-diene.

is one where an electron passes from one orbital to that of another of exactly the same type, except that it has one or more extra nodes along the direction of the nuclei; the *N* state is the lower electronic state, and *V* is the upper one. For example, in the case of buta-1 : 3 diene, a particular *V* state will be one which has a greater anti-bonding nature than that of the corresponding *N* state.

It is interesting to note that if the length of the conjugated chain is increased as from ethylene to butadiene and then to hexatriene, the first $V \leftarrow N$ transition in each case shifts to longer wavelengths with increased conjugation. Thus, the first $V \leftarrow N$ transitions for ethylene, butadiene, and hexatriene are, respectively, at about 1600, 2100, and 2500 Å. This shift to longer wavelengths with increased conjugation is a general phenomenon, and, in fact, highly conjugated molecules are usually coloured, that is they absorb energy in the visible region of the electromagnetic radiation.

A←N and B←N transitions

These types of transitions may be illustrated by considering the carbonyl group in aldehydes and ketones. The keto group is formed in the ground state by having two electrons in a σ bond and two in a π bond. These are bonding orbitals. However, in the excited state of the carbonyl group either σ or π anti-bonding orbitals are feasible. For the electrons in the π-state a $V \leftarrow N$ transition is possible. In addition to the bonding electrons, the oxygen possesses lone pair electrons, and a transition may take place from one of these electrons to π or σ anti-bonding orbitals. When the upper level in such a transition is an anti-bonding π level, the transition is termed an $A \leftarrow N$ one.

If, however, the upper level is a σ anti-bonding orbital, then the transition is classified as of the $B \leftarrow N$ type.

It is to be expected, and it is indeed borne out by ionisation potential data, that the electrons in a π orbital are more weakly bound than those in σ orbitals. In addition, for carbonyl compounds the first ionisation potential corresponds to the removal of one of the oxygen lone pair electrons. Thus, the binding energies for the electrons in a carbonyl group are in the following order:

σ bonding electrons > π bonding electrons > non-bonding electrons

Hence, it may be anticipated that an $A \leftarrow N$ transition would be at a longer wavelength then either the $V \leftarrow N$ or $B \leftarrow N$ types. Since the longest wavelength absorption for aldehydes and ketones of three different electronic transitions is found in the 2900 Å region, then a reasonable interpretation is that this is of the $A \leftarrow N$ type. The $V \leftarrow N$ and $B \leftarrow N$ transitions may be distinguished from each other by the wavelength dependence of the $V \leftarrow N$ transition on the conjugation of the carbonyl group with the remainder of the molecule. By studying a series of molecules with varying degrees of conjugation, it is to be anticipated that the $V \leftarrow N$ transition will shift to longer wavelengths with increased conjugation. For $B \leftarrow N$ transitions where the non-bonding electrons are concerned a much less dependence on conjugation would be expected. It is to be noted, however, that in $A \leftarrow N$ transitions the upper electronic state is dependent on the extent of conjugation within the molecule. The dependence of the absorption wavelength on these different types of transitions for a number of aldehydes may be seen in Table 5.9.

TABLE 5.9

Absorption wavelengths (Å) *of different types of transitions for a number of aldehydes*

Aldehyde	$A \leftarrow N$	$B \leftarrow N$	$V \leftarrow N$
Formaldehyde	2900	1745	1560
Acetaldehyde	—	1800	1650
Acraldehyde	3300	1750	1935
Crotonaldehyde	3300	1800	2030

In Table 5.9 the $B \leftarrow N$ transition is to be detected by its insensitivity to conjugation and the $A \leftarrow N$ by its occurrence at longer wavelengths and its dependence on conjugation.

It would appear that the $B \leftarrow N$ type of transition may occur in any diatomic group where one of the atoms has a lone pair of electrons. No limitation is placed on this type of transition by the type of bond between the two atoms which may be of the σ or π type or both. Such transitions are observed in many types of molecules which have lone pairs, and these include the alcohols, ethers, thiols, and alkyl halides.

A review by Walsh[11] should be consulted for the types of electronic transitions in polyatomic molecules.

Ionisation potentials of polyatomic molecules and R←N transitions

For transitions taking place between the ground state and orbitals far removed from the nuclear framework, absorption of high frequencies of electromagnetic radiation is necessary. In these higher orbitals the influence of the nuclear framework is diminished, and the spacing of the observed bands has a similar appearance to the Rydberg series of lines observed in atomic spectra. In fact, wave-numbers of the band heads of such series may even be fitted to the following Rydberg type of formula:

$$\nu = A - \frac{B}{(n+m)^2} \tag{5.81}$$

where A and m are specific constants ($m<1$) for the given series, B is a universal constant, and n takes integral values. When n is very large, the second term on the right-hand side of equation (5.81) becomes very small, and $\nu = A = \nu_\infty$. where ν_∞ is the wave number corresponding to the ionisation potential whose value would be $hc\nu_\infty$ ergs. The ionisation potential may be obtained by extrapolation of the wave-numbers to the series limit, and this can lead to a most accurate value for the ionisation potential.

A Rydberg series of bands for the methyl and deuterated methyl radical in the vacuum ultra-violet is given in Fig. 5.19. (See p. 223).

The excitation of the strongly bonded σ-electrons generally tends to cause dissociation of the molecule which results in diffuse absorption. With lone pairs, however, excitation leads to bands which have a line-like appearance, which may be readily and precisely fitted to a Rydberg series. Numerous ionisation potentials of lone pair electrons have been determined. A smaller number of ionisation potentials of π-orbitals is also known, and one of the types studied has been benzene and its substituents. It may be observed that the bands converge to a limit. The limit itself corresponds to the ejection of an electron, and at frequencies higher than this continuous absorption would occur.

When the excitation corresponds with the progressive removal of a σ electron (e.g. in a C—H bond) away from both of the atoms forming the bond, followed by ejection of the electron from the molecule, then the transition is termed a *Rydberg* or an *R←N transition.* Such a transition is characterised by having a progression of bands followed by a continuum. The transitions usually occur at low wavelengths; for example, both the *R←N* transitions for the C═C group in ethylene and those for the C═O group in formaldehyde occur in the 1200–1800 Å region.

Vacuum ultra-violet spectroscopy

Introduction

The development of the electromagnetic region of the spectrum at wavelengths from about 2000 to ~10 Å was delayed because of the experimental difficulties. The main difficulties are:

(*a*) Below about 1950 Å an absorption spectrum is seriously interfered with by the absorption of certain constituents of the atmosphere,† and although it is possible to work with the oxygen displaced from the spectrograph by such gases as H_2, N_2 and the rare gases, for many experiments it becomes necessary to design an apparatus from which foreign gases can be totally excluded.

(*b*) The only materials which are transparent and which may be used for cell windows and prisms when the transmission limit of quartz has been exceeded (below about 1850 Å) are lithium and calcium fluorides, and these cease to be useful at about 1250 Å.

(*c*) The gelatine of the photographic plate absorbs in this region.

(*d*) Light sources are often not sufficiently intense and not very stable.

Experimental technique and types of study

Vacuum spectrographs are evacuated by means of an oil diffusion pump backed by a rotary pump. The pressure at the backing pump and in the instrument itself may be measured by means of Pirani gauges.

Both emission and absorption spectra may be studied with vacuum spectrographs. Absorption cells fitted with fluorite windows for the study of gases and liquids may be attached to the entrance aperture of the spectrograph. This work is, of course, limited to the transmission region of fluorite. It is also possible to study the absorption of gases by introducing the gaseous sample into the spectrograph housing itself; the pressure of the gas is adjusted to give suitable absorption intensity. In some vacuum spectrographs the slit system is so arranged that gas discharge spectra may be studied without employing a window.

To examine the absorption spectrum at wavelengths less than about 2000 Å a continuous source of radiation is required. Unfortunately, the normal hydrogen lamp continuum ceases at about this value, and for shorter wavelengths the so-called hot spark in vacuum can be used. To produce this spark a high breakdown potential between the electrodes is required, and by the use of large capacitors, charged to about 50 000 to 100 000 V, bright sparks may be obtained with a high emissivity in the vacuum ultra-violet. The light source may be attached to the spectrograph by means of a ring seal.

As already indicated it is possible to use lithium and calcium fluoride prisms as dispersing elements in the vacuum ultra-violet region. Prisms constructed from these materials may possess a good dispersive power and are suitable for both absorption and emission spectral studies. An early vacuum ultra-violet prism spectrograph is described in a paper by McLennan, Ainslie, and Fuller.[13] One prism instrument manufactured by Hilger and Watts Ltd. employs fluorite prisms and covers the wavelength region from 1600 to 1850 Å. Light enters the evacuated spectrograph through a fluorite window and is incident on an entrance slit. The beam is then collimated

† O_2 absorbs between $\sim$1950 to 1300 Å and 1100 to $\sim$300 Å. N_2 and H_2O vapour also absorb.

TABLE 5.10

Comparison of four Hilger vacuum ultra-violet spectrographs

Instrument	Dispersing element	Reciprocal linear dispersion	Wavelength range	Detector
(*a*) Fluorite spectrograph	Three fluorite prisms	6 Å/mm at 1775 Å 4.5 Å/mm at 1670 Å	1600 to 1850 Å	Photographic plate Photomultiplier
(*b*) Three-metre grazing incidence vacuum grating spectrograph	Concave grating (5 × 1 cm) with a radius of curvature of 3 m. 14 400 lines/in. ruled on glass set at grazing incidence	2.7 Å/mm at 2000 Å 0.8 Å/mm at 100 Å	Up to 2200 Å	Photographic plate
(*c*) Three-metre normal incidence vacuum grating spectrograph	Concave grating (8 × 5 cm) with a radius of curvature of 3 m. 14 400 lines/in. ruled on aluminium on glass set at normal incidence	5.9 Å/mm in the first order	About 400 to 2900 Å	Photographic plate up to about 2900 Å Photomultiplier up to about 2500 Å
(*d*) One-metre normal incidence vacuum grating spectrograph	5 × 3.5 cm concave grating with a radius of curvature of 1 m. 14 400 lines/in. ruled on aluminium on glass set at normal incidence	About 16.7 Å/mm in the first order	About 400 to 4000 Å	Photographic plate up to about 4000 Å Photomultiplier up to about 3000 Å

and suffers dispersion by means of three fluorite prisms with refracting angles of 66°, the spectrum being brought to a focus on a photographic plate. The reciprocal linear dispersion of the spectrograph and other relevant data are collected together under (*a*) in Table 5.10. Provision is made on the spectrograph for conversion into a direct-reading instrument using a photomultiplier attachment.

For spectroscopic studies below the transmission limits of lithium and calcium fluorides a concave grating instrument is normally employed. Owing to the fact that the reflecting power of metals and other materials falls off seriously in the vacuum ultra-violet region the grating surface is important for determining the range of the instrument.

When the grating is to be illuminated at nearly normal incidence,† that is when the angle between the normal to the grating and the incident beam is small, suitable materials are: aluminium at wavelengths longer than about 1000 Å, and platinum and glass at wavelengths below this. Typical instruments of this kind are the Hilger 1- and 3-m normal incidence vacuum grating spectrographs the data for which are presented in (*d*) and (*c*) of Table 5.10. Fig. 5.20(*a*) is the diagrammatic arrangement of the 3-m spectrograph where the light from a source (not shown in Fig. 5.20(*a*)) mounted on the accessory bar and sealed to the spectrograph passes through the entrance slit and strikes the grating at nearly normal incidence. The spectrum is focused on the photographic plate or photomultiplier located below the entrance slit by means of the concave grating. The plate-holder and grating are mounted on the Rowland circle, and change of the wavelength region is facilitated by means of one external control which operates a link mechanism. The link arms, pivoted in the centre and rigidly secured at their other ends to the plate-holder and grating mount, respectively, always form radii of the Rowland circle. A scale indicates the wavelength setting.

Much better suited to short wavelength (less than 400 Å) studies is the grazing incidence spectrograph. In this type of instrument the angle between the normal to the grating and the incident beam is of the order of 80° or more. At this high angle of incidence the reflecting power of surfaces improves in the far ultra-violet, and glass is a suitable material for the grating surface. The Hilger 3-m grazing incidence vacuum grating spectrograph is illustrated in Fig. 5.20(*b*) and the relevant data collected together in (*b*) of Table 5.10. Light from a source (not shown in Fig. 5.20(*b*)) sealed to the spectrograph passes through the entrance slit and strikes the grating at an angle of incidence of about 85°, the spectrum being brought to a focus at the photographic plate located at the end of the spectrograph opposite to that of the slit. Change of the wavelength region is effected by means of a wavelength change control motor, operated externally, which causes the plate-holder to traverse the Rowland circle as illustrated in the figure. A second motor, the

† The advantages of using a diffraction grating at nearly normal incidence for wavelengths greater than 400 Å are (i) a large grating can be employed, (ii) astigmatism is small permitting rapid exposures to be made.

plate-racking motor, enables the photographic plate to be moved vertically permitting seven spectra to be taken on one plate.

The photographic plates employed in the vacuum ultra-violet region are specially prepared with the silver halide sensitive layer on top of the gelatine to minimise absorption of the ultra-violet radiation by the gelatine. Substances with fairly tightly bound electrons often exhibit electronic transitions in the vacuum ultra-violet region. The magnitude of the energy

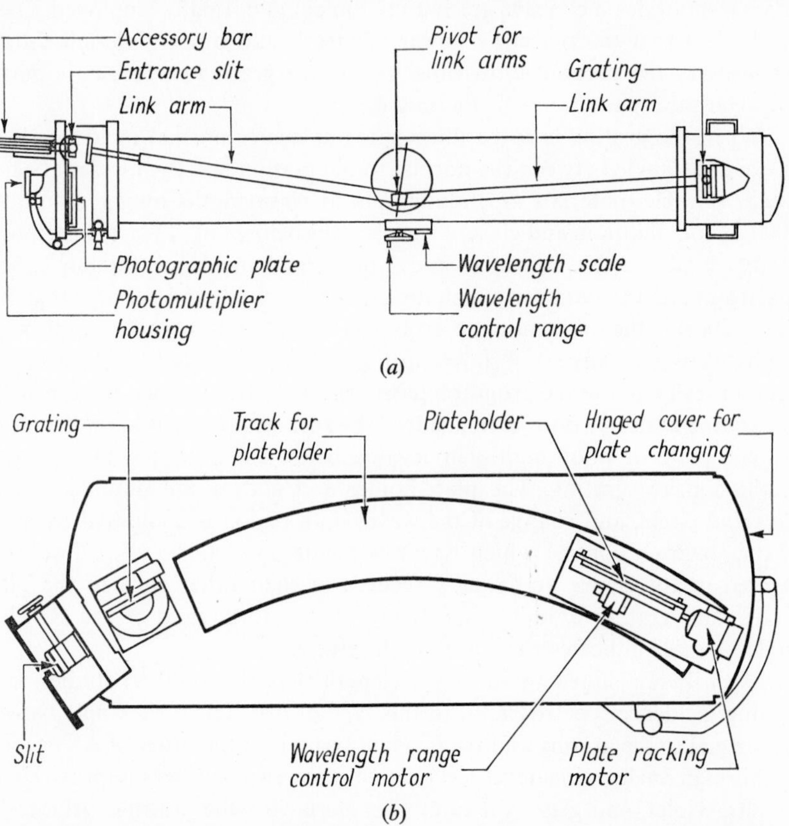

FIG. 5.20 Vacuum ultra-violet spectrographs: (*a*) 3-m normal incidence spectrograph, (*b*) 3-m grazing incidence spectrograph. (*Courtesy of Hilger and Watts Ltd.*)

change involved in transitions between possible electronic states is high. As we shall see later absorption in the visible and ultra-violet region is often dependent on the excitation of fairly loosely bound electrons (e.g. π-electrons) such as those associated with double bonds and lone pairs.† For many atoms the singly- and multiply-ionised spectra occur principally in the vacuum ultra-violet.

† It is not to be inferred that systems with double bonds and conjugation do not also absorb in the vacuum ultra-violet. In fact, many such systems (e.g. benzene) exhibit absorption in this region.

Generally, in the case of electronic spectra of small molecules in the far ultra-violet region the vibrational structure of a band but not the rotational structure is resolvable, though sometimes the vibrational structure is so complex that it too is not resolvable.

Normally in the ultra-violet and visible regions a molecular spectrum consists of a series of bands which does not by any means approximate to a Rydberg series† However, as has already been indicated, a Rydberg series of bands may be observed in absorption in the vacuum ultra-violet. Some of the diatomic species which have been investigated in the vacuum ultra-violet are:[14]

$$H_2, N_2^+, N_2, O_2, S_2, I_2, \text{and NO}.$$

One example of such a study is that by Rowlinson and Barrow[15] who examined the absorption bands of GeO and SiO in the 1250 to 2000 Å region. The bands were photographed with a 1-m normal incidence grating instrument with a reciprocal dispersion of about 8.5 Å/mm. A Lyman discharge was used as the source of radiation. Vibrational analyses were carried out on two systems of red-degraded bands for both SiO and GeO, and the constants ω_e and $x_e\omega_e$ were obtained for each of the electronic states, and an estimate was made of the upper limit for the dissociation energy in one of these states.

Herzberg and Shoosmith[16] have carried out a most striking vacuum ultra-violet study by employing a flash photolysis technique (see p. 243) on mercury dimethyl and definitely identified the methyl radical, showing that it has a slightly pyramidal structure in its ground state. In addition, from the Rydberg series limit they determined its ionisation potential as being 9.48 eV. A number of molecular ionisation potentials have been determined in the vacuum ultra-violet from the analysis of the spectra in terms of Rydberg series; the method is somewhat limited as it is restricted to the molecules which have sharp absorption bands. Most molecules do not exhibit sharp absorption in this region and, thus, cannot be satisfactorily analysed by this approach. A more fruitful approach is the photoionisation method which consists of:

(i) A concave grating, an absorption cell, and a photodetector.

(ii) A high-voltage hydrogen discharge tube as the light source.

(iii) A pumping system for evacuating the housed grating and absorption cell.

(iv) An electrometer for measuring the ionisation current.

These features are illustrated in Fig. 5.21.

By rotation of the grating about a fixed axis the wavelengths are scanned, and the mono-energetic photons are directed into the cell containing the gas being examined. The gas pressure is measured with an Alphatron vacuum ion gauge. The photodetector is placed behind the exit slit and measures the absorption quantitatively at these short wavelengths employed in the

† One exception is the band spectrum of He_2 in the visible and near ultra-violet regions.

vacuum ultra-violet. At a certain wavelength ionisation of the molecule occurs, and the ion current (i) in this photoionisation process sets in sharply for a slight decrease in wavelength; this ionisation current is detected on the electrometer. Initially the grating is set to give a particular wavelength and the current (I_0) from the photomultiplier is recorded with the cell evacuated.

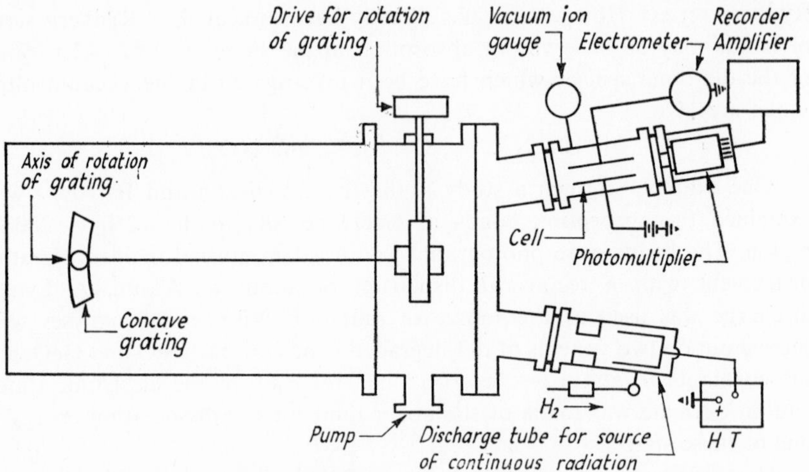

FIG. 5.21 Photo-ionisation spectrophotometer. (*After Price, Bralsford, Harris and Ridley.*[17] *Courtesy of Pergamon Press Ltd.*)

The gas is admitted to the cell, and the photomultiplier current (I) together with the ion current (i) are then recorded. The process is repeated at a number of different wavelengths, and a plot is made of $Ki/(I_0-I)$ against the wavelength where K is a known constant for the apparatus. At the frequency $\bar{\nu}_\infty$ corresponding to the wavelength at which a sudden bend in the curve occurs the ionisation potential is simply $h\bar{\nu}_\infty$. Ionisation potentials have now been obtained for numerous hydrocarbon molecules and radicals.[17]

Correlation of ultra-violet and visible absorption of organic compounds with their molecular structure

As has been seen the whole of the electromagnetic spectrum from approximately 10 Å to 10^4 cm can now be studied, but the ultra-violet and visible regions are particularly interesting to the chemist, since the interaction between the substance and this radiation is determined by the electronic structure of the molecule. So far the majority of the work has been on the absorption spectra of organic compounds in dilute solution, and the studies have been made on prism instruments working in a region from about 2000 to 10 000 Å. It would seem, though, that in future the trend will be to employ greater dispersion and to extend the range of wavelength studied.

Experimental

The Unicam SP 500 spectrophotometer is illustrated in Fig. 5.22(*a*), and this represents a typical instrument that may be employed in the region from 1860 to 10 000 Å to obtain absorption curves of the type shown in Figs. 5.23 and 5.24. Two light sources are provided on the SP 500, a hydrogen discharge lamp for the region from 1860 to 3200 Å and a tungsten filament

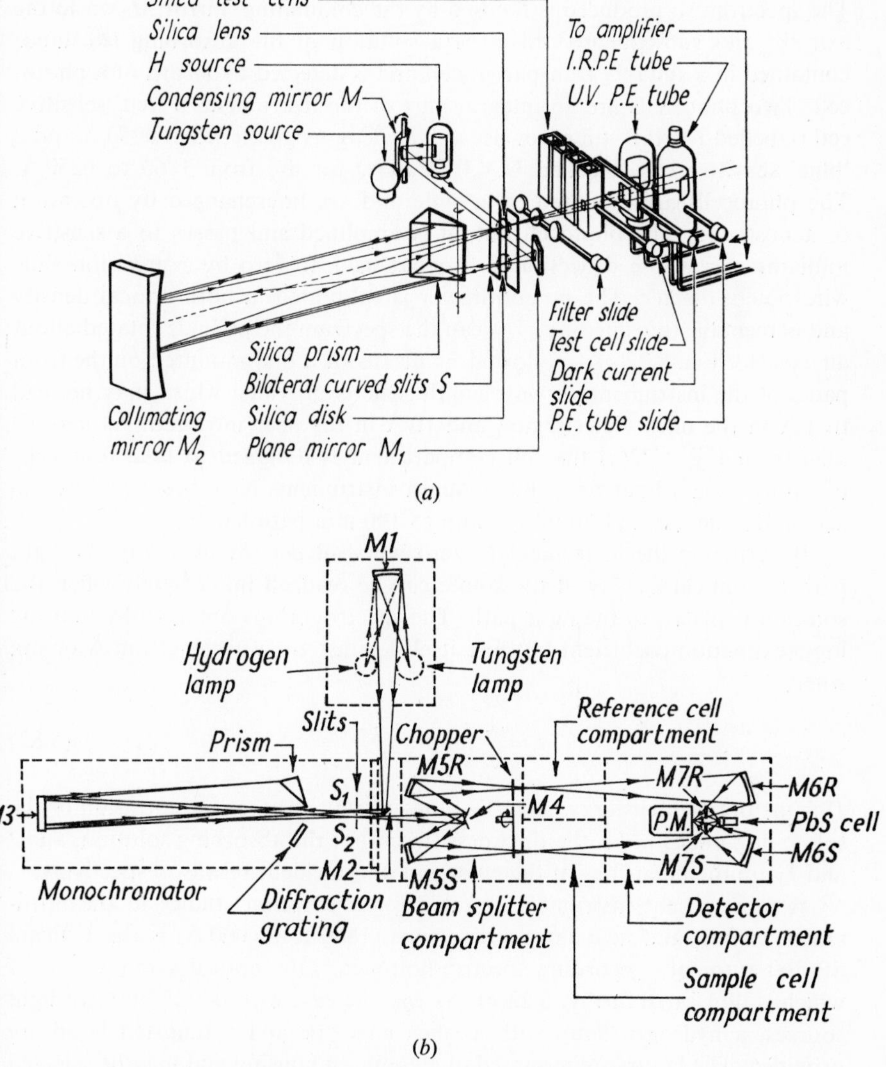

FIG. 5.22 (*a*) Unicam SP500 spectrophotometer, (*b*) Unicam SP700 spectrophotometer. (*Courtesy of Unicam Instruments Ltd.*)

lamp for the range 3200 to 10 000 Å. The two sources are mounted in the same housing, and changeover is effected by means of a lever switch which adjusts the position of the condensing mirror M (see Fig. 5.22(*a*)). The image of the light source is reflected by the mirror M on to a small plane mirror M_1 which reflects the light through the lower of two slits S placed at the focus of

M. After passage through the entrance slit of the monochromator the beam is collimated by a front surface mirror M_2 of 50 cm focal length and is incident on a 30° fused silica prism with an aperture of 50 mm. The back surface of this prism is aluminised, so that radiation suffers double dispersion. The spectrum so produced is focused by the collimating mirror M_2 on to the exit slit and subsequently traverses a solution of the absorbing substance contained in a suitably transparent cell and is detected by means of a photocell. Two photocells are an integral part of the instrument, a 'red' sensitive cell (labelled I.R.P.E. tube) for use at wavelengths greater than 6250 Å and a 'blue' sensitive cell (labelled U.V.P.E. tube) for use from 1860 to 6250 Å. The photocells are mounted on a slide and are interchanged by operation of a push rod. The photocell output is amplified and passes to a sensitive milliammeter whose deflection is brought back to zero by a precision slide wire potentiometer. The potentiometer is calibrated in both optical density and percentage transmission. To scan the spectrum the prism is rotated about an axis (see Fig. 5.22(*a*))—followed by means of a dial mounted on the front panel of the instrument. A wavelength scale is provided which may be read to 1 Å in the ultra-violet region and 10 Å in the near infra-red. As may be seen from Fig. 5.22(*a*) the cell compartment is designed to take four cells of up to 40 mm light path, but modern instruments have been modified to accommodate gas and liquid cells up to 100 mm path length.

By bringing the instrument to zero with solvent (or blank) in the light path the optical density of the solute can be read off immediately when the solution is placed in the light path. The spectrogram is obtained by plotting $\log_{10}$(extinction coefficient (ε)) or ε itself against the wavelength in Å or mμ where

$$\varepsilon = \frac{1}{cl} \cdot \log_{10} \frac{I_0}{I} = \frac{D}{cl} \tag{5.82}$$

D is the optical density (where $D = \log_{10}(I_0/I)$), c is the concentration of the solute in g-moles/l., l is the thickness (in cm) of the absorbing solution, and I and I_0 are the intensities of the emergent and incident beams, respectively.

A more recent instrument suitable for absorption studies in the ultra-violet, visible, and near infra-red regions (1860 to 36 000 Å) is the Unicam SP 700 automatic recording spectrophotometer, the optical arrangement of which is illustrated in Fig. 5.22(*b*). As was the case with the SP 500 two light sources, a hydrogen lamp with a silica envelope and a tungsten lamp are provided. The lamps are mounted in a common housing and may be selected by means of a knob on the front of the instrument. Radiation from the source is reflected by the mirror M_1 on to a mirror M_2 which in turn reflects the light through the entrance slit S_1 on to the collimating mirror M_3. After suffering double dispersion by a 30° silica prism the radiation is brought to a focus on the exit slit S_2 of the monochromator. The prism may be employed at wavelengths up to 25 000 Å after which the dispersing element is changed by a lever switch to a Merton N.P.L. replica diffraction grating. The grating has

7500 lines/in. and covers the region from 25 000 to 36 000 Å in the first order, the unwanted orders being removed with filters (Ge 1860—30 300 Å Pbs 30 300—36 000 Å). The beam from the exit slit S_2 is split into two by means of the mirror M_4, and these beams are brought to a focus in the reference and sample cells by mirrors $M5R$ and $M5S$, respectively. Prior to passage through the sample and reference cells the incident radiation is interrupted by a chopper rotating at 25 c/s. Mirrors $M6R$ and $M6S$ recombine the chopped beams on the detector. The instrument is fitted with two detectors, a thirteen-stage photomultiplier (*PM*) with a silica window, and a lead sulphide photoconductive cell which functions in the near infra-red region. Changeover from the photomultiplier to the PbS detector is made by a switch which adjusts the mirrors $M7R$ and $M7S$ so that the reference and signal beams, respectively, are now recombined on the PbS detector, the changeover wavelength being 7690 Å. The output from the detector is amplified (see p. 76) and fed to a pen recorder which gives a plot of transmittance or absorbance on a linear wave-number scale. The spectrum is scanned by rotation of the appropriate dispersing element, the wave-number being indicated by a counter mounted on the front of the instrument and by marks in both chart margins at equal wave-number intervals. The scanning speed may be varied from 250 cm^{-1}/min up to 20 000 cm^{-1}/min. The slit width, which in normal operation is controlled automatically so as to maintain the energy in the reference beam constant at a value determined by the setting of a resolution control switch, may be manually adjusted. The absorption spectrum of benzene vapour between 2336 Å and 2688 Å as recorded on the SP 700 instrument is given in Fig. 5.17. In this case the scanning speed was 250 cm^{-1}/min, the chart speed 0.5 in./min, and 20 mins were taken for the whole run; the slit width was automatically controlled.

Interpretation of the absorption spectrum

Absorption by organic compounds in the region 2000 to 10 000 Å corresponds mostly to the excitation of lone pair electrons or π-electrons.† These are more easily excited than σ-bonded electrons.

The absorption bands of molecules in solution are fairly broad, the fine structure being masked by solute-solvent interaction, and only band envelopes are observed in the absorption curve. The absorption curve for benzene in solution (Fig. 5.23(*a*)) should be compared with its absorption spectrum in the vapour state (see Fig. 5.17) where in the former much of the detail exhibited by the latter is not resolved.

Ultra-violet absorption is generally concerned with certain groups known as *chromophores* rather than the molecule as a whole. The chromophores are generally covalently unsaturated groups such as those in Table 5.11. The main features of absorption depend on the number, conjugation, and position of the double bonds in the molecule, secondly on whether these are

† In addition the unpaired electron(s) in a free radical (e.g. CH) is often also excited in this region.

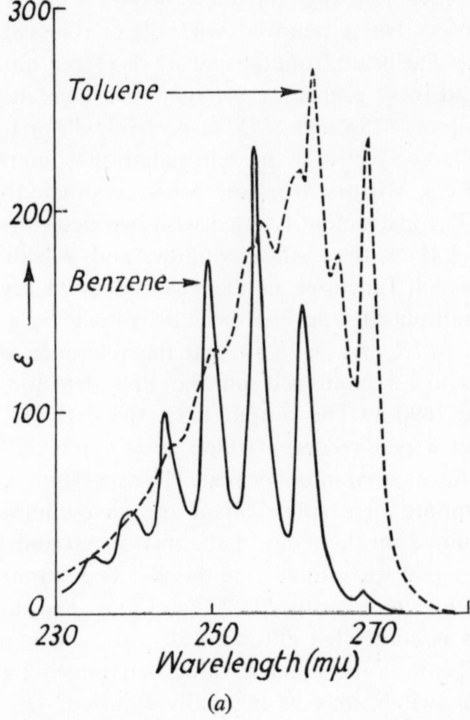

(a)

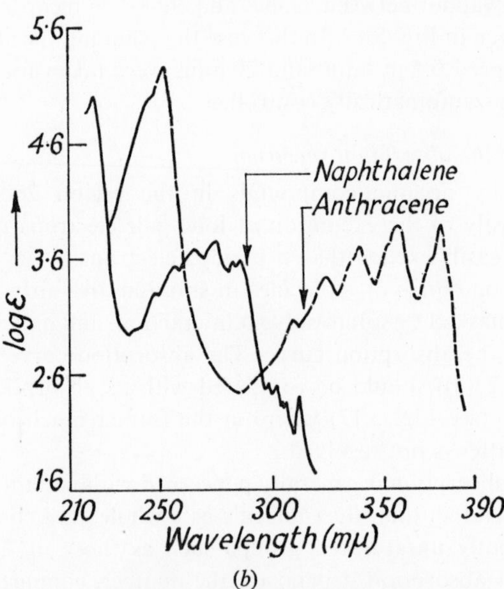

(b)

FIG. 5.23 Electronic absorption spectra of (*a*) benzene and toluene in cyclohexane, (*b*) naphthalene and anthracene in ethyl alcohol. (*After Gillam and Stern.*[18] *Courtesy of Messrs. Edward Arnold*)

conjugated with lone pairs, and thirdly upon the environment of the saturated groupings. Any increase in conjugation in a molecule is in practice usually accompanied by a shift of the absorption spectrum to longer wavelengths and intensity changes. Groups which cause this resonance extension are termed *auxochromes*; these are usually covalently saturated groups. Examples of auxochromes are hydroxyl, alkoxyl, aroxyl, amino, alkylamino, and arylamino, all of which promote conjugation of the unsaturated system with either the lone pairs on the oxygen or that on the nitrogen atom.

TABLE 5.11

Examples of chromophores† and their approximate λ_{max} *values (in* mμ)

ethylenic	>C═C<	185	nitro	—NO_2	270
acetylenic	—C≡C—	175	nitroso	—N═O	300
carbonyl	>C═O	188			
azo	—N═N—	410			

† Since some of these groups also have lone pairs which could conjugate to a small extent and auxochromes may sometimes have a number of resonant forms, the line of demarcation between chromophores and auxochromes is sometimes a fine one. Such terms have been given here because they are still in current use.

When two or more chromophores are present in the same molecule their absorption is usually additive provided they are separated by two or more single bonds. Two chromophores in conjugation, however, give rise to a much enhanced absorption with increases in λ_{max} and ε_{max}, and three conjugations result in still further increase of both the wavelength of maximum absorption and the extinction coefficient. When two or more chromophores are conjugated together this is called a *bathochromic effect* and can be explained by assuming that the conjugated system forms a new chromophoric entity and that the π-electrons associated with each double bond are able to move with increased freedom throughout the new structure. Substitution of the chromophore with an auxochrome once again results in the band maximum shifting to longer wavelengths.† For example, crotonaldehyde, which has the C═C—C═O grouping, has a λ_{max} of 217 mμ and an ε value of 16 000; this is to be compared with the C═C value of 185 mμ and 8000 in oct-3-ene. Another example is that of the C═C—C═C—C═C grouping which has a maximum absorption at 258 mμ and a ε_{max} equal to 35 000. Further lengthening of the conjugated chain to five or six conjugated groups causes the absorption to fall in the visible region.

If an aromatic nucleus is present in the molecule, the ultra-violet absorption spectrum differs considerably from a conjugated open chain containing the same number of carbon atoms. In Fig. 5.23(*a*) and (*b*) the electronic

† There is no theoretical justification for the shift towards the red, although it is generally observed in practice. Since, in general, it is not possible to predict where one of the many possible excited states of a molecule will lie with respect to the ground state, from a knowledge of that in another molecule, no theoretically justifiable prediction may be made as to which of the bands lies more towards the red.

absorption spectrograms for benzene, toluene, naphthalene, and anthracene in dilute solutions are given where the effect of increasing conjugation has caused a displacement to longer wavelengths.

The effects of substitution into an aromatic nucleus are many and varied; details of this and absorption by other types of molecules may be obtained from Gillam and Stern,[18] Mason,[60] and an account by Braude.[16] Substitution in the aromatic molecule usually, though not always, causes a shift in the maximum to longer wavelengths and modifies the intensity of absorption. As the molecule becomes more complex the effects decrease in magnitude. The vibrational structure observed also diminishes as the complexity of the molecular structure increases. The magnitude of the shift to longer wavelengths increases in the order:

$$NH_2 > OCH_3 > Cl > CH_3$$

The following data illustrate the effect of monosubstitution of benzene on the wavelength (in mμ) of the most intense band:

Benzene*, 255	Phenol, 273	Toluene*, 262
Anisole, 265	Thiophenol, 236	Aniline*, 280

where the asterisk indicates that the figure quoted is for the approximate centre of a group of bands.

Solvent influences

The absorption spectrum of a transparent layer of solid, liquid, solution or gas, may be obtained, though much of the routine work is carried out in solution, and here the influence of the solvent has to be considered. In a hydrocarbon series the effect of solvent on the position and intensity of the absorption maxima is very slight and can for most purposes be neglected. The carbonyl absorption band, on the other hand, varies considerably in position with the solvent used as may be seen for acetone in Table 5.12.

TABLE 5.12

The λ_{max} and ϵ_{max} values for acetone in various solvents

Solvent	H_2O	CH_3OH	CH_3CH_2OH	$CHCl_3$	Hexane
λ_{max}(mμ)	265	270	272	277	279
ϵ_{max}	17	16	17	17	15

This variation in the case of acetone has been attributed to enolisation being favoured by polar solvents. Above a certain concentration strong intermolecular hydrogen bonding must be involved for the majority of these solvents.

Scope of Analytical Electronic Absorption Spectroscopy

It follows from the principles outlined that any organic compound containing a chromophore, if it absorbs, will probably have a characteristic spectrum. The absorption spectrum, thus, provides a method of identifying structural components in molecules. In addition to the value of the wave-length position of maximum absorption as measured by λ_{max}, ε_{max} is also an important aid to both structural and qualitative analytical applications, since it is sometimes possible to differentiate by intensity measurements between two chromophoric groupings which absorb at the same wavelength.

Great care, however, must be exercised in suggesting structural relations from an observed absorption spectrum without fully exploring all possibilities. Absorption in a particular region may indicate the presence of a given group, and intensity measurements may lend support to that grouping, but a small amount of impurity of a substance with a high extinction coefficient may lead to erroneous conclusions.

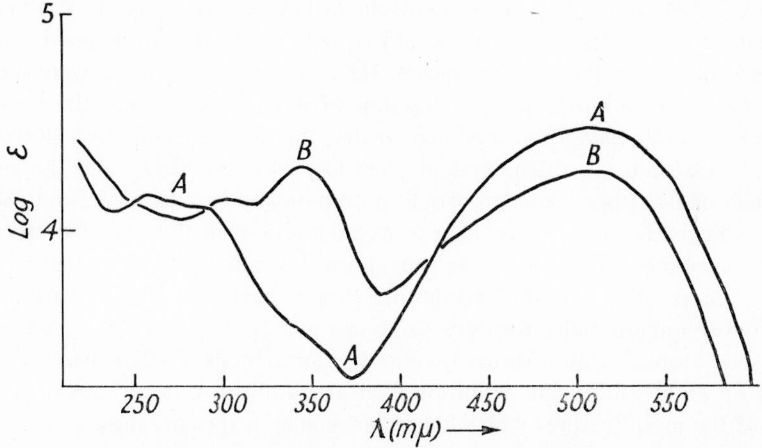

FIG. 5.24 Electronic absorption spectra of *A*, 4-[*p*-nitrophenyl-azo]-5-nitro-1-naphthylamine, *B*, 2-[*p*-nitrophenyl-azo]-5-nitro-1-naphthylamine. (*After Ward, Pearson, and Wells* [20])

The uses of this technique are many and varied for not only has it been applied to qualitative and quantitative analysis and the determination of molecular structure but also to the investigation of isomerism and steric hindrance, and it is applied extensively in control and specification of drugs and vitamins. Electronic absorption spectra studies in the visible and ultra-violet regions of solutions find numerous applications in both industry and in assisting research. In order to appreciate the variety of problems studied Gillam and Stern[18] should be consulted. As an example of its application the following procedure was employed for the qualitative estimation of two isomers which could not be readily studied by chemical means. When 5-nitro-1-naphthylamine or its nuclear-substituted derivatives react with diazotised amines, in general, coupling occurs simultaneously in the 2- and 4-positions. The reaction product can be separated by means of chromato-graphy. Since only relatively small amounts of material can be handled conveniently by the chromatographic procedure, a method was required whereby the separated isomers could be identified in small quantities. Their ultra-violet absorption spectra have proved excellent for this purpose, as may be observed from Fig. 5.24. The spectra of the 2 : 4-isomers of *p*-nitrophenylazo-nitronaphthylamines are similar, except in the region 300 to 360 mμ where the 2-azo compound (*B*) shows a double maximum while the 4-azo compound (*A*) is relatively weakly absorbing. Hence the 2- and 4-isomers may be readily distinguished, and a quantitative determination of the 2-isomer may be made, if previous calibration has been carried out.

Electronic spectra of free radicals

Introduction

A free radical is not readily defined. If the definition is that a free radical is an atom or a molecule which possesses one or more unpaired electrons, then O_2, NO, and ClO_2, which many chemists would not regard as radicals, would be termed as such. This would equally apply to paramagnetic compounds of certain transition elements. However, if the definition were that a free radical is a molecule or a fraction of a molecule, where the normal chemical bonds have been modified so that one or more unpaired electrons are left associated with the system, then O_2, NO, and ClO_2, and the compounds of transition elements would automatically be excluded from being free radicals. However, according to this definition, in the phosphorescence process the molecule would have to be termed a radical in the excited triplet state (see p. 291). Another borderline case is that of ionic crystals when irradiated unpaired electrons are produced which are often associated with localised atomic orbitals rather than molecular orbitals. Rather than concentrate on an all-embracing definition for a free radical, it is perhaps better to regard the main features which characterise such a species; these are:

(i) One or more unpaired electrons and as a consequence of this a magnetic moment owing to the uncompensated electron spin.

(ii) Usually a high reactivity.

Sometimes the word 'species' will be employed when it is not wished to be specific as to whether the unit being considered is a molecule with no unpaired electrons, a charged molecule, or a free radical.

On p. 218 it was indicated how from a satisfactory analysis of the rotational structure of the bands from an electronic transition excellent proof of the identity of a diatomic radical could be obtained. In fact, the electronic spectra approach provides one of the most convincing means for the identification of diatomic radicals. Many diatomic free radicals have been investigated; in numerous cases their emission spectra are readily obtained from flames and electric discharges (e.g. CH, CN, NH, and OH are readily produced in discharges). However, at the present time the most powerful means for the identification of radicals is that of absorption spectroscopy. This method possesses many advantages; in particular it can be used to observe spectra not obtainable in emission, and occasionally it is possible to determine the concentration of the radical by absorption spectroscopy whereas the emission spectrum of the radical would be of little use for this purpose.

The detection of radicals containing more than two atoms is generally difficult and often uncertain both in emission and absorption spectroscopy.

The main spectroscopic methods† employed for the detection of free radicals by their electronic spectra are the thermal dissociation technique, flash photolysis, and various strengths of discharges. Recently, two other methods have emerged. The first depends on the rapid heating developed in a shock wave and the second on the determination of the absorption spectrum of the radical trapped in a rigid medium at a low temperature where the radical is stabilised and prevented from combining with other similar radicals by means of the medium itself. All five methods will now be described, but first it must be pointed out that the two major obstacles in identifying radicals spectroscopically are the difficulty of generating them in sufficient concentration and of recording their spectrum during their brief existence.‡

Thermal dissociation method

The substance which is to be dissociated is introduced into a furnace which functions as a cell. The temperature is varied, and a continuous source of radiation from a hydrogen or tungsten lamp is directed through the furnace on to a spectrograph, the absorption spectrum of any dissociated radical and parent molecule being recorded photographically. By employing the King furnace, temperatures higher than 2500°C may be obtained, and most compounds dissociate below this temperature. This approach has been used for the detection of diatomic radicals. In addition, C_3 has been detected in a carbon tube furnace at 2800°C and SiC_2 in a carbon furnace charged with silicon at 2200°C.

Flash photolysis

Norrish and Porter[21] have employed a most fruitful technique for the detection of free radicals which have only a short life before reacting. The process involves generating an intense flash of light which produces extensive photolysis and liberates an unusually high concentration of radicals. In the case of short-life radicals there is no point in illuminating the molecules for any longer time than is necessary to achieve a stationary state concentration of the radicals. A rapid absorption spectrum is then taken using as the source of radiation an intense hydrogen continuum from which a sufficient concentration of radicals may absorb in a very short time. The objective is to record the absorption spectrum of the radical before it dimerises or reacts. By this approach very simple radicals may be identified by means of their absorption

† The detection of free radicals in flames is dealt with in Chapter 7 and by the electron spin resonance technique in Vol. 1, Chapter 4. The latter method has so far mainly detected either stable radicals in solutions or radicals in solids or solid solution.

‡ It should be noted that the time an electronically excited molecule exists in this state before it radiates is about 10^{-6} to 10^{-8} sec. At atmospheric pressure the molecule suffers about 10^{10} collisions per sec. Hence, a molecule would suffer about 100 to 10 000 collisions before emitting. Thus, for highly reactive radicals at atmospheric pressure the chances of reaction instead of giving an emission spectrum would be very great.

spectrum. The method is known as *flash photolysis*, and the experimental apparatus is illustrated in Fig. 5.25.

A high concentration of radicals is generated by means of a photolysis flash which is produced in a discharge tube. By charging a group of capacitors of capacity 35 μF, about 8000 V are placed across the electrodes in the discharge tube which contains argon at low pressure. The discharge is, however, initiated by means of the trigger electrode which is operated from an induction coil. A high-intensity flash of energy up to 1000 Joules and of duration about 10^{-4} sec is produced. The photochemical efficiency of this source is of the order of 6 per cent, and the flash consists mainly of continuous radiation.

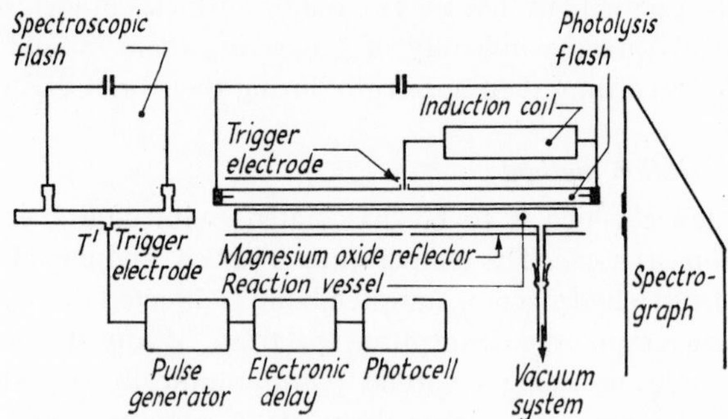

FIG. 5.25 Apparatus for investigation of free radicals by flash photolysis. (*After Norrish and Thrush.*[22a] *Courtesy of Professor R. G. W. Norrish, F.R.S. and The Chemical Society, London*)

The light is concentrated on the cell by means of the magnesium oxide reflectors. The generated radical is almost instantly detected by means of its electronic absorption spectrum. This is done by means of another discharge tube containing argon which is placed along the line of the cell and is operated by means of charging up another bank of capacitors (total capacity 35 μF). About 5000 V are applied across the electrodes, but no discharge takes place until the discharge is triggered by the third electrode T'. The flash produced is known as the *spectroscopic flash.* The delay between the spectroscopic and the photolysis flash is determined by means of the photocell and the electronic delay circuit. A hole in the reflector tube admits light to the photocell which initiates an electronic timer, and this governs the pulse generator. By adjustment of the electronic timer the spectroscopic flash may be produced between from 10^{-5} to 1 sec after the photolysis flash.† The radical in the cell is then detected by the spectrograph by means of its electronic absorption spectrum, and so far the majority of the radicals studied have shown absorption in the 2200 to 7000 Å region, and small, medium, and large quartz spectrographs have been used.

By varying the delay between the spectroscopic and photolysis flash the change in concentration of the radicals with respect to time may be followed.

† Hence, only species with a lifetime greater than about 10^{-5} sec may be detected.

This is illustrated in Fig. 5.26 for the concentration of the OH radical, in the explosive reaction between the hydrogen and oxygen to give water, where NO_2 is added as a sensitiser. This work was reported by Norrish, and the following mechanism was suggested. The initial stage is first the photolytic decomposition of nitrogen dioxide:

$$NO_2 \xrightarrow[\text{flash}]{\text{photolysis}} NO + O$$

And the subsequent reaction of this with hydrogen:

$$H_2 + O \rightarrow OH + H$$

$$OH + H_2 \rightarrow H_2O + H$$

In Fig. 5.26 it will be noted that there is an immediate appearance of the $1 \leftarrow 0$ band. The intensity of this band increases up to about 1.2 msec after the photolysis flash, but grows very weak after 7.2 msec. By noting the time interval necessary for the disappearance of the absorption bands of a radical an estimate of the lifetime of the radical may be made. In addition, from the decrease in the absorption intensity of the parent molecule(*s*) estimations can sometimes be made of the concentration of the radical from which rate constants and other important data can be calculated.

Norrish[23] also studied, by means of flash photolysis, the mechanism of the reaction

$$C_2H_2 + O_2 \rightarrow 2CO + H_2$$

One mixture which he employed contained 13 mm C_2H_2+10 mm O_2+ 1.5 mm of NO_2. The function of the nitrogen dioxide was again to act as a sensitiser and provide oxygen atoms as a result of the photolysis flash:

$$NO_2 \rightarrow NO + O$$

The concentration of the radicals taking part in the reactions is plotted in Fig. 5.27 against the time in milliseconds. It will be observed that there is an induction period of about 0.4 msec, and after this the radical concentration suddenly increases. In this region the explosion takes place, and this is followed by a relatively slow decay of radicals.

The photochemical reaction between chlorine and oxygen has been studied by the flash photolysis technique and the growth and decay of the ClO radical followed by means of its absorption spectrum. The radical had a half-life of a few milliseconds under the conditions of the experiment. The main feature of the relatively simple vibrational structure of its electronic absorption spectrum is a series of bands with fairly sharp heads degraded to the red. From the analysis of the bands ω_e', ω_e'', x_e', x_e'', and the dissociation energies in the upper and lower electronic states were evaluated. The SH and SD radicals have also been studied by the flash photolysis of H_2S and D_2S, the vibrational frequencies of both the radicals being determined.

Ramsay[24] has studied the CHO radical by flash photolysis of several aldehydes. The absorption bands occurred in the 4500 to 7500 Å region, and two red degraded bands with heads at 6138.2 and 5624.1 Å were studied in detail. These bands had a simple structure and were composed of only single

P-, *Q*-, and *R*-branches. From the rotational analysis it was shown that the bands were due to a transition from a lower state, where the valence angle was about 120°, to an upper electronic state where the nuclei were linear. In subsequent work[25] nine bands were obtained for CHO. Six of these bands were shown to form a progression of the bending vibration in the upper state,

120
80
40
0
Concentration
0·5
1·0
1·5
2·0
Time (ms)
CN
C_2
CH
OH

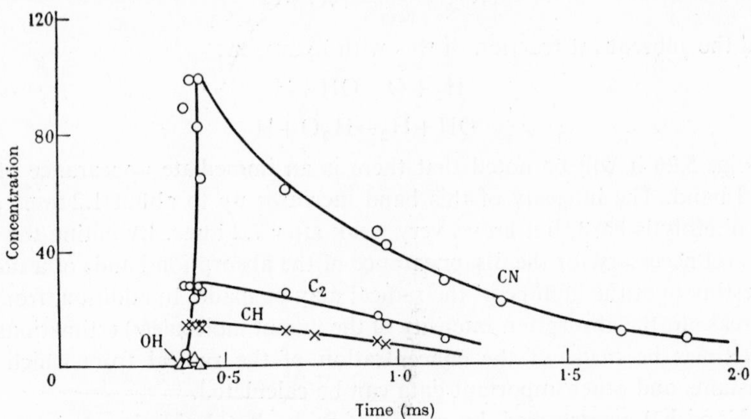

FIG. 5.27 The concentration of the radicals in the mixture plotted against time for a mixture of 13 mm of C_2H_2, 10 mm O_2, and 1·5 mm NO_2 when subjected to flash photolysis. (*After Norrish, Porter and Thrush.*[22c] *Courtesy of Professor R. G. W. Norrish, F.R.S. and the Council of the Royal Society*)

and the other three bands involved even quanta of the bending vibration in the upper state together with one quantum of the CH stretching vibration. A flash photolysis study was also made on CH_3CDO, and ten bands from the CDO radical were obtained. Eight of these bands were identified as a progression of the bending vibration in the upper state, and the other two involved even quanta of the bending vibration in the upper state in conjunction with one quantum of the CD stretching vibration. A rotational analysis was made on all the sharp bands of the CHO and CDO radicals, and the internuclear distances and bond angles determined from the rotational constants are given in Fig. 5.28.

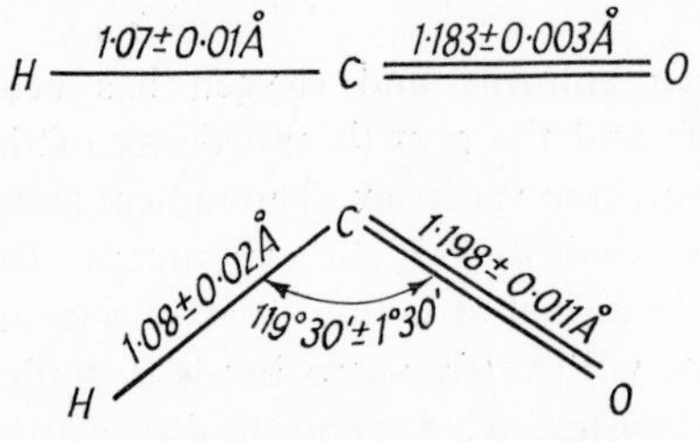

H
1·07±0·01Å
C
1·183±0·003Å
O
C
1·08±0·02Å
1·198±0·011Å
119°30′±1°30′
H
O

FIG. 5.28 The dimensions of the CHO radical in the ground and excited electronic states (uppermost diagram)

The values for the CH and CD internuclear distances were taken from the literature for the purposes of the analysis. It is interesting to note that the bond angle and the CO internuclear distance in the lower electronic state of the HCO radical are very similar to the corresponding values in the ground state of the formaldehyde molecule. In actual fact, the CO internuclear distance is 0.02 Å shorter than in the ground state of the formaldehyde molecule.

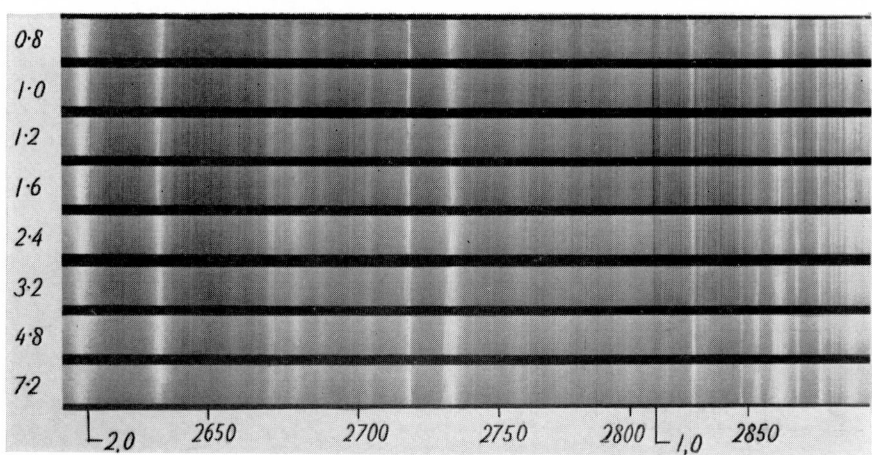

FIG. 5.26 The 1 ← 0 (absorption) band of the OH radical after various time intervals during an explosion of 10 mm H_2, 5 mm O_2 and with 0·75 mm of NO_2 as sensitiser. (*After Norrish and Porter* [22b]. *Courtesy of Professor R. G. W. Norrish, F.R.S. and the Council of the Royal Society*)

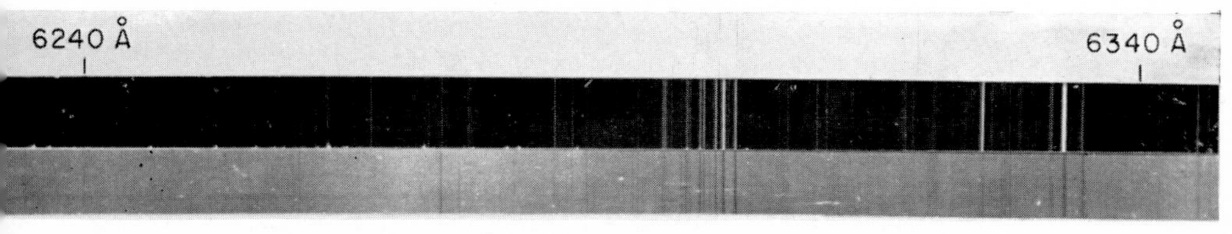

.29 (*a*) The emission spectrum of an oxyammonia flame, (*b*) the absorption spectrum of photodecomposed nia obtained by the flash photolysis technique. (*Courtesy of Dr. G. Herzberg*,[28] *F.R.S.C. and The Chemical Society, London*)

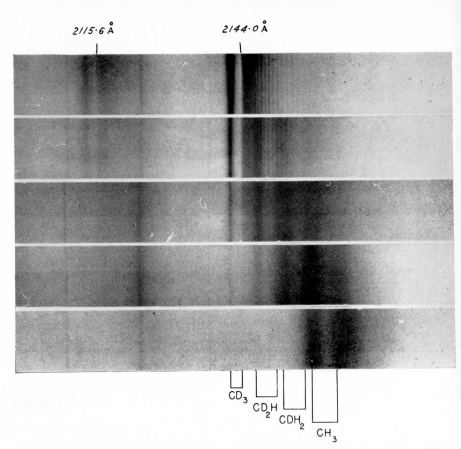

2115·6 Å 2144·0 Å

CD_3 CD_2H CDH_2 CH_3

FIG. 5.30 The flash photolysis of 100 per cent, 75 per cent, 50 per cent, 25 per cent, and 0 per cent, deuterated acetone reading from top to bottom of figure. (*Courtesy of Dr. G. Herzberg*,[28] *F.R.S.C. and The Chemical Society, London*)

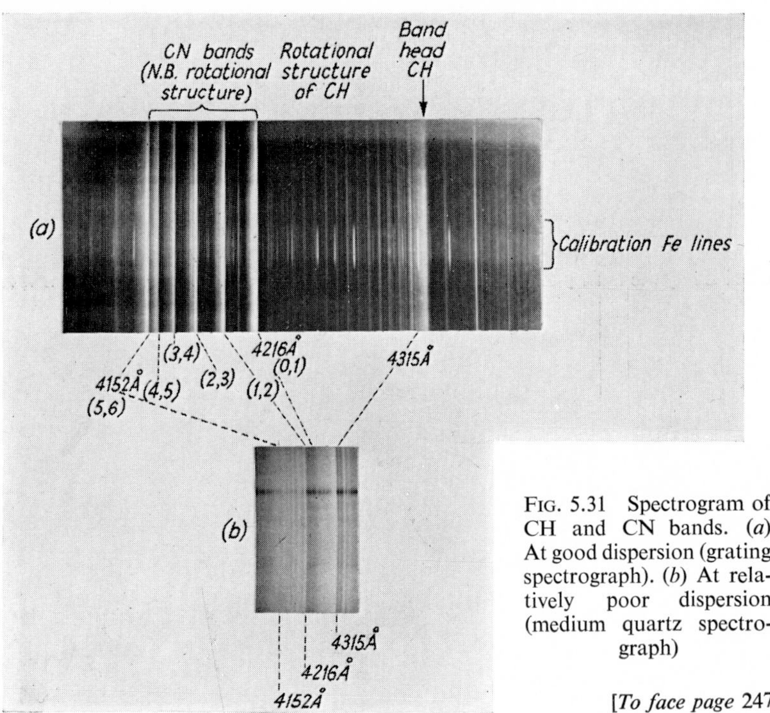

FIG. 5.31 Spectrogram of CH and CN bands. (*a*) At good dispersion (grating spectrograph). (*b*) At relatively poor dispersion (medium quartz spectrograph)

[*To face page* 247

The so-called α bands of ammonia have been studied for many years with a view to determining the identity of the emitter. These bands are produced in electric discharges, in oxy-ammonia flames, in the spectra from comets, and in flash photolysis experiments. In Fig. 5.29(*a*) the α bands between about 6240 and 6340 Å were obtained from the oxy-ammonia flame while in Fig. 5.29(*b*) from the flash photolysis of ammonia both were taken with the same 21 ft grating spectrograph. There is good correspondence between these emission lines from the flame, and the absorption lines from the flash photolysis. The α bands had for a long time been attributed to the NH_2 radical. The analysis of the lines in these α bands proved most difficult as the lines did not group together into recognisable bands. Ramsay[26,27] finally obtained a successful analysis and identified the α bands as being due to the NH_2 radical. It is interesting to note that in the excited electronic state the molecule is linear whereas in the ground state the $\angle$HNH is 103.5°. In addition, there is a contraction of 0.048 Å in the internuclear distance on passing from the O vibrational level in the ground state to the O vibrational level in the excited state.

The CH_3 radical has also been identified by flash photolysis work, and it appears that the CH_3 radical deviates slightly from a planar configuration in the ground electronic state and has a pyramidal form. However, in all the observed excited states the radical is planar. Herzberg and co-workers have made some most striking studies of this radical. In one set they followed the flash photolysis of varying degrees of deuteration of acetone. In Fig. 5.30 the spectra of the methyl and deuterated methyl are given for bands in the 2150 Å region. The isotopic effect on the spectra is observed, and in the 50 per cent deuterated compounds absorption bands due to CD_3, CD_2H, CDH_2, and CH_3 may be detected.

For absorption spectra in general, if the intensity of the spectra is weak, then it may be improved by a technique which consists of arranging three mirrors so that once the continuous radiation has entered the absorption tube the light is reflected up to about a hundred times through the tube before emerging. This is equivalent to increasing the path length of the absorbing gas up to a hundred times, hence considerably improving the sensitivity of detection. (See Fig 4.7*d* for infra-red arrangement.)

Of the radicals larger than CH_3 only a few have so far been identified by means of their electronic absorption spectra, and all these have contained conjugated systems. One such study was the flash photolysis of semiquinones, and an interesting aspect of this work was the direct spectroscopic measurement of the rate of proton separation from the durosemiquinone where the spectra of the radical and the anion may be readily distinguished.

Detection of radicals in discharges

Electric discharges have been widely employed for the study of the emission spectra of diatomic species. Vigorous discharges still offer the most ready means of achieving very high temperatures; these temperatures may sometimes be as high as 50 000°K. A discharge may be obtained by applying a suitable a.c. or d.c. potential (e.g. 2000 V) across two metal electrodes in a gas at a low pressure.† Many forms of discharges have been employed, and for details of the different types Sawyer[29] should be consulted.

A discharge functions by initial ionisation of some of the molecules, then by excitation of the resulting electrons and ions, and finally by bombardment of the other molecules with these excited particles. In this manner excited molecules are produced which may lose their excess energy by emitting a characteristic spectrum. If the energy of the discharge is sufficiently great, fission of the molecules into radicals or ions can result. The energy conditions required for a given type of discharge are greatly dependent on the ionisation potential of the gas examined and the pressure of the gas within the discharge. Most types of discharges tend to split polyatomic molecules into diatomic species. One milder kind of discharge is that of the Tesla type which may induce mild fission of the polyatomic molecule or even just electronic excitation of the polyatomic molecule itself.

CH is one of the best known radicals and may be obtained in almost any discharge, which is not too mild, through hydrocarbon compounds. Since the moment of inertia of the CH radical is small, the rotational structure is plainly resolvable; this is seen in the emission spectrogram Fig. 5.31(*a*) which was taken with a grating spectrograph. It is interesting to compare Fig. 5.31(*a*) with Fig. 5.31(*b*) as they both show the same CH emission band, but since Fig. 5.31(*b*) was taken with a medium quartz spectrograph the dispersion is much smaller, and the rotational structure is no longer apparent. In Fig. 5.31(*a*) can also be seen six bands due to an electronic transition in CN with their associated rotational fine structure. These bands form the (0,1), (1,2), (2,3), (3,4), (4,5), and (5,6) sequence. These six bands should be contrasted with those taken with the medium quartz spectrograph where once again with a prism as the dispersing element the rotational structure cannot be observed. Where the rotational structure may be analysed almost certain identification of the diatomic radical may be made.

To appreciate how involved is the identification of even a triatomic radical the following work may be considered. Mecke has obtained weak absorption bands at 4370 and 4020 Å, during the thermal decomposition of methane, which were at first considered to be due possibly to the methylene radical (CH_2). Further, Herzberg has obtained emission bands around 4050 Å from discharges through methane and from comets. These bands cannot be analysed as a diatomic species. The appearance of the bands resembles the perpendicular bands of an asymmetric top molecule. The spacing of the bands indicates a small moment of inertia, and they were provisionally assigned to a non-linear CH_2.[30] These same bands are reported to have been obtained from mild discharges in ketene and diazomethane, though irradiation of ketene ($H_2C{=}C{=}O$) with ultra-violet light has yielded no absorption band around 4050 Å. However, by the use of deuterated

† Mention of one simple type of discharge is made in Vol. 1, p. 3.

compounds the bands showed no isotope shift, and, therefore, the emitter could not contain hydrogen.[31] In addition, more recent work[32,33] using a 50 : 50 mixture of ^{13}C and ^{12}C has indicated that the bands at 4050 Å are actually due to C_3, since the principal band was replaced by six bands which could be attributed to $^{12}C—^{12}C—^{12}C$, $^{12}C—^{13}C—^{12}C$, $^{12}C—^{13}C—^{13}C$, $^{13}C—^{13}C—^{13}C$, $^{13}C—^{12}C—^{13}C$ and $^{12}C—^{12}C—^{13}C$. When the bands were analysed they gave a B value of 0.450 cm^{-1} corresponding to a C—C distance of 1.28 Å which lies between the value of a double bond and a triple carbon–carbon bond length. The conclusion that the emitter was the C_3 molecule was confirmed by work with the pure ^{13}C isotope. This 4050 Å system is now definitely assigned to C_3.

CF_2 was the first polyatomic radical to be definitely identified by means of its electronic spectrum which was first observed in emission by Venkateswarlu[34] in 1950 and later in the same year by Andrews, Laird, and Barrow[35] who obtained the absorption spectrum of CF_2, generated by passing discharges through fluorocarbon vapour. An electronic absorption spectrum of CF_2 has also been obtained where the radical was produced by the thermal decomposition of CF_4 at 900° K. The identification of the CF_2 radical was based mainly on the vibrational analysis because the rotational fine structure even at very high dispersion is most complex.

A detailed study has also been made by Schüler *et al.*[36] and Barrow and Walker[37] of numerous substituted benzene compounds in mild electric discharges (e.g. of the Tesla type) some of which yielded an emission spectrum in the 4500 Å region. Various emitters have been proposed for these bands including C_2H, C_6H_5, C_6H_5C, C_6H_5CH, and $C_6H_5CH_2$. The procedure employed in the identification of the radicals may be illustrated by considering the series:

$$C_6H_5X, \quad C_6H_5CH_2X, \quad C_6H_5CHX_2, \quad C_6H_5CX_3$$

If the same emission spectrum were obtained from each in a discharge and no ring fission took place, then the most probable radical would be $C_6H_5\cdot$ as this unit is common to all four types of molecules. The probable lack of ring fission may be indicated by the absence of an intense CH band. In practice a common emission spectrum is not obtained from all these four types. Molecules of the $C_6H_5CH_2X$ types where X = H, CH_3, CH_2CH_3, C_6H_5, and NH_2 give a common emission spectrum which is not obtained from the other three types. On these grounds the most probable radical would be expected to be $C_6H_5CH_2$. However, under certain discharge conditions *iso*propyl benzene also gives the same 4500 Å region bands as the $C_6H_5CH_2X$ type. Spectrograms of the 4500 Å region bands resulting from mild Tesla discharges through toluene-alpha-d_3 and *iso*-propyl benzene are given in Fig. 5.32. Bindley and Walker[38] showed that the radical from $C_6H_5CD_3$ exhibited an isotopic shift compared with that from toluene (see Fig. 5.32. (*a*) and (*b*)). Thus, C_6H_5 or C_6H_5C could not be the emitter. They carried out a vibrational frequency analysis of the electronic spectra and showed since the vibrational frequency in Fig. 5.33*a* was mass sensitive that the emitters must be $C_6H_5CH_2$ and $C_6H_5CD_2$. This was done by plotting the frequency of the vibrational mode against $1/(\text{mass})^{\frac{1}{2}}$ for the two radicals, $C_6H_5CH_3$, and $C_6H_5CD_3$ as in Fig. 5.33*b*. Finally, Watts and Walker [39a] showed that the $C_6H_5CH_2$ visible absorption spectrum could be interpreted by the emission upper state vibrational frequencies.

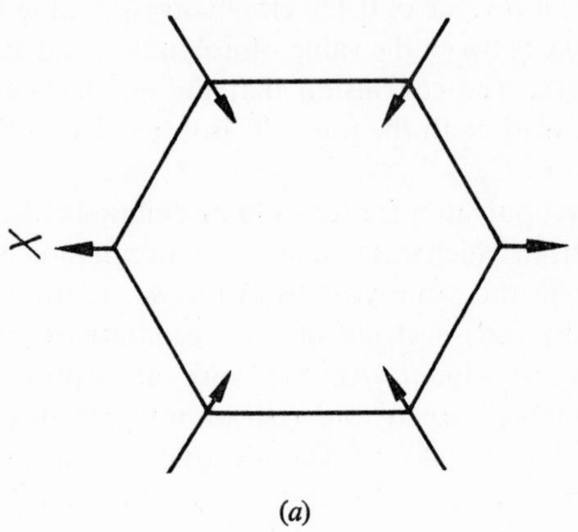

(*a*)

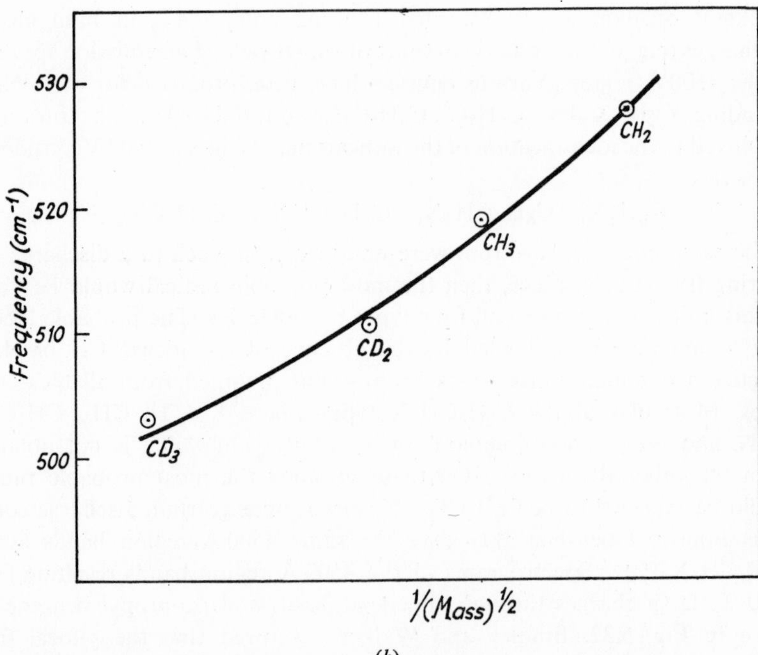

(*b*)

FIG. 5.33 (*a*) A mass sensitive vibrational mode of monosubstituted benzenes (*b*) Plot of this vibrational mode frequency (ordinate axis) for C_6H_5X where $X = CH_2$, CH_3, CD_2, and CD_3 against $1/(\text{mass of substituent})^{\frac{1}{2}}$ along the abscissa. (*After Bindley and Walker*[38])

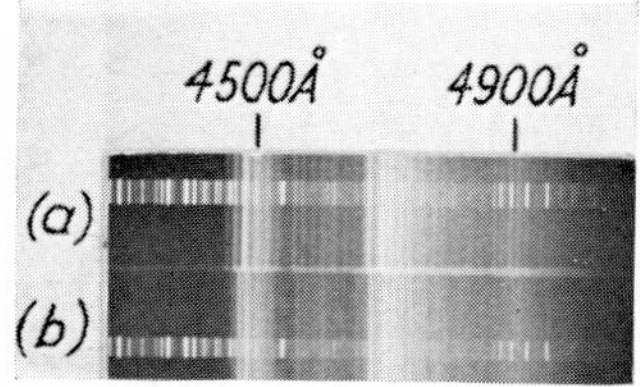

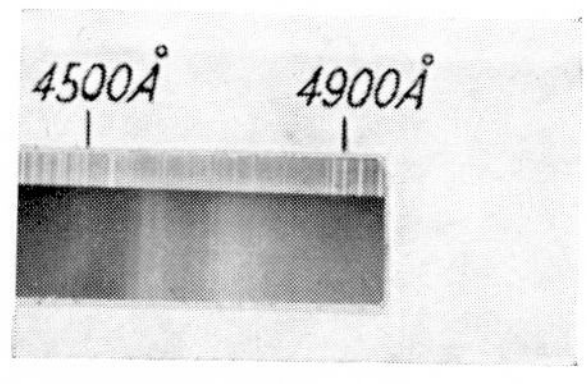

(c)

FIG. 5.32 Visible spectra resulting from a Tesla discharge through: (a) $C_6H_5CH_3$, (b) $C_6H_5CD_3$, (c) C_6H_5iPr. (*After Bindley and Walker* [38])

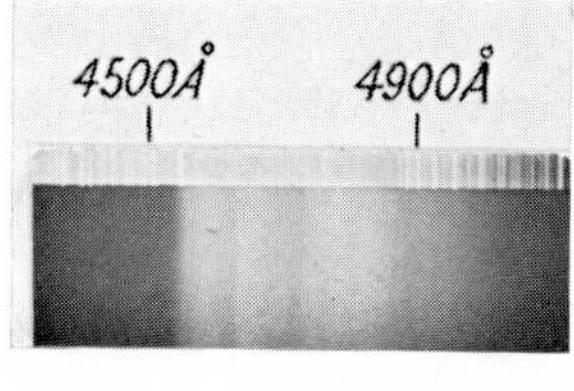

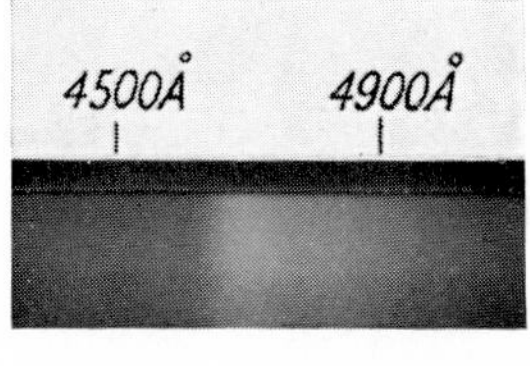

(a) (b)

FIG. 5.34 Visible spectra resulting from a Tesla discharge through: (a) p-xylene, (b) p-di-isopropylbenzene. (*After Watts and Walker* [39b])

In Fig. 5.34 (*a*) and (*b*) the spectra resulting from discharges through p-xylene and p-iPrC_6H_4iPr are given; Watts and Walker[39b] identified the emitters as being p-$CH_3C_6H_4CH_2$ and p-iPr$C_6H_4CH(CH_3)$ respectively.

Detection of radicals in shock tubes

Recent progress in spectroscopic studies of free radicals has been the development of a new method which depends on the rapid heating produced in a shock wave.[40] The shock tube is a long, narrow, cylindrical tube divided into two sections of unequal length separated from each other by a thin cellulose acetate or aluminium membrane. The larger section is filled with H_2 or He at several atmospheres pressure, while the smaller one contains the molecules (at a pressure of a few millimetres of Hg) from which as a result of the shock wave the radicals are to be generated. When the membrane is pricked, a shock wave travels forward, and a flash of light is emitted which is recorded photographically on a fast spectrograph. In a few cases one flash is sufficient to record the spectrum; otherwise, it might be necessary to repeat the process several times and build up the exposures on the photographic plate. Shock waves are capable of producing excited molecules, free radicals and ions. Ions have been identified in shock wave studies at temperatures up to 10 000°K. The method may be looked upon as an extension of the thermal method, and in the order of a microsecond a gas can be heated to several thousand degrees. After a brief initial equilibrium period the temperature of the gas which has suffered the shock wave remains constant until the wave is reflected from the end of the shock tube. From measurement of the absorption spectra and the velocity of the incident and reflected waves, information has been obtained on reaction rates and dissociation energies. So far such emission spectra have been obtained for a number of previously known radicals such as CN, CH, and OH. The method has been used to study a number of combustion reactions. Both this method and the flash photolysis technique have two important advantages over the discharge methods in that they enable a study of time dependence of the intermediates to be made, and their preparation is accomplished in a time which is short compared with the lifetime of the radical under the prevailing conditions of the experiment.

Shock tube spectra appear to offer a potential means of testing the various spectroscopic measurements of high temperatures as deduced by stellar spectroscopy and also for producing stellar types of spectra.

Low temperature stabilisation of free radicals

The low temperature stabilisation of free radicals may be divided into two categories:

(i) Those where the radicals are first formed and are then rapidly condensed on to a cold wall into a solid before they have the opportunity to react. The radical formation may be achieved by means of chemical reaction, electric discharges, or by high temperatures.

(ii) Those where a low concentration of the parent molecule is dissolved in a solvent mixture, then frozen to a low temperature. The radicals are then liberated from the parent molecule by irradiation with either X-rays, γ-rays, or ultra-violet light, or by bombardment with α-particles, electrons, neutrons, or protons. The solvent (or solvent mixture) is chosen so that it does not appreciably react with the liberated free radicals, nor give free radicals itself. Most important of all is that the resultant solid should be a transparent glass at the low temperature, if the detection is to be achieved by means of the radical's electronic absorption spectrum. The experiment is carried out in a quartz cell with optical windows.

The main methods of detection of the stabilised radicals have so far been accomplished by means of electronic absorption, or electron spin resonance spectra.† The latter method of detection has been dealt with in Vol. 1. As regards detection by means of their electronic absorption spectrum for those in category (ii), once the radicals have been stabilised, a source of continuous light (e.g. from a hydrogen or a tungsten lamp) is then directed through this transparent solid on to, for example, a medium quartz spectrograph where the absorption spectrum of the radicals may be recorded photographically. The experimental arrangement for category (ii) may be seen in Fig. 5.35 and is that used by Norman and Porter.[41]

They have used this technique in a number of free radical studies. The radicals were produced at 77°K by photolysis with light from a mercury lamp; the temperature of 77°K is that of the liquid nitrogen employed in the Dewar vessel which has quartz windows into which the quartz cell is inserted. Several solvent mixtures were used, the main one being a mixture of ether, *iso*pentane, and ethyl alcohol (known as E.P.A.). The free radicals were detected photographically by means of their electronic absorption spectrum on either a small or medium quartz spectrograph. The procedure was to irradiate first the solute plus solvent mixture in the Dewar with a mercury lamp, then to rotate the Dewar through 90° and to detect the presence of any liberated radicals by means of their absorption from the continuous radiation of the hydrogen lamp—Norman and Porter have detected CS and ClO from CS_2 and ClO_2, respectively. They have also studied a number of mono-substituted benzene compounds. The following compounds:

$$C_6H_5CH_2X \quad \text{where} \quad X = H, Cl, NH_2, CH, CN, CO_2H$$

gave three identical absorption bands at 3187, 3082, and 3047 Å where the respective relative intensities are 10, 3, and 3. *Iso*propyl benzene and *tert.*-butyl benzene gave different absorption bands. Their results indicated that the common absorption spectrum from $C_6H_5CH_2X$ irradiated type of molecule was due to the benzyl radical, since a completely different absorption spectrum was obtained from the $C_6H_5CHX_2$ and $C_6H_5CX_3$ type.[42]

This work has been extended by Porter and Strachan,[43] and later by Bindley and Walker,[39c] and evidence has been obtained for the identity of a

† In addition, the infra-red method has also been employed.

considerable number of polyatomic radicals from the photolysis of aromatic hydrocarbons and their substituents; the photolysis is such that the unsaturated ring is preserved in the detected free radicals.

As an example of the low temperature stabilisation procedure listed under category (i) the following work may be cited. Mador and Williams[44]

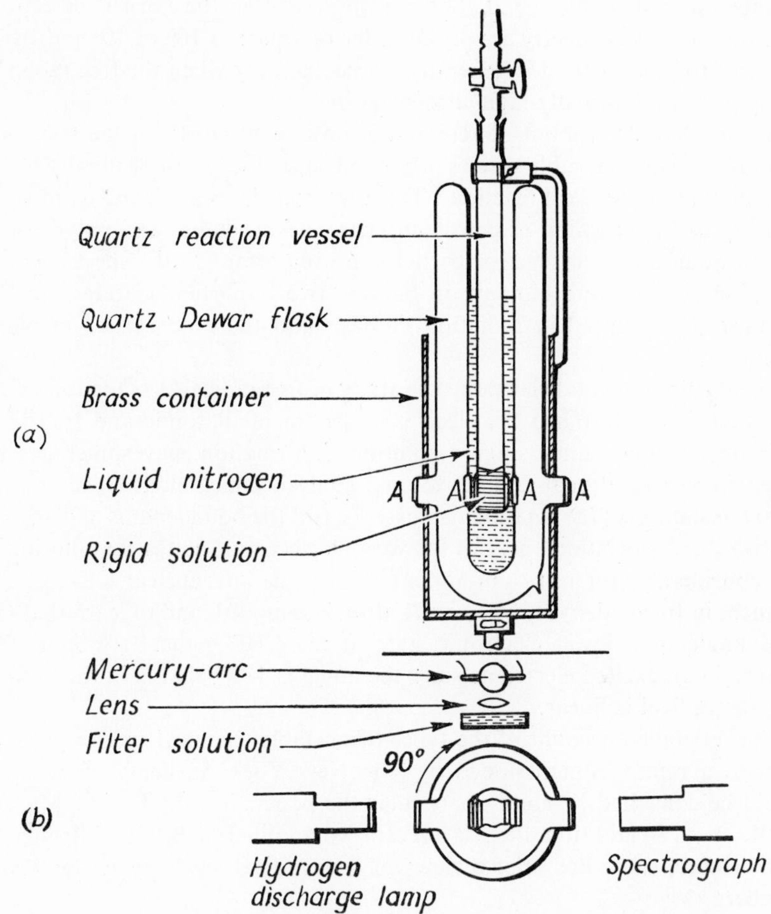

FIG. 5.35 Type of apparatus employed to liberate free radicals in a solid matrix and to record their electronic absorption spectrum. (*After Norman and Porter.*[41] *Courtesy of Professor G. Porter, and the Council of the Royal Society*)

passed an electric discharge through hydrazoic acid (N_3H) and froze the radicals in one experiment at 4°K and in another at 77°K. They measured the absorption spectrum in the near ultra-violet and the infra-red region. In the infra-red only bands assignable to N_3H were detected. Bands in the visible region were attributed to NH and NH_2; these bands disappeared on warming above 148°K and did not reappear on cooling to 77°K; this confirmed that the absorption could be attributed to an unstable species.

Conclusions

It must be stressed that the spectroscopic method is one of the most convincing ways of identifying simple radicals† Another useful approach, however, is mass spectrometry. For details of the qualitative and quantitative detection of free radicals by mass spectrometry a publication by Lossing[45] should be consulted. Lossing observes that the normal detection limits of mass spectrometry are of the order of 1 part in 10^3 or 10^4 and that, consequently, the method is generally applicable only when the free radicals are present in abnormally high concentrations.

A considerable amount of research is now in progress on the study of free radicals[46] and unstable species in general, since they must be involved in a large number of chemical reactions. These intermediates are involved in such processes as the cracking of petroleum, detonation, flames and polymerisation. In addition, such reactive particles are important in the spectroscopic side of astronomy and biology; in biology two important features are the free radicals produced in radiation damage and those concerned in plant growth.

From a fundamental viewpoint the study of free radicals has the following important features. When the electronic spectra of diatomic and triatomic types are examined under high resolution, information may sometimes be gained from a rotational and vibrational analysis concerning: (i) the vibrational constants, (ii) the rotational constants, (iii) the bond lengths and angles, and (iv) the dissociation energies for various electronic states. In addition it is of considerable interest to note the effect on the internuclear CH and CO distances in formaldehyde, when an H atom is removed, and to learn that the bond angle in a lower electronic state of the CHO radical is about 120° whereas in an excited electronic state the angle is 180°; that is in the excited state the radical is linear.

For a detailed account of the types of unstable chemical species work in progress a report commissioned by The New York Academy of Sciences should be consulted,[47a] and in particular the papers in it by Broida, Marcus and Ramsey. In addition, there is a recent work edited by Bass and Broida.[47b] Furthermore, there are brief reviews of free radical work by Porter[48] and Herzberg.[12]

Charge transfer spectra

In this chapter so far we have been concerned with electronic transitions within an isolated radical or molecule; this type of transition is concerned only with an intramolecular redistribution of charge. Charge-transfer spectra, however, involve an intermolecular or an interionic redistribution of charge

† Potentially the most promising spectral method for detecting free radicals seems to be the electron spin resonance method, although so far it has been applied mainly to stable or stabilised free radicals. The method is a very sensitive one for the study of radicals in the liquid and solid states. At present, however, the study of unstable gaseous free radicals by electron spin resonance absorption is very difficult.

where as a result of the transition an electron or a fraction of an electron is transferred from one ion or molecule to a different ion or molecule. To illustrate this kind of spectra the alkali halides will now be considered.

The ultra-violet absorption spectra of crystalline KBr, KI, RbI, and CsI are given in Fig. 5.36.

The crystalline alkali bromides have a pair of peaks separated by 0.48–0.60 eV, and the iodides also have a pair of peaks separated by 0.95–1.19 eV. In the bromine atom the two lowest electronic states are the $4^2P_{3/2}$ and the $4^2P_{1/2}$ with a 0.46 eV separation. In the case of the iodine atom the two lowest electronic states are $5^2P_{3/2}$ and the $5^2P_{1/2}$ with a 0.94 eV separation. Thus, the lowest value of the peak separations almost corresponds with the $^2P_{3/2}$ and $^2P_{1/2}$ level separations for each of the bromine and iodine atoms. This suggests quite strongly that free halogen atoms are formed from the corresponding ion during the electronic absorption and that the pairs of absorption peaks are to be related to the formation of some halogen atoms in the $^2P_{3/2}$ state and others in the $^2P_{1/2}$ state. Further support for this type of interpretation is received from bands in the spectra of the crystalline rubidium salts where the peak separation values are from 1.51 to 1.53 eV. This order of difference is in close agreement with the separation between the ground state and the first excited state of the rubidium atom itself. Furthermore, the spectra of the gaseous alkali bromides and iodides yield pairs of peaks whose separation is almost equal to that between the $^2P_{3/2}$ and $^2P_{1/2}$ states of the free halogen atom. In addition, some of these gaseous alkali halides yield further peaks, the separation between which indicates that the metal atoms are being produced in excited states.

The interpretation of the ultra-violet absorption spectra of the alkali halide crystals in terms of the transfer of an electron from a halide ion to a metal atom seems convincing. In actual fact, the process in the case of the crystalline halides is now considered to be the transfer of an electron from a set of halide ions to a set of metal ions. Such transitions are really photochemical oxidation-reduction reactions.

It is found that the frequency of the maximum absorption peak of the halides of a given metal follows the order:

$$\text{chloride} > \text{bromide} > \text{iodide}$$

Thus, more energy is required to transfer an electron from a chloride ion to the metal than for either a bromide or an iodide ion. It is interesting to note that their ionisation potentials fall in the same order. In fact, the electron charge transfer process is favoured by a low ionisation potential of the donor atom and a high electron affinity of the acceptor atom. The energy processes involved may be analysed in terms of the following model:

(i) An anion and a cation are removed from adjacent positions in the crystal lattice.

(ii) An electron is then removed from this anion and placed on the cation.

(iii) The atoms thus formed are returned to the original lattice positions.

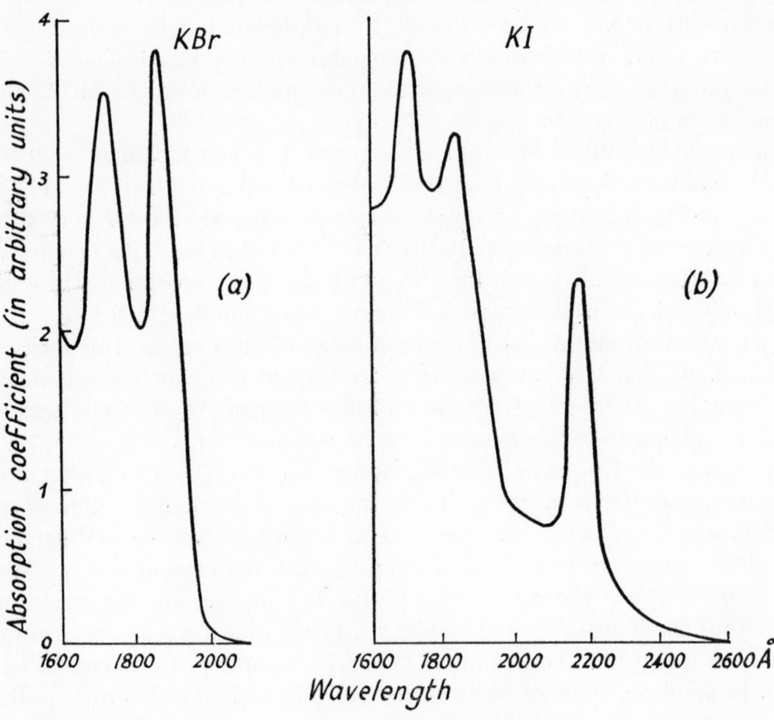

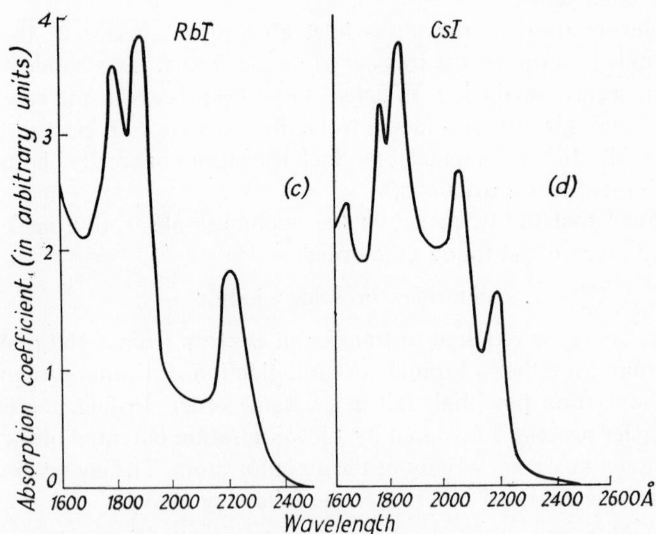

FIG. 5.36 The ultra-violet absorption spectra of crystalline (*a*) KBr, (*b*) KI, (*c*) RbI, and (*d*) CsI. (*After Hilsch and Pohl.*[49] *Courtesy of Springer-Verlag, Heidelberg*)

If W is the energy supplied by the system itself for the changes in (i), (ii), and (iii) then:

$$W = E - I + \Delta \tag{5.83}$$

where E is the electron affinity of the halogen, I is the ionisation potential of the alkali metal, and Δ is the difference between the energy of formation of the normal crystal and that of the crystal formed with a pair of adjacent atoms substituted for a pair of ions. If the metal ion has a high electron affinity and (or) the halide ion has a low ionisation potential, then the more the charge transfer process will be favoured. In addition, if the difference between the ionisation potential of the donor and the electron affinity of the acceptor is small, then the frequency of a charge-transfer absorption will tend to be small. In the case of crystalline solids the effect of the medium has to be taken into account. This is done so by means of the Δ term in equation (5.83). The Δ term varies from one halide to another. Attempts have been made to calculate Δ, since if E and I are known, then from the value of Δ as well the frequency of the absorption maximum in the charge transfer spectrum may be calculated from the equation:

$$h\bar{\nu} = I - E - \Delta \tag{58.4}$$

where $h\bar{\nu}$ is the energy supplied from outside the system itself to achieve the charge transfer. In some cases good agreement with the observed and calculated frequencies has been observed.[50,51]

Many other cases of charge transfer spectra have been examined, and a few of these are described below.

Inorganic anions and cations in aqueous solution

A rather striking study was made by Dainton[52] who plotted the energy corresponding to the long wavelength edge of the charge-transfer bands of the bivalent transition metals against the corresponding redox potential for the equilibrium,

$$\text{bivalent} \rightleftharpoons \text{trivalent} + e$$

If both these quantities are plotted in the same units, then the slope is approximately 45°, and this suggests that the minimum energy of the charge-transfer process corresponds with the energy of the process:

$$M(aq)^{2+} \rightarrow M(aq)^{3+} + e$$

It is considered that for such ions the charge-transfer process is from bivalent ion to the solvent.

Photochemical Reactions

Bates, Evans, and Uri[53] have studied a number of photochemical oxidations catalysed by ferric ions which may be interpreted as being free radical reactions initiated as for example:

$$Fe^{3+} + OH^- \xrightarrow{h\bar{\nu}} Fe^{2+} + OH$$

Then:

$$OH + RH \rightarrow H_2O + R\cdot$$

Organic systems

Numerous cases are known where, by mixing two components which would not be expected to react chemically, a definite and often pronounced colour change takes place. For example, certain aromatic nitro compounds when mixed with aromatic hydrocarbons give intense colours, and, in addition, stable solid complexes may be isolated. In solution, however, the complexes are usually considerably dissociated.

The electronic absorption spectrum of the complex is frequently removed by some thousands of Ångström units to the long wavelength side of the nearest absorption of either of the separate components of the mixture. This energy shift is of the order of 20 kcal/mole, but it is to be contrasted with the heat of formation of these complexes which are only of the order of $\frac{1}{2}$—4 kcal/mole. The absorption bands of these complexes are very broad and lack fine structure. This may probably be attributed to the loose attachment of the components of the complex in the ground state which would permit considerable relative nuclear motion, and since each nuclear configuration must lead to a slightly different absorption frequency, a broad absorption peak would ensue. In fact, the absorption peaks are often so broad that it is almost impossible to assess accurately the absorption maxima values.

It is interesting to note that the complexes are normally formed between two types of molecules. One member of the complex has a low ionisation potential, and the other partner has a high electron affinity. This is what might have been anticipated from the alkali halide charge-transfer work. Thus, one of the organic molecules acts as an electron donor and the other as an electron acceptor. If the two molecules are D and A, then Mulliken[54,55] has interpreted the complex formation as bonding due to resonance between two structures, which may be written formally as DA and D^+—A^-, where DA is a no-bond structure and corresponds to the two components held together by van der Waals' forces (this may include dipole-dipole or dipole-induced dipole forces). The other resonant structure, D^+—A^-, is identified with a D^+ ion formed from the donor atom and an A^- ion derived from the acceptor. These two ions are held together by electrostatic polarisation and possible covalent forces. In the ground state of the complex Mulliken considers there is a small admixture of D^+—A^- with DA. The wave-function for the ground state of the complex may be formulated as:

$$a\psi(\mathrm{DA})+b\psi(\mathrm{D}^+\text{—}\mathrm{A}^-)$$

where the contribution of the ionic state to the structure is approximately $b^2/(a^2+b^2)$. The wave-function of the corresponding excited state would be:

$$a\psi(D^+\text{—}\mathrm{A}^-)-b\psi(\mathrm{DA})$$

and an electronic transition between the two states would, in theory at least, be feasible. According to Mulliken the ionic contribution in the ground state is small, that is the value of b is small; hence, it follows from the wave-function of the excited state that the DA contribution is small in the excited state. Thus, on Mulliken's approach this excited state would be expected to be almost completely of the $D^+—A^-$ type. If $h\bar{\nu}$ is the energy required to bring about this electronic transition, then it follows from equation (5.84) that:

$$h\bar{\nu} = I_D - E_A - \Delta \tag{5.85}$$

where I_D is the ionisation potential of D, E_A is the electron affinity of A, and Δ is the stabilisation energy of the ion pair. When Δ is neglected then from equation (5.85), if I_D is decreased or E_A is increased the frequency of charge-transfer spectrum will be diminished. However, in some types of complexes the Δ term may be more important than the I_D and E_A changes.

One of the characterising features of the charge-transfer type of spectra in complexes is that they are most intense. This is to be anticipated for transitions from a *DA* type of complex to one in an ionic state. If assumptions are made as to the geometry of the complex and the magnitude of *b*, reasonable estimates of the intensity of the charge-transfer spectrum may sometimes be made.

Complexes formed between an organic and an inorganic molecule

Complex formation is not limited just to organic mixtures, and, in fact, mixtures of I_2 with either benzene, naphthalene or diphenyl form complexes which have respectively the following electric dipole moments: 1.8, 2.6, and 2.9D. Thus, a definite transfer of electric charge must have taken place in the complex formation since both I_2 and benzene separately have no dipole moments. Similar complexes have also been detected for Br_2, ICl, and O_2 with aromatic molecules. In the case of I_2 and benzene there is strong spectroscopic evidence for a 1 : 1 complex. The benzene molecule acts as the donor and the iodine as acceptor. It is interesting to note that the substitution of methyl groups into the benzene ring lowers the ionisation potential, and this has the expected effect of lowering the maximum absorption frequency of the complex (see above) and also of increasing the association constant of the complex. 1 : 1 complex formation has been detected for solutions of I_2 in alcohols and ethers where the donated electron may be probably attributed to an electron from a lone pair on the oxygen atom.

One striking feature of this iodine complex formation was detected by McConnell, Ham, and Platt[56] who found a linear relation between the wavelength of maximum absorption and the ionisation potential of the donor molecule. This relation has been employed to predict the positions of the absorption maxima of complexes in which the ionisation potential of the donor molecule was previously known. This linear dependence seems to indicate that in these cases the Δ term is practically independent of the shape of the donor molecule.

Finally, for charge-transfer and related phenomena reviews by Orgel[57] and Murrell[58] should be consulted and a book by Rao.[59]

References

1. Phillips, J. G. *Astrophys. J.* **108** (1948), 434.
2. Herzberg, G. *Spectra of Diatomic Molecules.* D. Van Nostrand (New York, 1950).
3. Johnson, R. C. *An Introduction to Molecular Spectra.* Methuen (London, 1949).
4. Gaydon, A. G. *Dissociation Energies and Spectra of Diatomic Molecules.* Chapman and Hall (London, 1947).
5. Schüler, H., Haber, H. and Gollnow, H. *Z. Phys.* **111** (1939), 484.
6. Jevons, W. *Report on Band-Spectra of Diatomic Molecules.* The Physical Society. (London, 1932).
7. Garforth, F. M., Ingold, C. K. and Poole, H. G. *J. Chem. Soc.* (1948), 406.
8. Ingold, C. K. and King, G. W. *J. Chem. Soc.* (1953), 2702.
9. Sponer, H. and Teller, E. *Rev. Mod. Phys.* **13** (1941), 75.
10. Sponer, H. and Teller, E. *Disc. Faraday Soc.* **9** (1950).
11. Walsh, A. D. *Quart. Rev.* **2** (1948), 73.
12. Herzberg, G. *Proc. Chem. Soc.* (1959), 116.
13. McLennan, J. C., Ainslie, D. S. and Fuller, D. S. *Proc. Roy. Soc.* (*Lond.*), **95A** (1919), 316.
14. Boyce, J. C. *Rev. Mod. Phys.* **13** (1941), 1.
15. Rowlinson, H. C. and Barrow, R. F. *J. Chem. Phys.* **21** (1953), 378.
16. Herzberg, G. and Shoosmith, J. *Canad. J. Phys.* **34** (1956), 523.
17. Price, W. C., Bralsford, R., Harris, P. V. and Ridley, R. G. *Molecular Spectroscopy. Institute of Petroleum Conference*, 1958.
18. Gillam, A. E. and Stern, E. S. *An Introduction to Electronic Absorption Spectroscopy in Organic Chemistry.* Edward Arnold (London, 1954).
19. Braude, E. A. and Nachod, F. C. (Editors). *Determination of Organic Structures by Physical Methods.* Academic Press (New York, 1955).
20. Ward, E. R., Pearson, B. and Wells, P. *J. Soc. Dyers Colourists*, **75** (1959), 484.
21. Norrish, R. G. W. and Porter, G. *Nature*, *Lond.* **164** (1949), 658.

22*a*. Norrish, R. G. W. and Thrush, B. A. *Quart. Rev.* **10** (1956), 149.

22*b*. Norrish, R. G. W. and Porter, G. *Proc. Roy. Soc.* (*Lond.*), **A210** (1952), 439.

22*c*. Norrish, R. G. W., Porter, G. and Thrush, B. A. *Proc. Roy. Soc.* (*Lond.*), **A216** (1953), 165.

23. Norrish, R. G. W. *Disc. Faraday Soc.* **14** (1953), 16.
24. Ramsay, D. A. *J. Chem. Phys.* **21** (1953), 960.
25. Herzberg, G. and Ramsay, D. A. *Proc. Roy. Soc.*, *Lond.* **233A** (1955), 34.
26. Ramsay, D. A. *J. Chem. Phys.* **25** (1956), 188.
27. Ramsay, D. A. *Mem. Soc. Roy. Sci.*, *Liège*, **18** (1957), 47.
28. Herzberg, G. *J. Chem. Soc.* (1959), 116.
29. Sawyer, R. A. *Experimental Spectroscopy.* Chapman and Hall (London, 1954).
30. Herzberg, G. *Astrophys. J.* (1942), 314.
31. Monfils, A. and Rosen, B. *Nature*, *Lond.* **164** (1949), 713.
32. Douglas, A. E. *Astrophys. J.* **114** (1951), 466.
33. Clusius, K. and Douglas, A. E. *Canad. J. Phys.* **32** (1954), 319.
34. Venkateswarlu, P. *Phys. Rev.* **77** (1950), 676.
35. Andrews, E. B., Laird, R. K. and Barrow, R. F. *Trans. Faraday Soc.* **46** (1950), 803.
36. Schüler, H. and Michel, A. *Z. Natursf.* **10a** (1955), 459.
37. Barrow, R. F. and Walker, S. *Trans. Faraday Soc.* **50** (1954), 541.
38. Bindley, T. F. and Walker, S. *Trans. Faraday Soc.* **58** (1962), 217.

39*a*. Watts, A. T. and Walker, S. *J. Chem. Soc.* (In press).

39*b*. Watts, A. T. and Walker, S. *Trans. Faraday Soc.*, **58** (1962), 849.

39*c*. Bindley, T. F., Watts, A. T. and Walker, S. *J. Chem. Soc.* (In press).

40. Payman, W. and Sheppard, W. C. F. *Proc. Roy. Soc.*, *Lond.* **186A** (1946), 293.
41. Norman, I. and Porter, G. *Proc. Roy. Soc.*, *Lond.* **230A** (1955), 399.
42. Porter, G. and Strachan, E. *Trans. Faraday Soc.* **54** (1958), 1595.
43. Porter, G. and Strachan, E. *Spectrochim. Acta*, **12** (1958), 299.
44. Mador, J. L. and Williams, M. C. *J. Chem. Phys.* **22** (1954), 1627.
45. Lossing, F. P. *Ann. N.Y. Acad. Sci.* **67** (1957), 499.
46. Fraenkel, G. K. *Ann. N.Y. Acad. Sci.* **67** (1957), 546.

47*a*. *Ann. N.Y. Acad. Sci.* **67** (1957).

47*b*. BASS, A. M. and BROIDA, H. P. (Editors). *Formation and Trapping of Free Radicals.* Academic Press (New York and London, 1960).
48. PORTER, G. *Molecular Spectroscopy. Institute of Petroleum Conference*, 1958.
49. HILSCH, R. and POHL, R. W. *Z. Phys.* **59** (1930), 812.
50. KLEMM, W. *Z. Phys.* **82** (1933), 529.
51. VON HIPPEL, A. V. *Z. Phys.* **101** (1936), 680.
52. DAINTON, F. S. *J. Chem. Soc.* (1952), 1533.
53. BATES, H. G. C., EVANS, M. G. and URI, N. *Nature, Lond.* **166** (1950), 869.
54. MULLIKEN, R. S. *J. Amer. Chem. Soc.* **74** (1952), 811.
55. MULLIKEN, R. S. *J. Phys. Chem.* **56** (1952), 801.
56. MCCONNELL, H., HAM, J. S. and PLATT, J. R. *J. Chem. Phys.* **21** (1953), 66.
57. ORGEL, L. E. *Quart. Rev.* **8** (1954), 423.
58. MURRELL, J. N. *Quart. Rev.* **15** (1961), 191.
59. RAO, C. N. R. *Ultraviolet and Visible Spectroscopy*. Butterworths (London, 1961).
60. MASON, S. F. *Quart. Rev.* **15** (1961), 287.

6

Effect of isotopes on the spectra of diatomic molecules

Introduction

THE isotope effect has already been considered several times. Examples of its use in microwave spectra were given on pp. 127 and 130 in Vol. 1. Other examples of its application may be found in the chapter on infra-red spectra, pp. 121 and 125. In addition a comparison of the infra-red ν_3 band of $^{14}N^{14}N^{16}O$ and $^{15}N^{14}N^{16}O$ may be made in Fig. 4.19. The use of isotopes is, in fact, a general procedure in microwave and infra-red spectra for the determination of internuclear distances and bond angles in certain simple polyatomic molecules. The technique has also been occasionally employed in Raman spectra for the determination of internuclear distances, and one example of its application was the evaluation of the C—C distance in benzene from C_6H_6 and C_6D_6 (see p. 224). Examples of the use of the isotope technique in simple polyatomic electronic spectra may be seen on (i) page 249 where by its application C_3 was identified, (ii) page 246 where the structure of the CHO radical was evaluated and compared with work on the CDO radical. The isotope effect, which is reflected in the spacing of the lines, in a band is dependent on the inverse value of the moment of inertia and for a diatomic molecule on:

$$\frac{m_A + m_B}{m_A m_B r_{AB}^2}$$

where m_A and m_B are the masses of the two atoms, and r_{AB} is their internuclear distance. The spacing of the lines in a band is thus dependent on the value of:

$$\frac{m_A + m_B}{m_A m_B}$$

and this is very dependent on the relative magnitudes of the masses of the atoms A and B. To illustrate this the following cases will be considered:

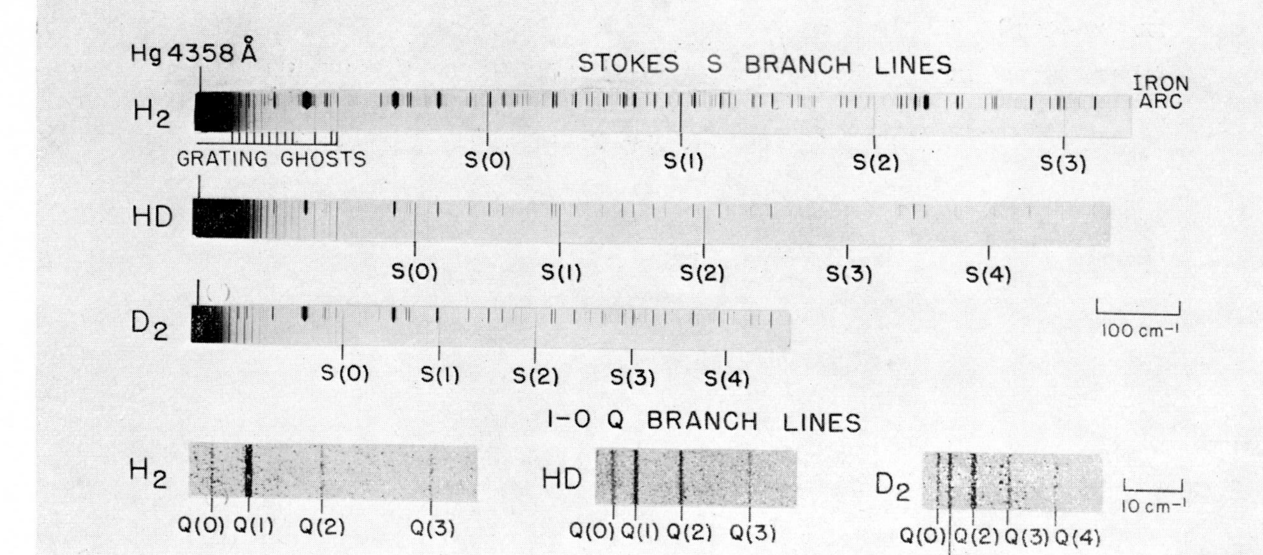

FIG. 6.1 Rotational Raman spectra of H_2, HD, and D_2 excited by the 4358 Å line of mercury and photographed with a 21 ft grating. The three upper spectrograms show the Stokes side of the pure rotational spectra, and the bottom strip shows the Q-branch lines of the $1 \leftarrow 0$ band. (*Courtesy of Dr. B. P. Stoicheff*[1a])

[*To face page* 262

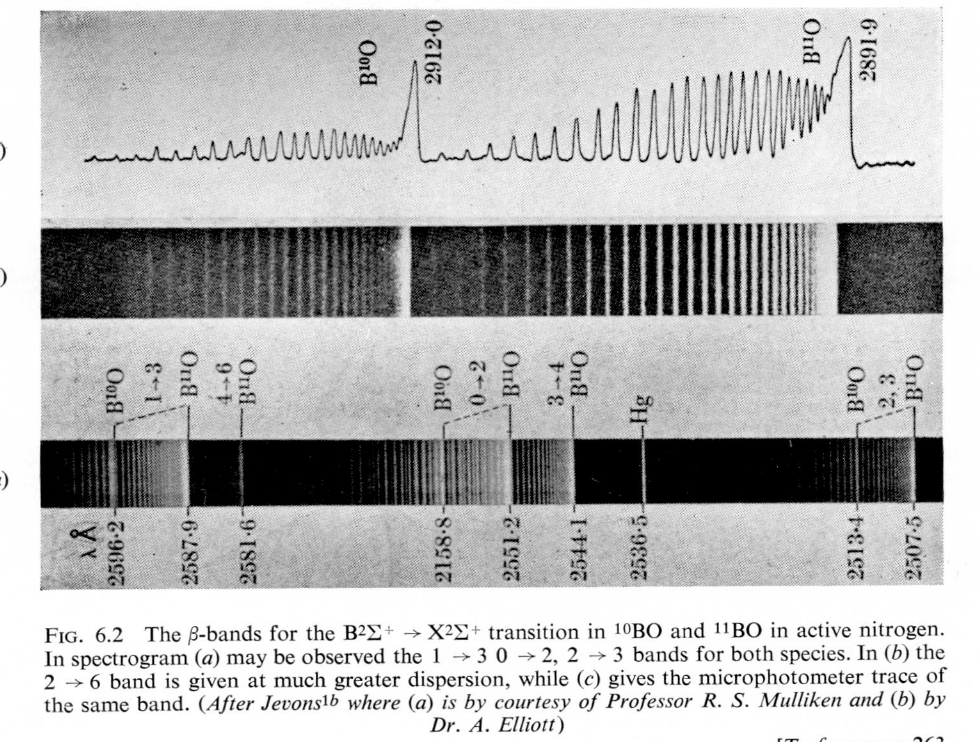

FIG. 6.2 The β-bands for the $B^2\Sigma^+ \rightarrow X^2\Sigma^+$ transition in ^{10}BO and ^{11}BO in active nitrogen. In spectrogram (*a*) may be observed the $1 \rightarrow 3$ $0 \rightarrow 2$, $2 \rightarrow 3$ bands for both species. In (*b*) the $2 \rightarrow 6$ band is given at much greater dispersion, while (*c*) gives the microphotometer trace of the same band. (*After Jevons*[1b] *where* (*a*) *is by courtesy of Professor R. S. Mulliken and* (*b*) *by Dr. A. Elliott*)

[*To face page* 263

(*a*) When $m_A = 1$ and $m_B = 200$, then $(m_A+m_B)/m_Am_B = 201/200$, and if m_A is now altered to the value of 2, then $(m_A+m_B)/m_Am_B = 202/400$.

(*b*) When $m_A = 200$ and $m_B = 202$, then $(m_A+m_B)/m_Am_B = 402/40\,400$, and if m_A is now altered to 201, then $(m_A+m_B)/m_Am_B = 401/40\,602$.

In case (*a*), where a light atom is joined to a heavy one, when the isotopic mass of the light atom was increased by 1 the value of $(m_A+m_B)/m_Am_B$ was almost halved, whereas in (*b*) there was only a very small change. In case (*a*) the isotopic effect would be readily observed, and for a given $v'-v''$ transition of the two isotopic molecules the band would be readily separated even at only moderate dispersion. However, in case (*b*) the separation would be difficult to achieve even at the highest resolution. In general, when the ratio of m_B/m_A differs appreciably from unity, then the better the chance of separating the lines in a given band due to the different isotope. Of course, in the examples taken the problem has been simplified, no account having been taken of the r^2_{AB} term, the value of which may differ appreciably if an electronic transition is being considered. However, for the infra-red and Raman rotation-vibration bands the r^2_{AB} term is less important, while for infra-red, Raman, and microwave rotational lines the change in the value of r_{AB} is negligible.

The pure rotational Raman spectra of H_2, HD, and D_2—Stokes branch only—are shown in Fig. 6.1. The rotational lines are very widely spaced with the separation decreasing in the order H_2, HD, D_2 due to the increasing moments of inertia. This is also the case for the Q branch lines of the (1,0) band.

As an example of the isotope effect in an electronic transition the spectrum of ^{10}BO and ^{11}BO may be seen in Fig. 6.2(*a*) and (*b*). This spectrogram is for β-bands in the $B^2\Sigma^+ \rightarrow X^2\Sigma^+$ electronic transition of ^{10}BO and ^{11}BO. Two sets of isotopic bands for the $1\rightarrow3$, $0\rightarrow2$, and $2\rightarrow3$ transitions are readily discernible. In Fig. 6.2(*b*) the $2\rightarrow6$ band is given at a much greater dispersion than that employed in Fig. 6.2(*a*), and the rotational structure of the two isotopic bands has been completely separated. In addition, the line intensities within this band are given in Fig. 6.2(*c*) in the microphotometer trace. Thus, in the case of BO the bands due to both the boron isotopes were fairly readily separated and were examined apart.

The introduction of an isotope into a molecule leaves essentially unchanged all the properties of the molecule associated with the electronic structure. In fact, the force constant of the bond is unchanged, and the same potential energy curve may be used to represent the energies of both isotopic molecules. The substitution, however, does affect those properties of the molecule which depend on the reduced mass and which are:

(*a*) The internuclear distances in the various vibrational levels.

(*b*) The moment of inertia.

The change referred to in (*a*) can be readily appreciated by reference to $H^{35}Cl$ and $D^{35}Cl$. The heavier molecule DCl, for a given value of v, will have a lower vibrational frequency than the lighter molecule HCl. The dependence of the equilibrium vibrational frequency ω_e on the mass of the two atoms is given by the equation:

$$\omega_e c = \frac{1}{2\pi}\sqrt{k\left(\frac{m_1+m_2}{m_1 m_2}\right)} \tag{6.1}$$

where k is the force constant and has the same value for both the isotopes. The dependence of the zero point energy on ω_e is given by equation (1.7), and if the x_e and y_e terms in this equation are neglected, then the zero point energy is $\frac{1}{2}hc\omega_e$, and from this and equation (6.1) it follows that DCl will have a smaller zero point energy than HCl. Thus, the internuclear separations in

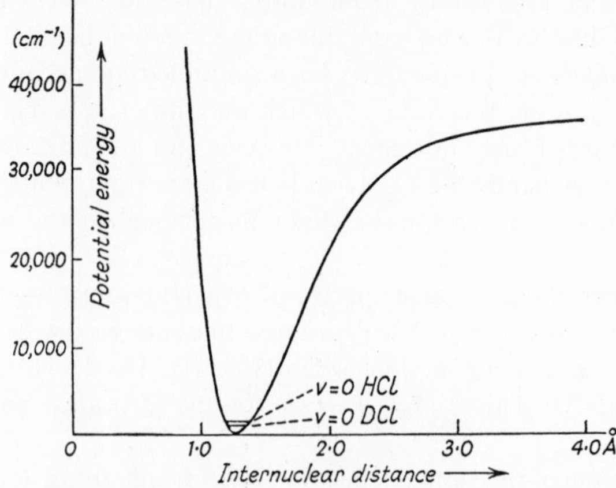

FIG. 6.3 The zero-point energies and the r_0 values for HCl and DCl

the ground vibrational levels are different, but the internuclear distance r_e, however, which corresponds to the hypothetical state of zero vibrational energy, is the same for both isotopic forms of the molecule. The dependence of the zero point energy on the isotopic mass in HCl and DCl is represented in Fig. 6.3.

Isotope effect on pure rotational spectra

The isotope effect in pure rotational spectra has already been partly treated in the chapter on microwave spectra (see Vol. 1), and it was considered with respect to symmetric- and asymmetric-top molecules, where the object was to assist in the evaluation of the moments of inertia. The dependence of the spacing of isotopic rotational lines with the same J value on the value of J for diatomic molecules will now be briefly considered.

If centrifugal stretching is neglected and it is assumed that the rotational constant $B = h/8\pi^2 cI$ is the same in both rotational levels, the wave-number of a pure rotational energy change is given by the formula:

$$\nu_r = B\{J'(J'+1)-J''(J''+1)\} \tag{6.2}$$

For an isotopic molecule the wave-number, ${}_i\nu_r$, of the corresponding transition would be:

$${}_i\nu_r = {}_iBJ'(J'+1) - {}_iBJ''(J''+1) \tag{6.3}$$

and

$$\nu_r - {}_i\nu_r = \Delta_i\nu_r = \frac{h}{8\pi^2 c}\left\{J'(J'+1) - J''(J''+1)\right\}\left\{\frac{1}{I} - \frac{1}{{}_iI}\right\} \tag{6.4}$$

hence

$$\Delta_i\nu_r = \nu_r\left(1 - \frac{I}{{}_iI}\right) \tag{6.5}$$

Since

$$I = \mu r_1^2 \quad \text{and} \quad {}_iI = {}_i\mu r_2^2 \tag{6.6}$$

and if it is assumed that r_1 is equal to r_2 then:

$$I/{}_iI = \mu/{}_i\mu \tag{6.7}$$

and it is customary to write ρ^2 for $\mu/{}_i\mu$; hence

$$\Delta_i\nu_r = \nu_r(1-\rho^2) \tag{6.8}$$

For most diatomic molecules, which exhibit pure rotational spectra, the isotopic masses are such that ρ^2 differs only slightly from unity; hence, the isotopic shift is small. However, in the case of a microwave spectrometer (Vol. 1) the resolution is so great that the isotopic shift could be readily detected. From the equation:

$$\Delta_i\nu_r = \nu_r(1-\rho^2) \tag{6.9}$$

and the facts that:

$$\rho^2 = \mu/{}_i\mu = \text{constant} \tag{6.10}$$

and:

$$\nu_r = (J+1)\frac{h}{4\pi^2 cI} \tag{6.11}$$

it follows that the separation of corresponding isotope lines has a linear dependence on J.

Isotope effect on vibrational spectra

The isotope effect has already been briefly considered in connexion with the effects on rotation-vibration spectra of spherical-, symmetric-, and asymmetric-top molecules in the chapter on infra-red and Raman spectra. Here we shall be mainly concerned with the alterations in wave-number of the origin of the vibrational band resulting from an isotopic change.

Since two isotopic forms of the same diatomic molecule have the same force constant, then:

$$k = 4\pi^2\omega_e^2 c^2\mu \tag{6.12}$$

and:

$$k = 4\pi^2\,{}_i\omega_e^2 c^2\,{}_i\mu \tag{6.13}$$

Hence:

$$\frac{{}_i\omega_e}{\omega_e} = \sqrt{\frac{\mu}{{}_i\mu}} = \rho \tag{6.14}$$

and:

$${}_i\omega_e = \rho\omega_e \tag{6.15}$$

It may be shown that the anharmonicity constant x_e is proportional to the equilibrium wave-number, and therefore on employing equation (6.15) it follows that:

$$_{i}x_e = \rho x_e \tag{6.16}$$

The energy levels of a non-harmonic oscillator are approximately given by:

$$E_v = (v+\tfrac{1}{2})hc\omega_e-(v+\tfrac{1}{2})^2 hcx_e\omega_e \tag{6.17}$$

For a vibrational energy change:

$$\nu_v = (v'+\tfrac{1}{2})\omega_e-(v'+\tfrac{1}{2})^2x_e\omega_e-\{(v''+\tfrac{1}{2})\omega_e-(v''+\tfrac{1}{2})^2x_e\omega_e\} \tag{6.18}$$

For the fundamental absorption frequency and its overtone bands $v'' = 0$ and $v' = v$; hence:

$$\nu_{v\leftarrow 0} = \{\omega_e-x_e\omega_e\}v-x_e\omega_e v^2 \tag{6.19}$$

and for the isotopic molecule since:

$$_{i}\omega_e = \rho\omega_e \tag{6.20}$$

and

$$_{i}x_e = \rho x_e \tag{6.21}$$

we have

$$_{i}\nu_{v\leftarrow 0} = \{\rho\omega_e-\rho^2x_e\omega_e\}v-\rho^2x_e\omega_e v^2 \tag{6.22}$$

Thus, for the isotopic shift

$$\nu_{v\leftarrow 0}-{_{i}\nu_{v\leftarrow 0}} = \Delta_i\nu_{v\leftarrow 0} \tag{6.23}$$

$$\Delta_i\nu_{v\leftarrow 0} = \omega_e(1-\rho)v-x_e\omega_e(1-\rho^2)v-x_e\omega_e(1-\rho^2)v^2 \tag{6.24}$$

$$\Delta_i\nu_{v\leftarrow 0} = (1-\rho)[\{\omega_e-x_e\omega_e(1+\rho)\}v-x_e\omega_e(1+\rho)v^2] \tag{6.25}$$

For the fundamental band $v = 1$, and

$$\Delta_i\nu_{1\leftarrow 0} = (1-\rho)\{1-2x_e(1+\rho)\}\omega_e \tag{6.26}$$

The first overtone $v = 2$, and

$$\Delta_i\nu_{2\leftarrow 0} = (1-\rho)\{1-3x_e(1+\rho)\}2\omega_e \tag{6.27}$$

The second overtone $v = 3$, and

$$\Delta_i\nu_{3\leftarrow 0} = (1-\rho)\{1-4x_e(1+\rho)\}3\omega_e \tag{6.28}$$

It may be deduced from equations (6.26) to (6.28) that if x_e is negligible, then the ratio of the isotope shifts, for the fundamental, the first overtone and the second overtone is roughly the ratio 1 : 2 : 3. This is borne out in Table 6.1 for the isotopic shifts for the $H^{35}Cl$ and $H^{37}Cl$ isotopic molecules.

TABLE 6.1

The isotopic shifts for the fundamental, first overtone, and second overtone bands of $H^{35}Cl$ *and* $H^{37}Cl$

Band	$\Delta_i\nu$ (cm^{-1})
1,0	2.10
2,0	4.00
3,0	5.83

Rotation-vibration spectra and isotope effect

If the resolution of the HCl bands just considered is sufficiently great, then each band is found to consist of pairs of lines, where the intensity of each member of the pair differs. In Fig. 6.4 the rotation-vibration change in

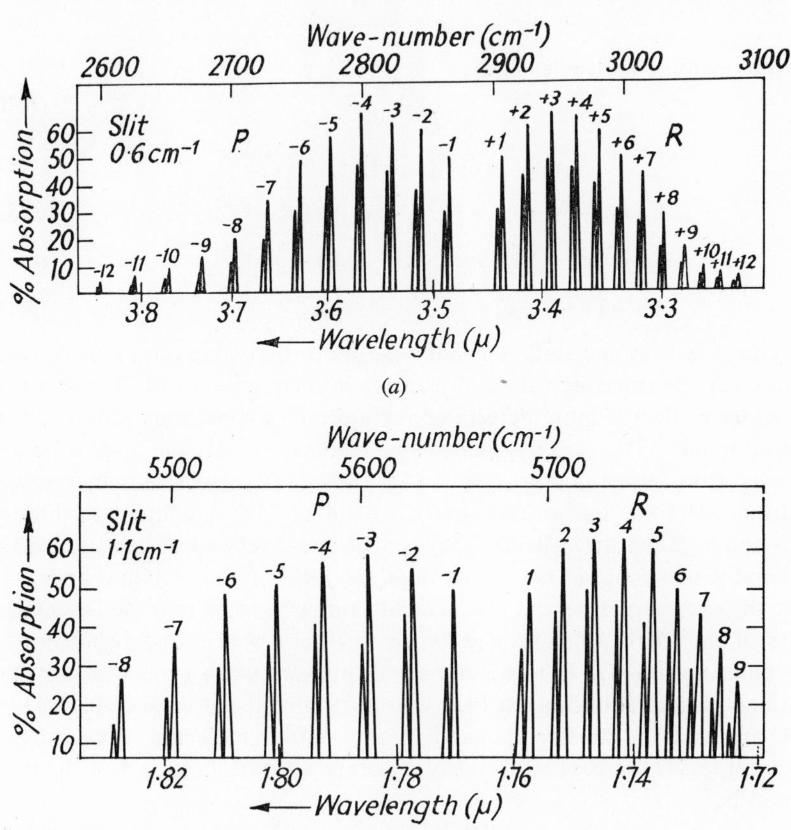

FIG. 6.4 The isotope effect on the rotation-vibration spectrum of $H^{35}Cl$ and H^{37} Cl for (*a*) the fundamental 3.46 μ band, and (*b*) the first overtone. The numbering above each pair of isotopic lines is the m-value. A line is missing in the centre of the bands (corresponding to m = 0) and to the left of this zero gap lies the *P*-branch while to the right the *R*-branch. (*After Meyer and Levin*[2], *Courtesy of 'The Physical Review'*)

the molecules $H^{35}Cl$ and $H^{37}Cl$ for the $1 \leftarrow 0$ and the $2 \leftarrow 0$ transitions, respectively, may be observed, where it will be noted:

(i) That there is duplicity of the band lines. The more intense member of each of the pairs of close lines is due to the molecule containing the more abundant isotope, that is $H^{35}Cl$.

(ii) That each $H^{35}Cl$ line occurs on the high-frequency side of the corresponding $H^{37}Cl$ line. This is what would be anticipated from theory since a vibrational frequency of $H^{35}Cl$ would be higher than that of $H^{37}Cl$.

Electronic spectra and isotope effect

The isotopic mass difference does not affect the ν_e (see p. 263) value between two electronic states, and if it is assumed that the vibration is simple harmonic, then for band origin wave-numbers:

$$\nu = \nu_e + \omega_e'(v'+\tfrac{1}{2}) - \omega_e''(v''+\tfrac{1}{2}) \tag{6.29}$$

For the isotopic molecule, since:

$$_i\omega_e = \rho\omega_e \tag{6.30}$$

then

$$_i\nu = \nu_e + \rho\omega_e'(v'+\tfrac{1}{2}) - \rho\omega_e''(v''+\tfrac{1}{2}) \tag{6.31}$$

$$\Delta_i\nu = \nu - {}_i\nu = (v'+\tfrac{1}{2})(\omega_e' - \rho\omega_e') - (v''+\tfrac{1}{2})(\omega_e'' - \rho\omega_e'') \tag{6.32}$$

$$\Delta_i\nu = (v'+\tfrac{1}{2})(1-\rho)\omega_e' - (v''+\tfrac{1}{2})(1-\rho)\omega_e'' \tag{6.33}$$

$$\Delta_i\nu = (1-\rho)\{(v'+\tfrac{1}{2})\omega_e' - (v''+\tfrac{1}{2})\omega_e''\} \tag{6.34}$$

Thus, the isotopic shift is greater the more the value of $(1-\rho)$ deviates from unity. By inserting values of μ and $_i\mu$ into equation (6.14) it is seen that the isotope effect is more detectable for molecules containing atoms of low atomic weight. The rare oxygen isotope of mass 18 was the first to be discovered from electronic spectra study. In the solar spectrum the oxygen molecule ($^{16}O^{16}O$) has an intense (0,0) band at 7596 Å containing thirteen lines and is called the *A*-band. Near this occurs a very weak band called the *A′* band which contains twenty-six lines. Both the *A* and *A′* bands appear to have the same structure, but the *A′* band cannot be fitted into the Déslandres table of the $^{16}O^{16}O$ bands, and hence this very weak band could not be attributed to $^{16}O^{16}O$. The explanation of this very weak band was provided by Giauque and Johnston[3] in 1929 who attributed the *A* band to the $^{16}O^{16}O$ molecule and the weaker *A′* band to the $^{16}O^{18}O$ molecule. According to equation (6.34) for the (0,0) band, the isotope shift of the origin of the band should be:

$$\Delta_i\nu = \tfrac{1}{2}(1-\rho)(\omega_e' - \omega_e'') \tag{6.35}$$

For the $^{16}O^{16}O$ molecule the ω_e' and ω_e'' values have been accurately determined as 1432.69 and 1580.36 cm^{-1} respectively, and therefore:

$$(\omega_e' - \omega_e'') = 1432.69 - 1580.36 = -147.67 \text{ cm}^{-1}$$

On substitution of this value into equation (6.35), and on the determination of ρ from $_i\mu$ for the $^{16}O^{18}O$, and μ for the $^{16}O^{16}O$ molecule, then a $\Delta_i\nu$ value of -2.1 cm^{-1} is obtained. The experimentally observed band origin shift is $\Delta_i\nu = -2.067$ cm^{-1} which is in good agreement with the over-simplified theoretical considerations. The negative sign implies that the shift due to the ^{18}O isotope has taken place towards shorter wavelengths. This close agreement was taken as proof of the existence of the ^{18}O isotope. A third band very close to the *A′* band, whose intensity was five times weaker than that of the *A′* band, was found shortly after the discovery of the *A′* band, and this, the *A″* band, was shown to be due to the $^{16}O^{17}O$ molecule, and the existence of ^{17}O

was thus established. The fact that for the $^{16}O^{18}O$ molecule the A' band contains twice as many rotational lines as the A band is due to the unsymmetrical nature of the $^{16}O^{18}O$ molecule. Owing to the symmetry of the $^{16}O^{16}O$ molecule, certain transitions are forbidden by the selection rules resulting in every other rotational line being missing. In the $^{16}O^{18}O$ molecule as in $^{16}O^{17}O$ because of the asymmetry no such restrictions are imposed by the selection rules, and double the number of rotational lines is observed. This is dealt with more fully on p. 62.

Further applications of isotope effect

(*a*) *For identification purposes*

From a vibrational analysis it is occasionally difficult to be certain of the diatomic species emitting a particular band system. On comparison of the experimentally determined value of ρ with that of the calculated one it is occasionally possible to confirm or reject the identity of a proposed emitter. One such case was the identification of the emitter of some bands produced in a discharge containing BCl_3 in active nitrogen. The emitter was first thought to be BN; however, the experimentally determined value of ρ taking into account the other boron isotopic species present was 1.0291, whereas the calculated value of ρ for BN was 1.0276. This value of ρ is, in fact, in excellent agreement with that to be anticipated for ^{10}BO and ^{11}BO the calculated value of which is 1.0292. Further investigation showed that the presence of a trace of oxygen was essential in this discharge for the production of these bands. Hence, there was no doubt that BO and not BN was the emitter.

The band spectra of a diatomic species is capable of distinguishing between certain isotopic species which could not otherwise be achieved with absolute certainty even by means of a mass spectrograph. For example, in the case of silicon, whose main isotope is ^{28}Si, a mass spectrograph could not distinguish between ^{30}Si and $^{28}SiH_2$ or ^{29}SiH produced from a volatile silicon hydride. Mulliken, however, from a study of the band spectrum of SiN definitely proved the presence of ^{30}Si isotope.

(*b*) *Abundance ratio*

The bands in the spectra from different isotopic species differ not only in their relative displacements but also in their relative intensities. The intensity ratio of the corresponding $v' \leftarrow 0$ bands in an absorption spectrum of isotopic molecules gives the abundance ratio of the molecules. For example, in the electronic absorption spectrum of Br_2 the intensity ratio of the isotopic species:

$$^{79}Br—^{79}Br,\ ^{79}Br—^{81}Br,\ ^{81}Br—^{81}Br \text{ is approximately } 1:2:1.$$

It follows, therefore, that the two isotopes of bromine are almost equally abundant, and, in fact, this is borne out by the atomic weight of bromine which is 79.916.

References

1*a*. Stoicheff, B. P. *Advances in Spectroscopy*. Interscience Publishers (N. Y. 1959), 91.
1*b*. Jevons, W. *Band Spectra of Diatomic Molecules*. Physical Society (London, 1932).
2. Meyer, C. F. and Levin, A. A. *Phys. Rev.* **34** (1929), 44.
3. Giauque, W. F. and Johnston, H. L. *Nature, Lond.* **123** (1929), 318, 831. *J. Amer. Chem. Soc.* **51** (1929), 1436, 3528.

7

Electronic spectra of flames

General considerations

WHEN combustion occurs electromagnetic radiation is emitted. Analysis of the band spectra of flames has been responsible for the identification of the presence of the radicals such as CH and OH in normal combustion processes. Some of the radicals present in the H_2+O_2 and the $C_2H_2+O_2$ flame reactions have been considered on p. 244 and p. 245, respectively. From the electromagnetic radiation emitted it may be possible to examine either: (*a*) the visible and ultra-violet emission spectra, or (*b*) the infra-red emission spectra, and although both types of emission have been studied, the greater proportion of the work has been done in the visible and ultra-violet regions. Most of the infra-red work appears to have been of an applied nature, e.g. to find out why gases behind a flame front still glow after the flame has passed by. The treatment given here will be confined to visible and ultra-violet emission, that is to electronic transitions in the molecules and radicals present in flames. In fact, the object will not be to understand the processes occurring in different types of flames, on which so much work has been directed, but only the more direct spectroscopic information which emerges.

One example which may be considered to illustrate the procedure of the identification of the emitter in a flame is the work on the band spectrum of stannous oxide. These bands were first observed in the oxy-coal-gas flame spectra of tin sulphide and tin chloride, and then later by Mahanti[1] in the arc spectrum of metallic tin on carbon electrodes. The feasible emitters of these bands were considered to be SnH, Sn_2, or SnO. Analysis of the bands showed that SnH could not be the emitter. In addition, Mahanti considered that it was improbable that Sn_2 was the emitter since no alternation of intensity in the lines of a given branch in a band could be observed even at high dispersion (Fig. 7.1). Such alternations are to be anticipated for a symmetrical diatomic emitter (see p. 63). This work was extended by Connelly[2] who employed the type of arc illustrated in Fig. 7.1.

In practice the arc was enclosed in a chamber and could be maintained in gases other than air. An arc was struck across the flame by means of an iron cup electrode which contained tin. The other electrode was a hollow copper rod which was cooled right up to the tip by flowing water. When the arc was struck the tin became molten, and when air was used in the arc

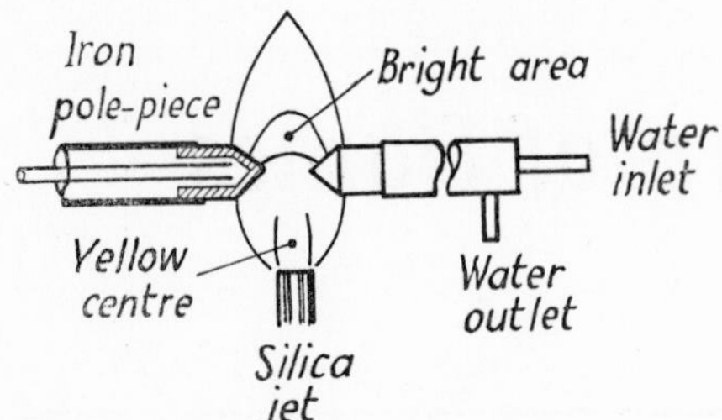

FIG. 7.1 Apparatus for the study of the emission spectrum of a flame with an arc across it. (*After Connelly.*[2] *Courtesy of the Council of the Physical Society*)

chamber the characteristic bands were readily obtained. These bands were also obtained by a hydrogen flame burning in a silica jet as in Fig. 7.1. The hydrogen was taken from a cylinder, then passed through a Woulffe's bottle containing anhydrous stannic chloride. A picture of the flame is given in Fig. 7.2. The flame was from hydrogen containing stannic chloride vapour while the electrodes had an oxide impurity.

The arc was fed by a transformer applying about 0.2 A at 5000 V. The wavelengths of the bands from the SnO spectra were arranged in a Déslandres table, where the v' values ranged from 0 to 8 and those of v'' from 0 to 9; the most intense bands lay on a Condon parabola. Connelly obtained the values of x_e'' and ω_e'' and the dissociation energy of the molecule in the ground state from the analysis, as well as x_e and ω_e values for one of the excited electronic states.

Mahanti had claimed three band systems for the SnO in emission, known as *A*, *B*, and *C* systems. Some doubt remained as to which of these systems involved a transition to the ground state of the molecule. This was settled by the work of Connelly when he took an absorption spectrum of the SnO in a flame by directing through it continuous radiation obtained from burning magnesium. The absorption spectrum of SnO is given in Fig. 7.3(*b*) and is to be compared with the emission bands in Fig. 7.3(*a*). The bands in Fig. 7.3(*a*) correspond in wavelength with some of those in Fig. 7.3(*a*), and these were the bands which Mahanti had attributed to band system *A*. The presence of only the *A* system in absorption indicates that the lower electronic state in this system must be the ground state.

Information derived from emission studies of flames

The work on flames not only helps to identify the emitter but yields information on the vibrational constants, dissociation energies, and the electronic states involved in the transition. Many such studies have been made on different types of flames and a number of radicals and molecules have been

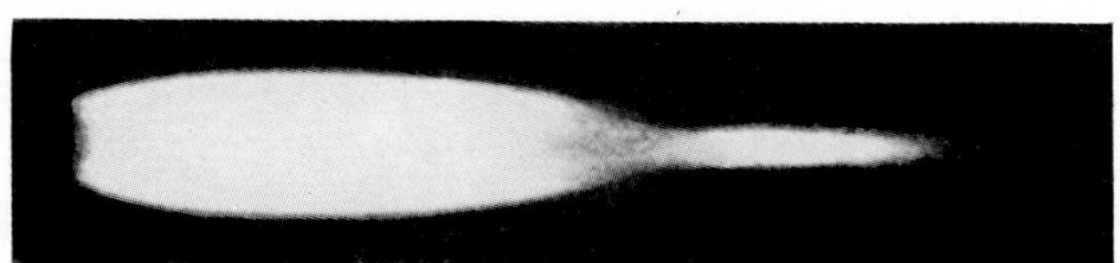

FIG. 7.2 The flame of hydrogen containing stannic chloride vapour. Iron and copper electrodes were employed containing oxide impurity. The inner region of the flame was yellow and the outer mantle a bright blue. (*After Connelly*[2]. *Courtesy of the Council of the Physical Society*)

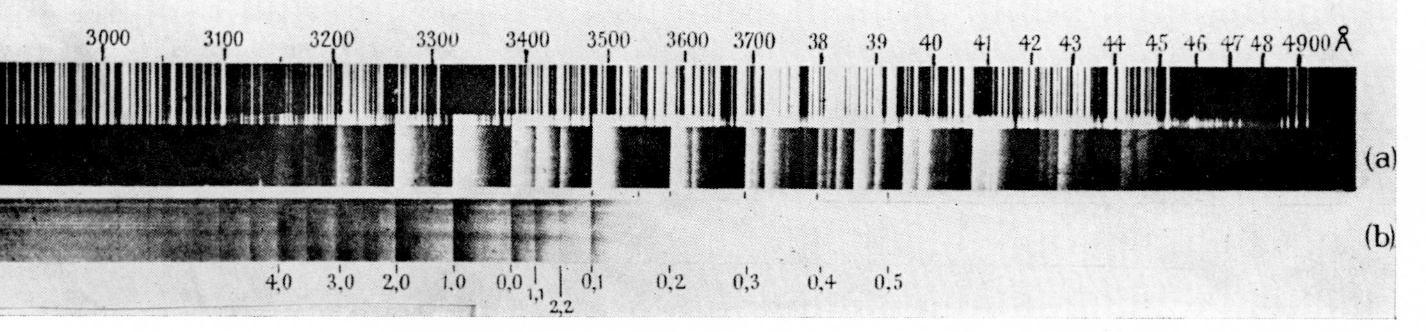

FIG. 7.3 (*a*) Emission spectrum of SnO obtained from a flame. (*b*) The corresponding absorption spectrum obtained by directing continuous radiation through the same flame. The reference spectrum at the head of the figure is that of the iron arc. (*After Connelly*[2]. *Courtesy of the Council of the Physical Society*)

[*To face page* 272

identified. Some of the radicals such as BrO and IO which have been recognised by means of the band spectra emitted by flames are not readily detectable from other sources. The BrO and IO radicals were identified by means of the band system produced from methyl bromide and methyl iodide flames, respectively.

Various types of flames have been studied. Organic compounds such as hydrocarbons and ethers when burning in air produce similar spectra. With the normal bunsen type of flame the inner cone from such gaseous mixtures yields electronic band spectra from which C_2, CH, and OH may be identified. The outer cone of the flame consists mainly of OH and CO emission. Quite a number of different types of inorganic flames have been examined, and one case was the spectra from an S_2 flame where emission bands of SO have been detected. The equation proposed to account for the SO bands is:

$$S_2 + O_2 \rightarrow S_2O_2 \rightarrow 2SO$$

In addition, S_2 emission bands are observed, and SO_2 absorption bands also occur. The burning of H_2S produces all these features and, besides this, shows an OH band.

There is no new principle in the procedure of spectrographically recording the emitted electronic radiation: in fact, the same medium quartz spectrograph employed for studies of certain electronic transitions (dealt with on p. 32) is suitable for most purposes. Since, however, flames are usually relatively weak emitters a wide slit is employed. Such studies may reveal the v' and v'' values in the upper and lower electronic levels, and a vibrational analysis may be performed in a similar way to that described on p. 194. An equation may be derived for the wave-number of the transition in terms of v' and v'' and the x_e and ω_e values which have been derived from the analysis. A few of the radicals and molecules whose band systems have been studied in electronic emission include CN, CO, NH, NO, CCl, CS, FeO, and NH_2.

In general, the study of the electronic emission spectra during combustion not only suggests some of the chemical reactions occurring during the oxidation process but also identifies some of the intermediate radicals. Band spectra are normally observed, and the most abundant information has been obtained on diatomic molecules and radicals.

In addition to band spectra, most flames emit a certain amount of continuous radiation which may result from the recombination of positive ions with free electrons. Sometimes, however, a strong continuum is obtained; this is particularly true of flames containing halogens and of halogens reacting with hydrogen. The cause of such a continuum has been ascribed to the reaction of normal and excited halogen atoms to form the halogen molecule, e.g. in the case of bromine:

$$\mathrm{Br}(^2P_{1/2}) + \mathrm{Br}(^2P_{3/2}) \rightarrow \mathrm{Br}_2 + \text{continuous radiation}$$

A large fraction of the radiation emitted by flames may be attributed to *chemiluminescence*. In such a process the chemiluminescence results from the formation of a radical in an excited electronic state by means of a chemical reaction. One case which has been explained this way is the intense emission from the hydroxyl radical in hydrocarbon flames where the reaction may be:

$$CH + O_2 \rightarrow CO + OH^{\star}$$

Line spectra are only detected from impurities in the flame (e.g. Na) since the atoms which could be present in flames, such as H, O, and C, require a greater excitation energy than can normally be supplied by means of a flame; an exception to this is the 2478 Å line of carbon. The exact cause of the electronic excitation of atoms and molecules in flames is as yet not certain. It is considered that although flames contain free electrons—these being the means of achieving excitation in discharges—their number and kinetic energy is insufficient to account for the intensity of the observed emission spectra. The excited electronic state in the emitter could be produced by a collision process involving some particle (atom, molecule, or ion) which itself possesses either electronic excitation energy or is in an excited vibrational state. A further possibility is that the emitter may become activated by being the third body present in combination of free atoms or radicals. Such low-energy processes can only produce excitation from the ground state to low-lying electronic levels in the radical or molecule which is to become the emitter. In fact, for all the electronic flame emission spectra observed the transition has always been from a low-lying excited state to the ground state itself. In molecules such as N_2, where there is no electronic state close to the ground one, no such emission spectrum is observed in flames.

Spectroscopic determination of the temperature of a flame

Generally, the rotational fine structure of the bands has not been examined. One of the reasons for this is that the intensity of the spectra is sometimes too weak to employ a diffraction grating. In some cases the radicals present in flames have been studied exhaustively by other means. In a few cases the rotational fine structure has been studied with a view to determining what is known as the effective rotational temperature. Normal methods of temperature measurement are often inadequate for assessing the thermal energy present in flames. A more satisfactory means is to consider the energy of the molecules as being composed of rotational, vibrational and translational contributions and so obtain a corresponding rotational, vibrational and translational temperature for the molecules. The rotational temperature is obtained by resolving the rotational fine structure, determining the rotational constant and measuring the intensities of the lines in a particular band. The intensity of a single line of the rotational fine structure in a band is given by:

$$I = C_{\mathrm{em}} P \nu^4 \exp\left(-\frac{E_r}{kT}\right)$$

where I is the intensity of the line; C_{em} is a constant and is the same for all the rotational lines in the band; P is a transition probability and may be evaluated (see equation (1.40)); ν is the wave-number of the line; $\boldsymbol{k}$ is the Boltzmann constant; E_r is the value of the rotational energy for the upper state and is obtained from the rotational analysis of the band spectrum; T is the effective rotational absolute temperature.

A plot is made of ($\log I - \log P\nu^4$) against E_r, and if a straight line is obtained its slope is $-1/2.303\,kT$, from which T, the effective rotational temperature, may be evaluated. This was done for the radical OH in hydrocarbon flames at atmospheric pressure which produces well-spaced lines in each band, and the effective rotational temperature in the flames studied was about 5700°C. The effective rotational temperature of CH was also evaluated from the rotational structure of one of its bands, and this was found to have a rotational temperature similar to that of the expected flame temperature.

By a similar type of study of the intensities of v' or v'' progressions an effective vibrational temperature may be determined; the value of the effective rotational temperature only coincides with this when there is thermodynamic equilibrium. This is also true of the effective translational temperature which is determined by measuring the Doppler broadening of spectrum lines (see p. 338). This broadening results from the random thermal motion of the hot emitter. When the molecule is moving towards the spectrograph, the spectrum line is displaced very slightly towards the violet, whereas when moving away the displacement is towards the red. Thus, when the process is considered for a number of molecules moving in various directions, the resultant effect is that the line is broadened. The line breadth due to the Doppler broadening varies as the square root of the temperature.

For a detailed account of combustion, the various types of flames, their theory and electronic spectra, and their infra-red emission and flame temperature books by Gaydon[3,6] should be consulted; there is also a review[4] article on the visible and ultra-violet emission spectra of flames by the same author and a most detailed book by Gaydon and Wolfhard.[5]

References

1. Mahanti, P. C. *Z. Phys.* **68** (1931), 114.
2. Connelly, F. C. *Proc. Phys. Soc.* **45** (1933), 791.
3. Gaydon, A. G. *Spectroscopy and Combustion Theory*. Chapman and Hall (London, 1942).
4. Gaydon, A. G. *Quart. Rev.* **4** (1950), 1.
5. Gaydon, A. G. and Wolfhard, H. G. *Flames, Their Structure, Radiation and Temperature*. Chapman and Hall (London, 1960), 2nd edn.
6. Gaydon, A. G. *The Spectroscopy of Flames*. Chapman and Hall (London, 1957).

8

Fluorescence and phosphorescence spectroscopy

Fluorescence

Introduction

THE majority of molecules in gases and solutions, when they absorb electromagnetic radiation and become electronically excited, do not re-radiate the absorbed quantum by a 'resonance' emission but suffer collision and lose the excess electronic energy. However, some substances, e.g. certain dyes in aqueous solution, can be electronically excited, then by collision lose their excess vibrational energy. They still retain the additional electronic energy which the water molecules are unable to take away and after a period of about 10^{-8} sec emit characteristic radiation and revert to the ground electronic state. That is they produce an emission spectrum from the lowest vibrational levels in the excited electronic state to certain of the vibrational levels in the ground state. This type of emission which takes place after an interval of about 10^{-8} sec is known as *fluorescence*. A fluorescence spectrum is characterised by lying at longer wavelengths than the corresponding absorption spectrum, and, within the limits of the absorption frequency range of the latter, is independent of the wavelength chosen for excitation. In addition, from an analysis of the frequencies obtained in a fluorescence spectrum the vibrational frequencies which emerge are those for the ground electronic state. At ordinary temperatures fluorescence is generally produced only by molecules whose electronically excited state is resistant to deactivation by collision. Two typical examples are: (i) the ions of transitional elements or of rare earths where the electron to be excited is a *d* or *f* electron and not an outer shell electron; (ii) conjugated systems of π electrons where the excitation of an electron to a higher orbit has only a small effect on the total electronic structure of the molecule, as for example in dyes.

The process of fluorescence described may be represented in diagrammatic form as in Fig. 8.1. The diagram is very much oversimplified as only $v' \leftarrow 0$

transitions have been inserted for absorption, and although the majority of molecules will be in the $v'' = 0$ level before absorption, some other transitions will take place from higher v'' vibrational states, and also all rotational energy considerations have been neglected. In addition, only one

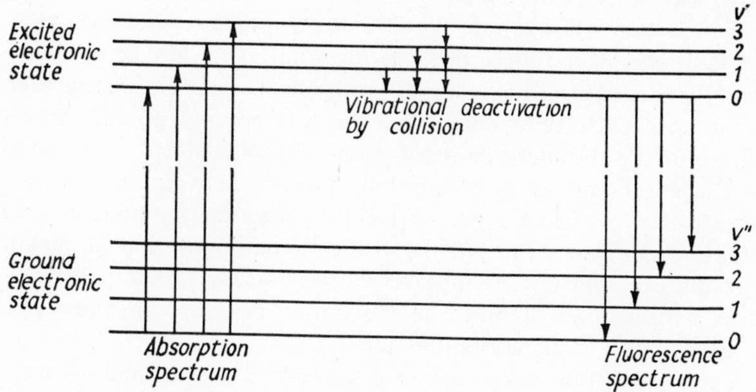

FIG. 8.1 Transitions involved in the process of fluorescence

vibrational frequency has been taken into account in the ground electronic state. This is also the case for the excited electronic state. Nevertheless, the diagram serves to illustrate:

(i) That the excess vibrational energy above the $v' = 0$ levels is lost by collision of the molecules before fluorescence occurs and that the vibrational energy is lost in a step-wise manner.

(ii) That the difference between the consecutive frequency values in the $(0,v'')$ progression of bands should on analysis yield the vibrational frequency of the molecule in the ground state.

Experimental

A fluorescence spectrum may readily be studied by means of a Unicam spectrophotometer (see p. 235). By rotation of a calibrated dial the position of a quartz prism is altered and consequently the wavelength. For each setting of the dial the instrument supplies a source of monochromatic light. The sample is mounted at the exit slit, suitable monochromatic light is selected to excite the molecules, and the fluorescence spectrum is detected photometrically. When, however, a vibrational analysis of the fluorescence spectrum is required a photographic recording of the spectrum is generally preferred to the photometric one. The photographic recording may be achieved by means of a spectrograph as, for example, that of the medium quartz type (see p. 32).

Fluorescence may sometimes be obtained at extremely low concentrations. This, however, is sometimes a disadvantage as a small amount of unknown impurity may lead to an erroneous interpretation of the observed spectrum.

Influence of phase on fluorescence

Numerous examples of the fluorescence of aromatic vapours are known. Such aromatic compounds are often also fluorescent in liquid solution and even in the solid state. The phenomenon of fluorescence requires that the excited electronic state should not be deactivated for about 10^{-8} sec or longer.† If the collision rate between the fluorescent molecule and other such molecules is too high, then the quantum yield may be diminished by loss of the excited electronic energy in collision. The collision rate is decreased in more viscous solvents and at low temperatures; in general, experiment confirms that substances fluoresce more intensely under such conditions. There is no all-embracing relationship, though, between the viscosity and fluorescence. For example, pure crystalline anthracene has an intense fluorescence, and this persists to just below the melting point, but on melting the fluorescence completely disappears. However, some other polycyclic condensed hydrocarbons fluoresce in the vapour state and in dilute solutions but hardly at all in the crystalline state.

A great deal of the fluorescence work is carried out in liquid solutions, and alcohol, hexane, and water are frequently employed as the solvents. In general, for unionised compounds, if the compound fluoresces in all the three phases, the bands are very slightly displaced to longer wavelengths on passing from the gaseous to the liquid to the solid state.

Approximate mirror image symmetry of absorption and fluorescence bands

There is often the appearance of almost mirror image symmetry between the absorption and fluorescence spectrum of a condensed ring hydrocarbon and also some of its derivatives. This is illustrated for eosin in Fig. 8.2, where the symmetry with respect to the wavelength, which lies half-way between the two peaks, is most striking. For the absorption and fluorescence spectrum of the triphenyl methyl radical given in Fig. 8.3, although there is a very approximate overall appearance of mirror image symmetry, the detailed structure differs appreciably. Such deviation in structural appearance may be explained by consideration of the much simpler case of a diatomic molecule. In Fig. 8.4 the fluorescence process is represented for a diatomic molecule. In this figure the most intense band in fluorescence would be expected to be the $0 \rightarrow 1$ whereas in absorption it would be the $1 \leftarrow 0$. The more the spacing of the vibrational levels differs in the upper and lower electronic states the greater the deviation in the mirror image symmetry between the fluorescence and the absorption spectrum. The symmetry of the fluorescence and absorption spectrum is fixed by the x_e', ω_e', and x_e'', and ω_e'' values which determine the shape of the potential energy curves (see p. 96) and the spacing of the vibrational levels. An additional factor is how one potential energy curve lies with respect to the other, that is how their equilibrium internuclear distances

† This value of 10^{-8} sec is quite an arbitrary value and should not on its own be employed as a criterion for fluorescence. In fact, some fluorescence processes involve appreciably longer lifetimes and give rise to the phenomenon known as *slow fluorescence* (see p. 289).

differ. When $x'_e \sim x''_e$ and $\omega'_e \sim \omega''_e$ in both the electronic states concerned in the fluorescence, then similarly shaped potential energy curves are obtained. If these curves lie directly one above the other, an intense (0,0) band should be observed in both fluorescence and absorption, and mirror image symmetry

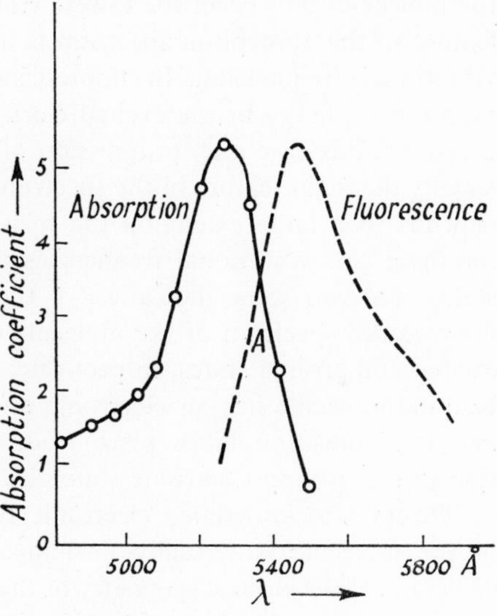

FIG. 8.2 Absorption and fluorescence of eosin where the approximate mirror image symmetry of the curves about A is apparent. The ordinate plot is that of the absorption coefficient, α, where α may be defined by $\alpha = \frac{1}{l}\log_e\frac{I_0}{I}$. (*After Nichols and Merritt*[1]. *Courtesy of 'The Physical Review'*)

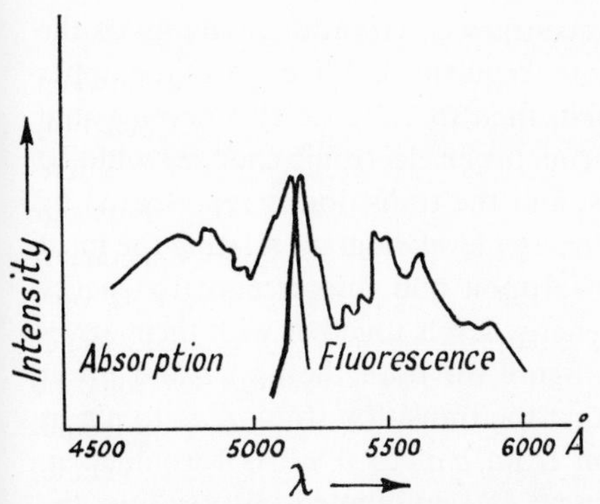

FIG. 8.3 Absorption and fluorescence of the triphenyl methyl radical in an ether, isopentane, and ethanol mixture at liquid nitrogen temperature. (*After Lewis, Lipkin and Magel*[2]. *Courtesy of 'The Journal of the American Chemical Society'*)

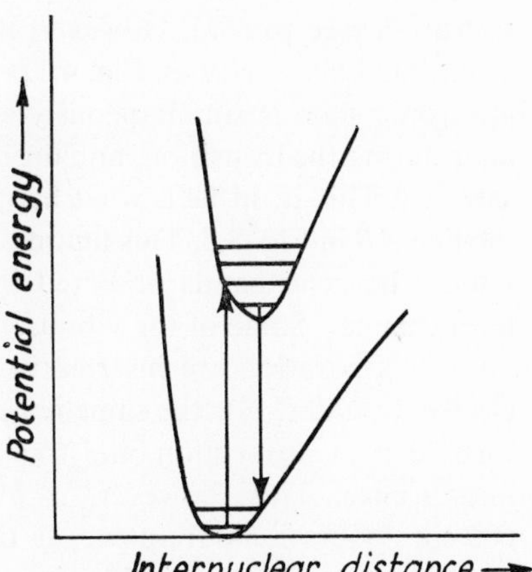

FIG. 8.4 Representation of the transitions involved in the fluorescence spectrum of a diatomic molecule

would result. In the case of fluorescence involving the two potential curves in Fig. 8.4, since the shape and relative abscissa positions of the curves differ considerably the mirror image symmetry between the absorption and fluorescence spectrum would be low.

As polyatomic molecules have a number of vibrational frequencies it might be anticipated that it would be much more difficult to account for a mirror image symmetry between the absorption and fluorescence spectrum. However, fortunately the main features of such a spectrum generally result from the excitation of one of these vibrational frequencies. If the absorption and fluorescence work is carried out at very low temperatures, then nearly all the molecules will be in the lowest vibrational level(s), and the dominating feature in the absorption spectrum is usually a v' progression of one of the vibrational frequencies. In fluorescence the molecules lose their excess vibrational energy in the excited electronic state by collision and then fluoresce. In this case a v'' progression of one of the vibrational frequencies is usually the main feature in the spectrum. Hence, the mirror image symmetry depends to a large extent on the relative spacing of the vibrational levels for these two vibrational frequencies in the ground and excited electronic states. To gain some indication of the dependence of the absorption and fluorescence spectrum of the molecule on the vibrational frequencies in the excited and ground states, respectively, benzene will now be considered. The benzene molecule has an electronic absorption band in the 2500 Å region, and this transition takes place from a hexagonally symmetrical benzene ring in the ground electronic state characterised by a vibrational frequency of 992 cm^{-1} to an excited electronic state, where the hexagonal symmetry of the molecule is virtually unchanged and the vibrational frequency is 923 cm^{-1}. If the electric symmetry of the molecule were completely unaltered, then this change would be forbidden by the selection rule for an electronic transition (see p. 365). However, if a quantum of vibrational energy of the vibrational mode ν_{18} (see Fig. 4.12) whose frequency is 520 cm^{-1} in the upper electronic state is simultaneously excited, then the electric symmetry would alter during the transition, and the criterion for an electronic change would be satisfied. This is, in fact, what happens, and the transition is represented by the line *AB* in Fig. 8.5. This figure is an energy level diagram relating the most intense benzene bands observed in absorption and fluorescence to energy level changes. Some of the vibrational energy levels together with their wave-number separation are inserted in the figure for both the upper and lower electronic states. For the same reason that the transition from $a''a''$ to $a'a'$ is forbidden in absorption, the transition from $a'a'$ to $a''a''$ is forbidden in fluorescence. This, however, is overcome by simultaneously exciting the 606 cm^{-1} vibrational frequency in the lower electronic state. The fluorescence spectrum is characterised by a progression where the spacing between consecutive members is 992 cm^{-1}. Thus, although the spectrogram at the head of the figure has a superficial appearance of symmetry, on closer scrutiny since the spacing of the absorption and emission bands differs there cannot be an exact mirror image relationship. Only the main features of the absorption and emission spectrum have been represented and, in fact, additional bands are observed both in absorption and fluorescence. One of the factors neglected is that a small proportion of the molecules may be in the $b''b''$ level at ordinary temperatures and that absorption may take place from this level. Another is that other vibrational frequencies may be excited.

As a result of the electronic absorption transition of the benzene molecule, the benzene ring has expanded (see p. 224) in the excited electronic state.[4] Although the absorption spectrum of the molecule is mainly concerned with the 923 cm^{-1} vibrational frequency in the upper electronic state, this vibration is sufficiently coupled with the other fundamental vibrational modes of the

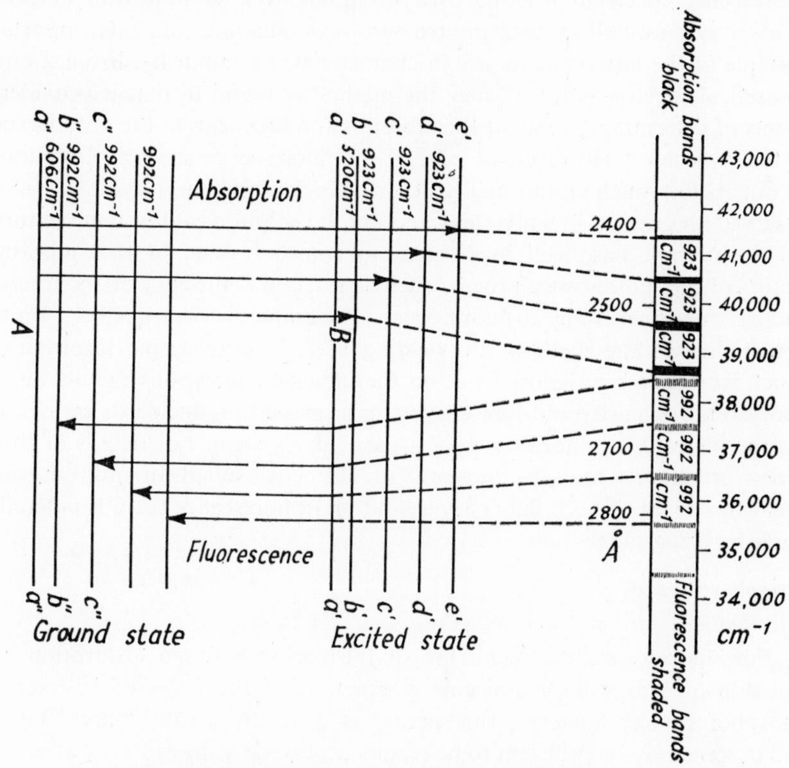

FIG. 8.5 An energy level diagram relating the most intense benzene bands observed in electronic absorption and fluorescence to energy level changes. (*Courtesy of Dr. E. J. Bowen*[3] *F.R.S. and the Chemical Society*)

molecule to make the vibrational motion of the nuclei a very complex pattern indeed. In fact, the nuclei may be regarded as undergoing Lissajous movement in a polydimensional surface.

Applications of fluorescence data

Two of the most important applications of fluorescence spectra have been to qualitative analysis and structural determination. Both of these are dependent on relating the electronic emission spectrum to a particular atom, group, or structural unit (e.g. an unsaturated ring in the molecule) and for this approach it is usually desirable to know the fluorescence spectra of similar systems. In general, the determination of the fluorescence spectrum of a compound does not solve a structural problem but rather assists in its solution in conjunction with other information.

A considerable amount of fluorescence work has been carried out on aromatic hydrocarbons and heterocyclic compounds, that is on substances which generally yield a highly characteristic fluorescence spectrum. Examples of the heterocyclic compounds studied are those of the pyrimidines and purines. Extensive investigations have been made on dye solutions. The fluorescence spectrum may be used for qualitative identification purposes or even as an auxiliary tool in structural examination, and one important example of the latter was its use in characterising vitamin B_2. From a more theoretical spectral point of view the method is useful in that it provides a means of determining some of the vibrational frequencies in the ground state of the molecule.† However, in general the fluorescence spectra of solutions do not exhibit much vibrational structure. Much more vibrational structure is observed for gases at low pressures and in solid solutions at low temperatures.

No attempt has been made here to consider some of the important factors of the fluorescence process such as quantum efficiency or the internal and external quenching of fluorescence. The emphasis here has been on the potentiality of the method for yielding useful spectroscopic information. Much work has been carried out on the influence of various factors on the fluorescence intensity and how they are concerned in reducing or extinguishing the intensity of fluorescence of a particular system. For details of this a review article or a book by Bowen[3,5] should be consulted. In addition, for a wider treatment of both fluorescence and phosphorescence there is a detailed book by Pringsheim.[6]

Phosphorescence

Introduction

For fluorescence the mean life of the period between absorption and emission of energy by a molecule is generally of the order of 10^{-8} sec. In phosphorescence, however, this period is generally greater than 10^{-4} sec, and in some cases is sufficient to be readily observed by the eye as an afterglow when the source of excitation is cut off. In fact, from the examination of a large number of organic compounds the lifetimes ranged from 10^{-4} to about 10 sec; the longer lifetimes of the order of seconds are exhibited only by the aromatic compounds. This property of afterglow was termed *phosphorescence*.

Systems which exhibit phosphorescence may be divided into two groups:

(i) Inorganic phosphors, where the active centres of phosphorescence cannot be identified with a single molecular species. Mineral phosphors are typical of this category. The phosphorescence of mineral phosphors after irradiation has been attributed to the ejection of an electron from some position in the phosphor. After a period of time the electron returns to this position and this results in the emission of light. Another example of inorganic phosphors is ZnS which has been heated above 800°C. Pure zinc sulphide exhibits practically no phosphorescence but when heated to above 800°C

† The fluorescence method has this feature in common with the infra-red and Raman methods. However, the fluorescence spectra of gases and vapours (e.g. toluene) can yield vibrational frequencies of the excited electronic state as well.

some of the sulphur is removed, and zinc atoms remain present in the zinc sulphide structure, and phosphorescence is now observed after the sample has been irradiated with ultra-violet light. For this phosphorescence both the zinc and the zinc sulphide are essential, and the property is related to a phosphorescent unit and not to individual atoms or molecules. This type of phosphorescence will not be considered further here, and for details Pringsheim[6] should be consulted.

(ii) The other kind of phosphorescence is that which may be ascribed to a certain type of molecule. Unsaturated organic molecules furnish typical examples of this type and the phenomenon of phosphorescence is a property of the molecule itself and may be explained in terms of its electronic energy states.

In general, most solid substances at room temperature do not exhibit phosphorescence. The most favourable conditions for the observation of the phosphorescence of organic molecules at room temperature after irradiation occur when the observed molecule is dissolved in a solid solvent such as boric acid glass. At low temperatures a solvent mixture of ether, *iso*pentane, and ethyl alcohol is generally preferred; this mixture may be frozen to give a transparent glass (see p. 252). In liquid solution phosphorescence is favoured by very viscous solvents, and the intensity of the phosphorescence is very much dependent on the viscosity of the solvent. The positions of the bands, however, in the emission (phosphorescence) spectrum observed are not appreciably dependent on the solvent employed, and the medium plays no major part in the excitation or emission processes. The role of the solvent is to prevent loss of electronic energy by deactivation on collision. At low concentration and at temperatures of the order of liquid nitrogen it would seem that a large number of substances phosphoresce.

The distinction between fluorescence and phosphorescence is only arbitrarily made on a time basis; in fact, the actual mechanism of the two processes differs. In fluorescence generally only two electronic states are involved, whereas with the phosphorescence of molecules three electronic states take part.†

One characteristic difference between fluorescence and phosphorescence is that the phosphorescence spectrum always lies at appreciably longer wavelengths. The longer period between absorption and emission of light in phosphorescence is related to the molecules being in an intermediate (metastable) state where the emission of light to the ground state is forbidden by a selection rule. This metastable state has been identified as being a triplet state. In fact, fluorescence spectra involve the emission of electromagnetic radiation in a transition between two electronic states of the same multiplicity, whereas phosphorescence involves an electronic transition between states

† More than two electronic states may be involved in fluorescence for the case where the initial excitation is to that of a higher singlet state (S_2). The electronic transition can be $S_2 \leftarrow S_0$ in absorption (where S_0 is the ground state) followed by the emission transitions $S_2 \rightarrow S_1$ and $S_1 \rightarrow S_0$, where S_1 is the first excited singlet state.

of different multiplicity (i.e. a triplet→singlet transition). For example, the nitrogen afterglow due to the first positive bands of N_2, which involve the $B^3\Pi_g \rightarrow A^3\Sigma_u^+$ transition, would be classed as fluorescence and not phosphorescence because it is a triplet→triplet transition.

However, before the mechanism of phosphorescence is dealt with we shall consider the meaning of the term 'triplet state', how such a state may come about, and the factors which determine the electronic transitions involved in the phosphorescence process.

More detailed consideration has been allotted to the topic of phosphorescence than fluorescence, for phosphorescence gives more insight into the energy states of polyatomic molecules and the transitions which may take place between them. In addition, it seems that there are signs that the long-lived electronic excited states involved in phosphorescence may play an important part in determining the reactivity of many organic molecules.

It must not, however, be inferred that phosphorescence has found wider application than fluorescence. In fact, under normal conditions a large number of aromatic molecules fluoresce whereas only a much smaller number phosphoresce. At low concentrations and low temperatures (e.g. 90°K), however, a large number of aromatic substances phosphoresce. Under these conditions nearly all substances would be expected to fluoresce. In general, fluorescence is applicable to a far wider range of compounds, and, in addition, from an experimental viewpoint fluorescence is more readily carried out.

Phosphorescence apparatus

The apparatus employed by Lewis and Kasha[7] for the study of phosphorescence spectra is represented in Fig. 8.6. *A* is a high-pressure mercury arc

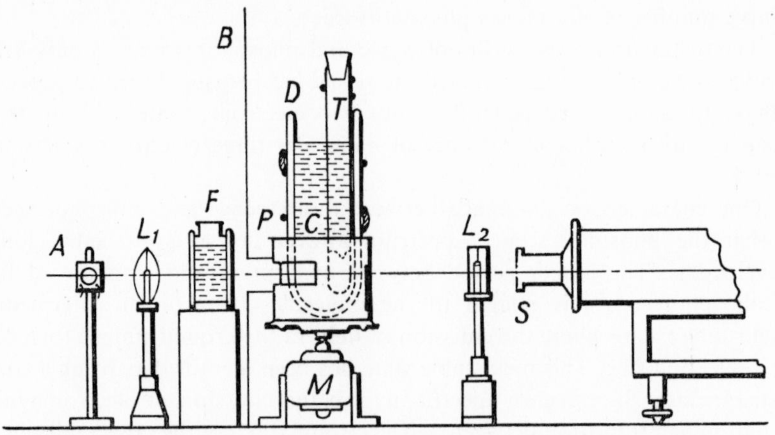

FIG. 8.6 The apparatus employed in the study of phosphorescence spectra. (*After Lewis and Kasha*[7]. *Courtesy of 'The Journal of the American Chemical Society'*)

enclosed in a quartz jacket. L_1 is a quartz condensing lens. *F* is a filter of aqueous copper sulphate used only when the material studied is subject to rapid photo-oxidation. *B* is a light baffle of blackened cardboard. *P* is a rotating can mounted on a variable speed motor (M) with a maximum of 1800 r.p.m. A section is cut out about a third of the way around the can so that the sample is alternately illuminated and viewed by the spectrograph. The Dewar, D, is supported so that it does not touch the can. The Dewar holds the liquid air, C, and the quartz sample tube, T, containing the solution to be studied. T is placed as far to the right of the Dewar as possible, partly to increase the apparent intensity and partly to diminish the absorption of the phosphorescence by the liquid air. L_2 is another lens which focuses the phosphorescence upon the slit of the spectrograph, S. The spectra were photographed by means of a Hilger medium quartz spectrograph.

The solvent Lewis and Kasha employed in the study of the phosphorescence of a large number of organic compounds was a mixture of five parts by volume of ether, five of *iso*pentane and two of ethanol. This solvent when frozen to the temperature of liquid nitrogen forms a rigid transparent glass. Thus, the phosphorescent molecule is trapped in this rigid structure, and deactivation by collision is minimised.

Triplet state in atoms and molecules

The great majority of atoms and molecules have ground states where all the spins of the electrons are paired and where the resultant spin (S) is zero. Such atoms and molecules have singlet ground states and are diamagnetic. When one of the paired electrons in the atom or molecule is excited, the resultant energy state may have both these electrons with either parallel or anti-parallel spins. When the electron spins are anti-parallel the energy state is an excited singlet but when parallel a paramagnetic triplet state results. In the triplet state the resultant electron spin quantum number S is equal to $\frac{1}{2}+\frac{1}{2}$, and the corresponding angular momentum due to these spinning electrons is:

$$\sqrt{2}\frac{h}{2\pi}$$

The resultant angular momentum of an atom is obtained by vectorially combining the total orbital angular momentum, which is governed by the quantum number L, with the total electron spin angular momentum governed by S as follows:

$$J = (L+S), (L+S-1) \ldots |L-S|$$

where the resultant angular momentum is thus $\sqrt{J(J+1)}h/2\pi$. There are $(2S+1)$ values of J, and since $S = 1$ for a triplet state it follows that the number of electronic energy states is three, since each different value of J may be identified with a different electronic state. Hence, the use of the term 'triplet' when the electron spins are parallel.

These three electronic states differ only very slightly in their energy. This may be verified in the case of an atom by viewing the energy level diagram for the calcium atom for the case of $L = 1$, where the $^3P_2$, $^3P_1$ and $^3P_0$ state have almost the same energy.[8] This is even more true of the $^3D_3$,

$^3D_2$, and $^3D_1$ terms where $L = 2$, and in the case where $L = 3$, the $^3F_4$, $^3F_3$, and $^3F_2$ energy levels are virtually identical. In the phosphorescence of molecules, it is general practice to treat the three close-lying electronic states of the triplet as though they were one electronic energy level.

In atoms and diatomic molecules, where the fine structure may normally be fairly readily resolved, the multiplicity of the energy levels involved in the electronic transitions may be determined from an analysis of the spectrum. However, in the case of polyatomic molecules the evaluation of the multiplicity from a direct analysis of the spectrum is either most involved or at present impossible. Even worse is the case of polyatomic molecules in solution where the fine structure cannot be observed. Since nearly all the molecules which phosphoresce fall into the category of having broad unresolved bands, the multiplicity of the states involved in such cases cannot be directly determined from the spectrum itself. To determine the multiplicity of the upper electronic state in these phosphorescent molecules more general considerations have to be applied, and these will be considered presently.

The question as to whether an electron when excited will result in the molecule being in a singlet or a triplet state is not generally easily determined. For light atoms and molecules containing them the spin angular momentum of the paired electrons may be regarded as quantised independently, and for these the spin angular momentum value is not permitted to change during an electronic transition. Hence, if the ground state is a singlet, then the excited state should also be a singlet, and the selection rule is that the change in the resultant electron spin (ΔS) between the two levels is zero. When, however, the molecule contains heavier atoms, these introduce an inhomogeneous magnetic field within the molecule, and the simple L,S coupling is no longer followed.† Only the total angular momentum $\sqrt{j(j+1)}\boldsymbol{h}/2\pi$ for each of the individual electrons is characteristic, and only this obeys the quantum rules. In this case the electron coupling is of the j, j type. Easy interconversion of the electron spin and orbital angular momentum occurs in j,j coupling, and this results in the spin energy no longer being conserved. Under such conditions the selection rule $\Delta S = 0$ no longer readily holds, and transitions may take place between singlet and triplet states. However, even then, such transitions are of lower probability than singlet-singlet transitions, and the observed absorption spectrum is much less intense and usually requires longer exposures or special techniques.

Any molecule which possesses a multiple bond may have a low-lying triplet state, and when the molecule is composed of light atoms such as carbon, hydrogen, and oxygen the triplet-singlet transitions will result in only a very weak absorption spectrum.

† A similar effect is observed in an atomic spectrum when the atom is present in an inhomogeneous magnetic field, and the selection rule $\Delta S = 0$ is disobeyed. In addition, for heavy atoms such as mercury the spin and orbit motions interaction becomes so great that electronic transitions between singlet and triplet states may readily occur. The 2537 Å line of mercury in absorption may be identified with the $6^3P_1 \rightarrow 6^1S_0$ transition.

For molecules containing heavy atoms such as bromine or iodine the triplet-singlet transitions usually become more intense. In fact, the spin-orbit interaction energy increases very rapidly with atomic number as the electron coupling gradually changes from L,S to j,j. This change in coupling by the heavy atoms is reflected in the value of the lifetime of the triplet state where, as the atomic number of the atom increases, the lifetime of the triplet state decreases, that is there is more ready conversion from the triplet to the singlet state. For example, it may be observed in Table 8.1 for the α- and β-mono-substituted isomers of naphthalene that on replacing the atom X by the next heavier one the lifetime of the triplet state is markedly decreased.

TABLE 8.1

Effect of heavy-atom substituents on phosphorescence lifetimes of monosubstituents of α- and β-naphthalene compounds in triplet-singlet emission (after McClure[9])

Substituent	Lifetime in triplet state (in sec)	
	of α-isomer	of β-isomer
F	1.5	—
Cl	0.30	0.47
Br	0.018	0.021
I	0.0025	0.0025

The data in Table 8.1 were taken from a paper by McClure.[9] He employed data from atoms to make estimates of the spin-orbit coupling in molecules, and his deductions were based on the assumption that the major contribution came from the heaviest atom, and from this he made estimates of the lifetime of the triplet state. He showed that for a series of molecules with different halogen substituents the relative lifetimes of their triplet states were approximately in the ratio to be anticipated from the spin-orbit coupling data for the heavy atom.

The heavy atom effect on the lifetime of the metastable state is considered to be strong evidence for the existence of the triplet state and indicates that spin-dependent forces govern the electronic transitions involved in the phosphorescence of organic molecules.

Mechanism of phosphorescence

Lewis and Kasha[7] in a paper published in 1944 were the first to clearly define the mechanism of phosphorescence. From a study of a large number of inorganic and organic molecules they came to a definite conclusion as to the nature of the electronic states involved in the process of phosphorescence. The type of process they visualised was as follows. Initially the molecule is in the ground state (S_0) (see Fig. 8.7), where all its electrons have their spins paired, and is then excited to another singlet state S_1 by the absorption of electromagnetic radiation. The molecule may then either lose its energy by radiation to the original state, that is undergo the transition $S_1 \rightarrow S_0$, as for example in the fluorescence process, or lose its energy by collision with other molecules, or undergo a radiationless transition. The radiationless transition may be explained in terms of Fig. 8.8 where the molecule excited to the state S_1 may then transfer to another potential curve T_1 which intersects S_1.

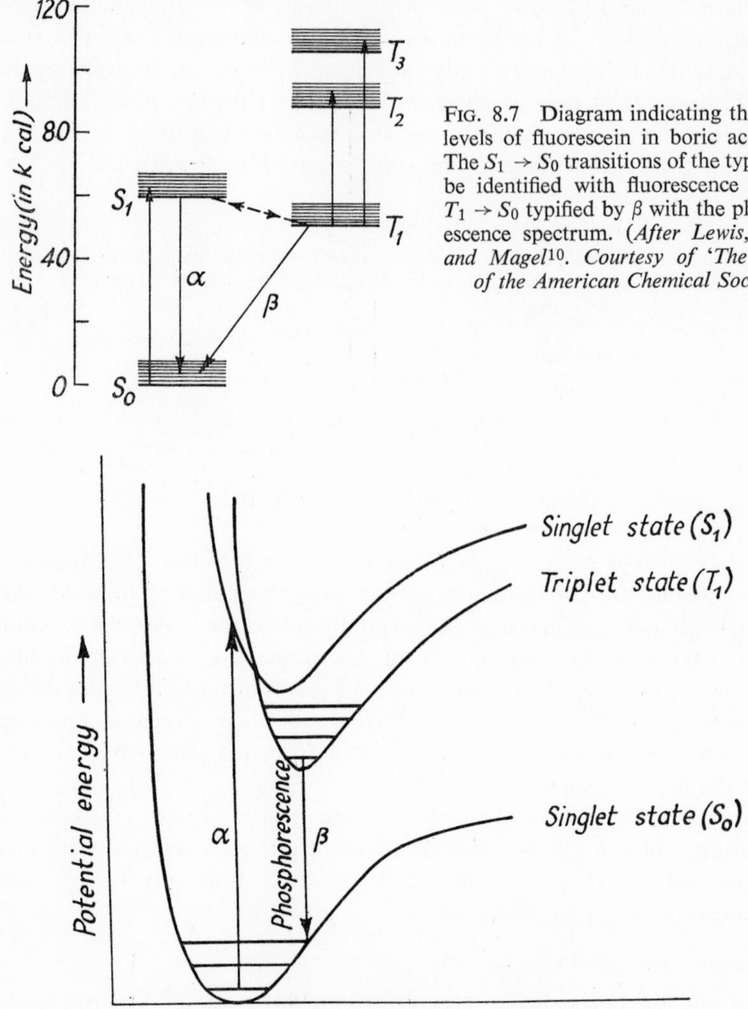

FIG. 8.7 Diagram indicating the energy levels of fluorescein in boric acid glass. The $S_1 \rightarrow S_0$ transitions of the type α may be identified with fluorescence and the $T_1 \rightarrow S_0$ typified by β with the phosphorescence spectrum. (*After Lewis, Lipkin, and Magel*[10]. *Courtesy of 'The Journal of the American Chemical Society'*)

FIG. 8.8 Type of transitions involved for a diatomic molecule if it exhibited phosphorescence. β is representative of phosphorescence and α of absorption. The point of intersection of the S_1 and T_1 potential energy curves is where the radiationless transition between S_1 and T_1 states occurs

Jablonski was the first to indicate that at least three electronic states of the molecule were involved in the process of phosphorescence. The energy state T_1 he identified as being a metastable state or phosphorescent state which always lies below the excited singlet state involved in the fluorescence process.

The great contribution of Lewis and Kasha[7] was to identify this metastable state as a triplet state.† The final step in the phosphorescence process they then identified as $T_1 \rightarrow S_0$. In both the fluorescence and phosphorescence processes the emitting state of a given multiplicity is the lowest excited electronic state of that multiplicity.

When a molecule is in the metastable state T_1 it has two probable fates. It may either phosphoresce and undergo the transition $T_1 \rightarrow S_0$, or may revert to its ground state S_0 by a non-radiative dissipative process in which the energy is given up as thermal energy. (A further possibility is that it may be thermally excited from the state T_1 to the state S_1 with subsequent emission of its normal fluorescence spectrum. The complete process would in this case be $S_1 \leftarrow S_0$ followed by radiationless transfer to T_1, then thermal excitation back to S_1, and finally fluorescence from $S_1 \rightarrow S_0$. Since the molecule may spend an appreciable time in the T_1 state, the time interval after the initial excitation at which fluorescence may occur can also be appreciable, and this type of process is termed *slow fluorescence*.)

Lewis and Kasha observed that phosphorescence is favoured by low temperatures and a rigid medium, since under these conditions the non-radiative dissipation process is minimised. This is borne out by examining the phosphorescence spectrum of a strong phosphor starting from a low temperature such as that of liquid nitrogen and gradually increasing the temperature. As the temperature rises the phosphorescence gradually diminishes in intensity. The main function of the solvent is its rigidity in that it protects the molecules in the phosphorescent state from the process of thermal dissipation. In general, the more viscous the solvent medium the longer the lifetime of the phosphorescence state. However, the phosphorescence often exists until the solvent becomes a pourable liquid. In addition, examples are known of phosphorescence in liquid and even gaseous media (one example is gaseous diacetyl) where the phosphorescence state is the same as that in the rigid solvent.

Evidence for the triplet state and the electronic transitions involved in phosphorescence

The observation employed by Lewis and Kasha[7] to indicate the existence of the triplet state in the phosphorescence of organic molecules was that there appeared to be two electronic states concerned between which transitions were strongly forbidden. From considerations based on the change in conjugation in the triplet state compared with the ground state singlet they concluded that the phosphorescence state could definitely be identified as a triplet level. However, this identification was by no means generally accepted. Definite physical confirmation of this was obtained by Lewis and Calvin.[11] They used a magnetic microbalance the main details of which are as follows.

† It is to be anticipated from Hund's multiplicity rule (see p. 90, Vol. I) that if both the singlet and triplet configurations are permitted with one set of orbitals, the triplet state will have a lower energy value than the corresponding singlet.

A horizontal bar was suspended by means of two extremely fine glass threads, and the phosphorescent sample was suspended in the capillary tip of the horizontal bar. A narrow strip of solid glass phosphor sample, produced by an extrusion process, was employed. The sample was then centred in a magnetic field, and the position of the capillary tip was observed by means of a microscope. Light from a high-pressure mercury arc was directed from below on to one half of the sample, and in the absence of a magnetic field no deflection was detected. On the application of the magnetic field, if unpaired electrons exist in the molecules, the illuminated half of the sample should be pulled into the field and the deflection observed by means of the microscope. Such a deflection was measured when the sample was fluorescein dissolved in a boric acid glass. Thus, the phosphorescent molecules are diamagnetic in the ground state and paramagnetic when excited. The fluorescein is present in the glass as the cation form

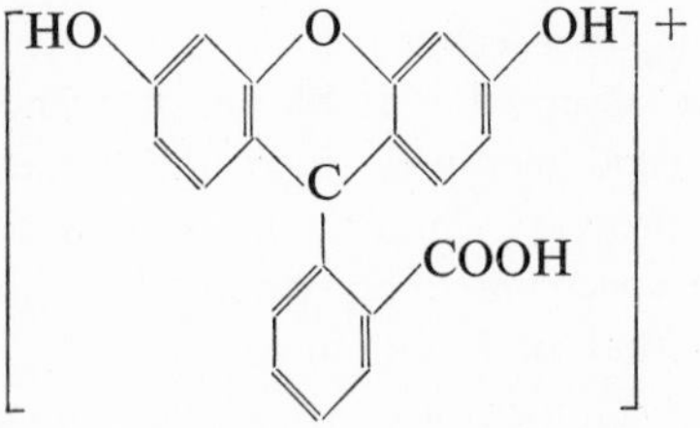

and exhibits an intense yellow phosphorescence with a half-life of the order of 2 sec. The deflection of the horizontal tip was proportional to the intensity of the blue light irradiated at the sample. From the work of Lewis and Calvin[11] and later of Lewis *et al.*[12] it was shown that there are two unpaired electrons per excited molecule when fluorescein is in the metastable electronic state. Thus, this state was definitely a triplet. In addition, it was estimated that as many as 85 per cent of the molecules were in the excited triplet state. Furthermore, an estimate of the molar paramagnetic susceptibility was made, and this was of the order to be anticipated if 88 per cent of the molecules were in the triplet state. The comparison of the molar susceptibility value was made with the oxygen molecule in its ground state, which is known from the spectroscopic data to be definitely a triplet state.

Further support for the existence of the triplet state in organic molecules was obtained from the appearance of additional absorption bands exhibited by the fluorescein in boric acid glass at low temperatures when the sample was exposed to a very high intensity mercury source. The absorption spectrum of fluorescein in boric acid glass is given in Fig. 8.9. *ABC* is the normal absorption spectrum of the sample and is identified with $S_1 \leftarrow S_0$ absorption. *DEF* represents the additional absorption at about 5050 and 6600 Å which results when the absorption spectrum is taken while the sample is being irradiated with very intense light. The mechanism which could account for the additional transitions was: (i) $S_1 \leftarrow S_0$ absorption, then radiationless transfer to the triplet state T_1. (ii) Because of the high intensity of the incident light the triplet state T_1 became sufficiently populated for absorption transitions to be detectable between T_1 and the higher triplet states T_2 and T_3.† Thus, the two additional absorption transitions could be accounted for by $T_2 \leftarrow T_1$ and $T_3 \leftarrow T_1$ transitions. These triplet states are represented in Fig. 8.7, and the transitions are indicated. Further details of $T_2 \leftarrow T_1$ transitions are given on p. 292.

It must be emphasised, though, that this interpretation of the absorption curve in terms of triplet-triplet transitions is not necessarily the only interpretation. In fact, it is extremely difficult to identify with certainty the presence of the triplet state. The first convincing proof of its existence was that of the

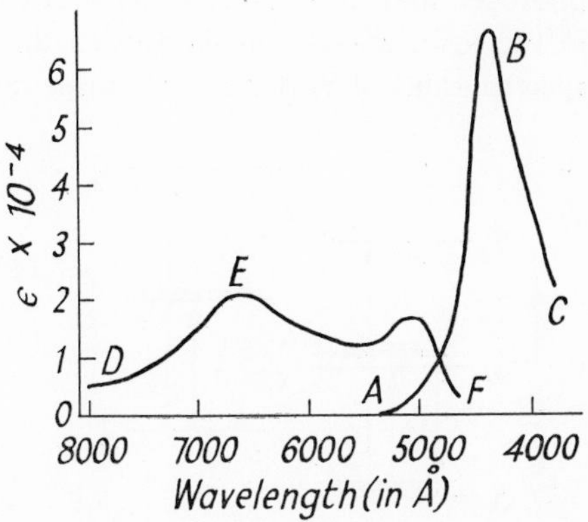

FIG. 8.9 Molal extinction-wavelength absorption curves in fluorescein in boric acid glass at − 95° C. Curve *ABC* may be interpreted as the normal $S_1 \leftarrow S_0$ transition but curve *DEF* is accounted for in terms of triplet-triplet absorption. (*After Lewis, Lipkin, and Magel*[10]. *Courtesy of 'The Journal of the American Chemical Society'*)

measured paramagnetism of fluorescein in boric acid glass. However, this is a very difficult experiment to perform, and until even recently this experiment had not been repeated or carried out on other molecules suspected of having triplet states.[13] To a large degree the evidence which we have so far quoted for the existence of the triplet state is indirect. The heavy atom effect mentioned on p. 286 is considered to be fairly strong support for the identification of the triplet state in phosphorescence processes.

The first conclusive proof that a (paramagnetic) triplet state was the state from which emission took place in the phenomenon of phosphorescence was given by Evans.[14] He showed experimentally that there was a parallel decay of phosphorescence and the magnetism of certain molecules in a rigid glass medium.

More recent proof that the upper electronic state is a triplet one in the phosphorescence process has been obtained by electron spin resonance studies.[15]

Further support for the existence of triplet states comes from the flash photolysis work of Porter *et al.* We shall consider this approach, since not only does it give further support to the now generally accepted view that the metastable state in phosphorescence is a triplet one, but it also gives insight

† In this case it was estimated that 75 per cent of the molecules occupied the phosphorescence state.

into the feasible electronic transitions in aromatic molecules. As was indicated on p. 244, the flash photolysis technique depends on producing a flash (the photolysis flash) of a very high intensity for a very short time (~35 μsec). This intense source of light may produce either fission of the molecule or excitation to higher electronic states. This flash is produced by the discharge of a condenser. In order to detect spectroscopically what has taken place a continuous source of most intense light is passed through the cell, and the absorption spectrum is recorded on, for example, a medium quartz spectrograph. This continuous source of light is produced in a discharge tube, triggered at a pre-set time interval after the photolysis flash, by means of a photocell and an electronic delay circuit. This continuum is also produced in the form of a flash—known as the *spectroscopic flash*. In Fig. 8.10 the spectrograms of Porter and Windsor taken for anthracene in hexane may be

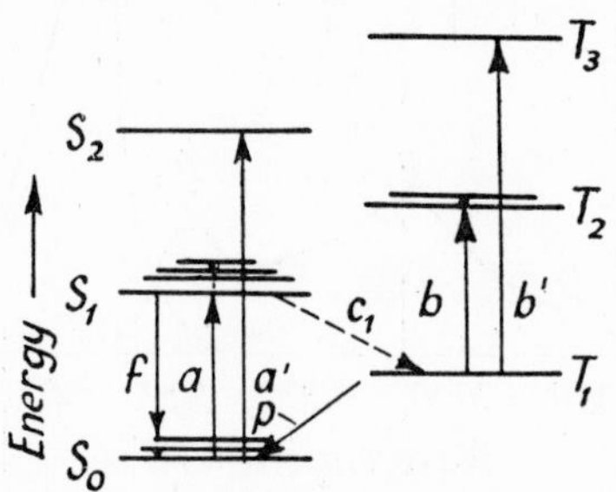

FIG. 8.11 Scheme of observed electronic transitions in a flash photolysis experiment on anthracene in hexane. (*After Porter and Windsor.*[16] *Courtesy of the Institute of Petroleum*)

observed. After the photolysis flash a number of absorption spectra were taken at the time intervals indicated in the figure. The bands observed may be accounted for in terms of singlet and triplet transitions, and this is done in Fig. 8.11. From Figs. 8.10 and 8.11 the following observations may be made.

(*a*) The part of the spectrum labelled 'first singlet' and represented by (*a*) in Fig. 8.11 consists of transitions from the vibrational levels in the S_0 electronic state to those in the S_1, i.e. $S_1 \leftarrow S_0$. The part designated 'second singlet' and represented by (a') in Fig. 8.11 is an $S_2 \leftarrow S_0$ transition, and in this case the transitions are from the vibrational levels in the S_0 electronic state to those of the electronic state S_2. These first and second singlet bands alone appear on the spectrogram in Fig. 8.10 labelled 'before' which is obtained when the spectroscopic flash only is employed. The spectrogram marked flourescence was obtained from the photolysis flash alone and is to be identified with molecules returning to the ground state from the S_1 state, that is the transition involved is $S_1 \rightarrow S_0$.

(*b*) The $T_1 \rightarrow S_0$ transition represented in Fig. 8.11 and labelled (*p*) is that of phosphorescence, and the dotted line (c_1) between levels S_1 and T_1 indicates a radiationless transfer.

(*c*) The 'first triplet' (*b*) involves the transition $T_2 \leftarrow T_1$.

(*d*) The 'second triplet' (b') is a $T_3 \leftarrow T_1$ transition.

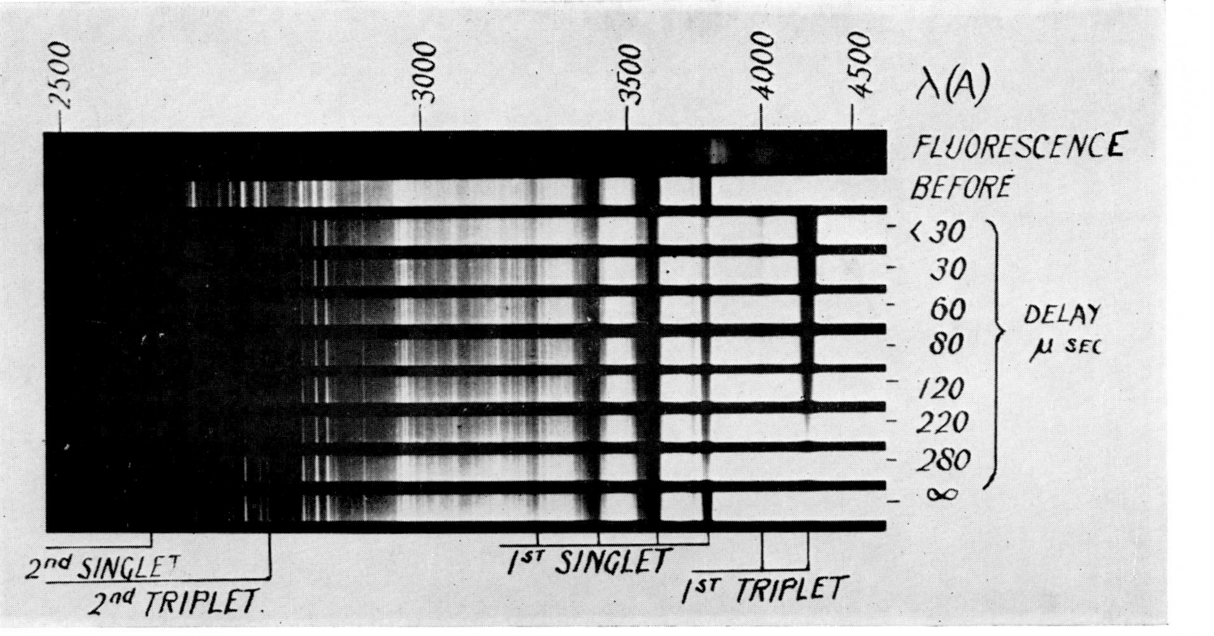

FIG. 8.10 Decay of the phosphorescent state of anthracene in hexane. (*After Porter and Windsor*[16]. *Courtesy of Professor G. Porter F.R.S. and the Institute of Petroleum*)

[*To face page* 292

In the electronic states S_0, S_1 and S_2 the electron spins are paired whereas in T_1, T_2, and T_3 two of the electron spins are parallel. Under the conditions of the experiment up to 20 per cent of the molecules in the excited singlet state (S_1) were considered to undergo a radiationless transition to the lowest triplet state T_1. Absorption then occurs from this T_1 level to the higher T_2 and T_3 levels. Molecules may be removed from the T_1 state by thermal deactivation, and as the time interval between the photolysis flash and the spectroscopic flash is increased, the intensity of the triplet absorption falls off; this may be readily observed for the $T_2 \leftarrow T_1$ transition in Fig. 8.10. It should be noted that in the exposure taken with <30 μsec delay the intensity of the first singlet is appreciably less while the first triplet intensity is its most intense. This clearly indicated that at <30 μsec the triplet state is sufficiently occupied to cause an appreciable depletion in the population of the ground state singlet level. After about 300 μsec, however, the first singlet bands are the most intense while the first triplet bands are too weak to be detected. Thus, the molecules must have been removed from the triplet state in this time interval by thermal deactivation.

In general, the flash photolysis studies give confidence in the identification of the transitions involved in the processes of fluorescence and phosphorescence. Not only this, though, for the method supplies a means of:

(i) Direct measurement of the lifetime of the triplet state. In the case of anthracene this was seen to be about 300 μsec.

(ii) Studying the variation of the triplet lifetime with different solvent viscosity.

(iii) Following the kinetics of decay of the phosphorescence state of a molecule.

In a flash photolysis study of the kinetics of decay of the phosphorescent state in anthracene, it was shown that the decay process is of the first order with respect to the concentration of the phosphorescent molecule. The main factor which affected the decay rate appeared to be the viscosity of the solvent used. The solvents employed range from ether, which has a viscosity of 0.233 centipoise (cP), to that of glycerol of viscosity 1490 cP. The results suggested an inverse proportionality between the rate constant and the square root of the viscosity. One effect of variation of the solvent is that the positions of the phosphorescence band maxima exhibit a small progressive shift to longer wavelengths, when passing from the gaseous phase through the solvents of increasing viscosity to that of the solid glass.

Vibrational information from phosphorescence studies

In view of the large number of vibrational frequencies in a polyatomic molecule and the fact that each vibrational mode has its own set of v values, even the identification of the vibrational frequencies in terms of their v' and v'' values from the absorption or emission (phosphorescence) spectrum would at first sight appear a formidable task. Fortunately, however, various factors may assist such analyses. One in particular is that the most intense transitions in an electronic spectrum are concerned with vibrational modes which are totally symmetrical. We have already considered the ultra-violet electronic absorption spectrum of benzene vapour on p. 223, and it was seen that the separation between a pair of the most intense maxima was 923 cm^{-1} (e.g. the separation between the A+B+C and A+B bands). This vibrational frequency may be identified with the totally symmetrical breathing frequency, that is the ν_2 vibrational mode (see Fig. 4.12) of the benzene ring in the excited electronic state. The corresponding breathing frequency in the ground state as determined by the Raman or fluorescence (see p. 280) spectrum of benzene is 992 cm^{-1}. In the intense benzene progression the main symmetry of the molecule is preserved in spite of the electronic transition.

Shull[17] has studied the phosphorescence $T_1 \rightarrow S_0$ transition of benzene in the rigid glass solution of 5 parts ether, 5 parts *iso*pentane, and 2 parts of ethanol at the temperature of liquid nitrogen. The microphotometer trace of this triplet-singlet emission spectrum is given in Fig. 8.12. Each band, for convenience, has been characterised by a number, and the observed wave-numbers of the corresponding bands are listed in column (2) of Table 8.2.

TABLE 8.2

Observed wave-numbers of the bands in the 3400 Å *triplet-singlet phosphorescence spectrum of benzene* (after Shull[17])

Number allotted to band	Observed wave-number (cm^{-1})
1	29 470
2	28 784
3	28 460
4	28 310
5	27 891
6	27 308
7	26 893
8	26 308
9	25 916
10	25 555
11	25 125
12	24 933
13	24 743
14	24 577
15	24 159
16	23 735
17	23 163
18	22 900
19	21 850

An inspection of the spectrum suggests that the bands 4, 6, 8, and bands 5, 7, 9, form two different series. Differences which may be fairly readily interpreted in terms of the known fundamental frequencies of benzene are the differences 1–4 of 1160 cm^{-1}, 1–5 of 1579 cm^{-1} frequencies already known from other sources. For reasons too complex to consider band 1 is shown to be the (0,0) band. Furthermore, since the emission was observed at the temperature of liquid nitrogen, the emission was considered to take place from the lowest vibrational level of the triplet state. It then follows that all the wave-number differences must be characteristic of the ground state. If now each wave-number in turn is subtracted from the wave-number of the (0,0) band, then an explanation of the resulting wave-numbers may be attempted in terms of the vibrational frequencies of the benzene molecule. This is done

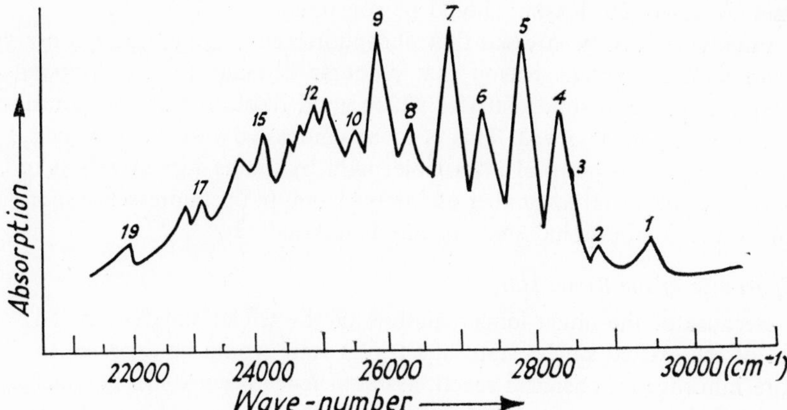

FIG. 8.12 Microphotometer trace of the phosphorescence $T_1 \rightarrow S_0$ transition of benzene in a rigid glass solution of 5 parts ether, 5 parts isopentane, and 2 parts ethanol at liquid nitrogen temperature. (*After Shull*[17]. *Courtesy of 'The Journal of Chemical Physics'*)

in Table 8.3 for the first eight bands. In column (4) of Table 8.3 the value of the wave-numbers of each band (x) is subtracted from the wave-number of the (0,0) band. The data are taken from Table 8.2. In column (3) of Table 8.3 are the corresponding calculated wave-numbers based on the fundamental benzene frequencies given by Herzfeld, Ingold, and Poole.[18] The calculation of these values from their data is carried out in column (2).

TABLE 8.3

Allotment of the vibrational frequencies to eight of the bands for the phosphorescence $T_1 \rightarrow S_0$ transition of benzene at 3400 Å

Number allotted to band (x)	Fundamental and combination frequencies on which the calculated value is based	Difference (band 1 − band x) (cm^{-1})	
		calc.	obs.
1	0	0	0
2	1 of 703	703	686
3	1 of 992	992	1010
4	1 of 1178	1178	1160
5	1 of 1596	1596	1579
6	1 of 1178+1 of 992	2170	2162
7	1 of 1596+1 of 992	2588	2577
8	1 of 1178+2 of 992	3162	3162

It will be observed that the vibrational frequency analysis is quite successful. In addition, for reasons which cannot be considered here, the analysis supports a hexagonally symmetrical planar molecule for the triplet state where the ring has expanded slightly.

For further examples of the employment of the phosphorescence spectrum in the study of the vibrational levels in the ground state of the molecule a paper by Lewis and Kasha[7] should be consulted.

Finally, it must be stressed that phosphorescence is only rarely observed in gases. It is for this reason that recourse is made to low temperature phosphorescence in solid matrices where good resolution of the vibrational structure may be achieved. This is to be contrasted with fluorescence. For example, the absorption of ultra-violet light by iodine vapour results in the appearance of the large number of narrow bands in the fluorescence spectrum from which a vibrational analysis may be carried out.

Importance of the triplet state

Because of the much longer lifetime of the triplet state compared with that of the excited singlet state, the triplet state would be expected to have more influence on chemical reactions. Sufficient evidence has now accumulated to indicate that a number of widely different types of chemical reactions involve a molecule in the triplet state. However, it is difficult to show with certainty that a particular reaction involves a triplet state, and the deductions are often based on kinetic quantum yields and quenching data. Three of the reactions which have given strong signs of taking place through a triplet state of one of the molecules are listed below:

(i) The photoreduction of all porphyrin-type molecules and also of phthalocyanines.

(ii) The reversible photoreaction of chlorophyll (X). If $\cdot X \cdot$ denotes the triplet state of chlorophyll, and HA the solvent, the following stages are probably involved:

$$X \xrightarrow{h\bar{\nu}} X^{\star} \rightarrow \cdot X \cdot$$

$$\cdot X \cdot + HA \rightarrow [\cdot XHA \cdot]$$

$$[\cdot XHA \cdot] \rightarrow \cdot X^{-} + HA^{+} \rightarrow \cdot XH + A \cdot$$

Then a similar process follows for $\cdot XH$ and XH_2 results.

(iii) Photo-oxidation reaction. The photo-oxidation mechanism involved in the production of photo-oxides of many substituted linear polyacenes probably takes place through a triplet state in the aromatic system. Two examples of photo-oxidation involving a triplet state are the formation of the peroxides of anthracene and pentacene, that is of

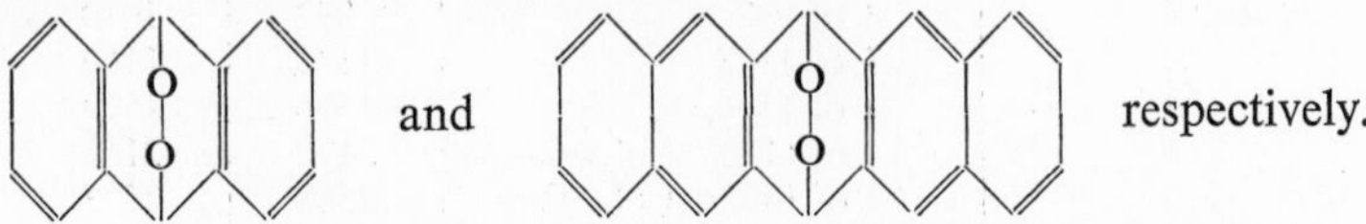

Two of the striking features about the photo-oxidation of the polyacenes are:

(*a*) That for the linear polyacenes the difference in energy between the first triplet and the ground state decreases appreciably on passing from one member to the next in the series:

naphthalene, anthracene, tetracene, and pentacene

(*b*) The corresponding non-linear polyacenes have much higher energy differences between the ground and the first triplet state.

It is probably significant that naphthalene, which has the highest first triplet energy level does not form a peroxide and that the peroxides of the non-linear polyacenes are very difficult to obtain. Information on the triplet state in aromatic hydrocarbons may be gained from fluorescence quenching data.

For details of fluorescence quenching of aromatic hydrocarbons by the paramagnetic molecules, O_2 and NO, a review by Stevens[19] should be consulted. It seems that the quenching mechanism is to be related to the magnetic field associated with the two unpaired electrons in the paramagnetic molecule which facilitates singlet-triplet conversion. The molecule may then either phosphoresce from the triplet state, or what is much more probable at normal temperatures, it may lose the excess electronic energy by collision. In either case, the fluorescence is quenched.

In general, though, it is not obvious which chemical reaction will take place through the triplet state of one or more of its reactants, and, in fact, each reaction has to receive a detailed study to determine whether a singlet or a triplet state is concerned. For further information on chemical reactions involving the triplet state a review by Reid[20] should be consulted.

References

1. NICHOLS, E. I. and MERRITT, E. *Phys. Rev.* **31** (1910), 376.
2. LEWIS, G. N., LIPKIN, D. and MAGEL, T. T. *J. Amer. Chem. Soc.* **66** (1944), 1579.
3. BOWEN, E. J. *Quart. Rev.* **1** (1947), 1.
4. GARFORTH, F. M., INGOLD, C. K. and POOLE, H. G. *J. Chem. Soc.* (1948), 406.
5. BOWEN, E. J. *Chemical Aspects of Light*. Oxford University Press (1942).
6. PRINGSHEIM, P. *Fluorescence and Phosphorescence*. Interscience Publishers (New York, 1949).
7. LEWIS, G. N. and KASHA, M. *J. Amer. Chem. Soc.* **66** (1944), 2100.
8. WALKER, S. and STRAW, H. *Atomic Microwave and Radiofrequency Spectroscopy*. Chapman and Hall (London, 1961), p. 40.
9. MCCLURE, D. S. *J. Chem. Phys.* **17** (1949), 905.
10. LEWIS, G. N., LIPKIN, D. and MAGEL, T. T. *J. Amer. Chem. Soc.* **63** (1941), 3005.
11. LEWIS, G. N. and CALVIN, M. *J. Amer. Chem. Soc.* **67** (1945), 1232.
12. LEWIS, G. N., CALVIN, M. and KASHA, M. *J. Chem. Phys.* **17** (1949), 804.
13. *Molecular Spectroscopy. Institute of Petroleum Conference*, 1955, p. 19.
14. EVANS, D. F. *Nature, Lond.* **176** (1955), 777.
15. HUTCHISON, C. A. and MANGUM, B. W. *J. Chem. Phys.* **29** (1958), 952.
16. PORTER, G. and WINDSOR, M. W. *Molecular Spectroscopy. Institute of Petroleum Conference*, 1955, p. 6.
17. SHULL, H. *J. Chem. Phys.* **17** (1949), 295.
18. HERZFELD, N., INGOLD, C. K. and POOLE, H. G. *J. Chem. Soc.* (1946), 316.
19. STEVENS, B. *Chem. Rev.* **57** (1957), 439.
20. REID, C. *Quart. Rev.* **11** (1958), 205.

9

Dissociation energies from spectroscopic data

Dissociation energies of diatomic molecules

Introduction

THE term 'dissociation energy' may be appreciated by reference to potential energy internuclear distance curves. At about 0°K all molecules have no rotational energy but are merely vibrating with their zero point energy. Thus, diatomic molecules are in the $v = 0$ vibrational level. The energy required to separate the stable molecule A—B initially in the $v = 0$ level into two unexcited atoms A and B, that is:

$$\text{A—B} \rightarrow \text{A} + \text{B}$$

is known as the dissociation energy (D), its value being represented in Fig. 9.1.

Another symbol which is often used by spectroscopists is D_e where

$$D_e = D + G(0) \qquad (9.1)$$

$G(0) = E_{v=0}/hc$ (see p. 11) and is the value of the vibrational energy in the $v = 0$ level. Since $G(0)$ is in cm^{-1} units, then D_e and D would also be in these units.

Dissociation energy values are most frequently expressed in kilocalories per gram molecule, although sometimes electron-volts or cm^{-1} are also employed. If the dissociation energy value is quoted in cm^{-1} this corresponds with the energy required to dissociate one molecule into two stable atoms and has to be multiplied by the Avogadro number to obtain the value for one gram molecule.

The value of D can be found by thermochemical methods. Infra-red spectroscopy can be used to determine D and D_e for the ground state of the molecule, while electronic spectra can be used to determine D and D_e, not only for the ground state of the molecule, but also for some of the excited states as well.

In the electronic spectra approach for the determination of the dissociation energy at least one of the products of dissociation is frequently in an excited state, and in some cases both the atoms are excited. In some instances the dissociation may even take place into ions.

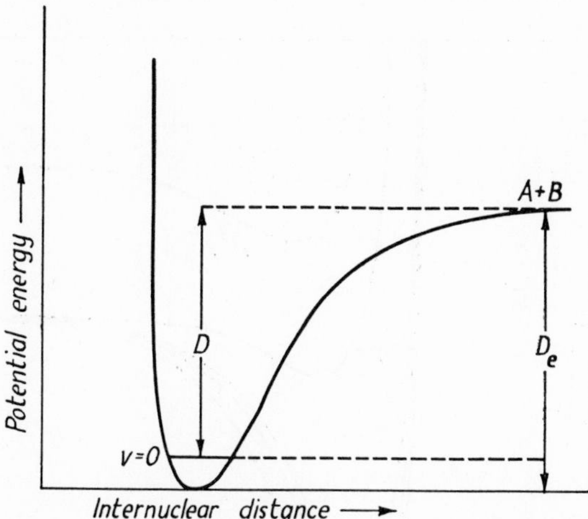

FIG. 9.1 Potential energy curve and the representation of thermal dissociation D and spectroscopic dissociation energy D_e

In order to determine the dissociation energy from spectroscopic data it is necessary either:

(1) (*a*) To determine the lowest absorption frequency which will produce dissociation of the molecule; (*b*) To identify the electronic state of the dissociation products, or:

(2) To determine the energy values of as many vibrational levels for the electronic state whose dissociation energy is required.

Electronic spectra may proceed by either (1) or (2) whereas the infra-red approach cannot be used to study actual dissociation and is, therefore, restricted to (2).

Evaluation of D by band convergence method

In Fig. 9.2 five of the potential energy curves are given for the oxygen molecule. When dissociation of the molecule takes place from any of the four lowest electronic states given in Fig. 9.2 it leads to two oxygen atoms each in a ^3P state, that is:

$$O_2 \rightarrow O(^3P) + O(^3P)$$

where both atoms would be released in their ground states. If, however, dissociation is produced in the $B^3\Sigma_u^-$ excited state, then one ^3P-state oxygen atom is produced and one in the excited ^1D state, that is:

$$O_2^\star \rightarrow O(^3P) + O(^1D)$$

Dissociation products differ in that those resulting from the lowest electronic states have both atoms in the ^3P states whereas in the other case one is in a ^3P-state and the other in a ^1D. If the energy absorbed in the $B^3\Sigma_u^- \leftarrow X^3\Sigma_g^-$ transition raises the energy of the diatomic molecule above the level *ab*, then the energy is sufficient to bring about dissociation of the molecule, and a

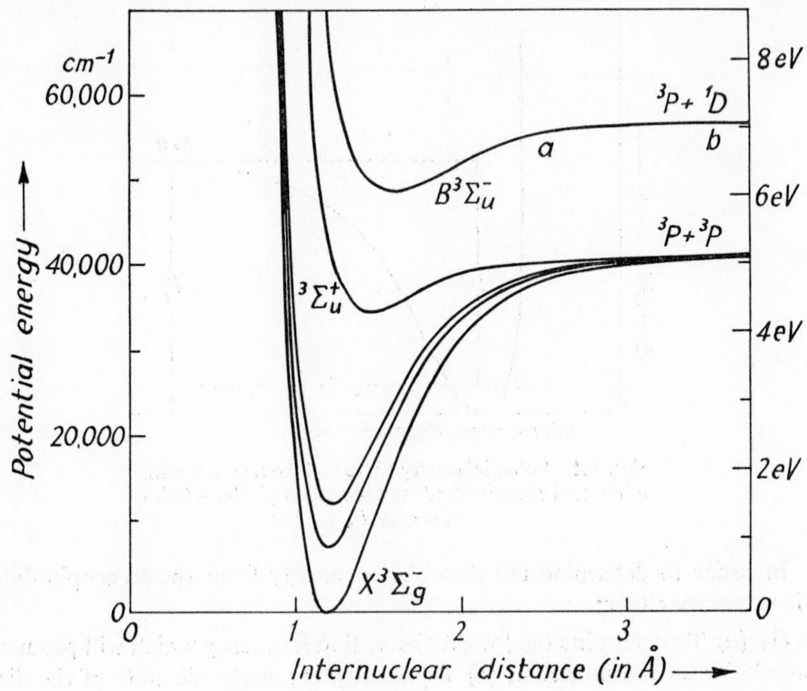

FIG. 9.2 Five potential energy curves of the oxygen molecule. (*After Gaydon*[1])

continuum is observed.† If ν_c is the lowest wave-number at which the continuum begins where the transition takes place from the v'' level, and D'' is the dissociation energy in the ground electronic state then it follows from Fig. 9.2 that

$$\nu_c = D'' + (^3P \rightarrow {}^1D) - \{G(v'') - G(0)\} \tag{9.2}$$

where $G(v'') = E_v/hc$ and $\{G(v'') - G(0)\}$ is the difference in vibrational energy (in cm^{-1}) between the v'' and the 0 level in the ground state of the molecule. When the transition involving ν_c takes place from the $v'' = 0$ level then

$$\nu_c = D'' + {}^3P \rightarrow {}^1D \tag{9.3}$$

where $^3P \rightarrow {}^1D$ represents the difference in energy for the two atomic states of oxygen. Hence, for this case if ν_c is observed and if from atomic spectra

† In addition, there may be a number of bands corresponding to transitions from the ground state to definite vibrational levels in the upper state. This is the case for the electronic transition of the oxygen molecule which is now being considered.

the energy corresponding to $^3P \rightarrow {}^1D$ is known, then the dissociation energy in the ground state, D'', may be determined.

In this particular O_2 electronic transition, known as the *Schumann–Runge* ($B^3\Sigma_u^- \leftarrow X^3\Sigma_g^-$), the bands converge to a readily discernible limit at 1759 Å and are then followed by a continuum. The convergence limit corresponds to 7.047 eV and is an upper limit for the dissociation energy for this electronic transition.

The ground state of the oxygen atom is a ^3P. The first excited state is a ^1D lying at 1.967 eV above the ground state, while the second and third excited states lie 4.188 and 9.1 eV above the ground state. If the $G(v'')-G(0)$ term is neglected, it follows from equation (9.2) that the 9.1 eV is unacceptable since it would lead to a negative value for D''. Hence, the only atomic states which need be considered as dissociation products for the Schumann–Runge bands are the ^3P, ^1D, and the second excited state which is a ^1S, since these would lead to positive D'' values. The feasible atomic states from the dissociated oxygen molecule in the higher electronic state are then:

$$^3P+{}^3P, \quad {}^3P+{}^1D, \quad {}^3P+{}^1S, \quad {}^1D+{}^1D, \quad {}^1D+{}^1S, \quad \text{and} \quad {}^1S+{}^1S$$

That is there are six possibilities.

From the rotational structure of the Schumann–Runge bands the spectroscopist can deduce that the upper electronic state must be a triplet. However, on the basis of quantum mechanics it may be shown that the combination of atoms in singlet states cannot result in a molecular triplet state.† Hence the

$$^1D+{}^1D, \quad {}^1D+{}^1S, \quad \text{and} \quad {}^1S+{}^1S$$

are not feasible atomic states for the dissociation products in this excited electronic state.

The $^3P+{}^3P$ combination may be eliminated since it is known from theory that from the combination of two such atomic states it is not possible to produce a $^3\Sigma_u^-$ molecular state. Thus, the two remaining possibilities are:

$$^3P+{}^1D \quad \text{and} \quad {}^3P+{}^1S$$

for the dissociation products in the upper electronic state. From the observed transition it is known that:

$$^3P \rightarrow {}^1D \quad \text{is } 1.967 \text{ eV}$$

and

$$^3P \rightarrow {}^1S \quad \text{is } 4.188 \text{ eV.}$$

Since the convergence limit ‡ is 7.047 eV, it follows from equation 9.2 that two feasible dissociation energies are given at least approximately by:

$$7.047-1.967 = 5.080 \text{ eV} \tag{9.4}$$

or

$$7.047-4.188 = 2.859 \text{ eV}$$

† This is one of the Wigner and Witmer correlation rules[2]. These rules govern the permissible atomic states which may result from the dissociation of a given molecular state.

‡ The convergence limit may be determined most accurately in this case because the $(v',0)$ progression may be followed to the beginning of the continuous absorption. This fixes the value of ν_c with great accuracy. In many other cases it is very difficult to decide exactly where the continuum begins.

However, the 2.859 eV value may be eliminated immediately as it is smaller than the energy of the highest observed vibrational level in the ground electronic state which lies 3.4 eV above the $v = 0$ level. Hence, the only possible value is 5.080 eV corresponding to a dissociation into $^3P+^1D$ oxygen atoms. This value is unambiguous since it was determined from a single accurately known dissociation limit. In the case of N_2 and NO and some other molecules, however, the spectroscopic approach has led to different values being quoted for the dissociation energy. If the dissociation energy concerned has also been obtained from thermochemistry or other independent methods, then this value may be used in identifying the atomic products in the spectroscopic dissociation process. This is done by determining which electronic state of the atom products would lead to a corresponding value of the dissociation energy in the ground state of the molecule.

The band convergence approach has also been applied to determine the dissociation energies of the halogens Cl_2, Br_2 and I_2. The ground state of the molecule is compounded of two halogen atoms each in a $^2P_{3/2}$ state. In the excited state where the convergence limit was observed† the molecule was composed of one atom in the $^2P_{3/2}$ state, but the other atom in a $^2P_{1/2}$ state where the latter state has the higher energy. Other systems analysed this way are H_2 and Na_2.

Under favourable circumstances this method of band convergence may probably give the most accurate of all values for dissociation energies. This occurs when in an electronic absorption spectrum one of the v' progressions may be followed almost to where the continuum begins, so that ν_c may be obtained directly or by a negligible extrapolation of the wave-numbers of the band heads. For example, if the first band in the v' progression is the $(0,v'')$ and the wave-number of its band head (or even better the band origin) is $\nu_{(0,v'')}$,and D' is the dissociation energy in the excited electronic state, then D' may be immediately obtained from the formula:

$$D' = hc(\nu_c - \nu_{(0,v'')}) \qquad (9.5)$$

To determine the dissociation in the ground state, however, as has already been indicated, it is necessary to be able to identify the atomic states of the dissociation products and know the value of this atomic excitation energy from the line spectrum of the relevant atoms.

Evaluation of D_e by extrapolation to convergence limits

In many cases the bands become too faint to trace a progression up to the convergence limit or even to any appreciable convergence at all. In such cases, if sufficient bands are observed, then an extrapolation method is employed such as that used by Birge and Sponer[3] who extrapolated the observed band head or band origin wave-number values to the convergence limit. Their initial method has been widely used to estimate dissociation energies and is

† The limit was determined by following the band convergence.

based on the vibrational energy in cm^{-1} units being represented by the following equation:

$$G(v) = (v+\tfrac{1}{2})\omega_e-(v+\tfrac{1}{2})^2x_e\omega_e+(v+\tfrac{1}{2})^3y_e\omega_e+\ \dots \tag{9.6}$$

where

$$G(v) = E_v/hc \tag{9.7}$$

If all the terms on the right hand side of equation (9.6) are neglected except the first two, then the mean interval between the successive levels $v+1$, v, and $v-1$ is given by:

$$\Delta G(v) = \tfrac{1}{2}\{G(v+1)-G(v-1)\} = \omega_e-2(v+\tfrac{1}{2})x_e\omega_e \tag{9.8}$$

where $\Delta G(v)$ may be regarded as the separation between the non-existent $(v+\frac{1}{2})$ or $(v-\frac{1}{2})$ levels, or, in fact, simply as $(\mathrm{d}/\mathrm{d}v)\{G(v)\}$.

From equation (5.20) it follows that as v increases the difference in energy between consecutive vibrational levels decreases; this is illustrated in Fig. 9.3, When $(\mathrm{d}/\mathrm{d}v)\{G(v)\} = 0$ the molecule dissociates, and if v_c is the corresponding value of the vibrational quantum number then from equation (9.8):

$$0 = \omega_e-2(v_c+\tfrac{1}{2})x_e\omega_e \tag{9.9}$$

Thus the value of the vibrational quantum number at which dissociation takes place is:

$$v_c = \frac{1}{2x_e}-\frac{1}{2} \tag{9.10}$$

and when this value of v_c is substituted in equation (9.6), then $G(v_c) = D_e$ where D_e is in cm^{-1} units. If only the first two terms on the right-hand side of equation (9.6) are considered, then on substitution for v_c the value of D_e obtained is:

$$D_e = \frac{\omega_e}{4x_e} \tag{9.11}$$

Thus, from the values of ω_e and x_e—determined from infra-red spectra (see p. 96), or from electronic spectra (see p. 199)—the spectroscopic heat of dissociation may be calculated. In the case of electronic spectra this Birge and Sponer method has been applied to data derived from the analyses of both emission and absorption band system data.

The experimental vibrational data† for the ground state of the carbon monoxide molecule may be fitted to the formula:

$$G(v) = [2167.4(v+\tfrac{1}{2})-12.70(v+\tfrac{1}{2})^2] \tag{9.12}$$

This formula was based on experimental data where the vibrational quantum number ranged from 0 to 25. From this formula v_c is found to be ~ 85, and if the dissociation energy corresponding to this v_c value is calculated from equation (9.12), it turns out to be about 40 kcal/mole higher than what is considered to be the correct value. In fact, this procedure rarely yields the correct result, and we shall now consider the reason for this.

† These data were obtained from the analysis of the fourth positive system of CO, which is the $A^1\Pi-X^1\Sigma^+$ transition.

If, for example, three or four experimental values for $(v+1) \leftarrow v$ transitions are available, then it follows from equation (9.8) that when $\Delta G(v)$ is plotted against v a straight line ought to be obtained which could then be extrapolated to $\Delta G(v) = 0$ to give $v = v_c$. This v_c value when inserted in equation (9.6) ought to give the dissociation energy (D_e). This procedure which should yield the same value of D_e as the method just outlined also rarely gives the correct value of the dissociation energy, and Gaydon suggested that a figure of about 20 per cent below that of the linear extrapolated value is generally best adopted, and this will then have a probable error of ± 20 per cent. In the case of hydrides and halides of group II elements the true dissociation energy may be even less than this 20 per cent lower value. When a few of the actual $\Delta G(v)-v$ experimental curves are viewed it becomes immediately

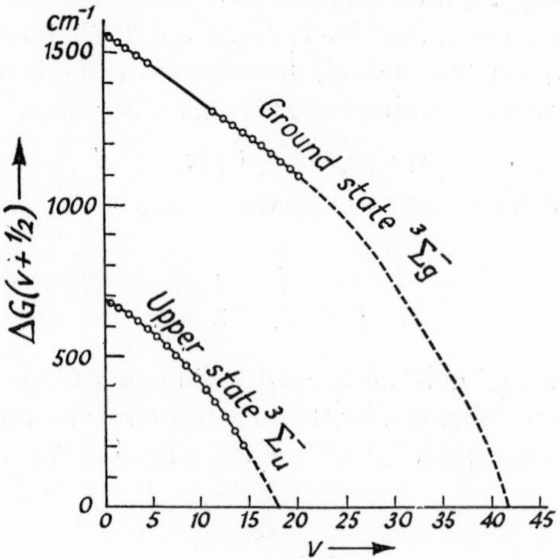

FIG. 9.3 $\Delta G\,(v + \frac{1}{2})$ against v for the ground and an excited state of the oxygen molecule. (*After Gaydon*[1])

obvious why this type of extrapolation yields an inaccurate result. In Fig. 9.3 $\Delta G(v+\frac{1}{2})$ is plotted against v for the ground and an excited electronic state of the oxygen molecule, and it is to be noted that curves result. It is interesting to observe that if only the data for the first five vibrational levels had been available for the ground electronic state, then it would have been possible to be misled into fitting a straight line whereas it ought to have been a curve. In general, the Birge–Sponer extrapolation gives an upper limit to the dissociation energy for covalent molecules and a lower limit to molecules where the ionic forces predominate. In the case of ionic molecules such as Na^+Cl^- no reliable estimate of the dissociation energy can be made by this Birge–Sponer type of approach since the curve approaches the v-axis asymptotically.

As has been indicated, equation (4.40) is frequently inadequate as it leads to a linear plot of $\Delta G(v)$ and $\Delta G(v+\frac{1}{2})$ against v. If, however, the equation:

$$G(v) = (v+\tfrac{1}{2})\omega_e - (v+\tfrac{1}{2})^2 x_e\omega_e + (v+\tfrac{1}{2})^3 y_e\omega_e \qquad (9.13)$$

had been used, the $\Delta G(v)$ values would no longer show linear dependence on v. However, even such an equation may prove inadequate, and, in fact, Birge showed that even a polynomial of the fourth degree failed to represent adequately the $\Delta G(v) - v$ data for some diatomic molecules. In fact, he demonstrated that the complete curve can never be exactly covered by a single function but that two functions were required.

One of the best procedures when a sufficient number of bands is available is to plot the experimental $\Delta G(v)$ values against v, and if the shape of the resulting curve seems reasonably certain to extrapolate the resulting curve until it cuts the v-axis at the point where $v = v_c$. The dissociation energy would then be obtained by finding the area enclosed by the curve and the two axes, that is

$$D = \int_0^{v_c} \Delta G(v) \mathrm{d}v \tag{9.14}$$

Evaluation of D by atomic fluorescence method

When a continuous or diffuse absorption spectrum is obtained for a molecule, and dissociation has taken place giving an excited atom and one in its ground state, if the excited atom is not metastable, then atomic fluorescence of this atom may accompany this photodissociation. The emitted atomic line may then be identified. The wavelength of the incident light is varied, and the lowest frequency which still produces this atomic line—owing to dissociation of the molecule—is sought. Thus, the lowest frequency of the incident light which will still cause the atom to fluoresce will lead to at least an upper limit for the dissociation energy. This process may be illustrated by considering the dissociation of sodium iodide by the absorption of light.

In its ground state sodium iodide is in the ionic form, and what takes place on the continuous absorption of light depends on the electromagnetic region in which absorption takes place. The dissociation products which occur in the different frequency regions are:

(i) An unactivated Na+unactivated I.
(ii) An activated Na+unactivated I.
(iii) An unactivated Na+activated I.

Case (ii) will now be considered. By the absorption of light an excited sodium iodide molecule (NaI)* is obtained, and this dissociates into an iodine atom in its ground state ($^2P_{1\frac{1}{2}}$) and an activated sodium atom (3^2P); thus:

$$\mathrm{Na}^+ + \mathrm{I}^- \xrightarrow{hc\nu} [\mathrm{NaI}]^\star$$

$$[\mathrm{NaI}]^\star \longrightarrow \mathrm{I}(^2P_{1\frac{1}{2}}) + \mathrm{Na}(3^2P)$$

and the excited Na then emits light (the sodium *D* lines) and falls to its ground state (3^2S), that is:

$$\mathrm{Na}(3^2P) \rightarrow \mathrm{Na}(3^2S) + hc\nu_0$$

where ν_0 represents the wave-number of the sodium *D* lines. The condition sought is that the minimum wave-number of the absorbed incident light should still produce this emission line (ν_0). If the wave-number of the incident light is ν_1, then:

$$\nu_1 - \nu_0 = D''\dagger \tag{9.15}$$

where D'' is the dissociation energy in the ground state in cm^{-1} units.

The great merit of this method is that it is possible to be reasonably certain of at least one of the atomic states in the dissociation products. The method has been applied to the halides of the alkali metals and thallium where the results agree fairly well with those from other methods. Only a bare outline of the process has been given here and for further details a paper by Sommermeyer[4] should be consulted.

Predissociation and its use in evaluating D

The phenomenon of predissociation was first observed in the electronic absorption spectrum of S_2, where for transitions from the v'' levels to low values of v' the bands appeared normal, and the rotational structure in each band consisted of sharp lines. However, for transitions from v'' to higher values of v', while the general appearance of the bands remains, some or all of the rotational fine structure of the band becomes diffuse.‡ This suggests that the molecule has definite vibrational energy in both the upper and lower electronic states but that above certain vibrational levels in the excited state some of the rotational energy is not quantised. Generally, predissociation may be detected when the sharp lines of a branch of a band due to the rotational fine structure suddenly end and the last few lines take on a diffuse appearance. There are several types of predissociation but two features stand out:

(*a*) The predissociation spectrum may be followed by a region of continuous absorption, or

(*b*) bands with no diffuse structure are found on both low and high frequency sides of the predissociation bands.

One of the simplest cases of predissociation will now be explained with respect to the potential energy curves in Fig. 9.4. The molecular electronic state quantum numbers for these three electronic states are such that the selection rules permit only transitions between curves 1 and 2. For transitions from the $v'' = 3$ level and higher, the potential energy of the excited molecule is greater than that at the point A, and during its vibration in this excited state, when the internuclear distance corresponds with that at A, it has the possibility of changing from curve 2 to 3. When this transition takes place it is termed a *radiationless* one. The time for a molecular vibration is of the order of 10^{-14} sec and for a molecular rotation 10^{-12} sec. Hence, a molecule may vibrate several times before completing a rotation, but when the molecule is excited to curve 2 it may during its vibration transfer to curve 3 before it has had time to rotate in excited state 2. Thus, in this case the rotational

† This equation is only strictly accurate providing the excitation producing the dissociation takes place from the $v'' = 0$ level.

‡ A spectrogram of CaH which illustrates this point may be observed in Gaydon.[1]

energy will no longer be strictly quantised, and the rotational fine structure of the band will become diffuse. However, the vibrational energy which fixes the gross structure will still be quantised and exhibit itself in the appearance of diffuse bands. Although the energy of the molecule was insufficient to cause dissociation in state 2, it is now sufficiently great in state 3 to bring about dissociation, and the dissociation limit may be fixed within a very narrow range.

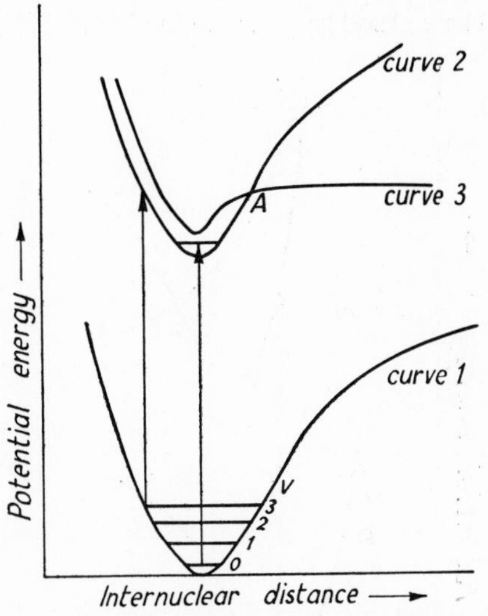

FIG. 9.4 Potential energy curves involved in the phenomenon of predissociation

However, if in some of the transitions from potential energy states 1 to 2, high values of v' are involved, this may lead to an energy relatively much greater than that at point A. In such a case the vibrational energy of the molecule, as it passes through the point A, may be sufficiently great to prevent the transition to state 3, and when this occurs the predissociation region resulting from the v'' transitions to lower v' values will be followed by bands showing sharp rotational structure.

One supporting fact which favours the given interpretation of predissociation is that where predissociation occurs in the absorption spectrum of S_2 bands, the same bands are completely absent in the same emission system. This would be anticipated if the given theory of predissociation were correct, since emission of such bands should be precluded by spontaneous dissociation of the molecule in such v' levels.

By employing a rather similar technique to that used in the band convergence method of determining dissociation energies and by estimating the lowest frequency at which the vibrational bands become diffuse, it might be expected that it would be possible to calculate the dissociation energy. There are many complicating factors; one of them is illustrated in Fig. 9.5, where the dissociation occurs through the point P, and the radiation along PM is non-quantised, and the dissociation limit of LPM lies below the predissociation limit.

Another complication in the predissociation determination of dissociation energies is that another type of phenomenon may give a similar appearance in the spectrum to that described to characterise predissociation. This phenomenon may occur if two potential energies nearly cross (see Fig. 9.6) and if the selection rules permit a transition between them. In such a case the energy levels may become perturbed, and the electronic spectrum from the ground state (III) to (I) may result in a radiationless transfer to II, which results in the spectrum having a similar appearance to what it would have had if the potential energy curves had actually crossed.

Generally, the commencement of predissociation gives at least a maximum value of D, and in some cases a very accurate value of D may be obtained. The method has been applied to N_2, H_2, CO, NO, and several other molecules.

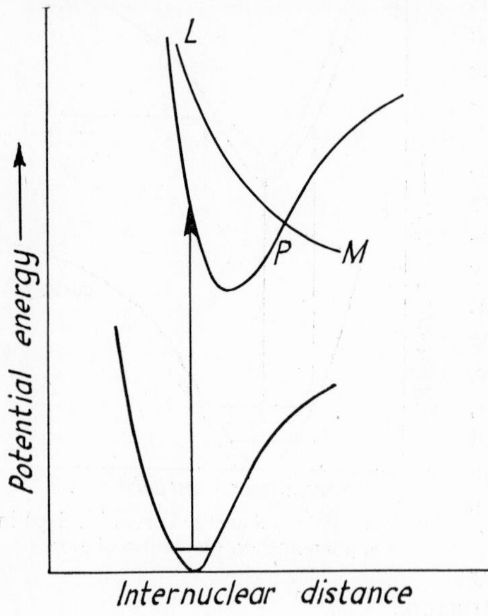

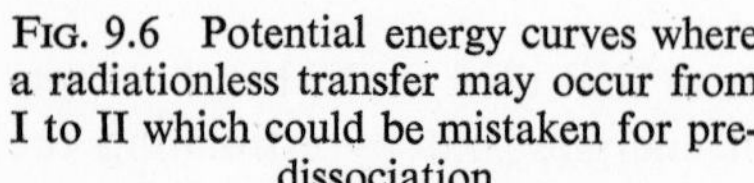

FIG. 9.5 Predissociation involving a non-quantised potential energy curve

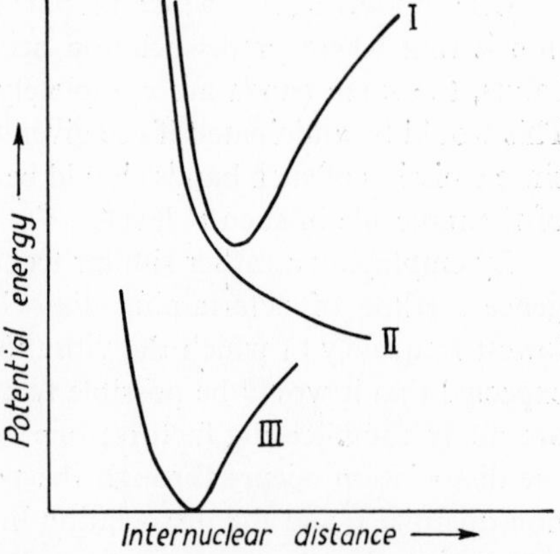

FIG. 9.6 Potential energy curves where a radiationless transfer may occur from I to II which could be mistaken for predissociation

As should be apparent from what has been indicated, the route to deduce such an accurate value is highly specialised and involves considerations of selection rules.† For the determination of dissociation energies by the predissociation method Gaydon[1] and Herzberg[2] should be consulted.

† Quantum mechanics has also shown that for these radiationless transitions the Λ and Σ selection rules (see p. 57) are the same as for radiative transitions. However, the selection rule for J is $\Delta J = 0$ while for the g and u states, it now becomes $g \rightarrow g$ and $u \rightarrow u$ instead of $g \rightarrow u$ and $u \rightarrow g$.

Conclusions on the determination of dissociation energies of diatomic molecules

The most prolific source of dissociation energies for diatomic molecules has been by means of electronic spectra. The infra-red approach has also been employed. A large number of dissociation energies of diatomic molecules and radicals is given by Herzberg.[2] In favourable cases the electronic spectra approach is capable of giving the most accurate dissociation energies for diatomic molecules. The band convergence method where a progression is followed to the region where dissociation commences is particularly good since the dissociation limit is fixed with reasonable certainty, and wavelengths can be measured most accurately. Except in the atomic fluorescence method, where at least one of the atomic states is identified with certainty, the identification of the excited state of the atomic products is difficult and sometimes uncertain and may lead to publication of considerably differing values for a particular dissociation energy. However, the atomic fluorescence method is very limited in application, while the band convergence method may lead to errors of ± 20 per cent. The predissociation method can sometimes yield most accurate results, but again this is limited in application.

Recent dissociation energy studies for diatomic molecules

(1) In the treatment outlined here one possible complicating factor has been omitted, i.e. it has been assumed that there is no maximum in the potential energy curve either in the excited or ground electronic states. Herzberg interpreted the electronic spectrum of NO by assuming a potential energy maximum was involved. Another case was that studied by Rowlinson

TABLE 9.1

Dissociation energies of diatomic molecules

Halogen molecule	Dissociation energy (kcal/mole)
F_2	37 ± 1.6
Cl_2	57
Br_2	45
I_2	36

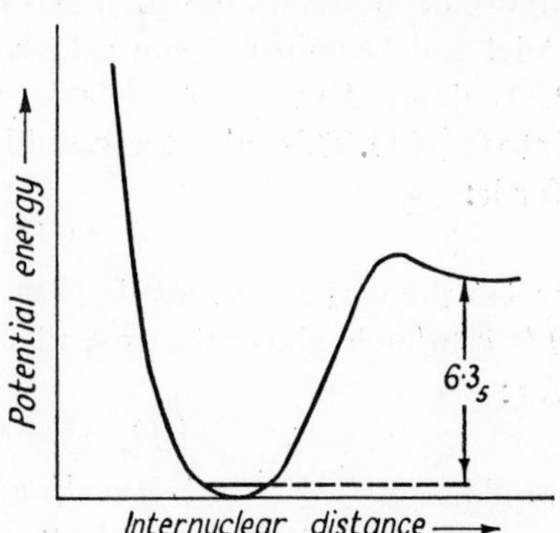

FIG. 9.7 Potential energy curve exhibiting a maximum

and Barrow[5] who examined the electronic emission spectrum of the diatomic AlF for the $A^1\Pi \rightarrow X^1\Sigma$ system. Their results indicate that the dissociation energy in the ground state must be greater than 6.51 eV, and from a short extrapolation of the vibrational levels they obtained a value of 7.2 ± 0.3 eV. The thermochemical value for the dissociation energy (D'') in the ground state is 6.35 eV. If the value of the dissociation energy from the electronic spectra is truly appreciably greater than this value, then it could most satisfactorily be explained by a maximum in the potential energy curve in the ground state. This is represented diagrammatically in Fig. 9.7.

(2) One of the most interesting of recent dissociation energy determinations is that of F_2 the value of which is not in the order which might be first anticipated in relation to the other halogens, as is illustrated in Table 9.1. In fact, for a number of years the dissociation energy of F_2 was thought to be 63 kcal/mole. In the last ten years a number of workers have tried to fix its value. The value quoted in Table 9.1 for F_2 was obtained by Caunt and Barrow[6] from extensive studies on the ultra-violet absorption spectra of the gaseous alkali metal fluorides, where the dissociation energy of the metallic fluoride was related to the dissociation energy of fluorine.† Altogether, they studied all the twelve gaseous potassium, rubidium and caesium halides and deduced the upper limits of the dissociation energy for each of these substances.

Dissociation energies of polyatomic molecules

With only a few exceptions spectroscopic methods have been concerned with the determination of the dissociation energies of diatomic molecules; the spectrum of a polyatomic molecule is normally too complex to permit this type of determination at present. However, combination of thermochemical data with dissociation energies for diatomic molecules determined by the spectroscopic methods, and the use of Hess's law enables heats of formation of polyatomic molecules to be calculated.

The spectroscopic determination of the dissociation energies of a few triatomic molecules has been carried out, and two cases will now be quoted. Adel and Dennison[8] from calculations based on the infra-red spectrum of CO_2 obtained a value of $\sim$300 kcal/mole for the heat of dissociation of CO_2 into $O+CO$. This value was considered much too high but could be accounted for if:

$$CO_2 \rightarrow O + CO^{\star}$$

where the carbon monoxide is in an excited electronic state ($^3\Pi$), which is 138 kcal/mole above the ground state for CO. Thus, the dissociation energy for:

$$CO_2 \rightarrow O + CO \text{ (ground state)}$$

would be $300-138 = 162$ kcal/mole which is a much more reasonable value.

Herzberg[9] studied the electronic absorption spectrum of formaldehyde and followed the rotational fine structure of a band, until it eventually merged into continuous absorption. This corresponded with the following dissociation:

$$CH_2O \rightarrow HCO + H$$

and he fixed the upper limit for this dissociation energy as 105 kcal/mole.

Generally, the spectroscopic determination of accurate dissociation energies of larger molecules is more in the realm of the mathematician than

† A recent analysis by Stamper and Barrow[7] of the pressure of partly dissociated F_2 has fixed the dissociation energy as 37.72 ± 0.13 kcal/mole.

the spectroscopist, and no appreciable progress has so far been made. In several cases, though, the study of photochemical processes such as the photolysis of acetaldehyde has yielded upper values for the dissociation energy. For example, if ν is the lowest wave-number responsible for the chain initiation:

$$CH_3—CHO \rightarrow CH_3 + CHO$$

it may then be concluded that the dissociation energy (in cm^{-1}) of acetaldehyde for the C—C bond is either equal to, or less than, this value. A review article on bond dissociation energies by Szwarc[10] should be consulted, and this includes the non-spectral methods such as the electron impact method, the thermochemical method, the kinetic method in addition to the spectral methods. For more detailed treatment there are excellent works by Cottrell,[11] Gaydon [12] and Jevons.[13]

References

1. Gaydon, A. G. *Dissociation Energies and Spectra of Diatomic Molecules.* Chapman and Hall (London, 1947), p. 102.
2. Herzberg, G. *Spectra of Diatomic Molecules.* D. Van Nostrand (New York, 1950).
3. Birge, R. T. and Sponer, H. *Phys. Rev.* **28** (1926), 259.
4. Sommermeyer, K. *Phys.* **56** (1929), 548.
5. Rowlinson, H. C. and Barrow, R. F. *Proc. Phys. Soc., Lond.* **A66** (1953), 437, 771.
6. Caunt, A. D. and Barrow, R. F. *Proc. Roy. Soc.* **A219** (1953), 120.
7. Stamper, J. G. and Barrow, R. F. *Trans. Faraday Soc.* **54** (1958), 1592.
8. Adel, A. and Dennison, D. M. *Phys. Rev.* **44** (1933), 99.
9. Herzberg, G. *Trans. Faraday Soc.* **27** (1931), 378.
10. Szwarc, M. *Quart. Rev.* **5** (1951), 22.
11. Cottrell, T. L. *The Strengths of Chemical Bonds.* Butterworths (London, 1954).
12. Gaydon, A. G. *Dissociation Energies and Spectra of Diatomic Molecules.* Chapman and Hall (London, 1947).
13. Jevons, W. *Report on the Band Spectra of Diatomic Molecules.* Physical Society (London, 1932).

10

Force constants

Introduction

FOR a diatomic molecule, if the bond connecting the atoms is distorted, e.g. lengthened, then a force comes into play to restore the bond length to its previous (known as *equilibrium*) value. If the displacement is small, the restoring force exerted by one nucleus on the other will be proportional to their relative displacement, and the proportionality constant relating the restoring force and the distortion is called the *force constant, k*. Expressed in equational form this is:

$$\text{restoring force} = -kq \tag{10.1}$$

where q is the displacement of a point mass, m, from the equilibrium position, and the restoring force is measured in a direction away from the equilibrium position. The value of the force constant is that it characterises a particular chemical bond; for example in the case of C—C, C=C, and C≡C, the values of the force constants are very approximately in the ratio 1 : 2 : 3, respectively, and, in fact, force constants have been used to assess bond order.

A diatomic molecule

The case of a diatomic molecule will now be considered, where the nuclei execute simple harmonic motion along the line between their centres, and

m_1 q_1 m_2 q_2

FIG. 10.1 Nuclear displacements during the vibration of a diatomic molecule.

q_1 and q_2 represent the displacements in a particular direction of the nuclei of masses m_1 and m_2, respectively (as in Fig. 10.1).†

For the nucleus of mass m_1, the relative displacement of this with respect to the other is (q_1-q_2), while for m_2 it is (q_2-q_1), and the restoring forces

† Although the vibration is really O→←O, ←O——O→, it is quite legitimate to represent it as in Fig. 10.1; it merely means that q_1 or q_2 has a negative value.

will be, respectively, $-k(q_1-q_2)$ and $-k(q_2-q_1)$. Since force = mass × acceleration we may write:

$$-k(q_1-q_2) = m_1\frac{d^2q_1}{dt^2} \tag{10.2}$$

$$-k(q_2-q_1) = m_2\frac{d^2q_2}{dt^2} \tag{10.3}$$

For a simple harmonic oscillator

$$q = q_0 \sin(2\pi\omega ct+\alpha) \tag{10.4}$$

where ωc is the frequency of vibration† and is the same for both nuclei, and q is the displacement at time t while q_0 is the amplitude of the vibration, and α the phase constant. It follows that:

$$\frac{d^2q_1}{dt^2} = -q_0 4\pi^2\omega^2c^2 \sin(2\pi\omega ct+\alpha) = -4\pi^2(\omega c)^2 q_1 \tag{10.5}$$

and substituting d^2q_1/dt^2 into equation (10.2) we get:

$$k(q_1-q_2) = m_1 4\pi^2(\omega c)^2 q_1 \tag{10.6}$$

In addition, $\quad m_1q_1+m_2q_2 = m\bar{q},\quad$ where $m_1+m_2 = m \qquad (10.7)$

If the condition is employed, that the displacement of the centre of gravity of the system $\bar{q}$ is zero—otherwise translational motion would be considered as well—then the equation becomes:

$$m_1q_1+m_2q_2 = 0 \tag{10.8}$$

and

$$q_2 = -\frac{m_1q_1}{m_2} \tag{10.9}$$

On substitution from (10.9) into (10.6) for q_2

$$k\left(\frac{1}{m_1}+\frac{1}{m_2}\right) = 4\pi^2(\omega c)^2 \tag{10.10}$$

$$\omega c = \frac{1}{2\pi}\sqrt{k\left(\frac{1}{m_1}+\frac{1}{m_2}\right)} = \frac{1}{2\pi}\sqrt{\frac{k}{\mu}} \tag{10.11}$$

where $\mu = m_1m_2/(m_1+m_2)$ and is known as the *reduced mass.* If the masses, m_1 and m_2, are known, then by substituting the experimentally determined frequency into (10.11) the force constant may be calculated. Generally, however, since the equation was derived for a very small displacement, the best frequency to use is the one corresponding to the minimum of the potential energy curve, that is the hypothetical frequency $\omega_e c$ (where $\omega_e c$ is the frequency of vibration of the nuclei with infinitesimal amplitude about their equilibrium positions) and equation (10.11) becomes:

$$\omega_e c = \frac{1}{2\pi}\sqrt{\frac{k}{\mu}} \tag{10.12}$$

† The symbol $\bar{\nu}$ is sometimes employed rather than ωc for the vibrational frequency symbol in force constant work.

Polyatomic molecules

For the two stretching fundamental frequencies of a linear triatomic molecule, by using similar principles to those employed in the case of a diatomic molecule, equations could be built up and solved for the vibrational frequencies in terms of their force constants.

For larger molecules where certain vibrations are often characteristic more of the molecule as a whole, e.g. for the symmetrical breathing vibrational mode of benzene (see p. 280), it would not be anticipated that the link between force constant, reduced mass, and measured frequency could be as neatly formulated as was the case for the diatomic and linear triatomic molecules. Generally, for polyatomic molecules, in order to obtain an expression for the frequencies in terms of the masses and the force constants, it is first necessary to derive expressions for the kinetic and potential energy of the molecule. It is the formulation of a suitable but reasonably accurate potential energy equation which presents the main difficulty. One way of expressing the potential energy (V) of a molecule would be:

$$V = \tfrac{1}{2}k_{11}q_1^2 + \tfrac{1}{2}k_{22}q_2^2 + \tfrac{1}{2}k_{33}q_3^3 + \ldots k_{12}q_1q_2 + k_Bq_1q_3 + \ldots \qquad (10.13)$$

where the force constants are k_{11}, k_{22}, k_{33} . . ., and the corresponding displacements are q_1, q_2, q_3 which represent the displacement of the various atoms in the course of a vibration. k_{12}, k_{13} are termed *interaction constants* and may be associated with the secondary influences the nuclei have on one another; their main function is to make the potential equation more exact. These parameters are introduced and adjusted by virtually what amounts to trial and error methods until a satisfactory potential energy function is found which reproduces certain of the measured vibrational frequencies in the force constant calculations.

Since $k_{ij} = k_{ji}$ the general form of equation (10.13) is:

$$V = \tfrac{1}{2}\Sigma k_{ij}q_iq_j \qquad (10.14)$$

The corresponding kinetic energy (T) is:

$$T = \tfrac{1}{2}(a_{11}\dot{q}_1^2 + a_{22}\dot{q}_2^2 + \ldots 2a_{12}\dot{q}_1\dot{q}_2 + 2a_{13}\dot{q}_1\dot{q}_3 + \ldots) \qquad (10.15)$$

where the a_{ij} terms are constant and related to the masses, $\dot{q} = \dfrac{\mathrm{d}q}{\mathrm{d}t}$ and the equation is of the form:

$$T = \tfrac{1}{2}\Sigma a_{ij}\dot{q}_i\dot{q}_j \qquad (10.16)$$

Equations (10.14) and (10.16) have been successfully applied to the calculation of force constants from measured vibrational frequencies.

Once the kinetic and potential energy equations have been formulated they are substituted in what is known as the Lagrange equation of motion.†

† For a reader unfamiliar with determinants, equations (10.17) to (10.32) and the corresponding text could well be omitted.

The Lagrange equation may be derived as follows:

$$T = \tfrac{1}{2}m_1\dot{q}_1^2$$

and

$$\frac{\partial T}{\partial \dot{q}_1} = m_1\dot{q}_1 = \text{momentum} \tag{10.17}$$

Force = mass × acceleration, and, therefore,

$$F_1 = m_1 \times \frac{\mathrm{d}\dot{q}_1}{\mathrm{d}t} = \frac{\mathrm{d}}{\mathrm{d}t}(m_1\dot{q}_1) \tag{10.18}$$

and substituting from equation (10.17) into (10.18)

$$F_1 = \frac{\mathrm{d}}{\mathrm{d}t}\left(\frac{\partial T}{\partial \dot{q}_1}\right) \tag{10.19}$$

For a small change in position δq_1 of the particle 1, the work done by the force F_1 is $F_1\delta q_1$, and this is equal to the decrease in potential energy as is expressed by the equation $F_1\delta q_1 \sim -\delta V_1$ which in the limit becomes:

$$F_1 = -\frac{\partial V}{\partial q_1} \tag{10.20}$$

On substitution from equation (10.19) into (10.20) we get:

$$\frac{\mathrm{d}}{\mathrm{d}t}\left(\frac{\partial T}{\partial \dot{q}_1}\right) + \frac{\partial V}{\partial q_1} = 0$$

and this is known as the *Lagrange equation of motion* which in its general form would be:

$$\frac{\mathrm{d}}{\mathrm{d}t}\left(\frac{\partial T}{\partial \dot{q}_l}\right) + \frac{\partial V}{\partial q_l} = 0 \tag{10.21}$$

where $l = 1, 2, 3 \ldots s$, and s is the number of degrees of vibrational freedom and in principle would be $3N-6$ for a non-linear molecule. Thus, there should be $3N-6$ equations of the form of equation (10.21). On differentiation of equation (10.14) for the displacement q_l we get:

$$\frac{\partial V}{\partial q_l} = \tfrac{1}{2}\Sigma_j(k_{jl} + k_{lj})q_j \tag{10.22}$$

$$= \Sigma_j k_{lj} q_j \tag{10.23}$$

while on differentiation of equation (10.16)

$$\frac{\partial T}{\partial \dot{q}_l} = \tfrac{1}{2}\Sigma_j(a_{jl} + a_{lj})\dot{q}_j = \Sigma_j a_{lj}\dot{q}_j \tag{10.24}$$

and, therefore,

$$\frac{\mathrm{d}}{\mathrm{d}t} \cdot \frac{\partial T}{\partial \dot{q}_l} = \Sigma_j a_{lj}\ddot{q}_j \tag{10.25}$$

On substitution from equations (10.23) and (10.25) into (10.21) we get:

$$\Sigma_j(a_{lj}\ddot{q}_j + k_{lj}q_j) = 0 \tag{10.26}$$

In order to solve equation (10.26)

$$q_j = A_j \sin(\sqrt{\lambda}t + \alpha) \tag{10.27}$$

may be tried. For this characteristic wave equation A_j is the amplitude and α the phase constant, while the frequency ωc is related to λ (note λ is not the wavelength) by:

$$\lambda = 4\pi^2(\omega c)^2 \tag{10.28}$$

On substitution from equation (10.27) into equation (10.26) it may be readily shown that:

$$\Sigma_j(k_{lj}-a_{lj}\lambda)A_j = 0 \tag{10.29}$$

for the following values of l:

$$1, 2, 3, 4, \ldots s$$

For each value of l an equation is obtained, and since l has s values then s equations result. These are as follows:

$$\begin{aligned}
&\text{when } l=1, \quad (k_{11}-a_{11}\lambda)A_1+(k_{12}-a_{12}\lambda)A_2+\ \ldots\ (k_{1s}-a_{1s}\lambda)A_s = 0\\
&\text{when } l=2, \quad (k_{21}-a_{21}\lambda)A_1+(k_{22}-a_{22}\lambda)A_2+\ \ldots\ (k_{2s}-a_{2s}\lambda)A_s = 0\\
&\qquad\qquad \cdots\cdots\cdots\cdots\cdots\cdots\cdots\cdots\cdots\cdots\\
&\qquad\qquad \cdots\cdots\cdots\cdots\cdots\cdots\cdots\cdots\cdots\cdots\\
&\text{when } l=s, \quad (k_{s1}-a_{s1}\lambda)A_1+(k_{s2}-a_{s2}\lambda)A_2+\ \ldots\ (k_{ss}-a_{ss}\lambda)A_s = 0
\end{aligned}$$

From these s equations each of the A values could be determined as follows:

$$A_1 = \frac{\begin{vmatrix} (0) & (k_{12}-a_{12}\lambda) & \ldots & (k_{1s}-a_{1s}\lambda)\\ (0) & (k_{22}-a_{22}\lambda) & \ldots & (k_{2s}-a_{2s}\lambda)\\ \cdot & \cdot & \cdot & \cdot\\ \cdot & \cdot & \cdot & \cdot\\ (0) & (k_{s2}-a_{s2}\lambda) & \ldots & (k_{ss}-a_{ss}\lambda)\end{vmatrix}}{\begin{vmatrix} (k_{11}-a_{11}\lambda) & (k_{12}-a_{12}\lambda) & \ldots & (k_{1s}-a_{1s}\lambda)\\ (k_{21}-a_{21}\lambda) & (k_{22}-a_{22}\lambda) & \ldots & (k_{2s}-a_{2s}\lambda)\\ \cdot & \cdot & \cdot & \cdot\\ \cdot & \cdot & \cdot & \cdot\\ (k_{s1}-a_{s1}\lambda) & (k_{s2}-a_{s2}\lambda) & \ldots & (k_{ss}-a_{ss}\lambda)\end{vmatrix}} \tag{10.30}$$

and similarly

$$A_2 = \frac{\begin{vmatrix} (k_{11}-a_{11}\lambda) & (0) & \ldots & (k_{1s}-a_{1s}\lambda)\\ (k_{21}-a_{21}\lambda) & (0) & \ldots & (k_{2s}-a_{2s}\lambda)\\ \cdot & \cdot & \cdot & \cdot\\ \cdot & \cdot & \cdot & \cdot\\ (k_{s1}-a_{s1}\lambda) & (0) & \ldots & (k_{ss}-a_{ss}\lambda)\end{vmatrix}}{\begin{vmatrix} (k_{11}-a_{11}\lambda) & (k_{12}-a_{12}\lambda) & \ldots & (k_{1s}-a_{1s}\lambda)\\ (k_{21}-a_{21}\lambda) & (k_{22}-a_{22}\lambda) & \ldots & (k_{2s}-a_{2s}\lambda)\\ \cdot & \cdot & \cdot & \cdot\\ \cdot & \cdot & \cdot & \cdot\\ (k_{s1}-a_{s1}\lambda) & (k_{s2}-a_{s2}\lambda) & \ldots & (k_{ss}-a_{ss}\lambda)\end{vmatrix}} \tag{10.31}$$

If a determinant contains a 'zero line', as is the case for the numerator in each of these solutions for A, then the particular determinant is equal to zero. If the denominator may be represented by Δ, then it follows in general that:

$$A \times \Delta = 0$$

However, since not all A are zero it follows that $\Delta = 0$, and therefore,

$$\begin{vmatrix} (k_{11}-a_{11}\lambda) & (k_{12}-a_{12}\lambda) & \ldots & (k_{1s}-a_{1s}\lambda)\\ (k_{21}-a_{21}\lambda) & (k_{22}-a_{22}\lambda) & \ldots & (k_{2s}-a_{2s}\lambda)\\ \cdot & \cdot & \cdot & \cdot\\ \cdot & \cdot & \cdot & \cdot\\ (k_{s1}-a_{s1}\lambda) & (k_{s2}-a_{s2}\lambda) & \ldots & (k_{ss}-a_{ss}\lambda)\end{vmatrix} = 0 \tag{10.32}$$

This determinant yields s values of λ (i.e. s frequency values) in terms of force constants, cross-terms, and the masses of the atoms (i.e. a_{ij} values). If sufficient experimental frequencies are available, since $\lambda = 4\pi^2(\omega c)^2$ it should be possible to solve the determinant and derive values of the force constants. An example of this procedure applied to one of the simplest cases, that of a linear unsymmetrical triatomic molecule, is given below.

It is generally true that the maximum number of determinable interaction constants and force constants cannot be greater than the number of measured fundamental frequencies—usually, the number is deliberately chosen to be less. The number of force constants and interaction terms used is fixed by the chosen potential energy expression; hence, if the maximum number of accurately measured frequencies is available, the accuracy of the ensuing force constants is determined by the exactness of the chosen potential energy equation. For CH_2Cl_2 the number of possible independent constants (interaction+force) for the most general type of the potential energy function is 17. However, it is possible only in theory to measure 9 fundamental frequencies ($3\times 5-6 = 9$), that is not more than 9 constants could be determined. However, if $CDHCl_2$ were also examined, there would now be $2\times 9 = 18$ fundamental frequencies available. This extra frequency would serve as an internal check to the whole procedure for deciding whether a suitable potential energy equation has been chosen.

Simple valence force field and simple central force field

The isotope procedure is not always feasible, and sometimes not all fundamental frequencies are available. The only avenue of approach, then, is to attempt to find a satisfactory potential energy function which uses a reduced number of independent constants. The two most important cases of simplified potential energy equations are the simple valence force field (S.V.F.F.) and the simple central force field (S.C.F.F.).

The S.V.F.F. assumes that the only forces in the molecule are associated with the valence bonds where:

(i) If a bond alters its length, there is a restoring force which is proportional to its change in length.

(ii) If the angle between two bonds alters, there is a restoring force proportional to the change in angle.

By the normal procedure for a linear triatomic molecule ABC as in

(A)→————(B)→————(C)→
m_1 q_1 m_2 q_2 m_3 q_3

the complete potential energy function would have been:

$$V = \tfrac{1}{2}k_{11}q_1^2+\tfrac{1}{2}k_{12}q_2^2+\tfrac{1}{2}k_{13}q_3^2+k_{12}q_1q_2+k_{13}q_1q_3+k_{23}q_2q_3$$

and to solve finally for these six unknown constants, six measured fundamental frequencies would be required. However, only three are observed, two for the stretching and one for the bending, and, therefore, by this approach the problem would be insoluble. By applying the S.V.F.F. the complete potential energy equation would be:

$$V = \tfrac{1}{2}k_1^1(\Delta r_1)^2+\tfrac{1}{2}k_2^1(\Delta r_2)^2+\tfrac{1}{2}k_\theta(\Delta\theta)^2 \tag{10.33}$$

where k_1^1 is the force constant of the A—B bond;
k_2^1 is the force constant of the B—C bond;
Δr_1 is the change in the bond length A—B;
Δr_2 is the change in the bond length B—C;
and k_θ is the force constant for the bending vibration, and $\Delta\theta$ is the change in angle.

Equation (10.33) is obviously an approximation as it neglects the interaction between the non-bonding atoms A and C, but it does often enable a reasonable solution to be gained. The neglect of interaction between non-bonded atoms is a general limitation to the method, since in molecules many non-bonded atoms do exert significant forces on one another. The determination of the stretching force constants (k_1^1 and k_2^1) will now be considered for this simplified approach. The potential energy equation for the parallel vibrations is obtained from equation (10.33):

$$V_{\parallel} = \tfrac{1}{2}\{k_1^1(\Delta r_1)^2 + k_2^1(\Delta r_2)^2\} \tag{10.34}$$

and the corresponding equation for the kinetic energy may be shown to be:

$$T_{\parallel} = \frac{1}{2}\left\{\frac{m_1(m_2+m_3)}{M}(\Delta \dot{r}_1)^2 + \frac{2m_1m_3}{M}\Delta\dot{r}_1\Delta\dot{r}_2 + \frac{m_3(m_1+m_2)}{M}(\Delta\dot{r}_2)^2\right\} \tag{10.35}$$

where

$$M = m_1+m_2+m_3 \quad \text{and} \quad T = \tfrac{1}{2}\Sigma a_{jl}\Delta\dot{r}_j\Delta\dot{r}_l \tag{10.36}$$

(see p. 314). Thus, the form of the kinetic energy equation is:

$$T_{\parallel} = \tfrac{1}{2}a_{11}\Delta\dot{r}_1^2 + \tfrac{1}{2}a_{12}\Delta\dot{r}_1\Delta\dot{r}_2 + \tfrac{1}{2}a_{21}\Delta\dot{r}_1\Delta\dot{r}_2 + \tfrac{1}{2}a_{22}\Delta\dot{r}_2^2 \tag{10.37}$$

$$T_{\parallel} = \tfrac{1}{2}a_{11}\Delta\dot{r}_1^2 + a_{12}\Delta\dot{r}_1\Delta\dot{r}_2 + \tfrac{1}{2}a_{22}\Delta\dot{r}_2^2 \tag{10.38}$$

On comparison of equations (10.35) and (10.38) it follows that

$$a_{11} = \frac{m_1(m_2+m_3)}{M}, \quad a_{12} = \frac{m_1m_3}{M} \quad \text{and} \quad a_{22} = \frac{m_3(m_1+m_2)}{M}$$

Substituting these values into the determinant, equation (10.32), we obtain for this case of two parallel vibrations of a linear molecule (i.e. $s = 2$):

$$\begin{vmatrix} \left\{k_{11} - \dfrac{m_1(m_2+m_3)}{M}\lambda\right\} & \left\{k_{12} - \dfrac{m_1m_3}{M}\lambda\right\} \\ \left\{k_{21} - \dfrac{m_1m_3}{M}\lambda\right\} & \left\{k_{22} - \dfrac{m_3(m_1+m_2)}{M}\lambda\right\} \end{vmatrix} = 0 \tag{10.39}$$

In the case being considered we have neglected cross terms, therefore $k_{12} = k_{21} = 0$, and k_{11} is taken as being equal to k_1^1 and k_{22} equal to k_2^1. The resulting equation is:

$$\left\{k_{11} - \frac{m_1(m_2+m_3)\lambda}{M}\right\}\left\{k_{22} - \frac{m_3(m_1+m_2)\lambda}{M}\right\} - \frac{m_1^2m_3^2\lambda^2}{M^2} = 0 \tag{10.40}$$

The roots, λ_1 and λ_2, of this quadratic equation are such that:

$$\lambda_1\lambda_2 = k_{11}k_{22}\frac{M}{m_1m_2m_3} \tag{10.41}$$

and

$$\lambda_1 + \lambda_2 = k_{11}\left(\frac{1}{m_1} + \frac{1}{m_2}\right) + k_{22}\left(\frac{1}{m_2} + \frac{1}{m_3}\right) \tag{10.42}$$

If the two measured frequencies for the normal parallel vibrations of the molecule ABC are $\omega_1 c$ and $\omega_2 c$, then the corresponding values of λ are given by:

$$\lambda_1 = 4\pi^2(\omega_1 c)^2 \tag{10.43}$$

and

$$\lambda_2 = 4\pi^2(\omega_2 c)^2 \tag{10.44}$$

Hence, on substitution of these values into equations (10.41) and (10.42) the values of k_{11} and k_{22} (i.e. $k_1^|$ and $k_2^|$, respectively) may be calculated in terms of the masses. Thus, by this procedure the values of the two stretching force constants are obtained.

The procedure for obtaining the bending force constant is simpler, since only one force constant is involved and for this perpendicular vibration:

$$V_\perp = \tfrac{1}{2}k_\theta(\Delta\theta)^2 \tag{10.45}$$

This is the other portion of the equation (10.33) where :

$$V = V_\parallel + V_\perp \tag{10.46}$$

It may be noted that the general form of the potential energy function for the S.V.F.F. is:

$$V = \Sigma\tfrac{1}{2}k_a(\Delta r_a)^2 + \Sigma\tfrac{1}{2}k_m(\Delta\theta_m)^2 \tag{10.47}$$

where Δr_a is the change in the length of the bond a from the equilibrium value, and $\Delta\theta_m$ is the distortion in the angle θ_m where the summations are carried out over all the bonds and angles.

In the case of CH_2Cl_2, where there are nine measured frequencies but seventeen unknowns in the general approach, when the S.V.F.F. is applied the number of unknown force constants is only five—k_CH, k_CCl, $k_{\theta\mathrm{ClCCl}}$, $k_{\theta\mathrm{HCH}}$, and $k_{\theta\mathrm{ClCH}}$. Hence, by this approach the problem is soluble without resorting to isotopes.

The S.C.F.F. is sometimes said to be a more suitable approach for the physicist than the chemist, as it assumes that the only forces between molecules are those between atoms along the line joining them, irrespective of whether they are bonded. This approach, unlike the S.V.F.F. one, places no emphasis on angular bending forces. The potential energy is represented by:

$$V = \Sigma\tfrac{1}{2}k_\mathrm{AB}(\Delta r_\mathrm{AB})^2 \tag{10.48}$$

where Δr_AB is the change in the distance between the atoms A and B from the equilibrium value, and k_AB is the force constant. The summation is made over all pairs of atoms; e.g. in CH_2Cl_2 there are five different constants, one being involved in each of the following:

(i) The carbon hydrogen (two of this type).
(ii) The carbon chlorine (two of this type).
(iii) The hydrogen-hydrogen separation (one of this type).
(iv) The chlorine-chlorine separation (one of this type).
(v) The chlorine-hydrogen separation (four of this type).

The S.V.F.F. is regarded as being closer to the truth than the S.C.F.F.—especially so for linear triatomic molecules where the S.C.F.F. does not take into account the bending vibrations of linear molecules, and it also fails to account for the out-of-plane vibrations of planar molecules. In addition, to this, the chemist requires information on individual chemical bonds for comparison in different molecules, and this is the type of knowledge which the S.V.F.F. yields.

An extension to the S.V.F.F. is by the inclusion of 'cross-terms' as in:

$$V = \Sigma\tfrac{1}{2}k_a\Delta r_a^2+\Sigma\tfrac{1}{2}k_m(\Delta\theta_m)^2+\Sigma\tfrac{1}{2}k_{ab}\Delta r_a\Delta r_b+\Sigma\tfrac{1}{2}k_{mn}\Delta\theta_m\Delta\theta_n+\Sigma\tfrac{1}{2}k_{am}\Delta\theta_m\Delta r_a \tag{10.49}$$

where a cross-term such as $\Delta r_a\Delta\theta_m$ is said to take into account that when the bond a changes its length, the equilibrium value of the bond angle θ is affected. The number of cross-terms which it is possible to introduce depends on the number of experimentally determined fundamental frequencies available, and the cross-terms are chosen on the grounds of what seems the most reasonable. Sometimes, however, there appears to be little physical significance for some of the cross-terms introduced, except that they make the data fit. It is always desirable to be able to check the cross-terms chosen and, therefore, the number of unknown constants should always be fewer than the number of frequencies available. The art of this type of research is to find a sufficiently general force field (a potential energy function) but yet not to have too many unknown constants for the considered molecule.

A few points on force constant work

(1) Bond force constants are measured in dyn/cm and measure the restoring force that would come into play if the bond were stretched 1 cm. Thus, the definition is an arbitrary one fixed by the formula: 10.1

(2) It may be misleading to use a force constant determined in one molecule for a similar bond in another molecule; e.g. the force constants for the C—H bond in the methyl halides vary as much as 6 per cent from one halide to another.

The force constants of a number of C—H bonds in different types of organic molecules vary from 4.4×10^5 in aldehydes to 5.9×10^5 dyn/cm in acetylene, that is a variation of 30 per cent. The factors affecting this variation appear to be:

(*a*) The type of hybridization of the carbon atom to which the atom is attached, since this affects the amount of overlap of the orbitals.

(*b*) The electrostatic nature of the bond.

(*c*) Resonance with various ionic structures.

Thus, the force constant approach is an important means of reflecting the difference in character of a particular type of bond in different molecules.

(3) As might be anticipated from the difficulty experienced in choosing a suitable potential energy function there is sometimes a variation in the value of the force constant quoted by different workers for a particular bond in the same molecule. For example, some of the quoted figures in the force constant of the C—Cl bond in CH_3Cl are:

3.35, 3.44, 3.61, 3.64, 4.42×10^5 dyn/cm

(4) It appears that less emphasis has been placed on the determination of bending force constants than on valence stretching force constants. More irregularities are observed in the former values, although some of them arise from using unsatisfactory force fields. In addition, since the values of bending force constants are small relative to stretching force constants, the former are much more dependent on the type of cross terms introduced.

(5) The bulk of the vibrational frequencies used in force-constant determinations for polyatomic molecules comes from the infra-red and Raman spectra, although for diatomic molecules electronic spectra have been quite prolific.

Errors in force constant work

Incorrect assignment of the determined frequency may lead to error. For example, in an infra-red determination of frequency a combination or overtone band may be mistaken for a fundamental.

The potential energy equations are based on simple harmonic motion, but the observed frequencies available are not normally values for infinitesimal displacements (i.e. not ω_e type values). This leads to error in the derived force constants. Thus in the H_2O molecule, if no correction is made for the anharmonicity of the vibrations, errors of the order of about 8 per cent ensue. In N_2O using uncorrected values the error in the force constant would be 3 per cent.

Other possible sources of error in force constant work are use of insufficient cross-terms or the choice of some wrong ones. In some cases measurements may not have been made on gaseous molecules but on those in the solid or liquid state where the vibrational frequencies may be slightly modified.

Application of force constants

For a particular bond A—X, where X is varied, the values of the force constants of the bonds are related to the positions of X in the periodic table. For example, when elements in the first short period of the periodic table are bonded to the hydrogen atom, the force constants for these bonds are:

B—H	C—H	N—H	O—H	F—H
3.6×10^5	5.0×10^5	6.5×10^5	7.6×10^5	$\sim9.0\times10^5$ dyn/cm

(where all the values are uncorrected for anharmonicity).

An empirical equation which relates the value of k to its position in the periodic table and its internuclear distance is that of Badger:

$$k = \frac{1.86\times10^5}{(r_e-d_{ij})^3} \tag{10.50}$$

where r_e is preferably the equilibrium internuclear distance, and d_{ij} is a constant which depends on the rows of the periodic table where the two atoms are contained.

One of the best of the empirical relationships between internuclear distance and force constant is that due to Gordy:

$$k = 1.67N\left(\frac{x_A x_B}{r_e^2}\right)^{\frac{3}{4}} + 0.30 \tag{10.51}$$

where x_A and x_B are the *Pauling electronegativities* of atoms A and B, N is the bond order (that is, the effective number of covalent or ionic bonds acting

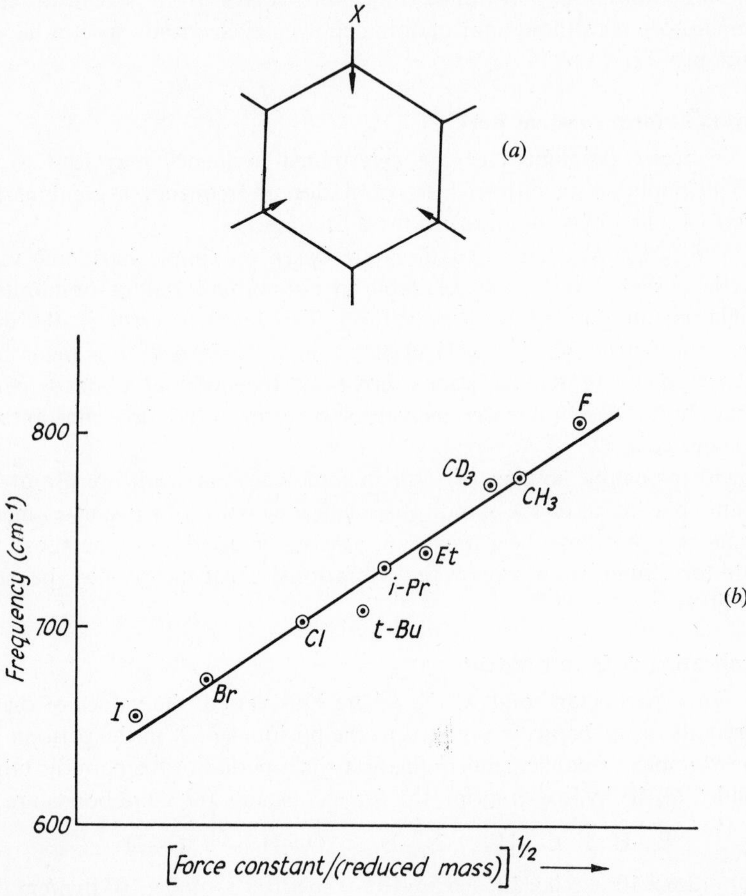

FIG. 10.2 (*a*) A vibrational frequency of monosubstituted benzene derivatives. (*b*) Plot of this vibrational frequency against $(k/\mu)^{\frac{1}{2}}$ for C_6H_5X molecules where $X = $ F, Cl, Br, CH_3, CD_3, C_2H_5, iPr, and tBu. μ is the reduced mass and is given by: $1/\mu = 1/m_C + 1/m_X$ where m_C is the mass of the ring carbon atom and m_X that of the attached group.

between the two atoms), and r_e is the equilibrium internuclear distance in Ångström units.

Attempts have been made to relate the heat of dissociation of a bond to its force constant, and for the C—C bond in different substances kr_e^2/D seems a constant quantity. However, it is very doubtful that there can be any precise correlation between dissociation energies and force constants, though there will be a general parallelism, as is borne out for the O—O bond in different substances, where the graphs of both k and D against r_e are smooth curves.

Bindley and Walker[1a] studied certain vibrational frequencies of monosubstituted benzene compounds and found that a plot of the vibrational frequency of the type in Fig. 10.2*a* against (CX stretching force constant/reduced mass)$^{\frac{1}{2}}$ gave a straight line (Fig. 10.2*b*). The fact that the force constant had to be included to obtain a linear plot suggested that the nature of the CX bond might be involved.

One of the aims in force constant work has been to bring about a better understanding of the chemical bond and to assist the development of the valence theory.

Generally, for bonds involving the carbon atom as one member the force constants of single bonds are about 5×10^5, those of double bonds about 10×10^5, and those of triple bonds about 15×10^5 dyn/cm. Thus, the force constants of single, double, and triple bonds are approximately in the ratio 1 : 2 : 3; hence, the force constant may be used to assess the bond order for bonds between a given pair of atoms. As an example of this the value of the CO link in the following molecules may be considered:

	carbon monoxide	carbon dioxide	formaldehyde
k(dyn/cm)	18.5×10^5	15.5×10^5	12.3×10^5

and this indicates that the carbon–oxygen link in CO_2 is intermediate between that in formaldehyde and carbon monoxide; that is, there is more than a double but less than a triple bond.

In a similar way for ClCN the C—Cl bond has a force constant of 5.3×10^5 whereas in CH_3Cl it is 3.4×10^5 dyn/cm. Thus, the C—Cl bond in ClCN by this simple approach would be judged to be more than a single bond and somewhere intermediate in structure between:

—Cl—C≡N and >Cl=C=N<

However, these considerations neglect the change in hybridisation of the C atom in the ClCN and CH_3Cl molecules.

It may well seem that from the examples given of the application of force constant work to chemical problems that such work does not merit such detailed consideration and that better methods are available for characterising a chemical bond. As yet the force constant work has not been directed at solving a large number of chemical problems. To some extent the method has not realised its inherent potentialities, and a limiting factor has been in the choice of a satisfactory potential energy function from which the force constants could be determined from the measured vibrational frequencies.

In the force constant work, greater emphasis has been placed on examining the merits of various force fields (potential energy functions) than in the study of direct chemical problems. This study of force fields is fundamental as it governs all the types of forces at work within the molecules—even the non-bonding forces—and Linnett,[1b] in what is called an *orbital force field approach*, has included terms for the repulsion between non-bonded atoms. In two later papers[2,3] this was extended to allow for the change in hybridisation of the carbon orbitals during the vibration. Another refinement of the valence-force is due to Urey and Bradley[4] which also takes into account the repulsive force between the non-bonded atoms. For example, in the analysis of methylene chloride a term taking into account the repulsion between the two chlorine atoms is added to those of the normal valence force approach.

It is in the development of improved force fields that the real potentiality of the work would appear to lie, and from that the extended chemical applications of force constants should follow. Thus, it might eventually be possible to predict the values of force constants in molecules—without experiment—and then to calculate their vibrational frequencies from the predicted force constants. One of the modes of attack is to use more isotopic molecules (e.g. of D, ^{13}C and ^{15}N); these provide more fundamental frequencies and enable a better potential energy function to be chosen.

There is a most comprehensive review on force constants by Linnett[5] and a more recent report by the same author.[6]

References

1a. BINDLEY, T. F. and WALKER, S. To be published.
1b. HEATH, D. F. and LINNETT, J. W. *Trans. Faraday Soc.* **44** (1948), 556, 561, 873, 878, 884.
2. LINNETT, J. W. and WHEATLEY, P. J. *Trans. Faraday Soc.* **45** (1949), 33, 39.
3. HEATH, D. F. and LINNETT, J. W. *Trans. Faraday Soc.* **45** (1949), 264.
4. UREY, H. C. and BRADLEY, C. A. *Phys. Rev.* **38** (1931), 1969.
5. LINNETT, J. W. *Quart. Rev.* **1** (1947), 73.
6. LINNETT, J. W. *Chem. Soc. Ann. Rept.* **49** (1952), 7.

11

Evaluation of thermodynamic functions from spectroscopic data

Introduction

To calculate thermodynamic functions such as entropy and free energy from spectroscopic data it is necessary to assign and measure the vibrational frequencies; infra-red and Raman spectra have been the main contributors to this work. In addition, it is necessary to evaluate the moments of inertia, which may be obtained for simple molecules from rotational studies in the microwave region, from the rotational structure of vibrational bands (mainly infra-red), or from methods which determine the internuclear distances (e.g. electron diffraction) and, thus, permit the calculation of the moment of inertia. For diatomic molecules electronic spectra are a prolific source of vibrational frequencies and moments of inertia.

From the vibrational frequencies, moments of inertia and the absolute temperature, it is possible to calculate what is known as the *total partition function*, and by substitution of this value into certain equations derived from statistical mechanics the thermodynamic function may be calculated.

For a system of N molecules in thermal equilibrium, if there are N_i molecules in a state of total energy ε_i, then according to the Maxwell-Boltzmann distribution law:

$$N_i \alpha g_i e^{-\varepsilon_i/kT} \tag{11.1}$$

where g_i is the total statistical weight (i.e. degeneracy—see later) of ε_i.

If N is the total number of molecules in a given volume of gas:

$$N \alpha \Sigma g_i e^{-\varepsilon_i/kT} \tag{11.2}$$

where

$$f = \Sigma g_i e^{-\varepsilon_i/kT} \tag{11.3}$$

Hence, it follows from equations (11.1), (11.2), and (11.3):

$$N_i = \frac{Ng_i e^{-\varepsilon_i/kT}}{f} \tag{11.4}$$

where f is termed the partition function to which all the thermodynamic quantities may be related. N_0 molecules possess energy ε_0, and N_1 molecules, energy ε_1 and so on, and the total number of molecules in the system is:

$$N = N_0+N_1+N_2+N_3+ \ldots = \sum_i N_i \tag{11.5}$$

The total energy of the system is:

$$\Sigma N_i\varepsilon_i = \varepsilon \tag{11.6}$$

Degeneracy

In some problems connected with partition functions certain energy levels may be so close together in value that for purposes of calculation they may be taken to coincide, i.e. to be degenerate. Such an example may be seen in the energy levels of the hydrogen atom, whose spectrum could almost be explained completely in terms of the principal quantum number. Thus, for the same value of n, different l values lead to virtually the same energy values, and if the energy level values for the 1s, 2s, 2p, 3s, 3p, and 3d were respectively ε_0, ε_1, ε_2, ε_3, ε_4 and ε_5 . . ., there would be negligible error in partition function calculations when the following assumptions are made:

$$\varepsilon_1 = \varepsilon_2, \quad \varepsilon_3 = \varepsilon_4 = \varepsilon_5 \tag{11.7}$$

Thus $g_0 = 1$, $g_1, = 2$, $g_2 = 3$, where the g values measure the degeneracy of the levels ε_0, ε_1, and ε_3, respectively.

For a diatomic molecule in a given electronic state the rotational energies are degenerate, and for a particular rotational energy state the degeneracy is $2J+1$, where J is the rotational quantum number of the molecule. In this case when

$$J = 0, 1, 2, 3 \ \ldots \ \text{then} \ (2J+1) = 1, 3, 5, 7 \ \ldots \tag{11.8}$$

and only the $J = 0$ level is non-degenerate, the other levels having a degeneracy of 3, 5, 7, . . . respectively.

The vibrational levels of all diatomic molecules have $g = 1$, that is they are non-degenerate.

Another form of degeneracy is associated with nuclear spin. In a heteronuclear diatomic molecule, where one of the nuclei has a spin quantum number of I_1, its degeneracy is $(2I_1+1)$, and if the other atom has a nuclear spin quantum number of I_2, its degeneracy is $(2I_2+1)$. The total spin quantum degeneracy for this heteronuclear diatomic molecule is then:

$$g = (2I_1+1)(2I_2+1) \tag{11.9}$$

Determination of translational, vibrational and rotational partition functions

The total energy of a perfect molecular gas may be divided up into the following energy contributions:

Total energy = translational+electronic+vibrational+rotational (11.10)

and the total partition function (f) is given by the product of the corresponding individual contributions:

$$f = f_T \times f_e \times f_y \times f_r \tag{11.11}$$

and the total statistical weight by:

$$g = g_T \times g_e \times g_v \times g_r \tag{11.12}$$

Nearly all molecules in the ground state, and the corresponding electronic energy is arbitrarily chosen to be zero, and consequently $f_e = 1$.

The translational, vibrational, and rotational partition functions may each be calculated separately from appropriate formulae.

The translational partition function is:

$$f_T = \left(\frac{2\pi mkT}{h^2}\right)^{3/2} \times V \tag{11.13}$$

where V is the volume of the system, the absolute temperature, and on the mass of the molecule. Thus, f_T may be readily calculated.

In the case of a diatomic molecule, if the vibration is taken to be simple harmonic,† and if the wave-number of the mechanical oscillator is ω, then $\varepsilon_v = hvc\omega$, where the energy is measured from the $v = 0$ level and $v = 0$, 1, 2, 3. . . . The vibrational partition function becomes:

$$f_v = \sum_i \exp(-\varepsilon_i/kT) = \{1 + \exp(-hc\omega/kT) + \exp(-2hc\omega/kT) + \ldots\} \tag{11.14}$$

and, therefore:

$$f_v = \{1 - \exp(-hc\omega/kT)\}^{-1} \tag{11.15}$$

Hence, by inserting the experimentally determined ω into equation (11.15) f_v may be calculated.

The rotational energy of a rigid diatomic molecule of moment of inertia I is:

$$E_r = \frac{J(J+1)h^2}{8\pi^2 I} \tag{11.16}$$

where the degeneracy is $2J+1$ and if nuclear spin is neglected, the partition function for the rotational part is:

$$f_r = \Sigma(2J+1) \exp\left\{-\frac{J(J+1)h^2}{8\pi^2 IkT}\right\} \tag{11.17}$$

† Negligible error often results in the calculated thermodynamic quantities if this assumption is employed.

This may be evaluated to:†

$$f_r = \frac{8\pi^2 IkT}{h^2} \tag{11.18}$$

If, however, the rotator is symmetrical, for example H_2 or X_2 in general, this partition function must be reduced by an integer:

$$f_r = \frac{8\pi^2 IkT}{\sigma h^2} \tag{11.19}$$

where σ is known as the *symmetry factor* and is equal to the number of indistinguishable positions obtained by rotation of the molecule as a whole through 360°. Thus, for H_2, Br_2, and O_2, $\sigma = 2$, because by turning the molecule of the type X_2:

$$X'—X''$$

through 180° the form

$$X''—X'$$

is obtained, where X′ is indistinguishable from X″. (The superscript marks are added to distinguish one atom from another.)

For asymmetrical molecules such as HCl, H—Cl and Cl—H are distinguishable and $\sigma = 1$.

For a complex molecule such as benzene resting in an XY plane, by rotating the molecule through 60° an indistinguishable configuration is produced from the previous one, and similarly at 120°, 180°, 240°, 300°, and 360°; that is six indistinguishable arrangements are obtained. In addition, if the molecule is turned through 180° about the X-axis, this gives six further indistinguishable arrangements. Thus, the symmetry number of benzene is 12.

Total partition function

(*a*) *For diatomic molecules*

If the only contributing factors are translational, vibrational, and rotational motions, then on substitution for f_T, f_v and f_r into equation (11.11) we get:

$$f = \left\{\frac{(2\pi mkT)^{3/2}}{h^3} V\right\} \times \left\{\frac{8\pi^2 IkT}{\sigma h^2}\right\} \times \{1 - \exp(-hc\omega/kT)\}^{-1} \tag{11.20}$$

(*b*) *For polyatomic molecules*

For a molecule with three different moments of inertia, I_x, I_y and I_z

$$f_r = \frac{\pi^{1/2}(8\pi^2 kT)^{3/2}(I_x I_y I_z)^{1/2}}{\sigma h^3} \tag{11.21}$$

If the molecule may be taken as being composed of n harmonic oscillators of vibrational frequencies $\omega_1, \omega_2 \ldots \omega_n$ in cm^{-1} units, then the corresponding f_v is given by:

† An approximation is involved in this evaluation, and the formula does not hold for light molecules at low temperatures.

$$f_v = \{1-\exp(-hc\omega_1/kT)\}^{-1} \times \{1-\exp(-hc\omega_2/kT)\}^{-1} \times \ldots$$
$$\ldots \{1-\exp(-hc\omega_n/kT)\}^{-1} \quad (11.22)$$

The translational partition function is still:

$$f_T = \frac{(2\pi mkT)^{3/2}V}{h^3} \quad (11.23)$$

Applying these f_T, f_v and f_r equations to a non-linear triatomic molecule with moments of inertia I_x, I_y, and I_z where the vibrational frequencies are ω_1, ω_2, and ω_3 we get:

$$f = \left\{\frac{(2\pi mkT)^{3/2}V}{h^3}\right\} \times \left\{\frac{\pi^{1/2}(8\pi^2 kT)^{3/2}(I_x I_y I_z)^{1/2}}{\sigma h^3}\right\} \times [\{1-\exp(-hc\omega_1/kT)\}^{-1} \times$$
$$\{1-\exp(-hc\omega_2/kT)\}^{-1}\{1-\exp(-hc\omega_3/kT)\}^{-1}] \quad (11.24)$$

Thermodynamic quantities from evaluated partition functions

It may be shown by statistical methods that the total partition function may be related to certain simple thermodynamic functions such as molar heat capacity at constant pressure (C°). Thus, the total energy ($E°$) of one mole of a perfect gas is given by:

$$E° = E_0° + N_1\varepsilon_1 + N_2\varepsilon_2 + N_3\varepsilon_3 + \ldots \quad (11.25)$$

where $E_0°$ is the zero-point energy and N_1, N_2 . . the number of molecules with energies ε_1, ε_2 . . . above the lowest energy. On substitution from equation (11.4) into (11.25):

$$E° = E_0° + \frac{N\Sigma g_i\varepsilon_i e^{-\varepsilon_i/kT}}{f} \quad (11.26)$$

$$= E_0° + NkT^2\frac{df/dT}{f} \quad (11.27)$$

$$= E_0° + RT^2\frac{d\ln f}{dT} \quad (11.28)$$

where N is the Avogadro number. It follows that the heat content $H°$ of one mole of a perfect gas is:

$$H° = E_0° + RT + RT^2\frac{d\ln f}{dT}$$

and hence the molar heat capacity at constant pressure is given by:

$$\frac{dH°}{dT} = C_p° = R + R\frac{d}{dT}\left[T^2\frac{d\ln f}{dT}\right]$$

Hence, if the partition function is obtained, then the heat capacity follows.

It may be shown also by means of statistical mechanics that for one mole of a perfect gas the entropy ($S°$) is given by the equation:

$$S° = R(1-\ln N) + RT\frac{d\ln f}{dT} + R\ln f$$

where N is Avogadro's number.

For further details on the evaluation of other thermodynamic functions and the application of partition functions to chemical equilibria more advanced works by Herzberg,[1] Rushbrooke,[2] and Fowler and Guggenheim[3] should be consulted. The aim here has been merely to define the terms and give a few of the basic equations. However, to emphasise the success of the statistical approach some entropy values obtained this way will now be compared with calorimetric values.

Comparison of statistical entropies with calorimetric values

In order to consider the success of the statistical approach based on spectral data in calculating thermodynamic functions a comparison will now be made of some of the statistical and calorimetric entropy values. Statistical entropies have been evaluated for a number of diatomic and simple polyatomic gases; a few examples are listed in Table 11.1 and are compared with the corresponding calorimetric values which are dependent on the assumption of the third law of thermodynamics.

TABLE 11.1

Entropy values in cal/mole per degree at 298.1°K

Gas (1 atm)	Statistical	Calorimetric
N_2	45.78	45.9
HCl	44.64	44.5
H_2S	49.10	49.15
NH_3	45.94	45.91
CH_3Br	58.74	58.61

For the majority of gases the two methods give agreement within about 0.2 cal/mole per degree, which can be the order of the experimental error. In the following cases serious disagreement results:

	Statistical	Calorimetric
CO	47.31	46.2
H_2	31.23	29.74
CH_3OH	58.38	56.63

The statistical value has been calculated on the assumption that there are only translational, vibrational, and rotational contributions. However, in these apparent divergences between the two methods the following factor have been neglected:

(i) In carbon monoxide the two atoms have a similar electronic structure. Even if the crystals of carbon monoxide were cooled very slowly as 0°K is approached, a perfectly regular lattice would not result. Instead the lattice would contain two different orientations of carbon monoxide (i.e. CO) and this type rotated through 180° (i.e. OC). Such a lattice containing two forms would have a maximum entropy of $R \ln 2$ at 0°K, that is, 1.4 cal/mole per degree. Since the calorimetric value is based on the assumption that the entropy at 0°K is zero, then the 1.4 cal/mole per degree has to be added to the calorimetric value; the resultant value is then in reasonable agreement with the statistical value.

(ii) The discrepancy between the two values in the case of hydrogen may be accounted for in terms of *ortho*- and *para*-hydrogen where these two forms have the different resultant nuclear spin of 1 and 0, respectively. In the *para*-form the nuclear spins are antiparallel, and the rotational quantum numbers for this form are 0, 2, 4, . . . , and the corresponding rotational energy levels are symmetric (see p. 61). The *ortho*-form, however, has both the nuclear spins parallel, and the rotational quantum numbers are 1, 3, 5, . . . and these energy levels are antisymmetric. For homonuclear molecules the selection rule forbids transitions between antisymmetric (a) and symmetric (s) levels. It follows, therefore, that since both *ortho*- and *para*-hydrogen are normally present at ordinary temperatures, then in the region of the absolute zero temperature both the $J = 0$ and $J = 1$ rotational levels will be occupied, since the $1 \rightarrow 0$ transition is forbidden, because the $J = 0$ level is symmetric and the $J = 1$ level antisymmetric. However, the selection rule $s \leftarrow\!/\!\rightarrow a$ is not rigid for such molecules as hydrogen where the nuclear spin quantum number is not zero, although the $1 \rightarrow 0$ transition may take months or years before it occurs; thus, unless the experiment were carried out extremely slowly, the calorimetric value for the entropy, based on the entropy of hydrogen being zero at 0°K, would not hold exactly.

(iii) In the case of CH_3OH the statistical method assumed in the calculation that there was free rotation between the CH_3 and OH groups in the molecule. In fact, evidence from many sources now indicates that rotation about the C—O bond is hindered, resulting in certain positions being preferred. Unless this were taken into account, agreement between the statistical and calorimetric values would not be expected.

Conclusions

The excellent agreement between the statistical and calorimetric entropy values confirms the validity of the assumptions in the statistical treatment and supports the concept that at 0°K many substances are perfect crystals.

The apparent initial disagreement between the statistical and calorimetric values is generally of great interest in that it indicates the neglect of a particular physical phenomenon which is contributing towards the total energy. Thus, it may be concluded that the statistical approach based on spectroscopic data is a highly successful one.

References

1. HERZBERG, G. *Spectra of Diatomic Molecules*. D. Van Nostrand (New York, 1950), and *Infra-red and Raman Spectra of Polyatomic Molecules*. D. Van Nostrand (New York, 1945).

2. Rushbrooke, G. S. *Introduction to Statistical Mechanics*, Oxford University Press (1949).
3. Fowler, R. and Guggenheim, E. A. *Statistical Thermodynamics.* Cambridge University Press, 1949.

12

Application of spectroscopy to astrophysics

Instrumentation

THE study of stellar spectra may be carried out using either one of the spectrographs described in Chapter 2 or by a slitless type. In the slitless type of spectrograph, instead of a series of monochromatic images of the slit leading to bands and lines on the photographic plate, a series of monochromatic images of the source are produced on the plate. A simple form of slitless spectrograph is the objective prism type where light collected by a telescope is dispersed by a large prism and focused on to a photographic plate situated in the focal plane of the telescope.

Slit spectrographs of both the prism and grating types are employed in conjunction with large light-gathering telescopes of both the refracting and reflecting types to study stellar spectra. The refracting telescopes have lenses which focus the image of the source on to the slit of the spectrograph, but these suffer from the disadvantage that different wavelengths are refracted to differing extents. Reflecting telescopes, however, which have large concave mirrors, do not have this drawback.

Reflecting telescopes are constructed so that secondary mirrors can be brought into the light path, and this gives a variety of positions at which the spectra may be recorded. Four such arrangements of a reflecting telescope are illustrated in Fig. 12.1. One of these positions is termed the *prime focus arrangement* and is illustrated in Fig. 12.1(*a*). Light from the source enters the telescope and is reflected by a large parabolic mirror M on to the slit of a spectrograph S which is situated at the focus of the parabolic reflecting mirror. If the reflecting telescope is not one of the largest, however, this prime focus arrangement is restricted in its use, since any spectrograph placed at the focus of the parabolic reflector would seriously reduce the amount of light from the source entering the telescope. Another arrangement of a reflecting telescope is shown in Fig. 12.1(*b*), and is known as the *Newtonian mounting*. A plane mirror M_1 placed in the light path just below the focus of the parabolic mirror, *M*, causes the light to pass through a small hole provided in the wall of the telescope and on to the spectrograph slit at *S*.

The *Cassegrain arrangement* illustrated in Fig. 12.1(*c*) involves a convex hyperbolic mirror M_2 set in the convergent beam of light below the focus of the parabolic reflecting mirror *M*. The mirror M_2 reverses the beam of light along a path through a hole in the centre of the main parabolic reflector, the slit of the spectrograph being located at *S*.

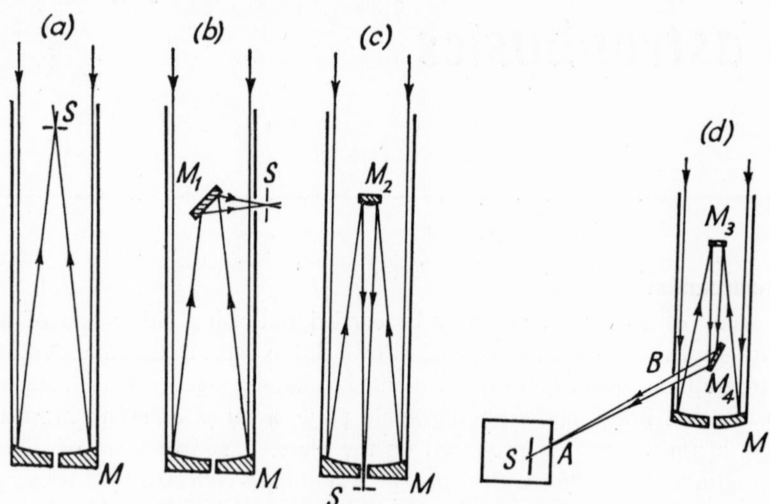

FIG. 12.1 (*a*) The prime focus, (*b*) Newtonian, (*c*) Cassegrain, and (*d*) coudé arrangements of a reflecting telescope

Another commonly used position is the *coudé focus* illustrated in Fig. 12.1(*d*), in which the light beam from the parabolic mirror *M* is reversed by a convex mirror M_3 (similar to that used in the Cassegrain arrangement but of different curvature) to a further mirror M_4 which deflects the converging beam along the hollow axis *AB* of the telescope. The spectrograph *S* is situated in an air-conditioned, temperature-controlled laboratory below the main reflecting mirror *M*.

While all of the described foci are employed, the Cassegrain and coudé positions are favoured, since larger spectrographs may be used in these arrangements. It is easier to mount the spectrograph at the Cassegrain focus without causing strain to be placed on the reflecting mirror *M* which must be very accurately supported. In the coudé arrangement the spectrograph is completely separated from the telescope. However, on account of the shorter focal length, the prime focus and the Newtonian positions are best for investigating electromagnetic radiation of low intensity.

A powerful modern type of reflecting telescope is the *Schmidt type* the optical arrangement of which is illustrated in Fig. 12.2. A spherical mirror *M*

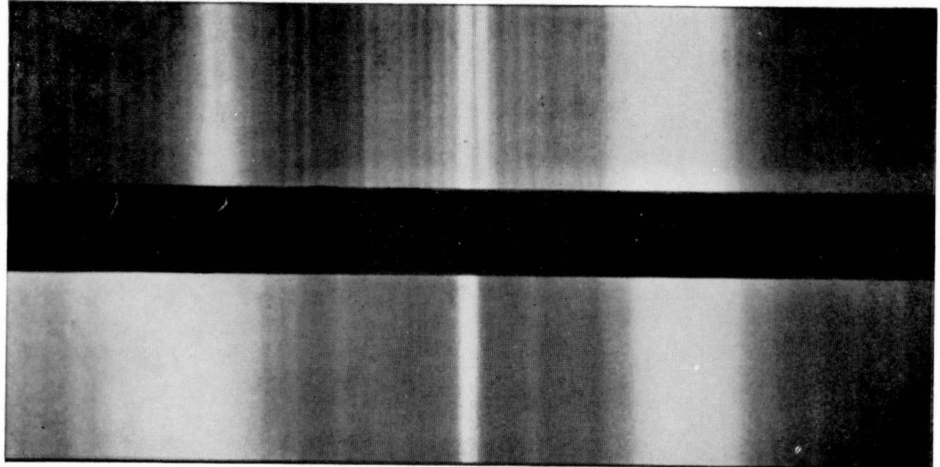

FIG. 12.4 Spectrogram of the binary star β-Aurigae. In the centre of the upper spectrogram (*a*) the doubling of the 3933·7 Å line of singly-ionised Ca may be observed while in the lower spectrogram (*b*) a single line may be seen. (*Courtesy of the Harvard Observatory.*) (See p. 339)

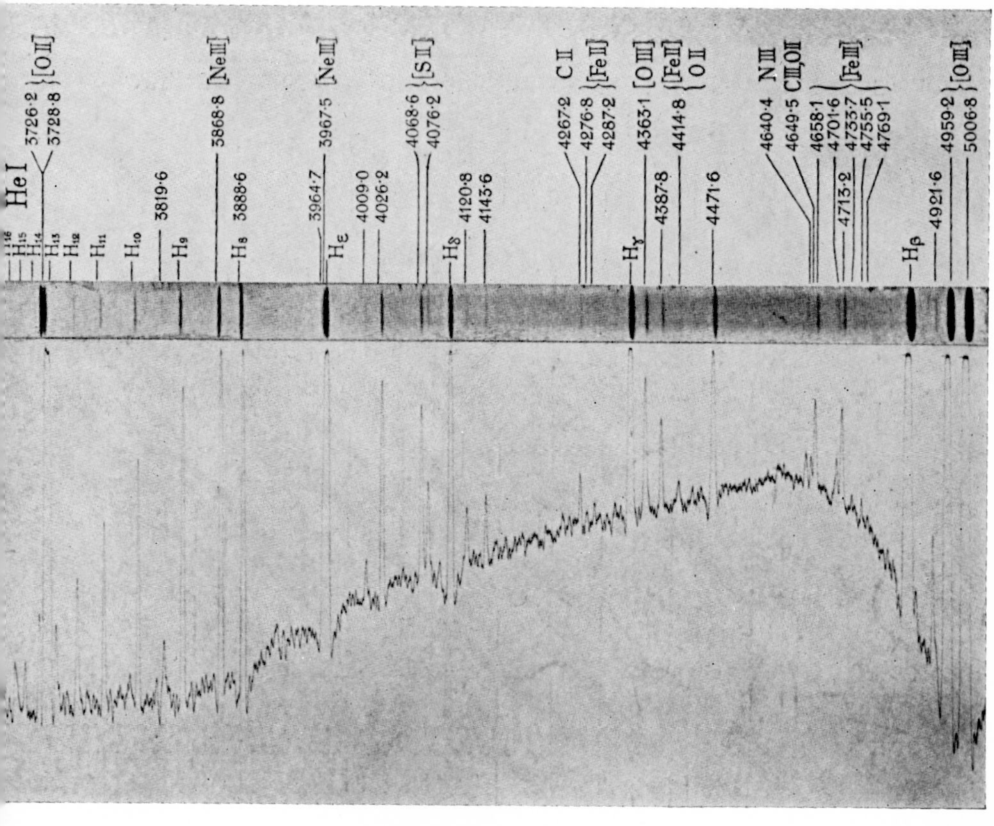

G. 12.5 Spectrogram and microphotometer trace of the Orion Nebula. The spectrogram was obtained ing a spectrograph with a single prism employed in conjunction with a 120 cm telescope. (*After Tcheng Mao-Lin and Dufay.*[8] *Courtesy of Professor J. Dufay and Messrs. Hutchinson.*) (See p. 343)

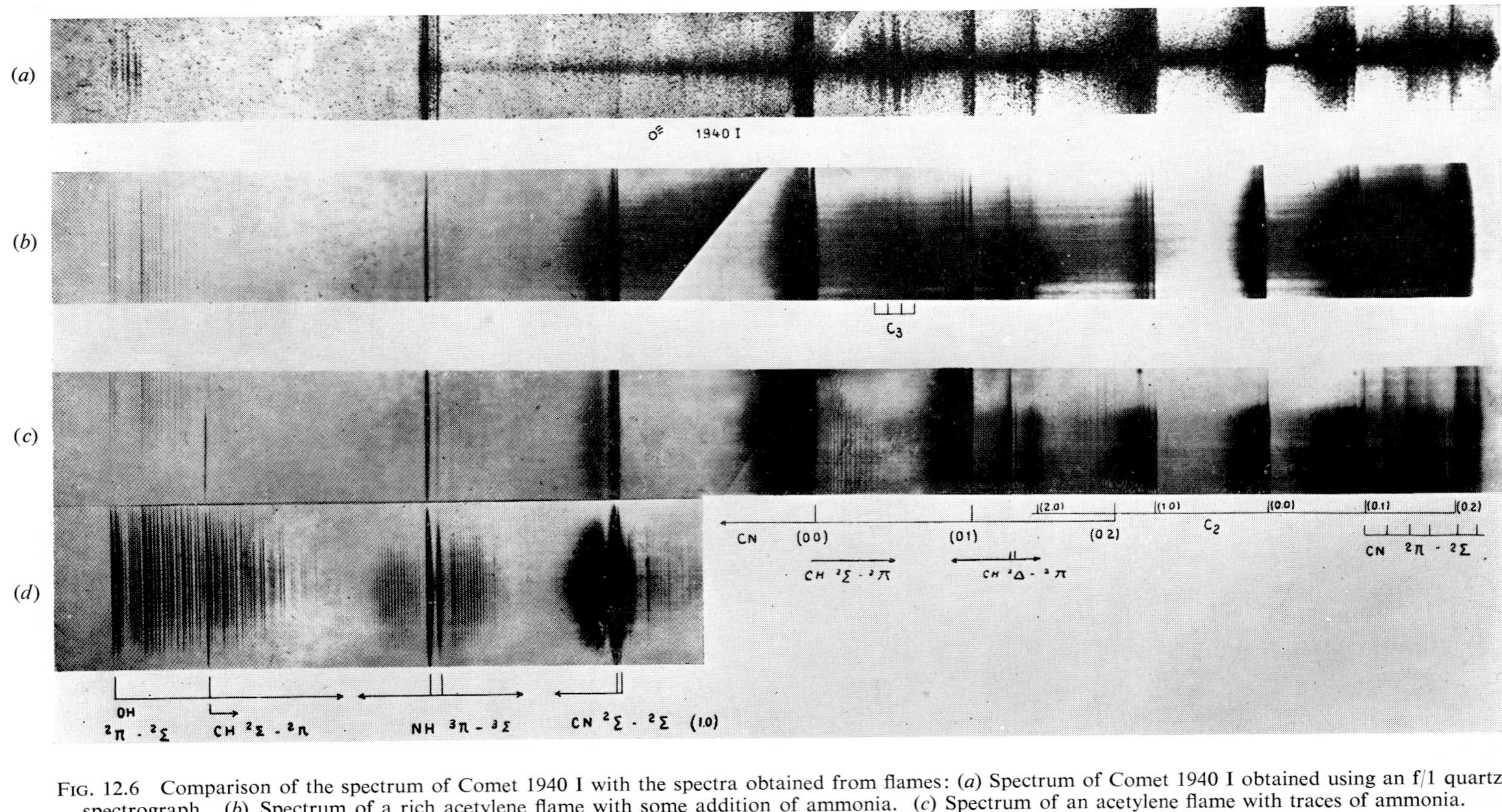

FIG. 12.6 Comparison of the spectrum of Comet 1940 I with the spectra obtained from flames: (*a*) Spectrum of Comet 1940 I obtained using an f/1 quartz spectrograph. (*b*) Spectrum of a rich acetylene flame with some addition of ammonia. (*c*) Spectrum of an acetylene flame with traces of ammonia. (*d*) Spectrum of an acetylene flame with ammonia. (*After Swings and Haser.*[14] *Courtesy of Dr. P. Swings.*) (See p. 346)

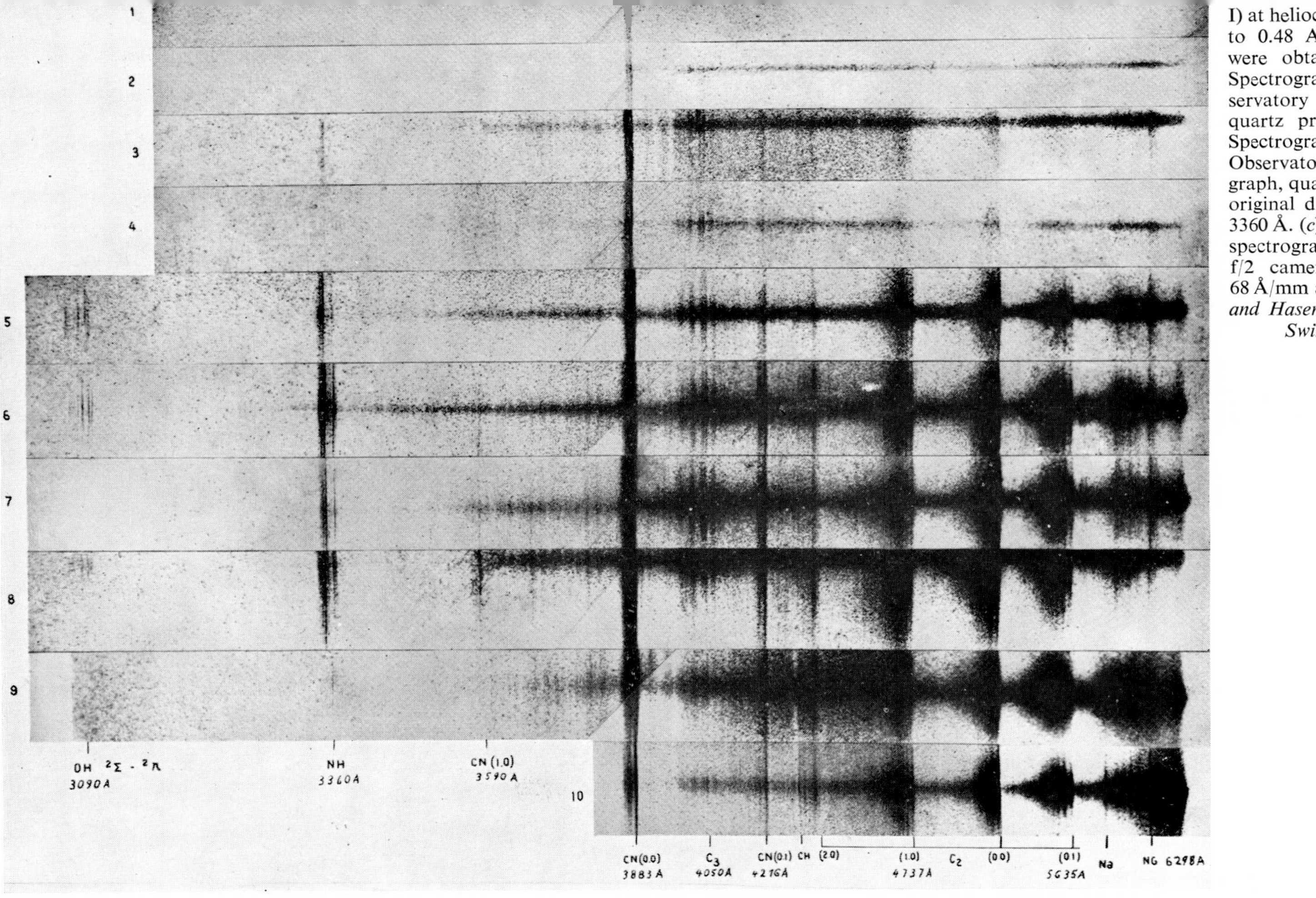

I) at heliocentric distances of 2.24 to 0.48 A.U. The spectrograms were obtained as follows: (*a*) Spectrogram 1: McDonald Observatory nebular spectrograph, quartz prisms, f/1 camera. (*b*) Spectrograms 2 to 9: McDonald Observatory Cassegrain spectrograph, quartz prisms, f/1 camera, original dispersion 137 Å/mm at 3360 Å. (*c*) Spectrogram 10: same spectrograph as in (*b*) but with an f/2 camera, original dispersion 68 Å/mm at 3360 Å. (*After Swings and Haser.*[14] *Courtesy of Dr. P. Swings.*) (See p. 347)

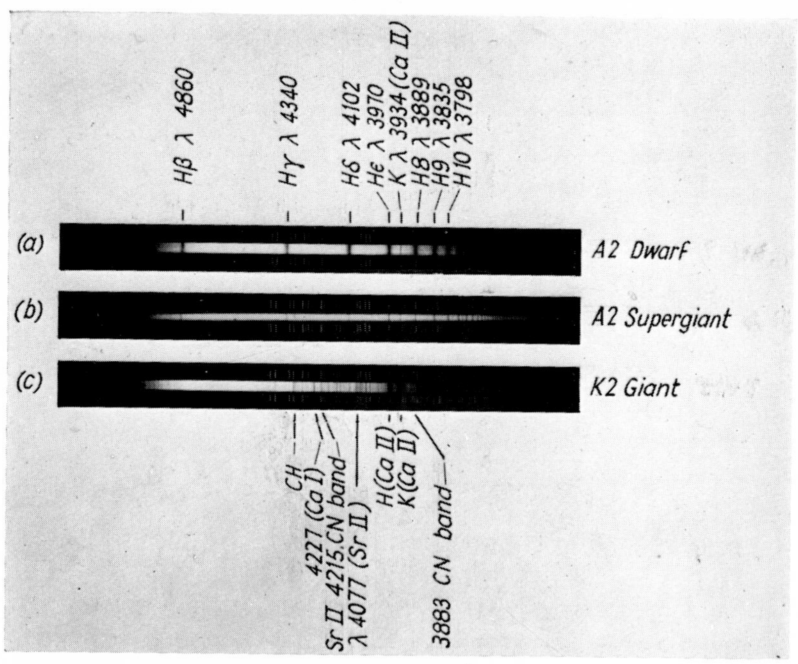

FIG. 12.8 Stellar spectrograms of (*a*) *A*2 dwarf, (*b*) *A*2 supergiant, (*c*) *K*2 giant. (*Courtesy of the Astronomer Royal.*) (See p. 349)

FIG. 12.12 Isotope effect in the C_2 Swan band $A^3\Pi_g \rightarrow X^3\Pi_u 1 \rightarrow 0$ produced in an electric furnace at approximately 2800°C. The $^{12}C^{12}C$ (1, 0) band lies at 4737.1 Å and that of $^{13}C^{12}C$ at 4744.5 Å. (*After King and Birge.*[16] *Courtesy of 'The Astrophysical Journal'*.) (See p. 354)

is employed in conjunction with a correcting lens C. The lens C is plane on one side whilst the other side is convex in the central portion and concave in the outer sections. The convex section acts as a converging lens and the concave portion as a diverging lens. The correcting lens C forms no image and does not necessarily alter the focal length or the magnification of the system. Its object is to correct for spherical aberration of the main spherical mirror M.

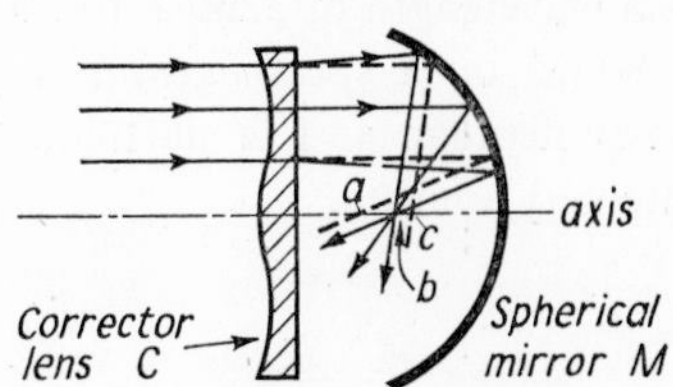

FIG. 12.2 The optical arrangement of a Schimdt telescope

With no correcting lens (broken lines) the rays cross the axis of the system at different points a, b, and c, while with the lens C in position the rays (full lines) cross the axis at the same point b, thus eliminating spherical aberration. The focal surface of the Schmidt telescope is curved so that the photographic plate or film must always be curved correspondingly to conform with the focal surface of the mirror M. The Schmidt telescope may be constructed to give a very short focal length, and in consequence a high photographic speed is possible. It also has good definition over a very wide field of view which is not possible with a parabolic mirror type reflector. In fact, Schmidt telescopes are often used for searching out objects to be viewed by the more restricted reflecting telescopes.

The optical arrangement of the Schmidt telescope makes possible high photographic speed and excellent definition of the image which are desirable features to have in the spectrograph camera itself, since a short-focus camera permits the entrance slit to be widened sufficiently to take in most of the star's image without losing resolution on the plate. The conventional arrangement of camera lens and plate holder may, therefore, be replaced in the spectrograph by a spherical mirror M and a correcting lens C of the same design as that employed in the Schmidt telescope. The plate holder P is mounted at the focus of the spherical mirror and curved so as to conform with the optical surface of this mirror. This arrangement is known as the *Schmidt camera*.

To illustrate the use of a Schmidt camera the type of spectrograph used to investigate the spectrum of the night sky or of nebulae† may be considered. Before it enters the spectrograph light from the source is reflected by a plane mirror M_1 (see Fig. 12.3(a)) provided with a shutter to a further mirror M_2. The shutter over the mirror M_1 limits its useful width, this mirror acting as the slit of the spectrograph. The distance between the mirrors M_1 and M_2 is 75 ft, and that between the mirror M_2 and the spectrograph is the same distance. The distance of the slit from the first prism makes a collimating lens unnecessary. The spectrograph illustrated in Fig. 12.3(b) consists of two 60° quartz prisms and an $f/1$ Schmidt camera with a focal length of approximately 10 cm. Light from the mirror M_2 (see Fig. 12.3(a)) enters the

† Clouds of gas or of fine solid particles.

spectrograph, is dispersed by the prisms, and passes through a corrector lens C. The spectrum is focused on the photographic film P by the spherical mirror M. The linear dispersion of such an instrument varies from 115 Å/mm at a wavelength of 3200 Å to 500 Å/mm at 5000 Å. The instrument described is based on a spectrograph employed by Struve[1] and his collaborators to study nebulae and is particularly suitable for the study of extended low-intensity sources.

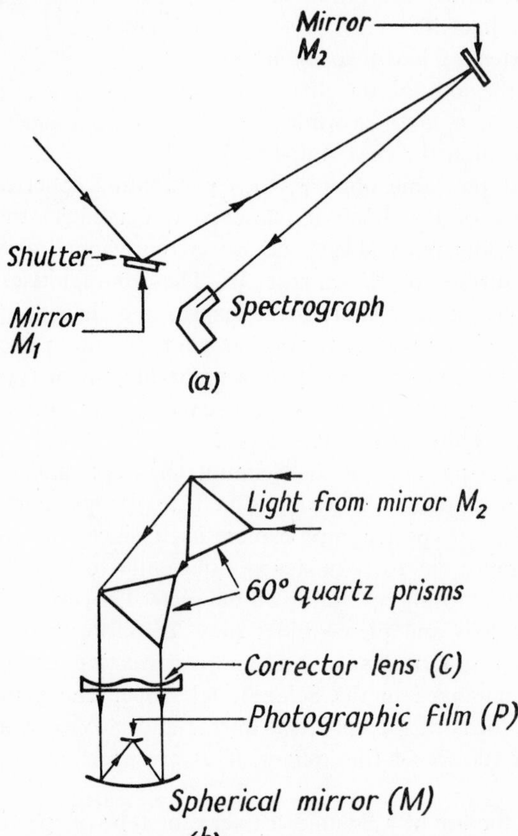

FIG. 12.3 (*a*) Mounting of spectrograph. (*b*) Optical arrangement of a spectrograph employing the Schmidt camera

The high intensity of electromagnetic radiation emitted by the sun makes feasible spectroscopic studies of a kind which are impossible for any other star. Spectrographs of high resolving power can be used to examine parts of the sun's surface. For example, one experimental arrangement makes use of a moving mirror mounted at the top of a tower; the mirror reflects the sunlight through an objective lens and focuses the light on to the slit of a grating spectrograph which is mounted in a laboratory below ground level.

For observations on the solar chromosphere, that is the thin envelope of relatively transparent gases which lies above the photosphere† of the sun, a slitless spectrograph may be used enabling the whole of the solar image to be recorded simultaneously which is not possible using a conventional slit instrument. These observations are made at the time of total solar eclipse (i.e. when the moon obscures the sun from view).

One of the advantages of a slitless spectrograph is the large field of view which can be recorded. Hitherto, the slitless arrangement has been used extensively for recording simultaneously the spectra of dozens of stars for the purpose of classification (see p. 347). In addition, slitless instruments are less wasteful of light than those employing slits and may, therefore, be used to investigate distant stars with low intensity in conjunction with a telescope of small aperture. Since the resolving power of a slitless spectrograph will be poor compared with that of the slit type, the former instrument is very inferior to the latter when fine structure studies are required. Until recently it was impracticable to record a reference spectrum (e.g. iron arc lines) alongside the unknown spectrum using the objective prism arrangement. Without these reference lines exact wavelength determinations are impossible. However, Fehrenbach[2] has developed a technique which overcomes this limitation and enables accurate wavelength determination.

The Doppler effect

Measurement of very high temperatures

The frequency of emitted radiation depends on the velocity of the source relative to that of the observer. The observed frequency increases if the motion is towards the observer and decreases if the motion is in the opposite direction. In the case of a spectral line only for those atoms which have no component of velocity in the direction of the observer will the frequency of the emitted light be equal to the natural frequency. If each of the atoms in a given gaseous system had roughly the same velocity due to the overall motion of the gas, the width of the spectral line would be unaffected, but the line would be displaced one way or the other according to the direction of motion. When, however, the centre of mass of the system is fixed, and the atoms are in random motion and have a Maxwellian distribution of velocities, the line is broadened but not displaced, that is the spectral line emitted by this gas consists of a range of frequencies symmetrically disposed about the natural frequency.

From the Doppler principle it follows that if a source of light of wavelength λ_0 is moving in the line-of-sight with velocity v relative to the observer, the apparent wavelength, λ, measured by the observer will be:

$$\lambda = \lambda_0(1+v/c) \tag{12.1}$$

where c is the velocity of light. Motion away from the observer produces a shift to longer wavelengths, and such motion is taken as being positive.

† The regions which contribute towards the continuous spectrum of a star.

Since the range of velocities increases with temperature so must the range of frequencies comprising the spectral line increase. The temperature of the atoms may be calculated in terms of the broadening of the spectral line and the mass, m, of the atoms. For a Maxwellian distribution of velocities it may be shown that when the extinction coefficient, ε, is plotted against the wavelength, λ, the total width of the line at half maximum (i.e. 0.5ε, see p. 137) is given by:

$$\delta\lambda = 1.67\frac{\lambda_0}{c}\sqrt{\frac{2kT}{m}} \tag{12.2}$$

where $\delta\lambda$ is the width of the spectral line at half maximum in Ångström units, λ_0 is the wavelength of the centre of the line also in Ångström units, c is the velocity of light, $\boldsymbol{k}$ is Boltzmann's constant, and T is the absolute temperature of the atoms of mass m. From a knowledge, then, of the values of the constants c, m, and $\boldsymbol{k}$ the temperature T may be calculated from the measurements of $\delta\lambda$ and λ_0. By this method the temperature of the solar corona† was estimated at over a million degrees. Actually only in the case of the sun can temperatures be obtained from line broadening. Even here, except in the case of the very hot and rarefied corona, lengthy analysis is needed to separate thermal broadening from other line broadening phenomena such as:

(1) Self absorption. When radiation from a hot gas passes through a layer of the same material, the central portion of the emission line is preferentially absorbed.

(2) Turbulence, that is the chaotic mass motion of stellar material, which introduces a Doppler broadening not due to thermal effects.

(3) Collisional or pressure broadening. A radiating or absorbing atom may be perturbed by forces due to any close neighbouring atom, ion, or electron. The broadening produced depends on the pressure and on the nature of the perturbing species.

(4) Magnetic and electric fields cause broadening and splitting of spectral lines.

Determination of radial velocities[3]

By the application of the Doppler principle relative velocities of, for example, stars and nebulae can be determined. Thus, from equation (12.1) it follows that:

$$\frac{\lambda-\lambda_0}{\lambda_0} = \frac{v}{c} \tag{12.3}$$

i.e.

$$\frac{\Delta\lambda}{\lambda_0} = \frac{v}{c}$$

and

$$v = c\Delta\lambda/\lambda_0 \tag{12.4}$$

Hence v may be determined from the experimental data.

† This is a tenuous gas cloud of pearly-white colour enveloping the sun and extending for at least a million miles.

Confirmation of the Doppler principle is obtained from numerous sources, but the shifts in planetary spectra are particularly suitable for this purpose. The relative motions of the planets are known very precisely, and in fact, are used for detecting systematic errors in line-of-sight velocity determinations given by a particular spectrograph.

The line-of-sight velocities of stellar bodies are determined by means of a spectrograph attached to a telescope at one of the positions already described (see p. 334). The spectrum is obtained, and on both sides of it is recorded the iron arc or other reference spectrum which serves to define a system of wavelengths of a source at rest relative to the observer. By the use of the Hartmann formula (see p. 42) the wavelengths of the stellar lines are determined. $\Delta\lambda$ is then merely the difference between this wavelength value and the wavelength of the same line measured from a laboratory source.

With a spectrograph of dispersion 15 Å/mm at a wavelength of 4340.48 Å (i.e. the Balmer H_γ line of hydrogen) a velocity of 1 km/sec corresponds to a shift on the photographic plate of 1μ. Stellar velocities are usually quoted to an accuracy of 0.1 km/sec.

Spectroscopic binaries

Another interesting application of the Doppler principle has been the discovery of pairs of stars so close together that no telescope has been able to resolve them. Such stars have been proved to be double by the behaviour of the lines in their spectra.

For two stars of approximately equal brightness revolving around each other, which possess spectral lines in common, when one star is receding and the other approaching the observer, each spectral line common to both stars is a doublet. This doubling of lines results from the frequency shift according to the Doppler principle. When, however, one star is in front of the other in the line of observation, the spectral lines are single.

Such double stars are called *spectroscopic binaries*, many hundreds of which are known. In Fig. 12.4(*a*) the spectrogram obtained from β Aurigae may be observed. This spectrogram shows the doubling of the 3933.7 Å line of singly-ionised Ca, whereas in Fig. 12.4(*b*), which was taken when one star was in front of the other, a single line may be seen. (Fig. 12.4, see p. 334.)

Planetary atmospheres†

Before the spectra of planetary atmospheres are dealt with it will be convenient to consider the absorption and emission spectrum of the earth's atmosphere. The reason for this is that radiation from all extraterrestrial sources will suffer considerable, if not complete, absorption, in the spectral

† A planet is a solid body having no light or heat of its own. In the solar system nine planets are recognised: Mercury, Venus, Earth, Mars, Jupiter, Saturn, Uranus, Neptune and Pluto. Of these nine planets, all of which move round the sun in nearly circular orbits, Mercury and Pluto have no atmosphere.

regions that are rendered either semi- or completely opaque by the absorbing species in our own atmosphere. The terrestrial absorption spectrum is completely molecular in origin.

Absorption spectrum of the earth's atmosphere

At wavelengths shorter than 3000 Å the earth's atmosphere is completely opaque. The opaqueness at wavelengths less than 3000 Å is partly due to ozone, which has a maximum concentration at a height of 20 to 30 km above the earth's surface. The ozone formation is dependent on the photodissociation of the oxygen molecule by the absorption of wavelengths of less than 2400 Å. The O_3 absorption extends to approximately 2200 Å but at about 2400 Å the $A^3\Sigma_u^+ \leftarrow X^3\Sigma_g^-$ bands of oxygen are found. Below 1950 Å intense O_2 absorption (the Schumann–Runge system $B^3\Sigma_u^- \leftarrow X^3\Sigma_g^-$) produces opaqueness down to about 1300 Å. Below this wavelength other systems of O_2 and N_2 cause complete absorption.

At the infra-red end of the electromagnetic spectrum intense rotation-vibration transitions of water vapour occur between 0.94 to 1.85 μ, 2.5 to 3.0 μ and 5 to 7.5 μ, and, in addition, rotational transitions of water vapour seriously deplete the solar spectrum at wavelengths greater than 16 μ and completely between 24 π and $\sim$1 mm. Other localised absorptions also occurring in the visible and infra-red regions are due to CO_2, N_2O, CH_4, and O_2.

Emission spectrum of the earth's atmosphere

On moonless nights the earth's atmosphere is still found to give a feeble illumination, and efforts have been made to account for this emitted electromagnetic radiation, Owing to the weakness of the source the type of instrument employed must have a high photographic speed, and consequently the dispersion and resolution are poor. The spectrograph described on p. 335 has been used for this type of investigation. The following are some of the difficulties encountered:

(i) It is not easy to determine by inspection of such spectrograms whether lines or bands are being observed.

(ii) The extent of any individual band may be small, possibly owing to the low temperature of the source.

(iii) Forbidden lines† are observed which are not easily reproduced in the laboratory.

From the work done so far, the majority of the spectrum of the earth's atmosphere is thought to be molecular in origin, though part of it is attributed to atoms.

The molecular bands identified so far are due to the oxygen and nitrogen molecules and also the rotation-vibration spectrum of OH.

The atomic lines which have been definitely identified are the O I $^1S_0 - ^1D_2$ transition at 5577 Å, the O I $^1D_2 - ^3P_{1,2}$ transition at 6300 Å and 6364 Å, and the sodium D lines. Other lines such as those attributed to Ca I and

† See p. 342 for a consideration of forbidden lines.

Ca II are doubtful and may be ascribed to low dispersion coincidence with molecular bands. Oxygen above 100 km is in the atomic state. At night recombination of the O atoms occurs mainly between 90 and 120 km. Oxygen is more easily photodissociated than nitrogen, and this together with the absence of nitrogen lines in the spectrum is taken to indicate that nitrogen in the upper atmosphere is mainly in the molecular state.

From the twilight glow the violet N_2^+ bands may be detected in emission. The sodium *D* lines and the red O I lines are also present, their intensity being greater than that observed in the night glow.

The spectra from auroral displays differs considerably from that of the twilight and night glows. Forbidden lines of O I and N I and molecular bands of N_2, and N_2^+ have been identified in auroral spectra. In addition the Balmer lines of hydrogen, the *D* lines of sodium, and some He lines are occasionally found.

For the OH bands at 10 440 Å the height at which the radiation is emitted has been estimated at about 70 km. The rotational structure of these bands has been resolved, and Meinel[4,5] determined the temperature of the OH stratum from the rotational intensity distributions† and obtained a value of $260 \pm 5°K$.

Other planetary atmospheres[6,7]

A number of criteria are available which enable the astronomer to decide whether a given planet is likely to have an atmosphere. The criteria depend on the observations of:

(i) Clouds, seasonal polar caps, twilight arcs, and atmospheric refractions.

(ii) Polarisation and reflection phenomena.

(iii) Whether sufficient gravitational attraction exists on the planet for it to retain an atmosphere. This can be computed from the mass, radius, and temperature of the planet.

These criteria are useful since they enable the astronomer to fix his attention on those planets where a definite possibility of an atmosphere exists.

The presence of absorption or emission bands in the spectrum of a planet is especially valuable in a number of ways. It gives definite proof of the existence of particular species (i.e. an atmosphere of some kind), identifies the substance(s), and enables estimates of the relative abundance of the various species to be made. On the other hand, spectroscopic observations are limited by:

(i) The transmission of the earth's atmosphere.

(ii) Sources of low spectral intensity. This leads to low dispersion spectra.

(iii) H_2, N_2, and the inert gases are not revealed and CO_2, CO, and N_2O only if the source is bright enough to make infra-red observations possible.

Gases which are common to the atmosphere of both the planet and the earth can sometimes be detected if the source is sufficiently intense for high

† A bare outline of this procedure is given on p. 274.

dispersion studies. This is achieved by virtue of the Doppler shift which results in a lack of coincidence of the two spectra.

The high percentage of water vapour and oxygen in the earth's atmosphere makes difficult the determination of these gases in extraterrestrial atmospheres. However, steps can be taken to avoid the terrestrial water vapour by, for example, working at high altitudes or on days of low humidity.

Table 12.1 summarises the major constituents in the atmospheres of the planets in the solar system.

TABLE 12.1

The main constituents in the atmospheres of the planets in the solar system

Venus	CO_2, H_2O
Mars	CO_2, H_2O, O_2
Jupiter	CH_4, NH_3
Uranus	CH_4, H_2
Neptune	CH_4, H_2
Saturn	CH_4, NH_3
Titan (largest satellite of Saturn)	CH_4

The observation of CH_4 in the atmosphere of Titan is interesting since this is the only large satellite in the solar system for which evidence of an atmosphere has been observed from its spectrum.

Spectrophotometric studies on the polar caps of Mars in the 1.5 μ region using a PbS detector have shown that these caps are composed of finely divided ice, and hence a very small amount of water vapour must be present in its atmosphere.

Spectra of nebulae and forbidden transitions

The unfamiliar conditions of extremely low density in nebulae (for example, the density of the Orion Nebula has been estimated at ~300 atoms/ml of that of air at normal temperature and pressure) give rise to spectra which are not normally encountered in the laboratory.

The Balmer lines of hydrogen H_α, H_β, H_γ, H_δ . . . are always prominent as are also the lines of neutral helium. Frequently also lines of He II are to be found in such spectra. In Fig. 12.5, which is the spectrogram and microphotometer trace for the Orion Nebula (NGC 1976), the hydrogen and helium lines are quite apparent†. Among weaker lines of the nebula are those attributed to C II, C III, and Ne III and sometimes also to O II and N III. In the near infra-red region some hydrogen lines belonging to the Paschen series have been observed, and in one particular nebula (NGC 6572) a line from the neutral oxygen atom has been detected. Lines from O III and N III have also been observed in the spectra of nebulae and are often quite intense.

In addition to the already indicated lines, other lines are observed which were not readily identified initially. The wavelengths of these lines have been

† This is the reference number of the nebula in the *New General Catalogue*.

measured quite accurately and the values obtained did not correspond to any known lines. These unknown lines were at first attributed to an unknown element, nebulium. Since, however, no suitable gaps were available in the periodic table it appeared more probable that nebulium was a known element under unfamiliar conditions.

The problem was solved by Bowen,[9,10] who showed that the frequencies were due to O, N, Ne, and S in various stages of ionisation. Some of these lines have now been produced in the laboratory, although the majority have not yet been obtained, since their emission is forbidden by the selection rules for electric dipole radiation. They are consequently called forbidden lines, examples of which can be seen in some of the lines in the spectrogram in Fig. 12.5 (p. 334).

The selection rules for atoms for electric dipole radiation† are:

(i) $\Delta J = 0, \pm 1, \quad J = 0 \not\rightarrow J = 0$.
(ii) $\Delta L = 0, \pm 1$ and $\Delta l = \pm 1$.
(iii) $\Delta S = 0$.
(iv) Even terms combine only with odd terms and vice versa.

However, for magnetic dipole and electric quadrupole radiation the selection rules are in some cases quite different, and although the normal conditions on earth are generally unsuitable for such transitions, in nebulae the reverse is true. Table 12.2 summarises the selection rules for electric and magnetic dipole and for electric quadrupole radiation.

TABLE 12.2

Comparison of some of the selection rules for atoms for electric dipole, electric quadrupole, and magnetic dipole radiation

	Electric dipole radiation	Electric quadrupole radiation	Magnetic dipole radiation
ΔJ	0 ± 1	$0 \pm 1 \pm 2 (J' + J'' \geqslant 2)$	0 ± 1
Terms	$+ \leftrightarrow -$	$+ \leftrightarrow +$ $- \leftrightarrow -$	$+ \leftrightarrow +$ $- \leftrightarrow -$
ΔL	0 ± 1	$0 \pm 1 \pm 2$	0 ± 1
ΔS	0	0	0

The Einstein transition probability of spontaneous emission A_{nm} is given by (see p. 365):

$$A_{nm} = \frac{64\pi^4 \nu_{nm}^3}{3h} \mid R^{nm} \mid ^2 \tag{12.5}$$

A_{nm} gives the fraction per sec of atoms in the initial state n undergoing transitions to the state m where n is the excited state. The mean life of state n is:

$$\mathscr{T} = 1/A_{nm} \tag{12.6}$$

For a permitted electric dipole transition $\mathscr{T}$ is approximately 10^{-8} sec, that is the average lifetime of the state n is 10^{-8} sec. If, however, no electric dipole

† These selection rules were considered in Vol. I, Chapter 1.

transition is allowed from state n to state m, A_{nm} will be very small, and $\mathscr{T}$ will consequently be large. It has been calculated that for transitions which take place by virtue of the electric quadrupole $\mathscr{T}$ is of the order of 1 sec, while for a magnetic dipole transition $\mathscr{T}$ is approximately 10^{-3} sec. Under these conditions n is termed a *metastable state.*

Generally, if a transition from n to m cannot take place by the electric dipole mechanism, then the other possibilities are by electric quadrupole or magnetic dipole transitions. However, on earth the probability of most gaseous atoms radiating by such means is very unlikely, because even in the highest vacuum attainable the atoms would lose their excess energy by collision with other atoms, before they had the opportunity to emit. At extremely low densities prevailing in the gaseous nebulae atomic collisions are very infrequent, occurring for a given atom at an average interval of several hours or even days. Under these conditions emission may take place by magnetic dipole and electric quadrupole transitions giving rise to the so-called forbidden lines.†[11,12] If in any portion of the nebula the predominant ion of an element X is X^{n+}, then usually only forbidden transitions of X^{n+} appear. However, recombination of X^{n+} with electrons produces permitted transitions of $X^{[n-1]+}$. In certain cases, for example, H, He II, O III, and N III, permitted transitions do arise.

One particular well known forbidden line—the green auroral line at a wavelength of 5577.35 Å, which is emitted after dark in the high terrestrial atmosphere and which is of great intensity during polar aurorae‡—was reproduced in the laboratory by McLennan and Shrum in 1924. They diluted oxygen with an inert monatomic gas in the discharge tube and concluded from the spectrum that the green line was due to the forbidden transition $^1S_0-{}^1D_2$ of the neutral oxygen atom: the transition was considered to take place through the electric quadrupole moment.

Forbidden lines belonging to Fe II, Fe III, Fe VI, and Fe VII have also been detected. The Solar corona has forbidden lines of Fe XI, Fe XIII, Fe XIV, A X, Ca XII, Ca XV, Ni XIII, Ni XV Ni XVI and Mg X. Elements in gaseous nebulae detected by their permitted lines are relatively few in number and include H, He, C, N, O, and possibly Fe, Si and Mg. The heavier atoms detected by their forbidden lines are, for example, F, Ne, S, Cl, A, K, Ca, Fe, and Ni.

The spectra of comets[13]

A comet consists of three parts:

(i) A nucleus of small dimensions of the order of a few kilometres or less.

† The concept of forbidden lines is based on the definition that lines which obey the selection rules for electric dipole radiation are the *permitted* ones whereas all the remaining lines are termed *forbidden*. This definition automatically classes any transition involving magnetic dipole or electric quadrupoles as forbidden transitions, even though they obey the selection rules for that type of interaction. Further consideration to forbidden lines is given on p. 44 of Vol. 1.

‡ Aurorae are glows in the atmosphere caused by electrically charged particles emitted by the sun entering the upper atmosphere. These charged particles are attracted towards the earth's magnetic poles and auroral displays are observed mainly at high latitudes.

(ii) A coma or head surrounding the nucleus and extending to perhaps hundreds of thousands of kilometres.

(iii) A tail, usually directed away from the sun, the length of which may well be of the order of millions of kilometres.

The nucleus of a comet is assumed to be a collection of meteorites, and the spectra observed from comets result from the gases in the head and tail. These gases are released from the solid particles under the influence of solar radiation.

Cometary spectra consist of a large number of strong emission bands together with lines due to sunlight reflected by the meteorites in the nucleus.

When a comet approaches the sun, the sodium *D* lines are observed from the comet and may have a very high intensity when the comet–sun distance is small. These are the only atomic lines observed in emission from comets.

The band spectrum from the head and nucleus is very different from that occurring in the tail. The species observed from their band spectra in the heads of comets are C_2, CN, C_3, OH, NH, CH, CH^+, and NH_2, while in the tails CO^+, N_2^+, CH^+, and CO_2^+ have been identified. The identification of the species OH, NH, CN, C_2, and C_3 in comet 1940 I may be seen in Fig. 12.6.

The intensity distribution within these cometary bands differs from those found in the laboratory sources even at low temperatures. The irregular distribution is very evident in, for example, the CN band near 3880 Å and also less prominent for the CH, OH, and CH^+ bands. Instead of showing a smooth rotational intensity distribution cometary spectra reveal complex band profiles with intensity minima in the branches. These minima appear even when the bands are incompletely resolved. The positions of the minima correspond perfectly with the wavelengths of strong absorption lines in the exciting sunlight, the absorption being due to the solar atmosphere. In addition, the radial velocity of the comet relative to the sun affects considerably the rotational profiles, since the positions of the minima are altered owing to the change in wavelength of the solar absorption lines in accordance with the Doppler principle.

From a study of the rotational structure of a band (see p. 274), estimates of the effective rotational temperature may be made. However, allowance has to be made for the effect of solar absorption. When this is done it is found that CH, OH, NH, CN, and CH^+ have, on the whole, low rotational temperatures of the order of 200° to 400°K depending on the distance of the comet from the sun. A study of the rotational intensity distribution in a C_2 band, however, leads to much higher rotational temperatures of about 3000° to 4000°K. These differences in rotational temperatures may be appreciated from the following facts:

(i) The rotational distributions are not brought about by collisions since collisions will be very infrequent at the low pressures prevailing.

(ii) The distribution of rotational energy is a result of the continued absorption of sunlight, and whereas the low rotational temperature types may undergo transitions in the far infra-red, since they have a permanent electric dipole moment (see p. 81), the C_2 molecule being homonuclear cannot dissipate its rotational energy in this manner. C_2, therefore, has a high rotational temperature, while the CH, OH, NH, CN, and CH^+ species have a low rotational temperature. The comet–sun distance will have an important effect on the rotational distribution (see Fig. 12.7, p. 334).

In Fig. 12.6 comparison is made between the spectrum of comet 1940 I and acetylene flame spectra. The spectrum of the comet was obtained by Swings[14] using an *f*/1 quartz spectrograph when the comet-sun distance was 0.87 A.U.† By comparing spectrogram (*a*) with those shown under (*b*), (*c*), and (*d*) the various bands due to OH, CH, NH, CN, C_2, and C_3 may be identified in the comet. In addition, it can be seen that the rotational and vibrational intensity distributions in the bands of OH, CH, NH, and CN are extremely different in the comet from those in the flames, while they are similar for the bands of C_2. The observed cometary lines within each band of OH, CH, NH and CN correspond to electronic transitions from the lowest rotational levels. The details of the acetylene flames are as follows:

Spectrogram (*b*) results from a rich acetylene flame with some addition of ammonia. The main features are bands of OH, NH (*Q*-branch), CN (violet system), C_3, C_2, and CH.

Spectrogram (*c*) is from an acetylene flame with traces of ammonia. The following bands are present in the inner cone of the flame: CH, NH, CN, CH, and C_2. In the outer cone of the flame are present bands due to OH, NH, CN, CH, and C_2.

Spectrogram (*d*) results from an acetylene flame with ammonia. The rotational structures of OH, NH, CH, and CN are clearly shown. (See p. 334.)

The abundance of molecules in comets can be estimated spectrophotometrically, although little work has been done along these lines. A very approximate estimate of C_2 molecules in the head of a comet gave 10^5 molecules per ml, while in the tail an estimate of CO^+ was found to be one molecule per ml. The effective vibrational and rotational temperature values may differ considerably and have little physical meaning. However, for systems at equilibrium these values should correspond. The lack of agreement serves to show that the prevailing densities are so low that thermal equilibrium in cometary systems cannot be established by collision processes. The upper limit for the total density is of the order of 10^6 molecules per ml.

The fundamental part of a comet is the collection of solid meteorites in the nucleus where almost the entire mass is concentrated, and from which the head and tail of the comet originate. The head and tail of a comet are formed by liberation of gas and dust from the nucleus, and since the nucleus has a small mass, that is it possesses little gravitational attraction, the head and tail need to be continuously replenished; otherwise they would disappear within a few days. As the comet approaches the sun the nucleus emits large

† A.U. is the astronomical unit, which is the earth's average distance (92 960 000 miles) from the sun.

quantities of gas and dust and eventually disintegrates. Sometimes the whole comet breaks up, and if fragments of it (meteorites) come under the gravitational attraction of the earth, then an opportunity of examining the fragments of former comets in the laboratory results. Molecules in a comet have a limited life in the radiation field of the sun, depending on the possibilities of photodissociation and photo-ionisation and on the amount of solar radiation available in the spectral region where dissociation or ionisation occurs.

The spectra of Comet Cunningham (1940 c,—1941 I) in the region 3000 6400 Å are given in Fig. 12.7. The spectrograms 1 to 10 inclusive were obtained at the following heliocentric distances: 2.24, 1.85, 1.47, 1.18, 1.03, 0.87, 0.75, 0.63, 0.50, and 0.48 A.U. respectively. The species detected are marked along the bottom edge of the figure. The resolution of the rotational structure of the OH and NH bands in spectrograms 5, 6, 7, and 8 enabled for the first time identification of these two radicals in comets. A study of comet 1948 I showed that the diameter to which radicals extend in the comet head varied with the heliocentric distance, e.g.:

$$r = 0.90 \text{ A.U.} \begin{cases} \text{the diameter of CN is 62 000 km;} \\ \text{the diameter of } C_3 \text{ is 4140 km;} \end{cases}$$

$$r = 2.21 \text{ A.U.} \begin{cases} \text{the diameter of CN is 166 000 km;} \\ \text{the diameter of } C_3 \text{ is 22 000 km.} \end{cases}$$

Over the comet-sun range 0.65 to 2.21 A.U. the profile of the CN band shows appreciable variation; the main systematic variation in profile of CN is due to its decrease in rotational temperature.

Stellar spectra

From a study of their spectra the surface temperature and chemical composition of the stars may be deduced. The majority of the stars show a continuous emission upon which are superimposed dark absorption lines. Some stars also show emission lines on this background.

The spectra of stars with very few exceptions can be grouped together into a limited number of spectral classes which form a sequence. The spectral sequence is:

```
                 R—N
                /
O—B—A—F—G—K—M
           /
          S
```

The sequence *O* to *M* is continuous while the *R*- and *N*-type stars, sometimes grouped together as *C*-type stars (i.e. carbon stars), follow on from group *G*, and *S* stars from group *K*.

The spectral sequence is also a colour sequence of the stars. Thus, stars of type *O* are bluish-white in colour, *M*-type stars are red; those of intermediate types range from white through orange to red. The colour sequence is a temperature sequence. The intensity of molecular bands in the late sequence stars suggests that these stars are comparatively cool while the early type stars, whose spectra are due to neutral and ionised atoms, are much hotter. This also agrees with the colours of the stars. A summary of the spectral types, their colours, temperatures, and main spectral characteristics, is given in Table 12.3.

TABLE 12.3

Colour, temperature and the main spectral features of stars of the various types

Type	Colour	Approximate temperature (°K)	Example of such a star	Chief spectral features	Some other spectral features
O	Bluish white	50 000	Alnitak	Absorption H; absorption He II; sometimes emission of He II at 4686 Å	Ionised C, N, O
B	Bluish white	20 000	Bellatrix	Absorption H; absorption He I	Ionised O, N, Si
A	White	10 000	Sirius	Hydrogen lines	Fe, Na, Ca II
F	Yellowish white	7000	Canopus	H and metallic lines	Lines of Ca II, Ca I; metallic lines
G	Yellow	5500	Sun, Capella	CH band at 4300 Å Metallic lines H lines still noticeable	CN, CH, C_2, Ca I, Ca II Fe I
K	Orange	4500	Arcturus	Metallic lines Ca I at 4226 Å	TiO, CN, CH, C_2, Ca II Fe I
M	Red	3000	Betelgeuse	Bands of TiO Ca I at 4226 Å	MgH, SiH, AlH, ZrO, ScO, YO, CrO, AlO, BO, Ca II, Fe I
S	Very red	3000	—	Bands of ZrO	TiO, YO, LaO
R, N	Very red	3000	—	Bands of C_2, CN	NH, C_3, CH

It may be observed from Table 12.3 that the temperature is one of the main factors which governs the excitation and ionisation in the atmospheres of the stars. It must be stressed that, although certain spectral features have been given to a particular class, they may well be met with in other classes; for example, the bands of TiO are dominant in class *M*, but they are also present in class *S* along with ZrO bands.

Each spectral class is sub-divided into groups called spectral types. These are identified by the numbers 0, 1, 2, 3, . . . placed after the capital letter of the class to which the star belongs. For example, *B*5 denotes a spectrum intermediate between *B* and *A* in appearance, while *F*8 indicates a spectrum resembling *G*0 closer than *F*0.

The spectral characteristics of the *O*-type stars are lines of H, He I, He II, O III, N III, and C III. In class *B*, lines of H and He I become stronger, while lines due to He II disappear. The hotter *B* stars show lines of O II, Si IV, and Si III while the colder *B* stars show Mg II, Si II and C II. Near *A*2 the lines of H attain their maximum intensity. The lines due to metals gain prominence in types *A* to *G* while the H lines weaken. Molecular bands occur weakly† in type *G* and increase in intensity together with the metallic lines from types *G* to *M*. Bands of TiO dominate *M*-type stars, bands of ZrO are shown by type S, while bands due to C_2 and CN are very prominent in the spectra of *R* and *N* types.

In Fig. 12.8(*b*) and (*c*) the spectrum of an *A*2 star is compared with that of type *K*2. It will be observed that in the hotter star the Balmer hydrogen lines can be seen as can also the 3934 Å line of Ca II. In the spectrogram of the cooler star many lines characteristic of metals have made an appearance and bands can be observed. The lines on either side of the spectrograms (*a*), (*b*), and (*c*) are the iron arc reference lines.

If the spectral classes of the stars are plotted against their absolute magnitudes,‡ the points are found to lie in a definite pattern. The plot is called the Russell–Hertzsprung diagram and is illustrated in Fig. 12.9. The majority of the points fall along a curve running diagonally across the diagram; the hot blue stars lie at one corner and the cool red ones at the other. This group of stars is called the *principal series* or *dwarf sequence*, generally referred to as the main sequence, of which the sun is one of type *G*2.

Above the dwarf sequence lie two other groups of stars called the *giants* and *supergiants*, while below the main sequence is found the group referred to as white dwarfs. The masses of dwarf and giant stars differ little, but as with their luminosities, the mean densities of these types are vastly different. The mean density of giants is very small and in the highly rarefied atmospheres of such stars ionised atoms will tend to be more abundant than in the compressed atmospheres of dwarf stars which possess a greater density.

† This is not true of the strong 4300 Å system of CH in *G*-type stars.

‡ The magnitude of a star expresses its brightness on a diminishing logarithmic scale. The absolute magnitude is the magnitude a star would have if it were placed at a distance of 10 parsecs, where 1 parsec is equal to 3.26 light years or 206 265 times the average distance of the sun from the earth, i.e. 206 265 A.U.

Thus, generally, an increased density will reduce the degree of ionisation in stellar atmospheres resembling somewhat the effect of decreasing temperature. The level of excitation of the atoms will, however, be unaffected. Consequently it might be expected that ionised lines would be stronger in the spectra of giants while neutral lines would gain more prominence in dwarf spectra.

However, since the spectral classification is based on the appearance of lines giants tend to be slightly cooler than dwarfs of the same spectral class. While the increased density of a dwarf star is largely compensated by a

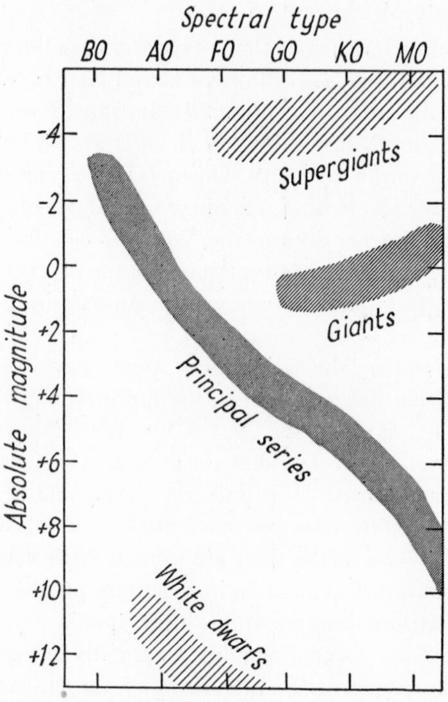

FIG. 12.9 The Russell-Hertzsprung diagram

somewhat higher temperature, the compensation is imperfect for a few elements. Lines belonging to ionised atoms, for example, the 4215 Å and 4077 Å lines of Sr II and the 4233 Å line of Fe II, are strong in giant star spectra. The 4227 Å line of Ca I, on the other hand, is more intense in dwarf than in giant spectra. The CN bands at 3590, 3883, and 4216 Å are important for distinguishing between giant and dwarf stars of the types *G* and *K*. If the spectra of these stars are compared, then the CN bands in giants are more intense than in dwarfs of the same spectral class. The detailed reasons for these differences cannot be considered here.

A further difference between the spectra due to giant and dwarf stars is the width of the spectral lines. The lines from giant stars are generally sharp and narrow while those from dwarfs are broad and rather diffuse. In Fig. 12.8(*a*) and (*b*) the spectra of an *A*2 dwarf and supergiant, respectively, are compared. The broadening of the spectral lines in the case of the dwarf star is clearly seen. This broadening may be due to:

(1) Greater rotation (see p. 338) in the hotter dwarf stars.

(2) More collisional broadening in dwarfs due to the increased density.

(3) Magnetic and electric fields may play a rôle in the line broadening phenomenon.

Such criteria as those given readily enable dwarf and giant stars of the same spectral type to be distinguished. The reason this is so important is that once the spectral type of the star is known, and it is established whether it is a dwarf or a giant or super giant, then from the Russell-Hertzsprung diagram the absolute magnitude of the star may be obtained. By comparison of the absolute magnitude with the apparent magnitude (i.e. the apparent brightness based on a logarithmic scale) the distance of the star may be estimated. The accuracy of such a determination is about 25 per cent, the relative error being independent of distance, but difficulties sometimes arise owing to absorption by dark interstellar matter.

The great variety of spectra from stars does not necessarily imply any difference in chemical composition of the stellar atmospheres. The apparent absence of certain elements in a given type is probably due to the different conditions prevailing at that type. So far as is known the majority of stellar atmospheres—apart from those of types *R*, *N* and *S*—are nearly identical in composition with only their temperatures and atmospheric pressures differing. The main constituent of stars is hydrogen. In the case of the sun 99.9 per cent by volume of the sun's atmosphere consists of H and He with hydrogen about five times more abundant than helium.

With these results, it is possible to establish the main processes of emission and absorption that give rise to the continuous background radiation on which these line spectra are superposed. At temperatures higher than about 4000°K, below which absorption by molecules begins to play an important part, the character of the continuous emission is fixed by the properties of hydrogen in the presence of free electrons. In the atmospheres of *O*- and early *B*-type stars, hydrogen is predominantly ionised and the continuous radiation (originally generated by thermonuclear processes in the deep interior of the star) is transferred through the atmosphere (that is the visible layers) mainly through Thomson scattering by free electrons. Shortward of the Lyman limit ($\lambda<912$), the residual neutral hydrogen in the ground state acts as an intense additional source of continuous absorption, so that one expects the intensity to be depressed below that of the corresponding black body in this extreme ultra-violet region, which has, however, not been observed so far except in the case of the sun (from rockets). For late *B* and *A* stars, free electrons become fewer (hydrogen only partially ionised), and the absorption is due to hydrogen in the second quantum level for the ultra-violet ($\lambda<3646$) and in the third quantum level for the visible ($\lambda<8208$).

This effect is confirmed by the presence of a strong absorption edge (the Balmer discontinuity) at λ 3650 in the continuous spectra of *B*-, *A*-, and early *F*-type stars.

When the temperature is reduced further, for example, in solar-type stars, the Balmer discontinuity weakens, contrary to what would be expected from pure hydrogen absorption, and indeed the continuous spectrum then approximates remarkably closely to that of a black body (except in the ultra-violet, where intense line and band absorptions occur). This is due to the combination of neutral hydrogen atoms with free electrons supplied by the metals, which are mostly in the singly-ionised state, to form the H^- ion, as was first suggested by R. Wildt. The light from the sun is the recombination continuum of H^-, and the continuous absorption is due to the photoelectric dissociation of H^- into $H+e$, the cross-section for which varies only slowly over the near ultra-violet, visible, and near infra-red regions. In giants, the electron pressure is lower than in dwarfs, owing to the lower surface gravity, and H^- is, therefore, less abundant in comparison with H; the Balmer discontinuity is consequently stronger in giants than in dwarfs of the same spectral class. In most cases significant amounts of both line and continuous absorption occur in the same atmospheric layers, so that both must be taken into account in the interpretation of line intensities, which essentially depend on the *ratio* of one to the other.

The spectrum of the sun has received special attention, since on account of its brightness, good dispersion and resolution have been obtained. In addition to many atoms and ions, the following molecular species have definitely been identified in the sun's atmosphere by means of their band spectra: CN, CH, C_2, NH, OH, SiH, MgH, TiO, CaH, ZrO, YO, AlO, and BH. Some evidence for MgO, ScO, MgF, and SrF also exists. The molecules H_2, N_2, O_2, NO, and SiO cannot be detected, since their spectra lie beyond the spectral regions accessible from the earth, though they must be present in great abundance in the solar atmosphere.

Stellar spectra are cut off at wavelengths less than 3000 Å by the ozone layer in the earth's atmosphere and by O_2 and N_2 at wavelengths less than about 2200 Å. However, with the availability of high-altitude rockets, which pass above the absorbing layers, it has been possible to photograph the extreme ultra-violet spectrum of the sun, and to examine this by recovery of the rocket. A series of such investigations has been carried out by Johnson, *et al.*[15] One of their spectrograms taken at an altitude of 115 km showed forty-five emission lines extending from 1892 to 977 Å which arise in the hot chromosphere and corona surrounding the visible disk of the sun. In Fig. 12.10 the microphotometer trace of this spectrum is given from 1850 to 950 Å. The main features of the solar spectrum in this region are an intense α-line of the hydrogen atom in the Lyman series and lines due to ionised C, Si, N, O, S, Fe, and Al. Except for the emission lines noted the irregular appearance in the spectrogram from 1850 to 1550 Å is due to absorption by the sun's atmosphere.

The spectrograph employed to obtain the ultra-violet spectrum of the sun, from which the microphotometer trace in Fig. 12.10 was obtained, is shown in Fig. 12.11. The spectrograph in a suitable housing was mounted

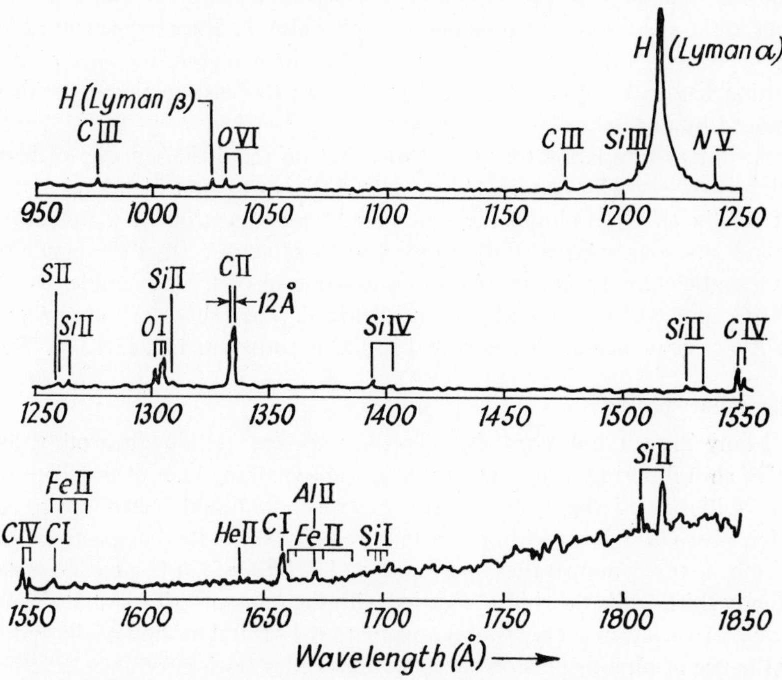

FIG. 12.10 Logarithmic densitometer trace of the solar spectrum from 950 to 1850 Å obtained at a height of 115 km above the earth's surface. (*After Johnson, Malitson, Purcell and Tousey.*[15] *Courtesy of 'The Astrophysical Journal'*)

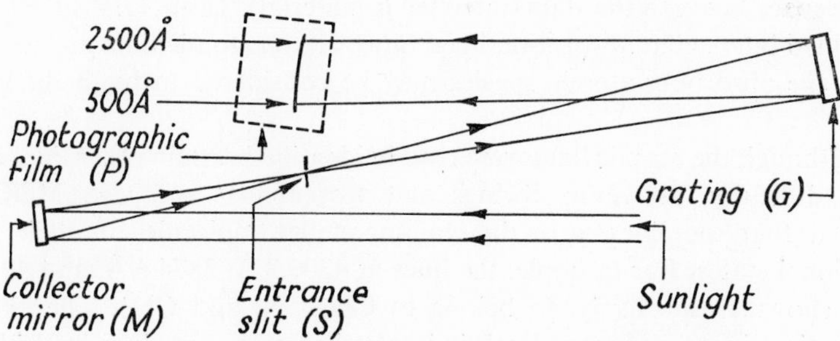

FIG. 12.11 Optical arrangement of the vacuum spectrograph employed to investigate the ultra-violet spectrum of the sun. (*After Johnson et. al.*[15] *Courtesy of 'The Astrophysical Journal'*)

on a rocket and was designed to cover the region from 2500 to 500 Å. By means of a photoelectric sensing device the spectrograph housing was kept directed so that the sun's image fell on the slit. Sunlight collected by a spherical quartz collector mirror, *M*, was reflected on to the entrance slit, *S*, of the spectrograph. Light from this slit, located at a distance of 21.3 cm from the mirror, *M*, was incident on a concave grating, *G*. The grating, which, set at normal incidence, had a radius of curvature of 40 cm and 6000 lines/cm blazed for maximum first-order efficiency at about 1200 Å, focused the spectrum on to the photographic film, *P*. Since oxygen and water vapour absorb strongly in the vacuum ultra-violet region, the spectrograph housing has to be either evacuated or, as was the case in this experiment, replaced by dry helium.

An interesting laboratory study was that on the 4050 Å group of bands which is observed in certain *C*-type stars.† This was first identified as CH_2 but finally as C_3, yielding the first correct identification of a polyatomic radical in stellar spectra. Furthermore, in these carbon stars the bands due to C_2 and CN are so intense that other isotopic species, for example, $^{13}C^{12}C$, $^{13}C^{13}C$, and $^{13}C^{14}N$ have also been identified. The laboratory spectrum of the $\Delta v=1$ sequence of $^{12}C_2$ enriched in ^{13}C is shown in Fig. 12.12, p. 335.

Interstellar spectra

Many distant hot stars show in their spectra certain absorption lines with a shift differing from that shown by the remaining lines of the spectrum. This is illustrated clearly by certain spectroscopic double stars (see p. 339) which give Ca II lines with a constant velocity shift. In the spectrum of δ Orionis it was demonstrated that the *H* and *K* lines of Ca II gave a constant velocity shift, while the shift associated with the remaining lines went through a cycle of variation every few days owing to the orbital motion of the system. By the use of high dispersion spectrographs other stationary lines have been detected including those of Na, I K, I Fe, I Ti, and II Ca I.

These stationary lines are really superimposed on the stellar spectrum and are due to the passage of light from the star through material dispersed in the space between the stars (interstellar material). Table 12.4 is a list of the identified interstellar absorption lines. Since all the atomic lines are resonance lines, the absorbing atomic species may be considered to be in the ground state.

Although the atomic lines were readily identified certain other lines caused more difficulty. However, Swings and Rosenfeld[17] and also McKellar[18] showed that the lines were due to interstellar molecules in their lowest rotational states. For example, the lines at 4300.3 Å, 3874.6 Å, and 4232.6 Å were shown, respectively, to belong to CH, CN, and CH^+. The observed absorption lines for these radicals in interstellar space are given in Table 12.4.

The lack of rotational energy of the interstellar molecules can be appreciated by a consideration of the conditions in interstellar space. Owing to the low density prevailing in these regions collisions are very infrequent, and excitation by radiation is either small or absent. Should any higher rotational energy levels become occupied, then depopulation can occur in the cases of CH, CN, and CH^+ by rotational energy emission.

† *C*-type stars are made up of *R* and *N* types and are often referred to as carbon stars.

In addition to the lines already mentioned, other more diffuse lines with a breadth of from 4 to 10 Å have been observed. So far these lines have defied interpretation. They occur in the region between 4430 and 6614 Å, and it has been suggested[19,20] that they are due to solid particles associated with the clouds of obscuring dust, rather than with the interstellar gas.

TABLE 12.4

Interstellar absorption

Atom or ion	Wavelengths (Å)
Na I	3302.3, 3303, 5890, 5896
K I	7664.9, 7699
Ca I	4226.7
Ca II	3968.5, 3933.7
Ti II	3073, 3229.2, 3242, 3383.8
Fe I	3719.9, 3859.9

Radical	Wavelengths (Å)	Remarks
CH	4300.3	This is the $R(1)$ line belonging to the (0,0) band of the $^2\Delta-^2\Pi$ transition.
	3890.2 3886.4 3878.8	These lines belong to the (0,0) band in the $^2\Sigma-^2\Pi$ transition.
CN	3875.8 3874.6 3874.0	$P(1)$ $R(0)$ These lines belong to the (0,0) band $R(1)$ in the $^2\Sigma-^2\Sigma$ transition.
CH$^+$	4232.6 3957.7 3745.3	These lines belong to the $^1\Pi-^1\Sigma$ transition. The 4232.6 Å line is the $R(0)$ line of the (0,0) band, the 3957.7 Å is the $R(0)$ line of the (1.0) band and the 3745.3 Å line is the $R(0)$ line of the (2,0) band.

Interstellar hydrogen and radio astronomy

Hydrogen is by far the most abundant element in the interstellar gas.† However, its detection by optical methods is not possible except in emission from those clouds that are close enough to hot stars for the hydrogen to be ionised. The ionisation is caused by ultra-violet radiation emitted by the hot stars, and such regions where this process occurs are called H II regions. The hydrogen atom emission results from the proton capturing an electron and becoming an excited hydrogen atom. These atoms then lose their excess energy by emitting radiation some of which lies in the visible region. At a certain distance from a star, depending on its size, temperature, and on the density of the gas, radiation is no longer available to ionise the hydrogen, and from these regions (called H I regions) no optically detectable hydrogen

† As it is also in normal stars.

atom emission can be observed.† H II regions are well defined volumes forming a sphere around a hot star and occupy only about one-tenth of the space occupied by the H I regions.

Neutral hydrogen in the H I regions can, however, be detected by radio astronomy from the 21.1 cm (1420 Mc/s) H I emission. This emission results from transitions between the $F = 1$ and $F = 0$ levels in the ground state of the atom ($n = 1$), where F is the total angular momentum quantum number of the whole atom. The two values of F arise since $S = \frac{1}{2} = J$ and $I = \frac{1}{2}$, where F takes the values

$$J+I,\ J+I-1,\ \dots\ |J-I|$$

The transition $F = 1$ to $F = 0$ corresponds with a reversal of the direction of the electron spin relative to that of the proton spin and takes place only very rarely, the mean life of an atom in the $F = 1$ state being approximately 11×10^6 years. Since, however, interstellar gas clouds are so extensive detectable amounts of the 21.1 cm radiation are emitted.

From the Doppler velocity shift of the 21.1 cm line and on the assumption of galactic rotation‡ it has been found possible to determine the spatial distribution of the neutral hydrogen clouds and to confirm the spiral structure of the galaxy.

Optical studies of the light from distant stars are restricted owing to attenuation by interstellar dust. Radio waves, on the other hand, can penetrate the dust and wider regions become available for investigation. Radio astronomy has the additional advantage in extragalactic research of being less handicapped by red shifts brought about by the rapid recession of the universe. In fact, the use of the 21.1 cm line emitted from cool hydrogen clouds surrounding the intense extragalactic radio source in Cygnus showed that the recession velocity of these clouds deduced from the Doppler shift of this line was in agreement with the value of 16 700 km/sec measured in the optical spectrum. This result confirms the view that the red shift observed in spectral lines of distant galaxies is a true velocity shift. Finally, two useful general reference books are by Allen[21] and Thackeray.[22]

References

1. Struve, O. and Elvey, C. T. *Astrophys. J.* **88** (1938), 364.
2. Fehrenbach, Ch. *J. Observateurs*, **41** (1958), 41.
3. Thackeray, A. D. *Occ. Notes. R. Ast. Soc.* **3** (1958), 189.

† It is from these H I regions that interstellar absorption originates.

‡ The galaxy is composed of the sun, with its attendant planets, and of the stars nebulae, and gas clouds, and the stars. The boundaries of the galaxy are not defined, but it is estimated that the galaxy is about 30 000 parsecs across and about 3000 parsecs thick. The sun is near the edge of the disk at a distance of about 10 000 parsecs from the centre. An important property of the galaxy is that it is rotating—otherwise it could not exist—and the hypothesis of rotation is supported by extensive observations of stellar velocities in the line of sight. On its outer parts it rotates not as a solid body but in the same manner as the solar system, the outer planets rotating more slowly than in inner ones. The distribution of interstellar matter and hot, bright stars in the galaxy is now known to lie along the arms of a spiral near the central plane of the disk, the width of the arms being of the order of 500 parsecs.

4. MEINEL, A. B. *Astrophys. J.* **111** (1950), 555.
5. MEINEL, A. B. *Rept. Progr. Phys.* **14** (1951), 121.
6. BOBROVNIKOFF, N. T. *Rev. Mod. Phys.* **16** (1944), 271.
7. KUIPER, G. P. *Rept. Progr. Phys.* **13** (1950), 247.
8. DUFAY, J. *Galactic Nebulae and Interstellar Matter.* (Translated by POMERANS, A. J.). Hutchinson (London, 1957).
9. BOWEN, I. S. *Astrophys. J.* **67** (1928), 1.
10. BOWEN, I. S. *Rev. Mod. Phys.* **8** (1936), 55.
11. MROZOWSKI, S. *Rev. Mod. Phys.* **16** (1944), 153.
12. HERZBERG, G. *Atomic Spectra and Atomic Structure.* Dover Publications (New York, 1944), p. 154.
13. SWINGS, P. *Vistas in Astronomy.* Pergamon Press (London, 1956), Vol. 2, p. 958.
14. SWINGS, P. and HASER, L. *Atlas of Representative Cometary Spectra.* University of Liège, Astrophysical Institute.
15. JOHNSON, F. S., MALITSON, H. H., PURCELL, J. D. and TOUSEY, R. *Astrophys. J.* **127** (1958), 80.
16. KING, A. S. and BIRGE, R. J. *Nature* (*Lond.*) **124** (1929), 127. *Astrophys. J.* **72** (1930), 19.
17. SWINGS, P. and ROSENFELD, L. *Astrophys. J.* **86** (1937), 483.
18. MCKELLAR, A. *Publ. Astron. Soc. Pac.* **52** (1940), 307.
19. MERRILL, P. W. *Astrophys. J.* **83** (1936), 126.
20. MERRILL, P. W. and WILSON, O. C. *Astrophys. J.* **87** (1938), 9.
21. ALLEN, C. W. *Astrophysical Quantities.* Athlone Press (London, 1955).
22. THACKERAY, A. D. *Astronomical Spectroscopy.* Eyre and Spottiswoode (London, 1961).

Appendix

THE object of this Appendix is to indicate how transition criteria, selection rules, the Franck–Condon principle, and the equation for the energy levels of the harmonic oscillator may be derived from quantum mechanics. A full mathematical treatment would have been too lengthy. In fact, the Appendix has been aimed at indicating the route along which this information emerges. The mathematics has been minimised, and for a fuller treatment Pauling and Wilson,[1] Kemble,[2] Eyring, Walter, and Kimball,[3] Wilson, Decius, and Cross[4] and Sillitto[5] should be consulted.

Energy levels of harmonic oscillator

According to classical mechanics the potential energy, (V), of a harmonic oscillator consisting of a reduced point mass μ is given by:

$$V = 2\pi^2\mu\omega^2c^2x^2 \tag{A.1}$$

where ω is the frequency of vibration (in cm^{-1}), c is the velocity of light, and x is the displacement of the point mass from its equilibrium position.

The Schrödinger equation for a one-dimensional oscillator is:

$$\frac{d^2\psi}{dx^2}+\frac{8\pi^2\mu}{h^2}(E-V)\psi = 0 \tag{A.2}$$

On substitution of equation (A.1) into equation (A.2) the wave equation for a one-dimensional oscillator is obtained:

$$\frac{d^2\psi}{dx^2}+\frac{8\pi^2\mu}{h^2}(E-2\pi^2\mu\omega^2c^2x^2)\psi = 0 \tag{A.3}$$

To simplify equation (A.3) let:

$$\lambda = \frac{8\pi^2\mu E}{h^2}\dagger \tag{A.4}$$

and

$$\alpha = \frac{4\pi^2\mu\omega c}{h} \tag{A.5}$$

On substitution of equations (A.4) and (A.5), equation (A.3) becomes:

$$\frac{d^2\psi}{dx^2}+(\lambda-\alpha^2x^2)\psi = 0 \tag{A.6}$$

To obtain satisfactory wave-functions (from equation (A.6), that is functions $\psi(x)$ which are continuous, single valued and finite throughout the region $+\infty$ to $-\infty$, the following procedure is adopted.

† This energy parameter λ is not to be confused with wavelength.

Initially, the form of ψ is studied in the regions of large positive and negative values of x, then subsequently the behaviour of ψ for small negative and positive displacements is examined. Each case will now be studied in turn.

1. *An approximate solution of the wave equation when* $|x|$ *is very large*

When $|x|$ is very large then, for any value of the total energy E, λ will be negligibly small compared to $\alpha^2 x^2$, and equation (A.6) becomes:

$$\frac{d^2\psi}{dx^2} = \alpha^2 x^2 \psi \tag{A.7}$$

Solutions to this equation are:

$$\psi = \exp\left(+\frac{\alpha}{2}x^2\right) \tag{A.8}$$

and

$$\psi = \exp\left(-\frac{\alpha}{2}x^2\right) \tag{A.9}$$

the first being unacceptable as a satisfactory wave-function since it tends too rapidly to infinity with increasing values of $|x|$.

2. *An accurate solution of the wave equation for small values of* $|x|$

In order to obtain an accurate solution of equation (A.6), a limiting factor has to be introduced into equation (A.9); this is achieved by multiplying by $f(x)$ a power series in x. Equation (A.9) becomes:

$$\psi = \exp\left(-\frac{\alpha}{2}x^2\right) . f(x) \tag{A.10}$$

On differentiation of equation (A.10) twice with respect to x, and writing f for $f(x)$, f' for $\frac{df}{dx}$, and f'' for $\frac{d^2f}{dx^2}$, we get

$$\frac{d^2\psi}{dx^2} = \exp\left(-\frac{\alpha}{2}x^2\right)(\alpha^2x^2f - \alpha f - 2\alpha x f' + f'') \tag{A.11}$$

On substitution for $\frac{d^2\psi}{dx^2}$ from equation (A.11) into equation (A.6)

$$\exp\left(-\frac{\alpha}{2}x^2\right)(\alpha^2x^2f - \alpha f - 2\alpha x f' + f'') + (\lambda - \alpha^2x^2)\psi = 0 \tag{A.12}$$

while from equation (A.10)

$$\exp\left(-\frac{\alpha}{2}x^2\right) = \frac{\psi}{f} \tag{A.13}$$

Thus, equation (A.12) becomes on substitution for $\exp\left(-\frac{\alpha}{2}x^2\right)$ from equation (A.13)

$$f'' - 2\alpha x f' + (\lambda - \alpha)f = 0 \tag{A.14}$$

For ease in manipulation it is convenient to introduce a new variable s such that

$$s = x\sqrt{\alpha} \tag{A.15}$$

and to replace $f(x)$ by $H(s)$ to which it is equal. On differentiation of equation (A.15) we obtain:

$$\mathrm{d}s = \sqrt{\alpha}\,.\,\mathrm{d}x$$

and

$$\frac{\mathrm{d}f}{\mathrm{d}x} = \frac{\mathrm{d}H}{\mathrm{d}s}\,.\,\frac{\mathrm{d}s}{\mathrm{d}x} = \sqrt{\alpha}\,.\,\frac{\mathrm{d}H}{\mathrm{d}s} \tag{A.16}$$

Also,

$$\frac{\mathrm{d}^2 f}{\mathrm{d}x^2} = \sqrt{\alpha}\,.\,\frac{\mathrm{d}}{\mathrm{d}s}\left(\sqrt{\alpha}\,.\,\frac{\mathrm{d}H}{\mathrm{d}s}\right) = \alpha\frac{\mathrm{d}^2 H}{\mathrm{d}s^2} \tag{A.17}$$

On substitution of equations (A.16) and (A.17) into equation (A.14)

$$\frac{\alpha \mathrm{d}^2 H}{\mathrm{d}s^2} - 2\alpha x\sqrt{\alpha}\frac{\mathrm{d}H}{\mathrm{d}s} + (\lambda - \alpha)H = 0 \tag{A.18}$$

or

$$\frac{\mathrm{d}^2 H}{\mathrm{d}s^2} - 2s\frac{\mathrm{d}H}{\mathrm{d}s} + \left(\frac{\lambda}{\alpha} - 1\right)H = 0 \tag{A.19}$$

To solve equation (A.19) $H(s)$ is represented as the power series:

$$H(s) = \Sigma a_\nu s^\nu = a_0 + a_1 s + a_2 s^2 + a_3 s^3 + \ \ldots \tag{A.20}$$

$$\frac{\mathrm{d}H}{\mathrm{d}s} = \Sigma \nu a_\nu s^{\nu-1} = a_1 + 2a_2 s + 3a_3 s^2 + \ \ldots \tag{A.21}$$

$$\frac{\mathrm{d}^2 H}{\mathrm{d}s^2} = \Sigma \nu(\nu - 1)a_\nu s^{\nu-2} = 1.2a_2 + 2.3a_3 s + \ \ldots \tag{A.22}$$

On substitution of equations (A.20) to (A.22) into (A.19) we get:

$$1.2a_2 + 2.3a_3 s + 3.4a_4 s^2 + 4.5a_5 s^3 + \ \ldots - 2a_1 s - 2.2a_2 s^2 - 2.3a_3 s^3 - \ \ldots$$
$$+\left(\frac{\lambda}{\alpha} - 1\right)a_0 + \left(\frac{\lambda}{\alpha} - 1\right)a_1 s + \left(\frac{\lambda}{\alpha} - 1\right)a_2 s^2 + \left(\frac{\lambda}{\alpha} - 1\right)a_3 s^3 + \ \ldots = 0 \tag{A.23}$$

For this series to vanish for all values of s, or in other words, for $H(s)$ to be a solution of equation (A.19) the coefficients of individual powers of s must vanish separately, that is:

$$\left.\begin{aligned} 1.2a_2 + \left(\frac{\lambda}{\alpha} - 1\right)a_0 &= 0 \\ 2.3a_3 - 2a_1 + \left(\frac{\lambda}{\alpha} - 1\right)a_1 &= 0 \\ 3.4a_4 - 2.2a_2 + \left(\frac{\lambda}{\alpha} - 1\right)a_2 &= 0 \\ 4.5a_5 - 2.3a_3 + \left(\frac{\lambda}{\alpha} - 1\right)a_3 &= 0 \end{aligned}\right\} \tag{A.24}$$

In general for the coefficients of s^v we may write:

$$(v+1)(v+2)a_{v+2}+\left(\frac{\lambda}{\alpha}-1-2v\right)a_v = 0 \tag{A.25}$$

or

$$a_{v+2} = -\frac{(\lambda/\alpha-2v-1)}{(v+1)(v+2)}a_v \tag{A.26}$$

Equation (A.26) is termed a *recursion formula* and enables coefficients $a_2, a_3, a_4, \ldots$ to be calculated successively in terms of a_0 and a_1. If $a_0 = 0$, then only odd powers appear while if $a_1 = 0$, only even powers are present in the series. For arbitrary values of the energy parameter λ the series consists of an infinite number of terms and increases too rapidly to correspond to a satisfactory wave-function.† Values of λ must be chosen such that the series $H(s)$ terminates leaving a polynominal with a finite number of terms. An odd or even polynominal of degree v will be obtained according as $a_0 = 0$ or $a_1 = 0$ respectively; it follows from (A.26) that the λ/α value which causes the series to cease at the Vth term is:

$$\frac{\lambda}{\alpha} = (2v+1) \tag{A.27}$$

On substitution of the values of λ and α from equations (A.4) and (A.5), respectively, (A.27) becomes:

$$E = (v+\tfrac{1}{2})hωc \tag{A.28}$$

where $v = 0, 1, 2, 3 \ldots$ This is one of the basic equations in vibrational spectra studies, since the vibrational energy (really E_v) is related to the vibrational quantum number which characterises a particular vibrational mode. For diatomic molecules in infra-red and electronic spectra studies the equation is usually modified to:

$$E_v = (v+\tfrac{1}{2})hc\omega_e-(v+\tfrac{1}{2})^2hcx_e\omega_e+(v+\tfrac{1}{2})^3hcy_e\omega_e+ \ \ldots$$

In polyatomic studies by the infra-red and electronic spectra approach the basic equation is usually retained, and for vibrational modes the vibrational energy is approximately given by:

$$E_v = \Sigma(v+\tfrac{1}{2})hc\omega$$

Calculation of eigenfunctions for a diatomic molecule

The series whose coefficients are characterised by equations (A.26) and (A.28) with $a_0 = 0$ (v odd), $a_1 = 0$ (v even) is the multiple of the Hermite polynominal $H_v(s)$ which can be expressed as:

$$H_v(s) = (-1)^v \exp(s^2)\frac{\mathrm{d}^v\{\exp(-s^2)\}}{\mathrm{d}s^v} \quad \text{(A.29}$$

The solution of equation (A.3) may be written in the form:

$$\psi_v = N_v \exp(-\tfrac{1}{2}s^2)H_v(s) \tag{A.30}$$

in which

$$s = x\sqrt{\alpha}$$

† This is shown to be the case on p. 71 of Pauling and Wilson.[1]

$H_v(s)$ is a polynominal of the vth degree in s. N_v is a constant such that ψ_v is normalised, that is:

$$\int_{-\infty}^{+\infty} \psi_v^\star \psi_v \mathrm{d}s = 1 \tag{A.31}$$

The value of the normalisation constant N_v is given by:

$$N_v = \left\{\left(\frac{\alpha}{\pi}\right)^{1/2} \frac{1}{2^v v!}\right\}^{1/2} \tag{A.32}$$

On substitution of equation (A.32) into equation (A.30) the complete wave-function becomes:

$$\psi_v = \left\{\left(\frac{\alpha}{\pi}\right)^{1/2} \frac{1}{2^v v!}\right\}^{1/2} \exp\left(-\tfrac{1}{2}s^2\right) . H_v(s) \tag{A.33}$$

The first four members of the Hermite polynominal are:

$$\begin{aligned} H_0(s) &= 1 \\ H_1(s) &= 2s \\ H_2(s) &= 4s^2 - 2 \\ H_3(s) &= 8s^3 - 12s \end{aligned} \tag{A.34}$$

For the lowest vibrational level ($v = 0$) the value of ψ_0 can be calculated by the use of equations (A.33) and (A.34) and is:

$$\psi_0 = \left(\frac{\alpha}{\pi}\right)^{1/4} \exp\left(-\tfrac{1}{2}s^2\right) = \left(\frac{\alpha}{\pi}\right)^{1/4} \exp\left(-\frac{\alpha}{2} \cdot x^2\right) \tag{A.35}$$

On substitution of $v = 1, 2, 3, \ldots$ in equation (A.33) the ψ_1, ψ_2, and ψ_3 values, respectively, may be determined.

From the known constants of a molecule α may be calculated and hence ψ_v obtained for a given displacement (x) of the nuclei in a diatomic molecule from the equilibrium position where one nucleus is treated as fixed and the other vibrating with respect to it. The form of the eigenfunctions for values of the vibrational quantum number equal to 0, 1, 2, 3, are shown in Fig. A.1 where the eigenfunctions are plotted on the ordinate axis and the displacement x from the equilibrium position along the abscissa. Since H_v is a polynominal of the vth degree with v real zero values, ψ_v will cross the abscissa v times as shown in the figure. For band intensity considerations the ψ_v values are plotted on the actual potential energy curves for both the upper and lower electronic states. An example of this procedure is given in Fig. 5.8 for the RbH molecule.

Criterion for a transition between two vibrational states of a harmonic oscillator

The probability of a transition between two states m and n produced by interaction of a system with electromagnetic radiation is dependent on the eigenfunctions ψ_n and ψ_m of the two states as follows:

$$R_x^{nm} = \int \psi_n^\star M_x \psi_m \mathrm{d}\mathcal{T} \tag{A.36}$$

$$R_y^{nm} = \int \psi_n^\star M_y \psi_m \mathrm{d}\mathcal{T} \tag{A.37}$$

$$R_z^{nm} = \int \psi_n^\star M_z \psi_m \mathrm{d}\mathcal{T} \tag{A.38}$$

where R_x^{nm}, R_y^{nm}, R_z^{nm}, are known as the matrix elements of the components of the variable electric dipole moment M whose components are M_x, M_y, and M_z along the x, y, and z axes (see Vol. 1). $d\mathscr{T}$ is a small volume element.†

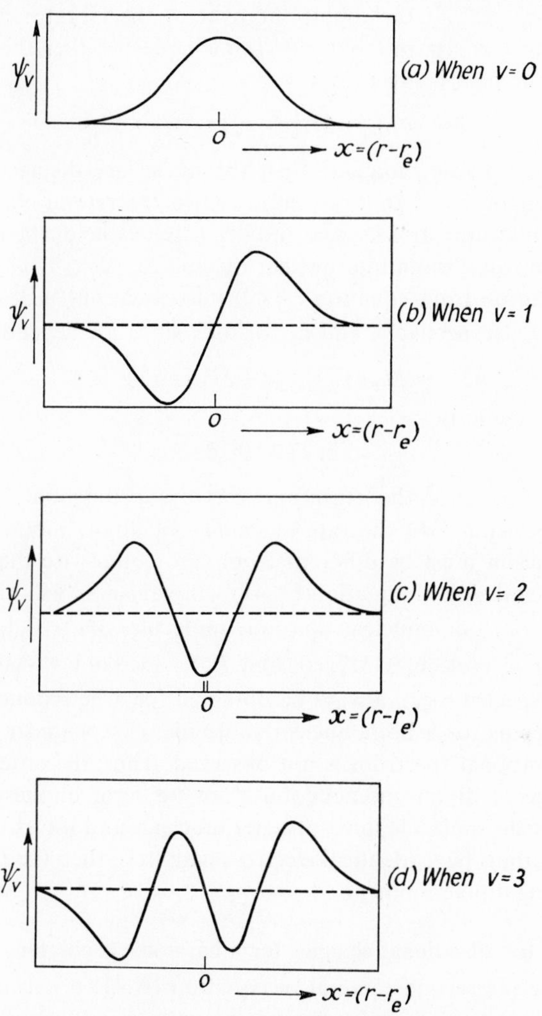

FIG. A.1 $\psi_v - x$ values for the vibrational levels 0, 1, 2, 3, of a harmonic oscillator

If the matrix element

$$R^{nm} = \int \psi_n^{\star} M \psi_m d\mathscr{T} \tag{A.39}$$

differs from zero for the two states n and m, then there exists a certain probability that the states n and m may combine with each other. If R^{nm} is zero, then the transition is forbidden as an electric dipole one.

† R and M are vector quantities and are frequently printed in bold type.

The particular problem of a transition between two vibrational states of a harmonic oscillator may conveniently be studied in one dimension. Hence, the matrix element of one component only is required. If the oscillator is orientated in the z direction, the matrix element component required will be R_z^{nm}. If the dipole moment of the vibrator varies linearly with the internuclear separation in a diatomic molecule, then the z component of the dipole moment is given by:

$$M_z = M_0 + M_1[r - r_e] = M_0 + M_1 z \tag{A.40}$$

where M_z is the dipole moment when the nuclei are displaced from their equilibrium separation r_e, to a position r, M_1 is the rate of change of dipole moment with internuclear distance, and M_0 is the value of the electric dipole moment at the equilibrium internuclear distance.

On substitution from equation (A.40) into equation (A.38), and writing $\psi_{v'}^{\star}\psi_{v''}$ for $\psi_n^{\star}\psi_m$, respectively, and dz for d$\mathscr{T}$, since M_z depends only on z

$$R_z^{v'v''} = M_0 \int \psi_{v'}^{\star}\psi_{v''} \mathrm{d}z + M_1 \int z\psi_{v'}^{\star}\psi_{v''} \mathrm{d}z \tag{A.41}$$

When $v' \neq v''$ the term:

$$M_0 \int \psi_{v'}^{\star}\psi_{v''} \mathrm{d}z \tag{A.42}$$

is equal to zero, since the eigenfunctions are orthogonal. Hence, for a vibrational spectrum, M_1, the rate of change of dipole moment with internuclear separation must be different from zero; otherwise the second term on the right-hand side of equation (A.41) will vanish as will also the matrix element $R_z^{v'v''}$. For homonuclear diatomic molecules $M_1 = 0$, but for heteronuclear diatomic molecules $M_1 \neq 0$, and $R_z^{v'v''}$ does not vanish. In practice a vibrational spectrum can always be obtained for a heteronuclear diatomic molecule, whereas for a homonuclear molecule, except under extreme conditions, a vibrational spectrum is not observed. Thus, the criterion, that the rate of change of dipole moment must not be zero, implies for diatomic molecules that the molecule must be heteronuclear, and if it is heteronuclear, since no two atoms have identical electronegativities, then the molecule must have an electric dipole moment.

Selection rule for vibrational changes for a harmonic oscillator

On solving the second integral in equation (A.41) it can be shown that under all conditions, except when $v' - v'' = \pm 1$, that $R_z^{v'v''}$ will vanish. The selection rule for a harmonic oscillator is, thus, that changes in v, the vibrational quantum number, are limited to ± 1 unit.

For a non-harmonic oscillator equation (A.40) should be:

$$M_z = M_0 + M_1 z + M_2 z^2 + \ . \ . \ . \tag{A.43}$$

where higher powers of z are included to account for the fact that the vibrations are not strictly harmonic. If instead of substituting equation (A.40) into equation (A.41), equation (A.43) is substituted, then transitions with $\Delta v = \pm 2, \pm 3, \ . \ . \ .$ become feasible. The motion of nuclei in diatomic molecules is not strictly a simple harmonic one, and, in fact, transitions corresponding to

$$\Delta v = \pm 2, \pm 3,$$

may usually be observed from the $v'' = 0$ level. However, such transitions as $2 \leftarrow 0$ (first overtone), $3 \leftarrow 0$ (second overtone) grow progressively weaker in intensity than the fundamental band ($1 \leftarrow 0$). This is considered on p. 96 with respect to the HCl molecule.

Intensity of a spectral line in emission and absorption

The intensity of a spectral line in emission resulting from a transition between the two states characterised by n and m, respectively, ($I^{nm}_{em.}$), is the energy emitted by the source per second. If the number of atoms in the state n is N_n, and if A_{nm} is the fraction of atoms in the initial stage undergoing transitions to the lower state m per sec, then

$$I^{nm}_{em.} = N_n \boldsymbol{h} c \nu_{nm} A_{nm} \tag{A.44}$$

where ν_{nm} is the wave-number of the emitted radiation. A_{nm} is called the *Einstein probability of spontaneous emission.* For dipole radiation A_{nm} is related to the matrix element R^{nm} of the transition by the equation:

$$A_{nm} = \frac{64\pi^4 \nu^3_{nm}}{3\boldsymbol{h}} \cdot | R^{nm} |^2 \tag{A.45}$$

On substitution of equation (A.45) into equation (A.44)

$$I^{nm}_{em.} = N_n \boldsymbol{h} c \nu_{nm} \frac{64\pi^4 \nu^3_{nm}}{3\boldsymbol{h}} \cdot | R^{nm} |^2 \tag{A.46}$$

or

$$I^{nm}_{em.} \propto \nu^4_{nm} \cdot | R^{nm} |^2 \tag{A.47}$$

The corresponding result for absorption is:

$$I^{nm}_{abs.} = \frac{8\pi^3}{3\boldsymbol{h}c} \cdot I^{nm}_0 \Delta x N_m \nu_{nm} \cdot | R^{nm} |^2 \tag{A.48}$$

where Δx is the thickness of the absorbing layer, I^{nm}_0 the intensity of the incident radiation, and N_m the number of atoms in the initial lower state m. The dependence of the intensity of the emitted radiation on the fourth power of the wave-number, while that of absorption depends on the first power, is the reason that, for a spectrum of low intensity, emission work is to be preferred to absorption.

Electronic transition probability and spectral intensity

The probability of a transition between two states n and m characterised, respectively, by the total eigenfunctions ψ' and ψ'' is given by the equation:

$$R = \int \psi'^{\star} M \psi'' d\mathscr{T} \tag{A.49}$$

where R is the matrix element, M the variable electric dipole moment (see p. 206), and $d\mathscr{T}$ is a small element of volume. $\psi^{\star}$ is the complex conjugate of ψ.

The total eigenfunction ψ is to a first approximation the product of the electronic ψ_e, vibrational ψ_v, and rotational ψ_r eigenfunctions, respectively, and the reciprocal of the internuclear separation r

$$\psi = \psi_e \frac{1}{r} \psi_v \psi_r \tag{A.50}$$

It may be shown that to a good approximation the rotation of the molecule may be neglected (see Herzberg[6]), and equation (A.50) is modified to:

$$\psi = \psi_e \psi_v \tag{A.51}$$

The variable electric dipole moment M may be divided into two components, the first depending on that for the electrons M_e and the second on that for the nuclei M_n. The two dipole moment components are related to M by:

$$M = M_e + M_n \tag{A.52}$$

On substitution of equations (A.52) and (A.51) into equation (A.49) the matrix element is given by:

$$R = \int M_e \psi_e'^{\star} \psi_v' \psi_e'' \psi_v'' \mathrm{d}\mathscr{T} + \int M_n \psi_e'^{\star} \psi_v' \psi_e'' \psi_v'' \mathrm{d}\mathscr{T} \tag{A.53}$$

The volume element $\mathrm{d}\mathscr{T}$ involved in the integrals in equation (A.53) is the product of two volume elements, namely the volume elements of the nuclear and electron co-ordinates $\mathrm{d}\mathscr{T}_n$ and $\mathrm{d}\mathscr{T}_e$, respectively. Thus, equation (A.53) may be written:

$$R = \int \psi_v' \psi_v'' \mathrm{d}\mathscr{T}_n \int M_e \psi_e'^{\star} \psi_e'' \mathrm{d}\mathscr{T}_e + \int M_n \psi_v' \psi_v'' \mathrm{d}\mathscr{T}_n \int \psi_e'^{\star} \psi_e'' \mathrm{d}\mathscr{T}_e \tag{A.54}$$

Since $\psi_e'^{\star}$ and ψ_e'' belong to different electronic states it can be shown that they are orthogonal (see Pauling and Wilson,[1] p. 64) to one another and therefore:

$$\int \psi_e'^{\star} \psi_e'' \mathrm{d}\mathscr{T}_e = 0 \tag{A.55}$$

Equation (A.54) then becomes

$$R = \int \psi_v' \psi_v'' \mathrm{d}\mathscr{T}_n \int M_e \psi_e'^{\star} \psi_e'' \mathrm{d}\mathscr{T}_e \tag{A.56}$$

Since the only co-ordinate on which ψ_v depends is the internuclear distance r, $\mathrm{d}\mathscr{T}_n$ may be replaced by $\mathrm{d}r$, and equation (A.56) becomes:

$$R = \int \psi_v' \psi_v'' \mathrm{d}r \int M_e \psi_e'^{\star} \psi_e'' \mathrm{d}\mathscr{T}_e \tag{A.57}$$

The matrix element

$$\int M_e \psi_e'^{\star} \psi_e'' \mathrm{d}\mathscr{T}_e$$

is called the *electronic transition moment* R_e, where $|R_e|^2$ is proportional to the electronic transition probability (see equation (A.45)).

Since for different internuclear distances the electron potential energy is different, it follows that the electron eigenfunction ψ_e must depend to some extent on the internuclear separation. Hence, R_e is also dependent on r, but since the variation of ψ_e with r is slow, this variation is often neglected, and R_e is replaced by an average value $\overline{R_e}$. For an electronic transition between the vibrational levels v' and v'' equation (A.57) becomes on substituting for $\overline{R_e}$

$$R^{v'v''} = \overline{R_e} \int \psi_v' \psi_v'' \mathrm{d}r \tag{A.58}$$

The integral over the products of the vibrational eigenfunctions of the two states in equation (A.58) is known as the *overlap integral.* On substituting equation (A.58) into equation (A.46) an expression is obtained for the band intensities in emission:

$$I_{\text{em.}}^{v'v''} = \frac{64}{3} \cdot \pi^4 c N_{v'} \nu_{v'v''}^4 \bar{R}_e^2 \left\{ \int \psi'_v \psi''_v \mathrm{d}r \right\}^2 \tag{A.59}$$

while the substitution of equation (A.58) into equation (A.48) leads to an expression for the band intensities in absorption:

$$I_{\text{abs.}}^{v'v''} = \frac{8\pi^3}{3hc} \cdot I_0^{v'v''} \Delta x N_{v''} \nu_{v'v''} \bar{R}_e^2 \left\{ \int \psi'_v \psi''_v \mathrm{d}r \right\}^2 \tag{A.60}$$

where $N_{v'}$ and $N_{v''}$ are the numbers of molecules in the upper and lower vibrational states, respectively, Δx is the thickness of the absorbing layer, and $I_0^{v'v''}$ the intensity of the incident radiation.

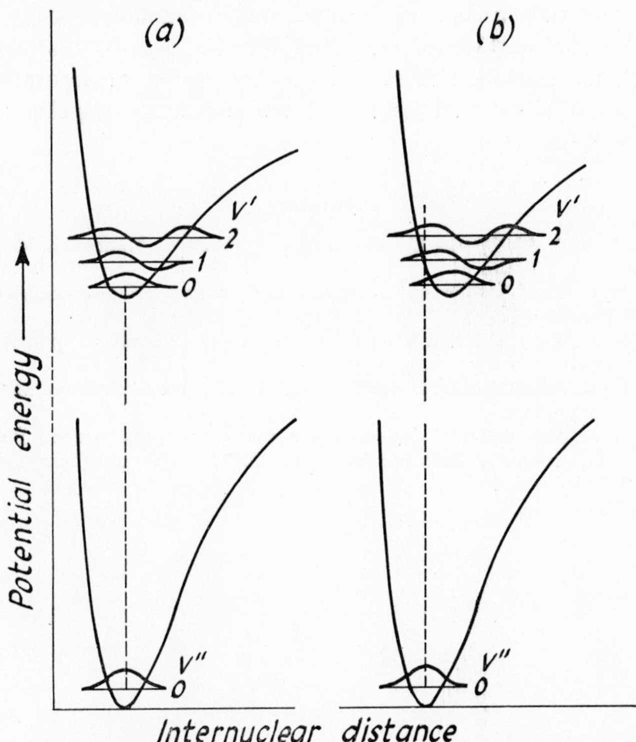

FIG. A.2 Electronic transition where (*a*) the r_e values for the upper and lower states are the same, (*b*) the r_e values differ

In Fig. A.2(*a*) and (*b*) potential energy curves for an upper and the lower electronic states may be observed. Superimposed on these curves are the vibrational eigenfunctions. In Fig. A.2(*a*) the minima of the potential energy curves lie one above the other while in Fig. A.2(*b*) the minima are displaced relative to one another. In Fig. A.2(a) the eigenfunctions for the vibrational levels $v' = 0$ and $v'' = 0$ have a maximum value at the same internuclear distance. It follows, therefore, that the value of the integral $\int\psi_{v'}\psi_{v''}\mathrm{d}r$ will have a maximum value for this (0,0) band, which in consequence will be a most intense band. As the minima of the potential energy curves are displaced relative to one another, then the overlap integral value becomes smaller, and the intensity of the (0,0) band is diminished. In Fig. A.2(b) the best overlap of the vibrational eigenfunctions is seen to be for the (2,0) band, and in accordance will, thus, be the most intense band.

Since for the higher vibrational levels in both the electronic states, the eigenfunctions have broad maxima or minima near the turning points of the vibrations, maximum values of the overlap integral are obtained when the maximum of the eigenfunction of the lower state lies vertically below the broad maximum or minimum of the upper state. These facts are in accordance with the elementary treatment of the Franck–Condon principle given on p. 18. Whether such transitions are observed in practice depends on there being a sufficient number of molecules present in the vibrational levels from which the transition takes place. For example, in absorption work only the lowest vibrational levels (v'') are sufficiently populated for the transition to be detected.

References

1. PAULING, L. and WILSON, E. B. *Introduction to Quantum Mechanics.* McGraw-Hill (New York, 1935).
2. KEMBLE, E. C. *The Fundamental Principles of Quantum Mechanics.* McGraw-Hill (New York, 1937).
3. EYRING, W. J., WALTER, J. and KIMBALL, G. E. *Quantum Chemistry.* John Wiley (New York, 1944).
4. WILSON, E. B., JR., DECIUS, J. C. and CROSS, P. C. *Molecular Vibrations.* McGraw-Hill (New York, 1955).
5. SILLITTO, R. M. *Non-relativistic Quantum Mechanics.* Edinburgh University Press (1960).
6. HERZBERG, G. *Spectra of Diatomic Molecules.* D. Van Nostrand (New York, 1950), p. 203.

Author Index

Subject Index

(N.B. The molecules and radicals are listed in alphabetical order under their formulae with the exception of aromatic molecules containing more than one ring.)